HIGHER GEOMETRY

HIGHER GEOMETRY

AN INTRODUCTION TO ADVANCED METHODS IN ANALYTIC GEOMETRY

BY

FREDERICK S. WOODS

PROFESSOR OF MATHEMATICS IN THE MASSACHUSETTS
INSTITUTE OF TECHNOLOGY

DOVER PUBLICATIONS, INC.
NEW YORK

This new Dover edition, first published in 1961, is an unabridged and unaltered republication of the work first published by Ginn and Company in 1922.

Manufactured in the United States of America

Dover Publications, Inc.
180 Varick Street
New York 14, N. Y.

PREFACE

The present book is the outgrowth of lectures given at various times to students of the later undergraduate and earlier graduate years. It aims to present some of the general concepts and methods which are necessary for advanced work in algebraic geometry (as distinguished from differential geometry), but which are not now accessible to the student in any one volume, and thus to bridge the gap between the usual text in analytic geometry and treatises or articles on special topics.

With this object in view the author has assumed very little mathematical preparation on the part of the student beyond that acquired in elementary courses in calculus and plane analytic geometry. In addition it has been necessary to assume a slight knowledge of determinants, especially as applied to the solution of linear equations, such as may be acquired in a very short course on the subject. But it has not been assumed that the student has had a course in higher algebra, including matrices, linear substitutions, invariants, and similar topics, and no effort has been made to include a discussion of these subjects in the text. This restriction in the tools to be used necessitates at times modes of expression and methods of proof which are a little cumbersome, but the appeal to a larger number of readers seems to justify the occasional lack of elegance.

In preparing the text one of the greatest problems has consisted in determining what matters to exclude. It is obvious that an introduction to geometry cannot contain all that is known on any subject or even refer briefly to all general topics. The matter of selection is necessarily one of individual judgment. One large domain of geometry has been definitely excluded from the plan of the book; namely, that of differential geometry. In the field which is left the author cannot dare to hope that his choice of material will agree exactly with that which would be made by any other teacher. He hopes, however, that his choice has been sufficiently wise to make the book useful to many besides himself.

iii

The plan of the book calls for a study of different coördinate systems, based upon various geometric elements and classified according to the number of dimensions involved. This leads naturally to a final discussion of n-dimensional geometry in an abstract sense, of which the particular geometries studied earlier form concrete illustrations. As each system of coördinates is introduced, the meaning of the linear and the quadratic equations is studied. The student is thus primarily drilled in the interpretation of equations, but acquires at the same time a knowledge of useful geometric facts. The principle of duality is constantly in view, and the nature of imaginary elements and the conventional character of the locus at infinity, dependent upon the type of coördinates used, are carefully explained.

Numerous exercises for the student have been introduced. In some cases these carry a little farther the discussion of the text, but care has been taken to keep their difficulty within the range of the student's ability.   FREDERICK S. WOODS

CONTENTS

PART I. GENERAL CONCEPTS AND ONE–DIMENSIONAL GEOMETRY

CHAPTER I. GENERAL CONCEPTS

CHAPTER II. RANGES AND PENCILS

CHAPTER III. PROJECTIVITY

PART II. TWO–DIMENSIONAL GEOMETRY

CHAPTER IV. POINT AND LINE COÖRDINATES IN A PLANE

CHAPTER IX. TETRACYCLICAL COÖRDINATES

CHAPTER X. A SPECIAL SYSTEM OF COÖRDINATES

PART III. THREE–DIMENSIONAL GEOMETRY

CHAPTER XI. CIRCLE COÖRDINATES

CHAPTER XII. POINT AND PLANE COÖRDINATES

PART IV. GEOMETRY OF FOUR AND HIGHER DIMENSIONS

CHAPTER XVII. LINE COÖRDINATES IN THREE-DIMENSIONAL SPACE

CHAPTER XVIII. SPHERE COÖRDINATES

CHAPTER XIX. FOUR-DIMENSIONAL POINT COÖRDINATES

CHAPTER XX. GEOMETRY OF N DIMENSIONS

HIGHER GEOMETRY

HIGHER GEOMETRY

PART I. GENERAL CONCEPTS AND ONE–DIMENSIONAL GEOMETRY

CHAPTER I

GENERAL CONCEPTS

1. Coördinates. A set of n variables, the values of which fix a geometric object, are called the *coördinates* of the object. The analytic geometry which is developed by the use of these coördinates has as its *element* the object fixed by the coördinates. The reader is familiar with the use of coördinates to fix a point either in the plane or in space. The point is the element of elementary analytic geometry, and all figures are studied as made up of points. There is, however, no theoretical objection to using any geometric figure as the element of a geometry. In the following pages we shall discuss, among other possibilities, the use of the straight line, the plane, the circle, and the sphere.

The *dimensions* of a system of geometry are determined by the number of the coördinates necessary to fix the element. Thus the geometry in which the element is either the point in the plane or the straight line in the plane is two-dimensional; the geometry in which the element is the point in space, the circle in the plane, or the plane in space is three-dimensional; the geometry in which the element is the straight line or the sphere in space is four-dimensional.

Since each coördinate may take an infinite number of values, the fact that a geometry has n dimensions is often indicated by saying that the totality of elements form an ∞^n extent. Thus the points in space form an ∞^3 extent, while the straight lines in space form an ∞^4 extent. If in an ∞^n extent the coördinates of an element are connected by k independent conditions, the elements

1

satisfying the conditions form an ∞^{n-k} extent lying in the ∞^n extent. Thus a single equation between the coördinates of a point in space defines an ∞^2 extent (a surface) lying in an ∞^3 extent (space), and two equations between the coördinates of a point in space define an ∞^1 extent (a curve).

2. The principle of duality. When the element has been selected and its coördinates determined, the development of the geometry consists in studying the meaning of equations and relations connecting the coördinates. There are therefore two distinct parts to analytic geometry, the analytic work and the geometric interpretation. Two systems of geometry depending upon different elements with the same number of coördinates will have the same analytic expression and will differ only in the interpretation of the analysis. In such a case it is often sufficient to know the meaning of the coördinates and the interpretation of a few fundamental relations in each system in order to find for a theorem in one geometry a corresponding theorem in the other. Two systems which have such a relation to each other are said to be *dualistic*, or to correspond to each other by the *principle of duality*.

It is obviously inconvenient to give examples of this principle at this time, but the reader will find numerous examples in the pages of this book.

3. The use of imaginaries. Between the coördinates of a geometric element and the element itself there fails to be perfect equivalence unless the concept of an imaginary element is introduced. Consider, for example, the usual Cartesian coördinates (x, y) of a point in a plane. If we understand by a " real point " one which has a position on the plane which may be represented by a pencil dot, then to any real pair of values of x and y corresponds a real point, and conversely. It is highly inconvenient, however, to limit ourselves in the analytic work to real values of the variables. We accordingly introduce the convention of an " imaginary point " by saying that a pair of values of x and y of which one or both is a complex quantity defines such a point. In this sense a " point " is nothing more than a concise expression for " a value pair (x, y)." From this standpoint many propositions of analytic geometry are partly theorems and partly definitions. For example, take the proposition that any equation of the first degree represents a straight line. This is a theorem as far as real points and real lines are concerned, but it is a definition for imaginary points satisfying an equation with real coefficients and for all points satisfying an equation with complex coefficients. The definition in question is that a straight line is the totality of all value pairs (x, y) which satisfy any linear equation.

Any proposition proved for real figures may be extended to imaginary figures provided that the proof is purely an analytic one which is independent of the reality of the quantities involved. One cannot, however, extend theorems which are not analytic in their nature. For example, it is proved for a real triangle that the length of any side is less than the sum of the lengths of the other two sides. The length of the side connecting the vertices (x_1, y_1) and (x_2, y_2) is $\sqrt{(x_1 - x_2)^2 + (y_1 - y_2)^2}$. We may extend this definition of length to imaginary points, but the theorem concerning the sides of a triangle cannot be proved analytically and is not true for imaginaries, as may be seen by testing it for the triangle whose vertices are $(0, 0)$, $(i, 1)$, and $(i, -1)$.

Similar considerations to those we have just stated for a point in a plane apply to any element. It is usual to have a real element represented by real coördinates, but sometimes it is found convenient to represent a real element by complex coördinates. In either case there will be found in the analysis certain combinations of coördinates which cannot represent real elements. In all cases the geometry is extended by the convention that such coördinates represent imaginary elements.

4. Infinity. Infinity may occur in a system of geometry in two ways: first, the value of one or more of the coördinates may increase without limit, or secondly, the element which we suppose lying within the range of action of our physical senses may be so displaced that its distance from its original position increases without limit.

Infinity in the first sense may be avoided by writing the coördinates in the form of ratios, for a ratio increases without limit when its denominator approaches zero. Coördinates thus written are called *homogeneous coördinates*, because equations written in them become homogeneous. They are of constant use in this book.

The treatment of infinity in the second sense is not so simple, but proceeds as follows: As an element of the geometry recedes indefinitely from its original position, its coördinates usually approach certain limiting values, which are said by definition to represent an "element at infinity." The coördinates of all elements at infinity usually satisfy a certain equation, which is said to represent the "locus at infinity." The nature of this locus depends upon the coördinate system. Thus, in the plane, by the use of one system of coördinates all "points at infinity" are said to lie on a "straight line at infinity"; by another system of coördinates the plane is said to have "a single real point at infinity"; by still another system of coördinates the plane is said to have "two lines at infinity." These various statements are not contradictory, since they are not intended to express any fact about the physical properties of the plane. They are simply conventions to express the way in which the coördinate system may be applied to infinitely remote elements. There is no more difficulty in passing from one convention to another than there is in passing from one coördinate system to another. The convention as to elements at infinity stands on the same basis as the convention as to imaginary elements.

5. Transformations. A transformation is an operation by which each element of a geometry is replaced by another element. The new element may be of the same kind as the original element or of a different kind. For example, a rotation of a plane about a fixed point is a transformation of points into points; on the other hand, a transformation may be made in the plane by which each point of the plane is replaced by its polar line with respect to a fixed conic. We shall consider in this book mainly *analytic transformations*, that is, those in which the coördinates of the transformed element are analytic functions of those of the original element.

A transformation may be conveniently expressed by a single symbol, such as T. If we wish to express the fact that an element, or a configuration of elements, a, has been transformed into another element or configuration b, we write

$$T(a) = b. \tag{1}$$

Suppose now, having carried out the transformation T, we carry out on the transformed elements another transformation S. The result is a single transformation G, and we write

$$G = ST, \qquad (2)$$

where G is called the *product* of S and T.

Similarly, the carrying out in succession of the transformation T, then S, and then R, is the product RST. This symbol is to be interpreted as meaning that the transformations are to be carried out in order from right to left. This is important, as the *product of transformations is not necessarily commutative*. For example, let T be the moving of a point through a fixed distance in a fixed direction and S the replacing of a point by its symmetrical point with respect to a fixed plane. It is evident in this case that

$$ST \neq TS. \qquad (3)$$

A product of transformations is, however, associative. To prove this, let R, S, and T be three transformations. We wish to show that

$$(RS)T = R(ST) = RST. \qquad (4)$$

In the sense of formula (1) let

$$T(a) = b, \qquad S(b) = c, \qquad R(c) = d.$$

Then $\qquad (RS)T(a) = RS(b) = R(c) = d.$

On the other hand, $\quad ST(a) = S(b) = c,$

so that $\qquad R(ST)\ (a) = R(c) = d.$

This establishes the theorem.

If T represents an operation, T^{-1} shall represent the *inverse* operation; that is, if T transforms any element a into an element b, T^{-1} shall transform every element b back into the original a. The product then of T and T^{-1} in any order leaves all elements unchanged. It is natural to call an operation which leaves all elements unchanged an *identical* transformation and to indicate it by the symbol 1. We have then the equation

$$TT^{-1} = T^{-1}T = 1. \qquad (5)$$

If S and T are two transformations, the operation

$$TST^{-1} = S' \qquad (6)$$

is called the *transform* of S by T.

If S_1' and S_2' are the transforms of S_1 and S_2 respectively, then $S_1'S_2'$ is the transform of S_1S_2. For

$$S_1'S_2' = (TS_1T^{-1})(TS_2T^{-1}) = TS_1T^{-1}TS_2T^{-1} = T(S_1S_2)\,T^{-1}.$$

1. State which of the following pairs of operations are commutative:

    (*a*) a translation and a rotation about a fixed point;

    (*b*) two rotations;

    (*c*) two translations;

    (*d*) a rotation and a reflection on a line.

2. If S is a transformation such that $S^2 = 1$, prove that $S^{-1} = S$, and conversely. Give geometric examples of transformations of this type.

3. Prove that the reciprocal of the product of two transformations is the product of the reciprocals of the transformations in inverse order; that is, prove that $(RST)^{-1} = T^{-1}S^{-1}R^{-1}$.

4. If S is a rotation in a plane and T a translation, find the transform of S by T and the transform of T by S.

5. Prove that the transform of the inverse of S is the inverse of the transform of S.

6. If the product of two transformations is commutative, show that each is its own transform by the other.

6. Groups. *A set of transformations form a group if the set contains the inverse of every transformation of the set and if the product of any two transformations of the set is also a transformation of the set.*

In general the definition of a group of operations involves also the conditions that the operations shall be associative and that the identical transformation shall be defined. These latter conditions being always true for geometrical transformations need not be specified in our definition nor explicitly looked for in determining whether or not a given set of transformations form a group.

As an example of a group consider the operations consisting of rotating the points in space around a fixed axis through any angle equal to any multiple of $\dfrac{2\pi}{5}$. Another example consists of all possible rotations around the same axis.

A set of operations forming a group and contained in a larger group form a *subgroup* of the larger group. For example, the rotations about a fixed axis through multiples of $\dfrac{2\pi}{5}$ form a subgroup of all rotations about the same axis. Again, all mechanical motions in space form a group. All translations form a subgroup of the group of mechanical motions. All translations in a fixed direction form a subgroup of the group of translations and hence a sub-subgroup of the group of motions.

The importance of the concept of groups in geometry lies in the fact that it furnishes a means of classifying different systems of geometry. The element of the geometry having been chosen, any group of transformations may be taken, and the properties of geometric figures may be studied which are unaltered by all transformations of the group. Thus the ordinary geometry of space considers the properties of figures which are unaltered by the group of mechanical movements.

Any property or configuration which is unaltered by the operations of a group is called an *invariant* of the group. Thus distance is an invariant of the group of mechanical motions, and a circle is an invariant with respect to the group of rotations in the plane of the circle about the center of the circle.

EXERCISES

1. If x is the distance of a point P on a straight line from a fixed point O, and P is transformed into a new point P' such that $x' = ax + b$, prove that the set of transformations formed by giving to a and b all possible values form a group.

2. If (x, y) are Cartesian coördinates in a plane, and a transformation is expressed by the equations

$$x' = x \cos \alpha - y \sin \alpha,$$
$$y' = x \sin \alpha + y \cos \alpha,$$

prove that the transformations obtained by giving α all possible values form a group.

3. If (x, y) are Cartesian coördinates in a plane, prove that the transformations defined by the equations

$$x' = x \cos \alpha + y \sin \alpha,$$
$$y' = x \sin \alpha - y \cos \alpha,$$

do not form a group.

4. Name some subgroups of the groups in Exs. 1–2.

5. Let G be a given group and G_1 a subgroup. If every transformation of G_1 is replaced by its transform by T, where T belongs to G, show that the transformations thus found form a subgroup of G.

CHAPTER II

RANGES AND PENCILS

7. Cartesian coördinate of a point on a line. Consider all points which lie on a line LK (Fig. 1). These points are called a *pencil* or a *range*, and the line LK is called the *axis* or the *base* of the range. Any point P on LK may be fixed most simply by means of its distance OP from a fixed origin

L———+———+———+———+———K
　　　A　　O　　B　　P

FIG. 1

O, the distance being reckoned positive or negative according as P lies on one side or another of O. We may accordingly place

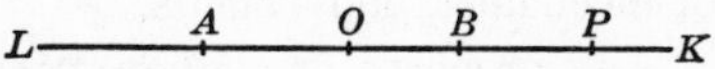

$$x = OP \qquad (1)$$

and call x the coördinate * of P. To any point P corresponds one and only one real coördinate x, and to any real x corresponds one and only one real point P. Complex values of x are said, as in § 3, to define imaginary points on LK.

The coördinate may be made homogeneous (§ 4) by using the ratio $x : t$, where $\dfrac{x}{t} = OP$. As P recedes indefinitely from O, t approaches the value 0. Hence, as in § 4, we make the convention that the line has one point at infinity with the coördinate $1 : 0$. When the nonhomogeneous x of (1) is used, the point at infinity has the coördinate ∞.

The coördinate x we call the Cartesian coördinate of P because of its familiar use in Cartesian geometry.

8. Projective coördinate of a point on a line. On the straight line LK (Fig. 1) assume two fixed points of reference A and B and two constants k_1 and k_2. Then if P is any point on LK we may take as the coördinate of P the ratio $x_1 : x_2$, where

$$x_1 : x_2 = k_1 \cdot AP : k_2 \cdot BP, \qquad (1)$$

---

* The word "coördinate" may be objected to on the ground that it implies the existence of at least two quantities which are coördinated in the usual sense. In spite of this objection we retain the word to emphasize the fact that we have here the simplest case of coördinates in an n-dimensional geometry.

8

in which the distances AP and BP are positive or negative according as P is on the one side or the other of A or B respectively. It is evident that the correspondence between real points on LK and real values of the ratio $x_1 : x_2$ is one to one. Complex values of the ratio define imaginary points on LK (§ 3).

The Cartesian coördinate of the preceding article may be considered as a special or limiting case of the kind just given. For if in (1) we place $k_1 = 1$, allow the point B to recede to infinity, and at the same time allow k_2 to approach zero in such a manner that the limit of $k_2 \cdot BP$ remains finite, equations (1) give the homogeneous Cartesian coördinates of P.

Considering (1), we see that as P recedes indefinitely from A and B the ratio $x_1 : x_2$ approaches the limiting ratio $k_1 : k_2$. Hence we say that the line has one point at infinity.

It is to be noticed that the ratio (which alone is essential) of the constants k_1 and k_2 is determined by the coördinate of any one point. Since this ratio is arbitrary the coördinate of any point may be assumed arbitrarily after the points of reference are fixed.

In particular any point may be given the coördinate $1 : 1$. This point we shall call the *unit point*. The coördinate of A is $0 : 1$ and that of B is $1 : 0$. Since the unit point and the points of reference are arbitrary, it follows that *in setting up the coördinate system any three points may be given the coördinates $0 : 1$, $1 : 0$, and $1 : 1$ respectively, and the coördinate system is fully determined by these points.*

The coördinate of this section we shall call the projective coördinate of P because of its use in projective geometry.

EXERCISES

1. Establish a coördinate system on a straight line so that the point B is 5 inches to the right of A and the unit point 1 inch to the right of A. Where is the coördinate negative?

2. Take the point B as in Ex. 1 and the unit point 1 inch to the right of B. What are the coördinates of points respectively 1, 2, 3, 4 inches to the right of A and 1, 2, 3 inches to the left of A?

9. Change of coördinates. The most general change from one system of projective coördinates to another may be made by changing the points of reference and the unit point, the latter change being equivalent to changing the ratio of the constants k_1 and k_2. Let

$x_1 : x_2$ be the coördinate of any point P (Fig. 2) referred to the points of reference A and B, with certain constants k_1 and k_2, and let $x_1' : x_2'$ be the coördinate of the same point referred to the points of reference A' and B', with constants k_1' and k_2'. Assume any point O and let $OA = a$, $OA' = a'$, $OB = b$, $OB' = b'$, and $OP = t$. Then from (1), § 8, we have

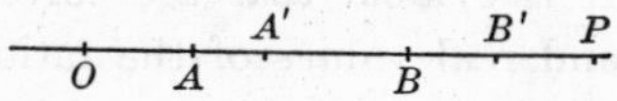

FIG. 2

$$x_1 : x_2 = k_1(t-a) : k_2(t-b), \quad x_1' : x_2' = k_1'(t-a') : k_2'(t-b'). \quad (1)$$

The elimination of t from these equations gives relations of the form

$$\begin{aligned} \rho x_1 &= \alpha_1 x_1' + \alpha_2 x_2', \\ \rho x_2 &= \beta_1 x_1' + \beta_2 x_2', \end{aligned} \quad (2)$$

which are the required formulas for the change of coördinates.

The ratio of the coefficients α_1, α_2, β_1, and β_2 will be determined if we know three values of $x_1 : x_2$ which correspond to three values of $x_1' : x_2'$, in particular to the three values $0 : 1$, $1 : 0$, $1 : 1$. For when $x_1' : x_2' = 0 : 1$ we have $x_1 : x_2 = \alpha_2 : \beta_2$; when $x_1' : x_2' = 1 : 0$ we have $x_1 : x_2 = \alpha_1 : \beta_1$; and when $x_1' : x_2' = 1 : 1$ we have $x_1 : x_2 = \alpha_1 + \alpha_2 : \beta_1 + \beta_2$.

It is obvious from the foregoing that if the reference points A and B are distinct, the coefficients in (2) must satisfy the condition $\alpha_1 \beta_2 - \alpha_2 \beta_1 \neq 0$, which is also necessary in order that the ratio $x_1 : x_2$ in equations (2) should contain $x_1' : x_2'$.

Equations (2) may be placed in a form which is of frequent use. Let us place $x_1' : x_2' = \lambda$, $\alpha_1 = z_1$, $\beta_1 = z_2$, $\alpha_2 = y_1$, $\beta_2 = y_2$, where $y_1 : y_2$ and $z_1 : z_2$ are the coördinates of the two points corresponding to $\lambda = 0$ and $\lambda = \infty$ respectively. Then equations (2) become

$$\begin{aligned} \rho x_1 &= y_1 + \lambda z_1, \\ \rho x_2 &= y_2 + \lambda z_2. \end{aligned} \quad (3)$$

Hence, *if $y_1 : y_2$ and $z_1 : z_2$ are the coördinates of any two points on a straight line, the coördinate of any other point may be written* $y_1 + \lambda z_1 : y_2 + \lambda z_2$.

EXERCISES

1. Find the formulas for the change from the coördinate in Ex. 1, § 8, to that in Ex. 2.

2. Find the formulas for a change from the coördinate in Ex. 1, § 8, to one in which the reference points are respectively 2 and 6 inches from A and the unit point 4 units from A.

3. Prove that all changes of coördinates form a group.

10. Coördinate of a line of a pencil. Consider all straight lines which lie in a plane and pass through the same point (Fig. 3). Such lines form a *pencil*, the common point being called the *vertex* of the pencil.

Let OM be a fixed line in the pencil, OP any line, and θ the angle MOP. Then it would be possible to take θ as the coördinate of OP, but in that case the line OP would have an infinite number of coördinates differing by multiples of 2π. We may make the relation between a line and its coördinate one to one by taking as the coördinate a quantity x defined by the equation

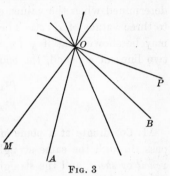

$$x = k \tan \theta, \qquad (1)$$

where k is an arbitrary constant. Then $x = 0$ is the line OM, $x = \infty$ is the line at right angles to OM, and

Fig. 3

any positive or negative real value of x corresponds to one and only one real line of the pencil, and conversely. Imaginary values of x define imaginary lines of the pencil as in § 3.

A more general coördinate may be obtained by using two fixed lines of reference OA and OB and defining the ratio $x_1 : x_2$ by the equation $\qquad x_1 : x_2 = k_1 \sin AOP : k_2 \sin BOP. \qquad (2)$

Equation (2) reduces to equation (1) when the angle AOB is a right angle, OA coincides with OM, and $x_1 : x_2 = x$.

In general let the angle $MOA = \alpha$ and the angle $MOB = \beta$. Then (2) may be written

$$x_1 : x_2 = k_1 \sin (\theta - \alpha) : k_2 \sin (\theta - \beta)$$
$$= k_1 (x \cos \alpha - k \sin \alpha) : k_2 (x \cos \beta - k \sin \beta), \qquad (3)$$

when x is defined by (1).

Now let $x_1' : x_2'$ be another coördinate of the lines of the pencil of the same form as in equation (2), but referred to lines of reference OA' and OB' and with constants k_1' and k_2'. Then $x_1' : x_2'$ is connected with $x_1 : x_2$ by a bilinear relation of the form

$$\rho x_1 = \alpha_1 x_1' + \alpha_2 x_2',$$
$$\rho x_2 = \beta_1 x_1' + \beta_2 x_2'. \qquad (4)$$

This follows from the fact that both $x_1 : x_2$ and $x_1' : x_2'$ are connected with x by a relation of the form (3).

Since a transformation of coördinates is effected either by change of the lines of reference or by change of the constants k_1 and k_2, it follows that any transformation of coördinates is expressed by a relation of form (4). The coefficients of the transformation are determined when the values of $x_1 : x_2$ are known which correspond to three values of $x_1' : x_2'$. The proof is as in § 9. Also, as in § 9, it may be shown that if $y_1 : y_2$ and $z_1 : z_2$ are the coördinates of any two lines of a pencil, the coördinate of any line may be written

$$\rho x_1 = y_1 + \lambda z_1,$$
$$\rho x_2 = y_2 + \lambda z_2. \tag{5}$$

11. Coördinate of a plane of a pencil. Consider all planes which pass through the same straight line (Fig. 4). Such planes form a *pencil* or *sheaf*, and the straight line is called the *axis* of the pencil. The coördinate of a plane of the sheaf may be obtained by first assuming two planes of reference a and b and a fixed constant k. Then, if p is any plane of the pencil and (a, p) means the angle between a and p, we may define the coördinate of p as the ratio $x_1 : x_2$ given by the equations

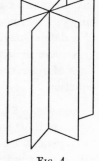

$$x_1 : x_2 = k_1 \sin (a, p) : k_2 \sin (b, p). \tag{1}$$

It is obvious that if a plane m be passed perpendicular to the axis of the pencil, the planes of the pencil cut out a pencil of lines in the plane m. The angle between two lines of this pencil is the

Fig. 4

plane angle of the two planes in which the two lines lie. Hence the coördinate $x_1 : x_2$ defined in (1) is also the coördinate of the lines of the pencil in the plane m, in the sense of § 10. The results of § 10 with reference to transformation of coördinates hold, therefore, for a pencil of planes. In particular, if $y_1 : y_2$ and $z_1 : z_2$ are the coördinates of any two planes of a sheaf, the coördinate of any plane of the pencil may be written

$$\rho x_1 = y_1 + \lambda z_1,$$
$$\rho x_2 = y_2 + \lambda z_2. \tag{2}$$

CHAPTER III

PROJECTIVITY

12. The linear transformation. We shall now consider the substitution

$$\rho x_1' = \alpha_1 x_1 + \beta_1 x_2, \qquad (\alpha_1\beta_2 - \alpha_2\beta_1 \neq 0) \qquad (1)$$
$$\rho x_2' = \alpha_2 x_2 + \beta_2 x_2$$

not as a change of coördinates, as in § 9, but as defining a transformation in the sense of § 5. Then $x_1 : x_2$ are to be interpreted as the coördinate of an element of a one-dimensional extent and $x_1' : x_2'$ as the coördinate of the transformed element of the same or another one-dimensional extent. If $x_1 : x_2$ and $x_1' : x_2'$ refer to different extents, the elements need not be of the same kind. For example, the transformation (1) may express the transformation of points into lines, of points into planes, of lines into planes, and so on.

To study the transformation we shall find it convenient to use a nonhomogeneous form obtained by replacing $x_1 : x_2$ by λ, $x_1' : x_2'$ by λ', and changing the form of the constants. We have

$$\lambda' = \frac{\alpha\lambda + \beta}{\gamma\lambda + \delta}. \qquad (\alpha\delta - \beta\gamma \neq 0) \qquad (2)$$

Here λ and λ' may be the point, line, or plane coördinates of §§ 7, 8, 10, 11 or may be the λ used in the formulas of §§ 9–11. More generally still, λ may be any quantity which can be used to define an element of any kind, even though not yet employed in this text.

In each case the element with coördinate λ is said to be transformed into the element with coördinate λ', and the two elements λ and λ' are said to correspond. There is one and only one element λ' corresponding to an element λ. Conversely, from (2) we obtain

$$\lambda = \frac{\delta\lambda' - \beta}{-\gamma\lambda' + \alpha}. \qquad (3)$$

Hence to an element λ' corresponds one and only one element λ. In other words, *the correspondence between the elements λ and the elements λ' is one to one.*

Any element whose coördinate is unchanged by the transformation is called a *fixed element* of the transformation. This definition has its chief significance when the elements λ and λ' are points of the same range, or lines of the same pencil, or planes of the same pencil. If, for example, λ and λ' are points of the same range, the point λ is transformed into the point λ', which is in general a different point from λ, but the fixed points are unchanged.

To find the fixed elements we have to put $\lambda = \lambda'$ in (2) or in (3). There results

$$\gamma\lambda^2 + (\delta - \alpha)\,\lambda - \beta = 0. \qquad (4)$$

Any linear transformation has, accordingly, two fixed elements, which may be distinct or coincident.

If α, β, γ, and δ are real numbers, and real coördinates λ and λ' correspond to real elements, we may make the following classification of the linear transformations:

(1) $(\delta - \alpha)^2 + 4\,\beta\gamma > 0$. The fixed elements are real and distinct. The transformation is called *hyperbolic.*

(2) $(\delta - \alpha)^2 + 4\,\beta\gamma < 0$. The fixed elements are imaginary with conjugate imaginary coördinates. The transformation is called *elliptic.*

(3) $(\delta - \alpha)^2 + 4\,\beta\gamma = 0$. The fixed points are real and coincident. The transformation is called *parabolic.*

By the transformation (2) an element P with coördinate λ is transformed into an element Q with the coördinate λ'. At the same time the element Q is transformed into an element R with coördinate λ''. In general, R is distinct from P, for λ'' is given by the equation

$$\lambda'' = \frac{\alpha\lambda' + \beta}{\gamma\lambda' + \delta} = \frac{(\alpha^2 + \beta\gamma)\lambda + \alpha\beta + \beta\delta}{(\alpha\gamma + \gamma\delta)\lambda + \beta\gamma + \delta^2}. \qquad (5)$$

In order that λ'' should always be the same as λ it is necessary and sufficient that the equation

$$(\alpha\gamma + \gamma\delta)\,\lambda^2 + (\delta^2 - \alpha^2)\,\lambda - (\alpha\beta + \beta\delta) = 0$$

should be true for all values of λ. The coefficients α, β, γ, and δ must then satisfy the equations

$$\alpha\gamma + \gamma\delta = 0,$$
$$\delta^2 - \alpha^2 = 0, \qquad\qquad (6)$$
$$\alpha\beta + \beta\delta = 0.$$

The second equation gives $\delta = \pm \alpha$. If we take $\delta = \alpha$ the other two equations give $\gamma = 0$, $\beta = 0$, and the transformation (1) reduces to the identical transformation $\lambda = \lambda'$. We must therefore take $\delta = -\alpha$, and all three equations (6) are satisfied.

The transformation then becomes

$$\lambda' = \frac{\alpha\lambda + \beta}{\gamma\lambda - \alpha}. \qquad (\alpha^2 + \beta\gamma \neq 0) \qquad (7)$$

A linear transformation of this type is called *involutory*. It has the property that if repeated once it produces the identical transformation. The correspondence between the elements λ and the transformed elements λ' is called an *involution*.

EXERCISES

1. Find the transformation which transforms 0, 1, ∞ into 1, ∞, 0, respectively. What are the fixed points of the transformation?

2. If x is the Cartesian coördinate of a point on a straight line, determine the linear transformation which interchanges the origin and the point at infinity. What are the fixed points of the transformation? Do all such transformations form a group?

3. If x is the Cartesian coördinate of a point on a straight line, determine the transformation which has only the origin for a fixed point and also that which has only the point at infinity for a fixed point. Does each of these types of transformation form a group?

4. If x is the Cartesian coördinate of a point on a straight line, determine a transformation with the fixed points $\pm i$. Do these form a group?

5. Show that the general linear transformation may be obtained as the product of two transformations of the type $\lambda' = a\lambda$, two of the type $\lambda' = \lambda + b$, and one of the type $\lambda' = \dfrac{1}{\lambda}$.

6. Show that any transformation with two distinct fixed elements a and b can be written $\dfrac{\lambda' - a}{\lambda' - b} = k\,\dfrac{\lambda - a}{\lambda - b}$.

7. Show that any transformation with a single fixed element a can be written $\dfrac{1}{\lambda' - a} = \dfrac{1}{\lambda - a} + b$.

8. Show that any involutory transformation can be written $\dfrac{\lambda' - a}{\lambda' - b} = -\dfrac{\lambda - a}{\lambda - b}$, where a and b are the fixed elements.

9. Show that all transformations with the same fixed elements form a group.

10. Consider the set of circles which pass through the same two fixed points, and the common diameter of the circles. Show that if P and Q are the two points in which any one of the circles meets the common diameter, P may be transformed into Q by an involutory transformation, the form of which is the same for all points P. Show that the transformation is elliptic or hyperbolic according as the two fixed points in which the circles intersect are real or imaginary.

11. Show, conversely to Ex. 10, that any involutory transformation may be geometrically constructed as there described.

13. The cross ratio. The linear transformation contains three constants; namely, the ratios of the four coefficients α, β, γ, and δ. These constants can be so determined that any three arbitrarily assumed values of λ can be made to correspond to any three arbitrarily assumed values of λ'. In other words,

I. By a linear transformation any three elements can be transformed into any other three elements, and these three pairs of corresponding elements are sufficient to fix the transformation.

To write the transformation in terms of the coördinates of three pairs of corresponding elements, we write first

$$\frac{\lambda' - \lambda_2}{\lambda' - \lambda_1'} = \alpha \, \frac{\lambda - \lambda_2}{\lambda - \lambda_1}, \tag{1}$$

which is obviously a transformation by which λ_1 is transformed into λ_1', and λ_2 into λ_2'. If, in addition, λ_3 is to be transformed into λ_3', α must be determined by the equation

$$\frac{\lambda_3' - \lambda_2'}{\lambda_3' - \lambda_1'} = \alpha \, \frac{\lambda_3 - \lambda_2}{\lambda_3 - \lambda_1}. \tag{2}$$

From (1) and (2) we have

$$\frac{\lambda' - \lambda_2'}{\lambda' - \lambda_1'} \cdot \frac{\lambda_3' - \lambda_1'}{\lambda_3' - \lambda_2'} = \frac{\lambda - \lambda_2}{\lambda - \lambda_1} \cdot \frac{\lambda_3 - \lambda_1}{\lambda_3 - \lambda_2}, \tag{3}$$

which is the required transformation.

If λ_4 and λ_4' are a fourth pair of corresponding elements, we have, from (3),

$$\frac{\lambda_4' - \lambda_2'}{\lambda_4 - \lambda_1'} \cdot \frac{\lambda_3' - \lambda_1'}{\lambda_3' - \lambda_2'} = \frac{\lambda_4 - \lambda_2}{\lambda_4 - \lambda_1} \cdot \frac{\lambda_3 - \lambda_1}{\lambda_3 - \lambda_2},$$

or, with a slight rearrangement,

$$\frac{\lambda_1' - \lambda_3'}{\lambda_1' - \lambda_4'} \cdot \frac{\lambda_2' - \lambda_4'}{\lambda_2' - \lambda_3'} = \frac{\lambda_1 - \lambda_3}{\lambda_1 - \lambda_4} \cdot \frac{\lambda_2 - \lambda_4}{\lambda_1 - \lambda_3}. \tag{4}$$

The quantity
$$\frac{\lambda_1 - \lambda_3}{\lambda_1 - \lambda_4} \cdot \frac{\lambda_2 - \lambda_4}{\lambda_2 - \lambda_3} \tag{5}$$

is called the *cross ratio*, or the *anharmonic ratio*, of the four elements λ_1, λ_2, λ_3, λ_4, and is denoted by the symbol $(\lambda_1 \lambda_2, \cdot \lambda_3 \lambda_4)$. Equation (4) establishes the theorem:

II. *The cross ratio of four elements is unaltered by any linear transformation.*

The cross ratio is accordingly independent of the coördinate system used in defining the elements.

The cross ratio depends not only on the four elements involved but also on the order in which they are taken. Now four things may be taken in twenty-four different orders, but there result only six distinct cross ratios. In fact, it is easy to show, by writing all possible cross ratios, that the six distinct ones are

$$r, \quad \frac{1}{r}, \quad 1-r, \quad \frac{1}{1-r}, \quad \frac{r-1}{r}, \quad \frac{r}{r-1},$$

where r is any one of them.

In naming the cross ratio of four elements it is therefore necessary to indicate the order in which the elements are to be taken. We have adopted the convention that if P_1, P_2, P_3, and P_4 are four elements with the coördinates λ_1, λ_2, λ_3, and λ_4 respectively, the cross ratio indicated by the symbol $(P_1 P_2, P_3 P_4)$ shall be given by the relation

$$(P_1 P_2, P_3 P_4) = \frac{\lambda_1 - \lambda_3}{\lambda_1 - \lambda_4} \cdot \frac{\lambda_2 - \lambda_4}{\lambda_2 - \lambda_3}. \tag{6}$$

If, then, we denote $(P_1 P_2, P_3 P_4)$ by r, it is evident that

$$(P_1 P_2, P_4 P_3) = \frac{1}{r}, \quad (P_1 P_3, P_2 P_4) = 1 - r, \quad (P_1 P_3, P_4 P_2) = \frac{1}{1-r},$$

$$(P_1 P_4, P_2 P_3) = \frac{r-1}{r}, \quad (P_1 P_4, P_3 P_2) = \frac{r}{r-1}.$$

A special form which the cross ratio takes for certain coördinates is of importance and is given in the following theorem:

III. *If the elements P and Q have the coördinates $y_1 : y_2$ and $z_1 : z_2$ respectively, and the elements R and S have the coördinates $y_1 + \lambda z_1 : y_2 + \lambda z_2$ and $y_1 + \mu z_1 : y_2 + \mu z_2$ respectively, then*

$$(PQ, RS) = (RS, PQ) = \frac{\lambda}{\mu}.$$

To prove this take $\lambda_1 = 0$ for the element P, $\lambda_2 = \infty$ for the element Q, $\lambda_3 = \lambda$ for the element R, and $\lambda_4 = \mu$ for the element S, and substitute in (6).

If λ is the Cartesian coördinate of a point on a straight line, then $\lambda_1 - \lambda_3 = P_3 P_1$, $\lambda_1 - \lambda_4 = P_4 P_1$, $\lambda_2 - \lambda_3 = P_3 P_2$, $\lambda_2 - \lambda_4 = P_4 P_2$, and

$$(P_1 P_2, P_3 P_4) = \frac{P_1 P_3}{P_1 P_4} \cdot \frac{P_2 P_4}{P_2 P_3}. \tag{7}$$

The cross ratio is accordingly found by finding the ratio of the segments into which the line $P_3 P_4$ is divided by P_1 and the ratio of the segments into which $P_3 P_4$ is divided by P_2, and forming the ratio of these ratios.

14. Harmonic sets. If a cross ratio is equal to -1, it is called a *harmonic ratio*. If P_1, P_2, P_3, and P_4 are four elements such that

$$(P_1 P_2, P_3 P_4) = -1,$$

the four elements form a harmonic set, and the points P_1 and P_2 are said to be harmonic conjugates to P_3 and P_4.

From III, § 13, it follows that the points $y_1 + \lambda z_1 : y_2 + \lambda z_2$ and $y_1 - \lambda z_1 : y_2 - \lambda z_2$ are harmonic conjugates to $y_1 : y_2$ and $z_1 : z_2$.

From (7), § 13, it follows that if four points on a straight line form a harmonic set, then

$$\frac{P_1 P_3}{P_1 P_4} = -\frac{P_2 P_3}{P_2 P_4}.$$

This shows that the two points in a harmonic set divide the distance between their harmonic conjugates internally and externally in the same ratio.

1. Show that the cross ratio of any point, the transformed point, and the two fixed points of any elliptic or hyperbolic transformation is constant. This is sometimes called the *characteristic cross ratio* of the transformation. What happens to the characteristic cross ratio as the two fixed points approach coincidence?

2. Show that by any involutory transformation any element is transformed into its harmonic conjugate with respect to the two fixed elements.

3. If λ_1, λ_2, λ_3, λ_4 form a harmonic set, prove that

$$\frac{2}{\lambda_2 - \lambda_1} = \frac{1}{\lambda_3 - \lambda_1} + \frac{1}{\lambda_4 - \lambda_1}.$$

In general, prove that if $(\lambda_1\lambda_2, \lambda_3\lambda_4) = k$,

$$\frac{1-k}{\lambda_2 - \lambda_1} = \frac{1}{\lambda_4 - \lambda_1} - \frac{k}{\lambda_3 - \lambda_1}.$$

4. Write the transformation by which each point on a line is transformed into its harmonic conjugate with respect to the points $\lambda = -a$, $\lambda = a$. What are the fixed points of the transformation?

5. Prove that an involution of lines of a pencil contains one and only one pair of perpendicular lines (that is, one case in which a line is perpendicular to its transformed line) unless all pairs of lines are perpendicular. When does the latter case occur?

6. Let $x_1 : x_2$ be the coördinate of a point on a line and consider the point pair defined by the equation

$$a_{11}x_1^2 + 2\,a_{12}x_1x_2 + a_{22}x_2^2 = 0.$$

Show that the equation may be reduced to one of three types by a real transformation of coördinates and give the analytic condition for each type.

7. Let A and B be two distinct points defined by the equation of Ex. 6, and $P\,(y_1 : y_2)$ and $Q\,(z_1 : z_2)$ and $R\,(w_1 : w_2)$ any three points. If the *projective distance* between two points is defined by the equation $D(PQ) = \dfrac{k}{2}\log(PQ, AB)$, show that $D(PQ) + D(QR) = D(PR)$.

Consider two cases:

1. A and B real. Take k real. Then any two points between A and B have a real distance apart. A and B are at an infinite distance from any other point. Any point not between A and B is at an imaginary distance from any point between A and B.

2. *A* and *B* conjugate imaginary. Take *k* pure imaginary. Any two real points are at a real finite distance apart. The total length of the line is finite.

8. Consider the point pair defined by the equation

$$a_{11}x_1^2 + 2\,a_{12}x_1x_2 + a_{22}x_2^2 = 0.$$

Then, if $y_1 : y_2$ is any given point, the equation

$$(a_{11}y_1 + a_{12}y_2)x_1 + (a_{12}y_1 + a_{22}y_2)x_2 = 0$$

defines a point which is called the *polar point* of *y* with respect to the point pair. Assuming $a_{11}a_{22} - a_{12}^2 \neq 0$, show that to any point corresponds a definite polar point and that any point is the polar point of a definite point *y*. Show that a point and its polar are harmonic conjugates with respect to the point pair. What happens to these theorems if $a_{11}a_{22} - a_{12}^2 = 0$?

15. Projection. Two one-dimensional extents are said to be in *projection* if the elements of the two extents are brought into correspondence by means of a linear relation,

$$\lambda' = \frac{\alpha\lambda + \beta}{\gamma\lambda + \delta}, \qquad (\alpha\delta - \beta\gamma \neq 0)$$

between their coördinates. The correspondence is called a *projectivity*. If the correspondence is involutory, the projectivity is an involution (§ 12). From the definition the following theorems may be immediately deduced:

I. The cross ratio of any four elements of a one-dimensional extent is the same as the cross ratio of the four corresponding elements of a projective extent.

II. Two one-dimensional extents may be brought into projection with each other in such a way that any three elements of one are made to correspond to any three elements of the other.

III. A projectivity is fully determined by three pairs of corresponding elements.

IV. Two extents which are in projection with the same third extent are in projection with each other.

EXERCISE

If the points of a circle are connected to any two fixed points of the circle, show that the two pencils of lines formed are projective.

16. Perspective figures. A simple case of a projectivity is that called a perspectivity, now to be defined. Noting that we have to do with pencils of different kinds, according as they are made up of points, lines, or planes, we say that two pencils of different kinds are in *perspective* when they are made to correspond in such a manner that each element of one pencil lies in the corresponding element of the other. Two pencils of the same kind are in *perspective* when each is

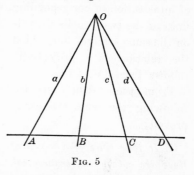

Fig. 5

in perspective to the same pencil of another kind. The correspondence between perspective figures is called a *perspectivity*.

A pencil of points and one of lines are therefore in perspective when they lie as in Fig. 5, where the lines a, b, c, d, etc. correspond to the points A, B, C, D, etc. To see that we are justified in calling this relation a projectivity, note that

$$\frac{AD}{BD} = \frac{OA \sin AOD}{OB \sin BOD} = \lambda.$$

Hence, if A and B are taken as fixed points and D as any point, the variable λ is a coördinate at the same time of the points of the pencil of points and of the lines of the pencil of lines. Since any change of coördinate of either of the pencils is expressed by a linear relation, the two pencils satisfy the definition of projective figures.

Two pencils (ranges) of points are in perspective when they are perspective to the same pencil of lines as in Fig. 6. The straight lines connecting corresponding

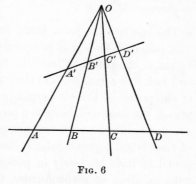

Fig. 6

points of the two ranges then pass through a common point. That the relation is a projectivity follows from **IV, § 15.**

Two pencils of lines are in perspective when they are in perspective to the same range of points as in Fig. 7. The points of intersection of corresponding lines of the two pencils then lie on the same straight line. That the relation is a projectivity follows from IV, § 15.

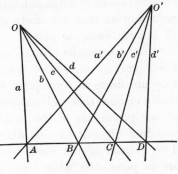

From these definitions the following theorems are easily proved:

I. If four lines of a pencil of lines are cut by any transversal, the cross ratio of the four points of intersection is independent of the

FIG. 7

position of the transversal and is equal to the cross ratio of the four lines.

II. If four points of a range are connected with any center, the cross ratio of the four connecting lines is independent of the position of the center and is equal to the cross ratio of the four points of the range.

III. If the straight lines connecting three pairs of corresponding points of two projective ranges meet in a point, all the lines connecting corresponding points meet in that point, and the ranges are in perspective.

IV. If the points of intersection of three pairs of corresponding lines of two projective pencils lie on a straight line, the points of intersection of all pairs of corresponding lines lie on that line, and the pencils are in perspective.

The last two theorems follow from III, § 15.

A pencil of lines is in perspective to a pencil of planes when the vertex of the pencil of lines lies in the axis of the pencil of planes and each line corresponds to the plane in which it lies. If the plane of the pencil of lines is perpendicular to the axis of the pencil of planes, the correspondence is a projectivity, since, by § 11, the same coördinate may be used for each pencil. If the plane of the pencil of lines is not perpendicular to the axis of the pencil of planes, the pencil of lines is clearly in perspective to another pencil of lines with its plane so perpendicular, for in Fig. 7 the two pencils are not necessarily in the same plane. Hence the relation here is also a projectivity.

EXERCISES

1. Consider any two projective pencils of lines not in perspective and construct the locus of the intersections of corresponding lines. Show that this locus passes through the vertices of the two pencils and that it is intersected by an arbitrary line in not more than two points.

2. Consider any two pencils of points not in perspective and construct the lines joining corresponding points. These lines envelop a curve. Show that not more than two of these lines pass through any arbitrary point and that the two bases of the pencils belong to these lines.

3. Consider the locus of the lines of intersection of corresponding planes of two pencils of planes not in perspective. Show that this locus contains the two axes of the pencils and that it is cut by any arbitrary plane in a curve such as is defined in Ex. 1.

4. Show that if the line connecting the vertices of two projective pencils of lines is self-corresponding (that is, considered as belonging to one pencil it corresponds to itself considered as belonging to the other pencil) the pencils are in perspective.

5. Show that if the point of intersection of the bases of two projective ranges is self-corresponding (see Ex. 4) the ranges are in perspective.

6. Given any two projective ranges of points. Connect any pair of corresponding points and take any two points O and O' on the connecting line. With O as a center construct a pencil of lines in perspective with the first range, and with O' as a center construct a pencil of lines in perspective with the second range. Prove by use of Ex. 4 that the two pencils are in perspective. Hence show how corresponding points of two ranges can be found if three pairs of corresponding points are known or assumed.

7. Given two projective pencils of lines. Take the point of intersection of two corresponding lines and through it draw any two lines o and o'. On o construct a range of points in perspective to the first pencil of lines and on o' construct a range of points in perspective to the second pencil of lines. Prove by use of Ex. 5 that the two ranges are in perspective. Hence show how corresponding lines of two projective pencils can be found if three pairs of corresponding lines are known or assumed.

17. Other one-dimensional extents. We have taken as an example of a one-dimensional extent of points the range, or pencil, consisting of all the points on a straight line. It is obvious, however, that this is not the only example of a one-dimensional extent of points.

In fact, any curve, whether in the plane or in space, is a one-dimensional extent, the coördinate of an element of which may be defined in a variety of ways. One of the simplest methods is to take the length of the curve measured from a fixed point to a variable point as the coördinate of the latter point, but other methods will suggest themselves to the reader familiar with the parametric representation of curves. In the case of a circle, for example, we may construct a pencil of lines with its vertex on the circle, take as the initial line of the coördinate system the tangent line to the circle through the vertex of the pencil, and then take as the coördinate of a point on the circle the coördinate of the line of the pencil which passes through that point.

Similarly, the tangent lines to a plane or space curve form an example of a one-dimensional extent of lines. Also the tangent planes to a cone or a cylinder or the osculating planes to a space curve are examples of a one-dimensional extent of planes. These extents, both of lines and planes, will be discussed later.

Moreover, it is not necessary that we confine ourselves to points, lines, and planes as elements. We may, for example, take the circle in a plane as the element of a plane geometry. In that case all the circles which pass through the same two points form a one-dimensional extent, a pencil of circles. Another example of a one-dimensional extent of circles consists of all circles whose centers lie on a fixed curve and whose radii are uniquely determined by the positions of their centers.

In like manner the sphere may be taken as the element of a space geometry. All the spheres which intersect in a fixed circle form then a one-dimensional extent of spheres, a pencil of spheres, and other examples are readily thought of.

In all these cases, when the coördinate λ of the element of the extent is fixed, the discussion of the previous sections applies.

One more remark is important. In all cases we have allowed λ to take complex values. That is, λ is a number of the type

$$\lambda = \lambda_1 + i\lambda_2,$$

where $i = \sqrt{-1}$. The variable λ may accordingly be interpreted in the usual manner on the complex plane. The significance of the linear transformation may then be studied from the standpoint of the theory of functions of a complex variable. This lies completely outside of the range of this book.

We notice, however, that in interpreting λ as the coördinate of a point on a straight line we have a one-dimensional extent of complex values, while in interpreting it as a complex point on a plane we have a two-dimensional extent of real values. That is, *the dimensions of an extent will depend upon whether it is counted in terms of complex quantities or of real quantities.* Usually we shall in this book count dimensions in terms of quantities each of which may take complex values.

Consider the complex quantity

$$\lambda = \lambda_1 + i\lambda_2, \tag{1}$$

where λ_1 and λ_2 are real, and let

$$\lambda_1 = f_1(t), \qquad \lambda_2 = f_2(t), \tag{2}$$

t being a real quantity and the functions real functions.

Then as t varies, the point λ traces out a curve on the complex plane which is one-dimensional. If λ is interpreted as the coördinate of a point on a straight line, then equations (2) define a one-dimensional extent of points on the straight line, which do not of course contain all the points of the line. Such a one-dimensional extent of points is called a *thread* of the line. Examples are the thread of real points ($\lambda_2 = 0$), the thread of pure imaginary points ($\lambda_1 = 0$), the thread of points $\lambda_1(1 + i)$ the square of whose coördinates is pure imaginary, and others which can be formed at pleasure.

REFERENCES

Students who wish to read more on the subject of projectivities may consult the following short texts:

LING, WENTWORTH, and SMITH, Elements of Projective Geometry. Ginn and Company.

LEHMER, Synthetic Projective Geometry. Ginn and Company.

DOWLING, Projective Geometry. McGraw-Hill Book Company, Inc.

These books differ from the present one in being synthetic instead of analytic in treatment, and they go beyond the content of our Part I in discussing two-dimensional extents. In spite of that they may easily be read at this point. If larger treatises are needed, consult the references at the end of Part II of this book.

PART II. TWO-DIMENSIONAL GEOMETRY

CHAPTER IV

POINT AND LINE COÖRDINATES IN A PLANE

18. Homogeneous Cartesian point coördinates. Let OX and OY be two axes of coördinates, which we take for convenience as rectangular. Then, if P is any point and PM is drawn perpendicular to OX, meeting it at M, the distances OM and MP, with the usual conventions as to signs, are the well-known Cartesian coördinates of P. To make the coördinates homogeneous we place

$$OM = \frac{x}{t}, \qquad MP = \frac{y}{t}. \tag{1}$$

Then to any point P corresponds a definite pair of ratios $x : y : t$. Conversely, to any real pair of ratios $x : y : t$, in which t is not equal to zero, corresponds a real point. In order that a point may correspond to any pair of ratios we need to make the following definitions, in harmony with the general conventions of §§ 3 and 4:

(1) The ratios $0 : 0 : 0$ shall not be allowable, for they make both OM and MP indeterminate, and the point P cannot be fixed.

(2) Complex ratios shall be said to represent an imaginary point (§ 3).

(3) A set of ratios in which $t = 0$ shall be said to represent a point at infinity (§ 4). In fact, it is obvious that as t approaches zero, P recedes indefinitely from 0, and conversely. In particular, the point $0 : 1 : 0$ is the point at infinity on the line OY (§ 7), the point $1 : 0 : 0$ is the point at infinity on the line OX, and $a : b : 0$ is the point at infinity on the line $OM = \frac{a}{b} MP$.

19. The straight line. It is a fundamental proposition in analytic geometry that any linear equation

$$Ax + By + Ct = 0 \tag{1}$$

represents a straight line. This is partly a theorem and partly a definition. It is a theorem as far as it concerns real points whose

27

coördinates satisfy an equation of the form (1), in which the coefficients are all real and A and B are not both zero. For proof of the theorem we refer to any textbook on analytic geometry.

The proposition is a definition as far as it refers to imaginary points, to equations with complex coefficients, or to the equation $t = 0$. In this sense "straight line" means simply the totality of pairs of ratios $x : y : t$ which satisfy equation (1).

In particular, the equation $t = 0$ is satisfied by all points at infinity. Hence *all points at infinity lie on a straight line, called the line at infinity.*

If one or more of the coefficients of (1) are complex the straight line is said to be imaginary. It is interesting to note that *an imaginary straight line has one and only one real point.* To prove this let us place in (1)

$$A = a_1 + ia_2, \quad B = b_1 + ib_2, \quad C = c_1 + ic_2.$$

Then (1) is satisfied by real values of x, y, and t when and only when

$$a_1x + b_1y + c_1t = 0,$$
$$a_2x + b_2y + c_2t = 0.$$

These equations have one and only one solution for the ratios $x : y : t$, and the theorem is proved. Of course the real point may be at infinity.

Consider now any two straight lines, real or imaginary, with the equations

$$A_1x + B_1y + C_1t = 0,$$
$$A_2x + B_2y + C_2t = 0.$$

These equations have the unique solution

$$x : y : t = B_1C_2 - B_2C_1 : C_1A_2 - C_2A_1 : A_1B_2 - A_2B_1,$$

which represents the common point of the two lines. This point is at infinity when $A_1B_2 - A_2B_1 = 0$, in which case, as is shown in any textbook on analytic geometry, the lines, if real, are parallel. If the lines are imaginary they will be called parallel by definition. We may say

Two straight lines intersect in one and only one point. If the lines are parallel, the point of intersection is at infinity.

If (x_0, y_0) is a fixed point on the line (1), we have

$$A(x - x_0) + B(y - y_0) = 0 ; \tag{2}$$

whence

$$\frac{y - y_0}{x - x_0} = - \frac{A}{B}.$$

Whether A and B be real or complex quantities, there exists a real or imaginary angle θ such that

$$\tan \theta = - \frac{A}{B}.$$

Then, from equation (2),

$$\frac{x - x_0}{\cos \theta} = \frac{y - y_0}{\sin \theta}.$$

By placing these equal ratios equal to r we have, as another method of representing a straight line analytically, the equations

$$x = x_0 + r \cos \theta,$$
$$y = y_0 + r \sin \theta. \tag{3}$$

These are the parametric equations of the straight line. In them x_0, y_0, and θ are constants and r a variable parameter to each value of which corresponds one and only one point on the line, and conversely. If the quantities involved are all real, the relation between them is easily represented by a figure. In all cases

$$r = \sqrt{(x - x_0)^2 + (y - y_0)^2} \tag{4}$$

and is defined as the distance between the points (x, y) and (x_0, y_0).

This work breaks down only when $A^2 + B^2 = 0$. In that case either $A = B = 0$, and the line (1) is the line at infinity, or equation (1) takes the form

$$x \pm iy + C = 0. \tag{5}$$

Here we may still place

$$\tan \theta = \pm i,$$

but $\sin \theta$ and $\cos \theta$ become infinite and equations (3) are impossible. In fact, equation (2) becomes

$$(x - x_0) \pm i(y - y_0) = 0$$

and

$$r = \sqrt{(x - x_0)^2 + (y - y_0)^2} = 0.$$

This shows that the distance between any two points on the imaginary lines (5) must be taken as zero. For that reason they are called *minimum lines*. They play a unique and very important part in the geometry of the plane.

EXERCISES

1. Prove that through every imaginary point goes one and only one real line.

2. Prove that if a real straight line contains an imaginary point it contains also the conjugate imaginary point (that is, the point whose coördinates are conjugate imaginary to those of the first point).

3. Prove that if a real point lies on an imaginary line it lies also on the conjugate imaginary line (that is, the line whose coefficients are conjugate imaginary to those of the first line).

4. If the usual formula for the angle between two lines is extended to imaginary lines, show that the angle between a minimum line and another line is infinite and that the angle between two minimum lines is indeterminate.

5. Given a pencil of lines with its vertex at the origin. Prove that if the pencil is projected on itself by rotating each line through a constant angle, the fixed points of the projection are the minimum lines.

6. Show that a parametric form of the equations of a minimum line is

$$x = x_0 + t,$$

$$y = y_0 \pm it,$$

where t is a parameter, not a length.

20. The circle points at infinity. The circle is defined analytically by the equation

$$a(x^2 + y^2) + 2fxt + 2gyt + ct^2 = 0, \tag{1}$$

the form to which equation (4), § 19, reduces when x_0, y_0, and r are constants and (x, y) are replaced by $x : y : t$.

If $a \neq 0$, the circle evidently meets the line at infinity in the two points $1 : i : 0$ and $1 : -i : 0$, no matter what the values of the coefficients in its equation. These two points are called the *circle points at infinity*. If $a = 0$ in (1), the circle contains the entire line at infinity and, in particular, the circle points. Hence we may say that *all circles pass through the two circle points at infinity*.

The circle points $1 : \pm i : 0$ are said to be at infinity because they satisfy the equation $t = 0$. Their distance from the center of the circle is not, however, infinite. The distance between two points with the nonhomogeneous coördinates (x, y) and (x_0, y_0) is

$$d = \sqrt{(x - x_0)^2 + (y - y_0)^2},$$

which can be written in homogeneous coördinates as

$$d = \frac{\sqrt{(xt_0 - x_0t)^2 + (yt_0 - y_0t)^2}}{tt_0}, \tag{2}$$

and this becomes indeterminate when $x : y : t$ is replaced by $1 : \pm i : 0$.

This perhaps makes it easier to understand the statement that these points lie on all circles.

If $x_0 : y_0 : t_0$ is the center of the circle and r its radius, equation (1) can be written (compare equation (2))

$$(xt_0 - x_0t)^2 + (yt_0 - y_0t)^2 - r^2t_0^2t^2 = 0.$$

When $r = 0$ this equation becomes

$$(xt_0 - x_0t)^2 + (yt_0 - y_0t)^2 = 0, \tag{3}$$

the locus of which may be described as a circle with center (x_0, y_0) and radius zero. When the center is a real point the circle (3) contains no other real point and is accordingly often called a *point circle*. A point circle, however, contains other imaginary points. In fact, equation (3) may be written as

$$[(xt_0 - x_0t) + i(yt_0 - y_0t)][(xt_0 - x_0t) - i(yt_0 - y_0t)] = 0,$$

which is equivalent to the two linear equations

$$\begin{aligned} t_0(x + iy) - (x_0 + iy_0)t &= 0, \\ t_0(x - iy) - (x_0 - iy_0)t &= 0, \end{aligned} \tag{4}$$

each of which is satisfied by one of the circle points at infinity. Hence we have the result that *a point circle consists of the two imaginary straight lines drawn from the center of the circle to the two circle points at infinity.*

The distance from the point (x_0, y_0) to any point on either of the two lines just described is zero, by virtue of equation (3). There are therefore the minimum lines of § 19, as is also directly visible from equations (4). It is obvious that through any point of the plane go two minimum lines, one to each of the circle points at infinity.

EXERCISES

1. Show that an imaginary circle may contain either no real point, one real point, or two real points.

2. Consider the pencil of circles composed of all circles through two fixed points. Show that the pencil contains two point circles and one circle consisting of a straight line and the line at infinity. Show also that the point circles have real centers when the fixed points of the pencil of circles are conjugate imaginary, and that the point circles have imaginary centers when the fixed points are real.

3. If a pencil of circles consists of circles through a fixed point and tangent at that point to a fixed line, where are the point circles and the straight line of the pencil?

21. The conic. An equation of the second degree,

$$ax^2 + 2\,hxy + by^2 + 2\,fxt + 2\,gyt + ct^2 = 0, \tag{1}$$

represents a locus, called a *conic*, which is intersected by a general straight line in two points. For the simultaneous solution of the equation (1) and the equation

$$Ax + By + Ct = 0 \tag{2}$$

consists of two sets of ratios except for particular values of A, B, and C.

Let the equation (1) be written in the nonhomogeneous form by placing $t = 1$, and let (2) be written in the form (§ 19)

$$x = x_0 + r \cos \theta, \qquad y = y_0 + r \sin \theta. \tag{3}$$

The values of r which correspond to the points of intersection of the straight line (2) with the curve (1) will be found by substituting in (1) the values of x and y given by (3). There results

$$Lr^2 + 2\,Mr + N = 0, \tag{4}$$

where $\qquad M = (ax_0 + hy_0 + f)\cos \theta + (hx_0 + by_0 + g)\sin \theta.$

This will be zero for all values of θ when x_0 and y_0 satisfy the equations $\qquad ax_0 + hy_0 + f = 0, \qquad hx_0 + by_0 + g = 0. \tag{5}$

In this case the point (x_0, y_0) will be called the *center* of the curve, since any line through it meets the curve in two points equally distant from it and on opposite sides of it. Now equation (5) can be satisfied by a point not on the line at infinity when and only when $h^2 - ab \neq 0$. Hence *the conic* (1) *is a central conic when* $h^2 - ab \neq 0$, *and is a noncentral conic when* $h^2 - ab = 0$.

The conic (1) is cut by the line at infinity $t = 0$ in two points for which the ratio $x : y$ is given by the equation

$$ax^2 + 2\,hxy + by^2 = 0. \qquad (6)$$

This has equal or unequal roots according as $h^2 - ab$ is equal or unequal to zero. Hence *a central conic cuts the line at infinity in two distinct points; a noncentral conic cuts the line at infinity in two coincident points.*

So far the discussion is independent of the nature of the coefficients of (1). If, however, the coefficients are real the classification may be made more closely, as follows:

(1) $h^2 - ab < 0$. The curve cuts the line at infinity in two distinct imaginary points. It is an ellipse in the elementary sense, or consists of two imaginary straight lines intersecting in a real point not at infinity, or is satisfied by no real point.

(2) $h^2 - ab > 0$. The curve cuts the line at infinity in two distinct real points. It is a hyperbola or consists of two real nonparallel lines.

(3) $h^2 - ab = 0$. The curve cuts the line at infinity in two real coincident points. It is a parabola, or two parallel lines, or two coincident lines. In the very special case in which $h = a = b = 0$ it degenerates into the line at infinity, and the straight line $fx + gy + ct = 0$.

EXERCISES

1. Show that for a given conic there goes through any point, in general, one straight line such that the segment intercepted by the conic is bisected by the point.

2. Show that for a given conic there go through any point, in general, two lines which have one intercept with the conic at infinity.

3. Prove that through the center of a central conic there go two straight lines which have both intercepts with the conic at infinity. These are the *asymptotes*. Show that the asymptotes of an ellipse are imaginary and those of a hyperbola real, and find their equations.

4. Show from (3) that if $x_0 : y_0 : t_0$ is a point on the conic, the equation of the tangent line is

$$(ax_0 + hy_0 + ft_0)\,x + (hx_0 + by_0 + gt_0)\,y + (fx_0 + gy_0 + ct_0)\,t = 0.$$

5. Show that the condition that (1) should represent straight lines is

$$\begin{vmatrix} a & h & f \\ h & b & g \\ f & g & c \end{vmatrix} = 0.$$

22. Trilinear point coördinates. Let AB, BC, and CA (Fig. 8) be three fixed straight lines of reference forming a triangle and let k_1, k_2, and k_3 be three arbitrarily assumed constants. Let P be any point in the plane ABC and let p_1, p_2, and p_3 be the three perpendicular distances from P to the three lines of reference. Algebraic signs are to be attached to each of these distances according to the side of the line of reference on which P lies, the positive side of each line being assumed at pleasure.

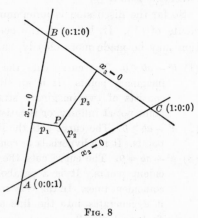

The coördinates of P are defined as the ratios of three quantities x_1, x_2, x_3 such that
$$x_1 : x_2 : x_3 = k_1 p_1 : k_2 p_2 : k_3 p_3. \quad (1)$$

It is evident that if P is given, its coördinates are uniquely determined. Conversely, let real ratios $a_1 : a_2 : a_3$ be assumed for $x_1 : x_2 : x_3$. The ratio $x_1 : x_2 = a_1 : a_2$ furnishes the condition $\dfrac{p_1}{p_2} = $ constant, which is satisfied by any

Fig. 8

point on a unique line through A. Similarly, the ratio $x_2 : x_3 = a_2 : a_3$ is satisfied by any point on a unique line through C. If these lines intersect, the point of intersection is P, which is thus uniquely determined by its coördinates.

In case these two lines are parallel we may extend our coördinate system by saying that the coördinates $a_1 : a_2 : a_3$ define a point of infinity. These are, in fact, the limiting ratios approached by $x_1 : x_2 : x_3$ as P recedes indefinitely from the lines of reference.

We complete the definition of the coördinates by saying that complex coördinates define imaginary points of the plane, and the coördinates $0 : 0 : 0$ are not allowable.

The coördinates of A are $0 : 0 : 1$, those of B are $0 : 1 : 0$, and those of C are $1 : 0 : 0$. The ratios of k_1, k_2, and k_3 are determined when the point with the coördinates $1 : 1 : 1$ is fixed. This point we shall call the unit point, and since the k's are arbitrary it may be taken anywhere. Hence the *coördinate system is determined by three arbitrary lines of reference and an arbitrary unit point.*

The trilinear coördinates contain the Cartesian coördinates as a special limiting case, in which the line BC is the line at infinity. If BC recedes indefinitely from A, p_3 becomes infinite, but the factor k_3 can be made to approach zero in such a way that $Lim\ k_3p_3 = 1$. (There is an exception only when P is on the line BC and remains there as BC becomes the line at infinity; in this case $k_3p_3 = 0$.) If in addition we place $k_1 = k_2 = 1$, the coördinates $x_1 : x_2 : x_3$ become the coördinates $x : y : t$ of § 18.

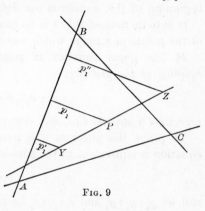

Fig. 9

23. Points on a line. If $y_1 : y_2 : y_3$ and $z_1 : z_2 : z_3$ are two fixed points, the coördinates of any point on the straight line joining them are $y_1 + \lambda z_1 : y_2 +$ $\lambda z_2 : y_3 + \lambda z_3$, and any point with these coördinates lies on that line. To prove this let Y and Z (Fig. 9) be the two fixed points and P any point on the straight line YZ. Place $\dfrac{YP}{PZ} = m$. Then, if p_1', p_1, and p_1'' are the perpendiculars from Y, P, and Z respectively on AB, it is evident from similar triangles that

$$\frac{p_1 - p_1'}{p_1'' - p_1} = m\ ;$$

whence

$$p_1 = \frac{p_1' + mp_1''}{1 + m}.$$

Similarly,

$$p_2 = \frac{p_2' + mp_2''}{1 + m},$$

$$p_3 = \frac{p_3' + mp_3''}{1 + m}.$$

From (1), § 22, $\quad p_i = \dfrac{\rho x_i}{k_i}, \quad p_i' = \dfrac{\rho' y_i}{k_i}, \quad p_i'' = \dfrac{\rho'' z_i}{k_i},$

where ρ, ρ', and ρ'' are proportionality factors. By substitution we have

$$x_1 : x_2 : x_3 = y_1 + \frac{m\rho''}{\rho'} z_1 : y_2 + \frac{m\rho''}{\rho'} z_2 : y_3 + \frac{m\rho''}{\rho'} z_3,$$

which is the required form, where $\lambda = \dfrac{m\rho''}{\rho'}$.

The above proof holds for any real point P. Conversely, any real value of λ determines a real m (the coördinates of Y and Z being real) and hence determines a real point of P. For complex values of λ or for imaginary points Y and Z the statement at the beginning of this section is the *definition* of a straight line.

It is to be noticed that λ is an example of the kind of coördinates of the points of a range which was discussed in § 8.

24. The linear equation in point coördinates. *A homogeneous equation of the first degree,*

$$a_1x_1 + a_2x_2 + a_3x_3 = 0,$$

represents a straight line, and conversely.

To prove this theorem it is necessary to show that the linear equation is equivalent to the equations of § 23. Let us have given

$$a_1x_1 + a_2x_2 + a_3x_3 = 0 \tag{1}$$

and let $y_1 : y_2 : y_3$ and $z_1 : z_2 : z_3$ be two points on the locus of (1). Then

$$a_1y_1 + a_2y_2 + a_3y_3 = 0,$$
$$a_1z_1 + a_2z_2 + a_3z_3 = 0.$$

From these three equations we have

$$\begin{vmatrix} x_1 & x_2 & x_3 \\ y_1 & y_2 & y_3 \\ z_1 & z_2 & z_3 \end{vmatrix} = 0.$$

Then from the theory of determinants there exist three multipliers $\lambda_1, \lambda_2, \lambda_3$ such that

$$\lambda_1x_1 + \lambda_2y_1 + \lambda_3z_1 = 0,$$
$$\lambda_1x_2 + \lambda_2y_2 + \lambda_3z_2 = 0,$$
$$\lambda_1x_3 + \lambda_2y_3 + \lambda_3z_3 = 0;$$

whence $\quad x_1 : x_2 : x_3 = y_1 + \lambda z_1 : y_2 + \lambda z_2 : y_3 + \lambda z_3. \tag{2}$

Conversely, if equations of the form (2) are given we may write them as

$$\rho x_1 = y_1 + \lambda z_1,$$
$$\rho x_2 = y_2 + \lambda z_2,$$
$$\rho x_3 = y_3 + \lambda z_3.$$

The elimination of ρ and λ then gives

$$\begin{vmatrix} x_1 & y_1 & z_1 \\ x_2 & y_2 & z_2 \\ x_3 & y_3 & z_3 \end{vmatrix} = 0,$$

which is a linear equation in x_1, x_2, and x_3.

Hence equation (1) is equivalent to equation (2), and the theorem at the beginning of this section is proved.

25. Lines of a pencil. *If*

$$a_1 x_1 + a_2 x_2 + a_3 x_3 = 0, \tag{1}$$

$$b_1 x_1 + b_2 x_2 + b_3 x_3 = 0 \tag{2}$$

are two fixed lines, the equation of any line through their point of intersection is

$$a_1 x_1 + a_2 x_2 + a_3 x_3 + \lambda (b_1 x_1 + b_2 x_2 + b_3 x_3) = 0. \tag{3}$$

It is evident that (3) represents a straight line and that the coördinates of any point which satisfy (1) and (2) satisfy also (3).

Furthermore, λ is uniquely determined by the coördinates of any point not on (1) and (2). Hence for all values of λ, (3) defines the lines of a pencil.

The parameter λ in (3) is of the type of coördinates defined in § 10. To show this let us take $Y(y_1 : y_2 : y_3)$, a point on (1), and $Z(z_1 : z_2 : z_3)$, a point on (2). Then $y_1 + \lambda z_1 : y_2 + \lambda z_2 : y_3 + \lambda z_3$ is a point on (3) and also a point of the range determined by Y and Z. By § 9, λ is the coördinate of a point on the range, and hence, as shown in § 16, the coördinate of a line of the pencil in the sense of § 10.

EXERCISES

1. Show that the equation of any line through the point A of the triangle of reference is $x_1 + \lambda x_2 = 0$, and find the coördinates of the point in which it intersects any line $a_1 x_1 + a_2 x_2 + a_3 x_3 = 0$. Distinguish between the cases in which $a_3 \neq 0$ and $a_3 = 0$.

2. Write the equations of two projective pencils of lines with the vertices A and B respectively. Find the equation satisfied by the coördinates of the points of intersection of corresponding lines. Hence verify Ex. 1, § 16.

3. Write the coördinates of the points of two projective ranges on AB and AC respectively. Find the equations of the lines connecting corresponding points. Hence verify Ex. 2, § 16.

4. Show that homogeneous point coördinates are connected by the relation

$$\rho\,(ak_1x_1 + bk_2x_2 + ck_3x_3) = K,$$

where a, b, and c are the lengths of the sides of the triangle of reference and K is its area. Hence show that

$$ak_1x_1 + bk_2x_2 + ck_3x_3 = 0$$

is the equation of the straight line at infinity.

5. Consider the case in which B is at infinity, A and C are right angles, and $k_1 = k_2 = k_3 = 1$. Show, for example, that $x_1 + x_3 = 0$ is the equation of the straight line at infinity and that $x_1 + x_3 + \lambda x_2 = 0$ is the equation of any straight line parallel to AC.

26. Line coördinates in a plane. The coefficients a_1, a_2, a_3 in the equation of a straight line are sufficient to fix the line. In fact, to any set of ratios $a_1 : a_2 : a_3$ corresponds one and only one line, and conversely. These ratios may accordingly be taken as coördinates of a straight line, or *line coördinates*, and a geometry may be built up in which the element is the straight line and not the point.

A variable or general set of line coördinates we shall denote by $u_1 : u_2 : u_3$, and the line with these coördinates is the straight line which has the point equation

$$u_1x_1 + u_2x_2 + u_3x_3 = 0. \tag{1}$$

This equation may also be considered as the necessary and sufficient condition that the line $u_1 : u_2 : u_3$ and the point $x_1 : x_2 : x_3$ are "united"; that is, that the point lies on the line and the line passes through the point.

It is obvious that the definition of line coördinates holds for Cartesian as well as for trilinear coördinates. With the use of trilinear coördinates any straight line may be given the coördinates $1 : 1 : 1$. For the substitution

$$\rho x_1 = \frac{x_1'}{a_1}, \quad \rho x_2 = \frac{x_2'}{a_2}, \quad \rho x_3 = \frac{x_3'}{a_3},$$

which amounts to a change in the constants k_1, k_2, k_3 in (1), § 22, changes the equation $a_1x_1 + a_2x_2 + a_3x_3 = 0$ into the equation $x_1' + x_2' + x_3' = 0$.

27. Pencil of lines and the linear equation in line coördinates. If $v_1 : v_2 : v_3$ and $w_1 : w_2 : w_3$ are two fixed lines, it follows immediately from § 25 that

$$v_1 + \lambda w_1 : v_2 + \lambda w_2 : v_3 + \lambda w_3 \qquad (1)$$

represents any line of the pencil determined by the two lines v_i and w_i.

Consider now an equation of the first degree in line coördinates,

$$a_1 u_1 + a_2 u_2 + a_3 u_3 = 0. \qquad (2)$$

It may be readily shown, as in § 24, that if $v_1 : v_2 : v_3$ and $w_1 : w_2 : w_3$ are two sets of coördinates satisfying (2), the general values of $u_1 : u_2 : u_3$ which satisfy (2) are of the form (1). Hence (2) represents a pencil of lines.

Or we may argue directly from (1), § 26, and say at once that any line whose coördinates satisfy (2) is united with the point $a_1 : a_2 : a_3$ and, conversely, that any line united with the point $a_1 : a_2 : a_3$ has coördinates which satisfy (2). We have, therefore, the theorem:

The equation $a_1 u_1 + a_2 u_2 + a_3 u_3 = 0$ represents a pencil of lines of which the vertex is the point $a_1 : a_2 : a_3$.

Compare the linear equation in point coördinates,

$$a_1 x_1 + a_2 x_2 + a_3 x_3 = 0, \qquad (3)$$

and the linear equation in line coördinates,

$$a_1 u_1 + a_2 u_2 + a_3 u_3 = 0. \qquad (4)$$

Equation (3) is satisfied by all points on a range of which the base is the line with the line coördinates $a_1 : a_2 : a_3$. It is the *point equation of that line.*

Equation (4) is satisfied by all lines of a pencil of which the vertex is the point with the point coördinates $a_1 : a_2 : a_3$. It is the *line equation of that point.*

EXERCISES

1. If ABC is the triangle of reference, as in Fig. 8, show that the line coördinates of AB are $1 : 0 : 0$, those of BC are $0 : 0 : 1$, and those of CA are $0 : 1 : 0$. Show also that the equation of the point A in line coördinates is $u_3 = 0$, that of B is $u_2 = 0$, and that of C is $u_1 = 0$.

2. What does the equation $u_1 + \lambda u_2 = 0$ represent? What line is represented by the line coördinates $\lambda : 1 : 0$?

3. Find in line coördinates the equations of the points of the range which lie on the line $1:1:1$; also the point coördinates of the same range.

4. Find in point coördinates the equations of the lines of the pencil with vertex $1:1:1$. Find also the line coördinates of the lines of the same pencil.

5. Show that line coördinates are proportional to the segments cut off by the line on the sides of the triangle of reference, each segment being multiplied by a constant factor.

6. Show that line coördinates are proportional to the three perpendiculars from the vertices of the triangle of reference to the straight line, each perpendicular being multiplied by a constant factor.

28. Dualistic relations. The geometries of the point and the line in a plane are dualistic (§ 2). This arises from the fact that the algebraic analysis is the same in the two geometries. The difference comes in the interpretation of the analysis. In both cases we have the two independent ratios of three variables which are used homogeneously. In the one case these ratios are interpreted as the coördinates of a point; in the other case they are interpreted as the coördinates of a line. In both cases we have to consider a linear homogeneous equation connecting the variables which is satisfied by a singly infinite set of ratio pairs. In the point geometry this equation is satisfied by the singly infinite set of points which lie on a straight line. In the line geometry this equation is satisfied by the singly infinite set of straight lines which pass through a point.

From the above it appears that any piece of analysis involving two independent variables connected by one or more homogeneous linear equations has two interpretations which differ in that " line " in one is " point " in the other, and vice versa. Hence a geometric theorem involving points and lines and their mutual relations may be changed into a new theorem by changing "point " to " line " and " line " to "point." In making this interchange, of course, such other changes in phraseology as will preserve the English idiom are also necessary. For example, " point on a line " becomes " line through a point," and " a line connecting two points " becomes " a point of intersection of two lines."

We restate some of the results thus far obtained in parallel columns so as to show the dualistic relations.

The ratios $x_1 : x_2 : x_3$ determine a point.

A linear equation $a_1x_1 + a_2x_2 + a_3x_3 = 0$ represents all points on the line of which the coördinates are $a_1 : a_2 : a_3$. It is the equation of the line.

If y_i and z_i are fixed points the coördinates of any point on the line connecting them are $y_i + \lambda z_i$.

If $\quad a_1x_1 + a_2x_2 + a_3x_3 = 0$

and $\quad b_1x_1 + b_2x_2 + b_3x_3 = 0$

are the equations of two lines, the equation of any line through their point of intersection is

$$a_1x_1 + a_2x_2 + a_3x_3 \\ + \lambda(b_1x_1 + b_2x_2 + b_3x_3) = 0.$$

Three points y_i, z_i, t_i lie on a straight line when

$$\begin{vmatrix} y_1 & z_1 & t_1 \\ y_2 & z_2 & t_2 \\ y_3 & z_3 & t_3 \end{vmatrix} = 0.$$

Three straight lines

$$\sum a_ix_i = 0, \ \sum b_ix_i = 0, \ \sum c_ix_i = 0$$

meet in a point when

$$\begin{vmatrix} a_1 & b_1 & c_1 \\ a_2 & b_2 & c_2 \\ a_3 & b_3 & c_3 \end{vmatrix} = 0.$$

The ratios $u_1 : u_2 : u_3$ determine a straight line.

A linear equation $a_1u_1 + a_2u_2 + a_3u_3 = 0$ represents all lines through the point of which the coördinates are $a_1 : a_2 : a_3$. It is the equation of the point.

If v_i and w_i are fixed lines the coördinates of any line through their point of intersection are $v_i + \lambda w_i$.

If $\quad a_1u_1 + a_2u_2 + a_3u_3 = 0$

and $\quad b_1u_1 + b_2u_2 + b_3u_3 = 0$

are the equations of two points, the equation of any point on the line connecting them is

$$a_1u_1 + a_2u_2 + a_3u_3 \\ + \lambda(b_1u_1 + b_2u_2 + b_3u_3) = 0.$$

Three lines v_i, w_i, u_i meet in a point when

$$\begin{vmatrix} v_1 & w_1 & u_1 \\ v_2 & w_2 & u_2 \\ v_3 & w_3 & u_3 \end{vmatrix} = 0.$$

Three points

$$\sum a_iu_i = 0, \ \sum b_iu_i = 0, \ \sum c_iu_i = 0$$

lie on a straight line when

$$\begin{vmatrix} a_1 & b_1 & c_1 \\ a_2 & b_2 & c_2 \\ a_3 & b_3 & c_3 \end{vmatrix} = 0.$$

29. Change of coördinates. We will first establish the relation between a set of Cartesian coördinates and a set of trilinear coördinates. Let AB, BC, and CA be the lines of reference of the trilinear coördinates and let their equations referred to any set of Cartesian coördinates be respectively

$$a_1x + b_1y + c_1t = 0,$$
$$a_2x + b_2y + c_2t = 0,$$
$$a_3x + b_3y + c_3t = 0.$$
(1)

Then by a familiar theorem in analytic geometry,

$$p_1 = \frac{a_1x + b_1y + c_1t}{\pm\sqrt{a_1^2 + b_1^2}\,t},$$

$$p_2 = \frac{a_2x + b_2y + c_2t}{\pm\sqrt{a_2^2 + b_2^2}\,t},$$

$$p_3 = \frac{a_3x + b_3y + c_3t}{\pm\sqrt{a_3^2 + b_3^2}\,t}.$$

We may take without loss of generality

$$k_1 = \pm\sqrt{a_1^2 + b_1^2}\,t, \quad k_2 = \pm\sqrt{a_2^2 + b_2^2}\,t, \quad k_3 = \pm\sqrt{a_3^2 + b_3^2}\,t,$$

since each of the equations (1) may be multiplied by a factor without changing the lines represented.

Therefore we have

$$\rho x_1 = a_1x + b_1y + c_1t,$$
$$\rho x_2 = a_2x + b_2y + c_2t,$$
$$\rho x_3 = a_3x + b_3y + c_3t,$$
(2)

where ρ is a proportionality factor.

Since the lines AB, BC, and CA form a triangle, the determinant $|a_1b_2c_3|$ does not vanish and equations (2) may be solved for x, y, and t.

Suppose now another triangle $A'B'C'$ be taken, the equations of its sides being

$$a_1'x + b_1'y + c_1't = 0,$$
$$a_2'x + b_2'y + c_2't = 0,$$
$$a_3'x + b_3'y + c_3't = 0,$$
(3)

and let $x_1' : x_2' : x_3'$ be trilinear coördinates referred to the triangle $A'B'C'$. Then, as before,

$$\rho'x_1' = a_1'x + b_1'y + c_1't,$$
$$\rho'x_2' = a_2'x + b_2'y + c_2't,$$
$$\rho'x_3' = a_3'x + b_3'y + c_3't.$$
(4)

Equations (2) may be solved for x, y, and t and the results substituted in (4). There result relations of the form

$$\sigma x_1' = \alpha_1 x_1 + \alpha_2 x_2 + \alpha_3 x_3,$$
$$\sigma x_2' = \beta_1 x_1 + \beta_2 x_2 + \beta_3 x_3, \qquad (5)$$
$$\sigma x_3' = \gamma_1 x_1 + \gamma_2 x_2 + \gamma_3 x_3,$$

which are the equations of transformation of coördinates from $x_1 : x_2 : x_3$ to $x_1' : x_2' : x_3'$.

In (5) the right-hand members equated to zero give the equations in trilinear coördinates of the sides of the triangle of reference $A'B'C'$. Since these do not meet in a point the coefficients are subject to the condition that their determinant does not vanish, and this is the only condition imposed upon them.

By the transformation (5) the equation of the straight line

$$u_1 x_1 + u_2 x_2 + u_3 x_3 = 0$$

becomes

$$u_1' x_1' + u_2' x_2' + u_3' x_3' = 0,$$

where

$$\rho u_1 = \alpha_1 u_1' + \beta_1 u_2' + \gamma_1 u_3',$$
$$\rho u_2 = \alpha_2 u_1' + \beta_2 u_2' + \gamma_2 u_3', \qquad (6)$$
$$\rho u_3 = \alpha_3 u_1' + \beta_3 u_2' + \gamma_3 u_3'.$$

These are the formulas for the change of line coördinates.

In connection with the change of coördinates three theorems are of importance.

I. The degree of an equation in point or line coördinates is unaltered by a change from one set of trilinear coördinates to another.

II. If the coördinates y_i and z_i are transformed into the coördinates y_i' and z_i', the coördinates $y_i + \lambda z_i$ are transformed into the coördinates $y_i' + \lambda' z_i'$, where $\lambda' = c\lambda$, c being a constant.

III. The cross ratio of four points or four lines is independent of the coördinate system.

Theorem I follows immediately from the fact that equations (5) and (6) are linear.

To prove theorem II note that from (5), if the coördinates $y_i + \lambda z_i$ are transformed into x_i', then

$$\sigma x_1' = \alpha_1(y_1 + \lambda z_1) + \alpha_2(y_2 + \lambda z_2) + \alpha_3(y_3 + \lambda z_3)$$
$$= (\alpha_1 y_1 + \alpha_2 y_2 + \alpha_3 y_3) + \lambda(\alpha_1 z_1 + \alpha_2 z_2 + \alpha_3 z_3)$$
$$= \sigma_1 y_1' + \sigma_2 \lambda z_1',$$

where σ_1 and σ_2 are used, since in transforming y_i and z_i by (5) the proportionality factors may differ.

Similar expressions may be found for x_2' and x_3'. Hence we have

$$x_1 : x_2' : x_3' = y_1' + \frac{\sigma_2}{\sigma_1}\lambda z_1' : y_2' + \frac{\sigma_2}{\sigma_1}\lambda z_2' : y_3' + \frac{\sigma_2}{\sigma_1}\lambda z_3',$$ which proves the

theorem. The same proof holds for line coördinates using equations (6).

Theorem III follows at once from II.

30. Certain straight-line configurations. A *complete n-line* is defined as the figure formed by n straight lines, no three of which pass through the same point, together with the $\frac{1}{2}n(n-1)$ points of intersection of these lines. A complete three-line is therefore a triangle consisting of three sides and three vertices. A complete four-line is called a complete quadrilateral and consists of four sides and six vertices. Thus in Fig. 10 the four sides are a, b, c, d and the six vertices are K, L, M, N, P, Q. Two vertices not on the same side are called opposite, as K and M, L

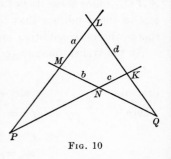

Fig. 10

and N, P and Q. A straight line joining two opposite vertices is a *diagonal line*. The complete quadrilateral has three diagonal lines.

A *complete n-point* is defined as the figure formed by n points, no three of which lie on a straight line, together with the $\frac{1}{2}n(n-1)$ straight lines joining these points. A complete three-point is therefore a triangle consisting of three vertices and three sides. A complete four-point is called a complete quadrangle and consists of four vertices and

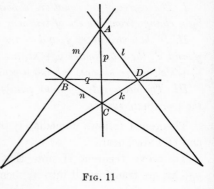

Fig. 11

six sides. Thus in Fig. 11 the four vertices are A, B, C, D and the six sides are k, l, m, n, p, q. Two sides not passing through the same vertex are called opposite, as k and m, l and n, and p and q.

The point of intersection of two opposite sides is a diagonal point. The complete quadrangle has three diagonal points.

It is obvious that a complete n-point and a complete n-line are dualistic. A triangle is dualistic to a triangle, and a complete quadrangle to a complete quadrilateral. The diagonal lines of a complete quadrilateral are dualistic to the diagonal points of a complete quadrangle.

For the complete triangle we shall prove the following dualistic theorems:

I. The theorem of Desargues. *If two triangles are so placed that the straight lines connecting homologous vertices meet in a point, then the points of intersection of homologous sides lie on a straight line.*

II. If two triangles are so placed that the points of intersection of homologous sides lie on a straight line, then the lines connecting homologous vertices meet in a point.

Let there be given two triangles with the vertices A, B, C and A', B', C' respectively (Fig. 12) and with the sides a, b, c and a', b', c' respectively, the side a lying opposite the vertex A etc.

We shall denote by AA' the straight line connecting A and A', and by aa' the point of intersection of a and a'. Then the two theorems stated above are respectively:

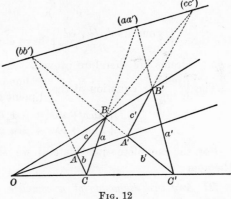

Fig. 12

If the straight lines AA', BB', and CC' meet in a point O, the points aa', bb', and cc' lie on a straight line o.

If the points aa', bb', and cc' lie on a straight line o, the straight lines AA', BB', and CC' meet in a point O.

The proofs of these theorems may be given together, the upper line of the following sentences being read for theorem I and the lower line for theorem II.

Take $\left\{\begin{matrix} ABC \\ abc \end{matrix}\right\}$ as triangle of reference and $\left\{\begin{matrix} O \\ o \end{matrix}\right\}$ as the unit $\left\{\begin{matrix} \text{point} \\ \text{line} \end{matrix}\right\}$. Then the coördinates of $\left\{\begin{matrix} A \\ a \end{matrix}\right\}$ are $0 : 0 : 1$, those of $\left\{\begin{matrix} B \\ b \end{matrix}\right\}$ are $0 : 1 : 0$, those of $\left\{\begin{matrix} C \\ c \end{matrix}\right\}$ are $1 : 0 : 0$, and those of $\left\{\begin{matrix} O \\ o \end{matrix}\right\}$ are $1 : 1 : 1$. By § 28 the coördinates of $\left\{\begin{matrix} A' \\ a' \end{matrix}\right\}$ are $1 : 1 : 1 + \lambda$, those of $\left\{\begin{matrix} B' \\ b' \end{matrix}\right\}$ are $1 : 1 + \mu : 1$, and those of $\left\{\begin{matrix} C' \\ c' \end{matrix}\right\}$ are $1 + \nu : 1 : 1$.

The coördinates of any $\left\{\begin{matrix} \text{point on } A'B' \\ \text{line through } a'b' \end{matrix}\right\}$ are therefore $1 + \rho : 1 + \rho(1 + \mu) : 1 + \lambda + \rho$, and if this $\left\{\begin{matrix} \text{point lies also on } AB \\ \text{passes also through } ab \end{matrix}\right\}$ we must have $\rho = -1$. Hence the coördinates of $\left\{\begin{matrix} cc' \\ CC' \end{matrix}\right\}$ are $0 : -\mu : \lambda$. Similarly, the coördinates of $\left\{\begin{matrix} bb' \\ BB' \end{matrix}\right\}$ are $\nu : 0 : -\lambda$ and the coördinates of $\left\{\begin{matrix} aa' \\ AA' \end{matrix}\right\}$ are $-\nu : \mu : 0$. Since

$$\begin{vmatrix} 0 & -\mu & \lambda \\ \nu & 0 & -\lambda \\ -\nu & \mu & 0 \end{vmatrix} = 0,$$

the three $\left\{\begin{matrix} \text{points } aa',\ bb',\ cc' \\ \text{lines } AA',\ BB',\ CC' \end{matrix}\right\}$ have a common $\left\{\begin{matrix} \text{line } o \\ \text{point } O \end{matrix}\right\}$. The two theorems are therefore proved.

The $\left\{\begin{matrix} \text{point} \\ \text{line} \end{matrix}\right\}$ equation of the $\left\{\begin{matrix} \text{line } o \\ \text{point } O \end{matrix}\right\}$ is

$$\left\{\begin{matrix} \lambda\mu x_1 + \nu\lambda x_2 + \mu\nu x_3 = 0 \\ \lambda\mu u_1 + \nu\lambda u_2 + \mu\nu u_3 = 0 \end{matrix}\right\}.$$

For the complete quadrilateral we shall prove the following theorem:

III. Any two diagonals of a complete quadrilateral intersect the third diagonal in two points which are harmonic conjugates to the two vertices which lie on that diagonal.

In Fig. 13 let the two diagonals LN and MK intersect the third diagonal PQ in the points R and S respectively. We are to prove that R and S are harmonic conjugates to P and Q.

Since by III, § 29, the cross ratio is independent of the coördinate system, we shall take the triangle LPQ as the triangle of reference and the point N as the unit point, so that the coördinates of P are $0:0:1$, those of Q are $1:0:0$, those of L are $0:1:0$, and those of N are $1:1:1$. Then by § 23 it is easy to see that the coördinates of R are $1:0:1$, those of M are $0:1:1$, those of K are $1:1:0$, and finally that those of S are $-1:0:1$. By § 14 the theorem follows.

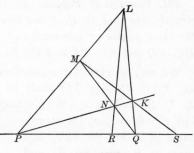

FIG. 13

The dualistic theorem to III is as follows:

IV. *If any two diagonal points of a complete quadrangle are joined by straight lines to the third diagonal point, the two joining lines are harmonic conjugates to the two sides of the quadrangle which pass through that third diagonal point.*

The proof is left to the reader.

Since the cross ratio of any four lines of a pencil is equal to the cross ratio of the four points in which the four lines cut any transversal (§ 16), theorem IV leads at once to the following:

V. *The straight line connecting any two diagonal points of a complete quadrangle meets the sides of the quadrangle which do not pass through the two diagonal points, in two points which are harmonic conjugates to the two diagonal points.*

Similarly, theorem III may be replaced by the theorem, dualistic to V, as follows:

VI. *If the intersection of any two diagonal lines of a complete quadrilateral is connected with the two vertices of the quadrilateral which do not lie on the two diagonals, the two connecting lines are harmonic conjugates to the two diagonals.*

Theorem III gives a method of finding the fourth point in a harmonic set when three points are known. In Fig. 13 let us suppose P, Q, and R given, and let it be required to find S. The point L may be taken at pleasure and the lines LP, LR, and LQ drawn. Then the point N may be taken at pleasure on LR and the points M and K determined by drawing QN and PN. The line MK can then be drawn, determining S.

We will now prove the following theorem:

VII. Theorem of Pappus. *If P_1, P_3, P_5 are three points on a straight line and P_2, P_4, P_6 are three points on another straight line, the three points of intersection of the three pairs of lines P_1P_2 and P_4P_5, P_2P_3 and P_5P_6, P_3P_4 and P_6P_1 lie on a straight line.*

We may so choose the coördinate system that the line containing P_1, P_3, P_5 (Fig. 14) shall be $x_1 = 0$ and the line containing P_2, P_4, P_6 shall be $x_2 = 0$. We may then take the line P_1P_2 as the line $x_3 = 0$, so that the coördinates of P_1 are $(0:1:0)$ and those of P_2 are $(1:0:0)$, and may so take the unit point that the coördinates of P_3 are $(0:1:1)$ and those of P_4 are $(1:0:1)$. Call the coördinates of P_5 $(0:1:\lambda)$ and those of P_6 $(1:0:\mu)$. Then the equation of P_1P_2 is $x_3 = 0$ and that of P_4P_5 is $x_1 + \lambda x_2 - x_3 = 0$. These lines intersect in the point K $(\lambda:-1:0)$. The equation of P_2P_3 is $x_2 - x_3 = 0$ and that

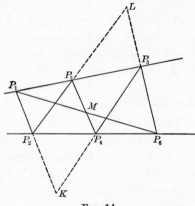

Fig. 14

of P_5P_6 is $\mu x_1 + \lambda x_2 - x_3 = 0$. These lines intersect in the point L $(1-\lambda:\mu:\mu)$. The equation of P_3P_4 is $x_1 + x_2 - x_3 = 0$ and that of P_6P_1 is $\mu x_1 - x_3 = 0$. These lines intersect in M $(1:\mu-1:\mu)$. Since

$$
\begin{vmatrix}
\lambda & -1 & 0 \\
1-\lambda & \mu & \mu \\
1 & \mu-1 & \mu
\end{vmatrix} = 0,
$$

the three points L, K, M lie in a straight line, as was to be proved.

Dualistic to this theorem is the following:

VIII. *If p_1, p_3, p_5 are three straight lines through a point and p_2, p_4, p_6 are three straight lines through another point, the three lines connecting the three pairs of points p_1p_2 and p_4p_5, p_2p_3 and p_5p_6, p_3p_4 and p_6p_1 meet in a point.*

The proof is left to the reader.

1. Prove theorem IV.

2. Prove theorem VIII.

3. A triangle is so placed that its vertices P, Q, R are on the sides AB, AC, and BC, respectively, of a fixed triangle and its sides PR and RQ pass through two fixed points in a straight line with A. Prove that the side PQ passes through a fixed point.

4. A triangle is so placed that its sides QR, PR, PQ pass through the vertices C, B, A, respectively, of a fixed triangle and its vertices Q and P lie on two fixed lines which intersect on BC. Prove that the vertex R lies on a straight line.

5. Given a straight line p and two fixed points A and B. Take any two points on p and connect each of them with A and B. These lines determine two new points C and D by their intersections. Prove that the line CD passes through a fixed point on AB.

6. Given a point P and two fixed lines a and b. Draw any two lines through P and connect their points of intersection with a and b. This determines two new lines c and d. Prove that the point of intersection of c and d lies on a fixed straight line through ab.

7. Three lines f, g, h are drawn through the vertex A of the triangle ABC. On g any point is taken and the lines l and m are drawn to C and B respectively. The line l intersects f in D and the line m intersects h in E. Prove that DE passes through a fixed point on BC.

8. Three points F, G, H are taken on the side BC of the triangle ABC. Through G any line is drawn cutting AB and AC in L and M respectively. The lines FL and HM intersect in K. Prove that the locus of K is a straight line through A.

9. Show that if a, a' and b, b' are any two pairs of corresponding lines of two projective pencils not in perspective, the line connecting the points ab' and $a'b$ passes through a fixed point. This is called the *center of homology* of the two pencils. Show that it is the intersection of the two lines which correspond to the line connecting the vertices of the pencils, considered as belonging first to one pencil and then to the other.

10. Show that if A, A' and B, B' are any two points of two projective ranges which are not in perspective, the point of intersection of the lines AB' and $A'B$ lies on a fixed straight line. This is called the *axis of homology* of the two ranges. Show that it intersects the base of each range in the point which corresponds to the point of intersection of the two bases, considered as belonging to the other range.

31. Curves in point coördinates. The equations

$$x_1 : x_2 : x_3 = \phi_1(t) : \phi_2(t) : \phi_3(t), \tag{1}$$

where t is an independent variable and the ratios of the functions $\phi_i(t)$ are not constant or indeterminate, define a one-dimensional extent of points called a *curve*. It is not necessary that any point of the curve should be real. We shall limit ourselves to those curves for which the functions $\phi_i(t)$ are continuous and have derivatives of at least the first order.

If $\phi_3(t)$ is identically zero the curve is the straight line $x_3 = 0$. Otherwise we may write equations (1) in the form

$$\frac{x_1}{x_3} = \frac{\phi_1(t)}{\phi_3(t)} = F_1(t), \qquad \frac{x_2}{x_3} = \frac{\phi_2(t)}{\phi_3(t)} = F_2(t). \tag{2}$$

It is then possible to eliminate t between the equations (2) with the result,

$$\frac{x_1}{x_3} = \Phi\left(\frac{x_2}{x_3}\right). \tag{3}$$

Conversely, let there be given an equation

$$f(x_1, x_2, x_3) = 0, \tag{4}$$

where f is a homogeneous function in x_1, x_2, x_3. By a homogeneous function we mean one which satisfies the condition

$$f(\lambda x_1, \lambda x_2, \lambda x_3) = \lambda^n f(x_1, x_2, x_3),$$

where λ is any multiplier, not zero or infinity. In particular, if we place $\lambda = \dfrac{1}{x_3}$ we have

$$f(x_1, x_2, x_3) = x_3^n f\left(\frac{x_1}{x_3}, \frac{x_2}{x_3}, 1\right)$$

for all points for which x_3 is not zero. Equation (4) may then be written

$$f(s, t, 1) = 0, \tag{5}$$

where

$$s = \frac{x_1}{x_3}, \qquad t = \frac{x_2}{x_3}.$$

We shall limit ourselves to functions f which are continuous and have partial derivatives of at least the first order.

We shall also assume that (4) is satisfied by at least one point $y_1 : y_1 : y_3 \ (y_3 \neq 0)$, at which one of the partial derivatives $\left(\text{say } \dfrac{\partial f}{\partial x_1}\right)$

does not vanish. Then similar conditions hold for (5), and by the theory of implicit functions * we have, from (5),

$$s = \phi(t),$$

which is valid in the vicinity of $t_0 = \dfrac{y_2}{y_3}$, $s_0 = \dfrac{y_1}{y_3}$.

This last equation may be written

$$x_1 : x_2 : x_3 = \phi(t) : t : 1,$$

which is of the type of equations (1). Hence, under our hypotheses equation (4) represents a curve.

The above discussion leaves unconsidered the points for which $x_3 = 0$. These may be found by direct substitution in (4) or we may repeat the discussion, dividing by some other coördinate, perhaps x_1.

Let $P\,(y_1 : y_2 : y_3)$ be a point of (1) corresponding to the value $t = t_0$, and let $Q\,(y_1 + \Delta y_1 : y_2 + \Delta y_2 : y_3 + \Delta y_3)$ be a point corresponding to $t_0 + \Delta t$. These two points fix a straight line with the equation

$$a_1 x_1 + a_2 x_2 + a_3 x_3 = 0, \tag{6}$$

the coefficients of which are determined by the two equations

$$a_1 y_1 + a_2 y_2 + a_3 y_3 = 0,$$
$$a_1(y_1 + \Delta y_1) + a_2(y_2 + \Delta y_2) + a_3(y_3 + \Delta y_3) = 0.$$

From these it follows that

$$a_1 : a_2 : a_3 = y_2 \Delta y_3 - y_3 \Delta y_2 : y_3 \Delta y_1 - y_1 \Delta y_3 : y_1 \Delta y_2 - y_2 \Delta y_1. \tag{7}$$

It is to be noticed that these involve the ratios of the increments Δy_1, Δy_2, Δy_3. If now Δt approaches zero, the point Q approaches P, the ratios $\Delta y_1 : \Delta y_2 : \Delta y_3$ approach the ratios $dy_1 : dy_2 : dy_3$, and the ratios $a_1 : a_2 : a_3$ approach the limiting ratios

$$a_1 : a_2 : a_3 = y_2 dy_3 - y_3 dy_2 : y_3 dy_1 - y_1 dy_3 : y_1 dy_2 - y_2 dy_1. \tag{8}$$

The straight line (6) with the coefficients defined by (8) is the limit of the secant PQ and is called the *tangent* to the curve.

If the equation of the curve is in the form (4), the equation of the tangent may be modified as follows:

Since $f(y_1 : y_2 : y_3)$ is a homogeneous function we have, by Euler's theorem,

$$\frac{\partial f}{\partial y_1} y_1 + \frac{\partial f}{\partial y_2} y_2 + \frac{\partial f}{\partial y_3} y_3 = n f(y_1, y_2, y_3) = 0. \tag{9}$$

* See Wilson's "Advanced Calculus," p. 117.

On the other hand, dy_1, dy_2, dy_3 satisfy the condition

$$df = \frac{\partial f}{\partial y_1} dy_1 + \frac{\partial f}{\partial y_2} dy_2 + \frac{\partial f}{\partial y_3} dy_3 = 0. \tag{10}$$

Equations (9) and (10) give

$$y_2 dy_3 - y_3 dy_2 : y_3 dy_1 - y_1 dy_3 : y_1 dy_2 - y_2 dy_1 = \frac{\partial f}{\partial y_1} : \frac{\partial f}{\partial y_2} : \frac{\partial f}{\partial y_3}.$$

Hence the equation of the tangent line is, from (8) and (10),

$$x_1 \frac{\partial f}{\partial y_1} + x_2 \frac{\partial f}{\partial y_2} + x_3 \frac{\partial f}{\partial y_3} = 0. \tag{11}$$

The equation (11) is fully and uniquely determined for any point on the curve except for a point $y_1 : y_2 : y_3$ at which

$$\frac{\partial f}{\partial y_1} = 0, \quad \frac{\partial f}{\partial y_2} = 0, \quad \frac{\partial f}{\partial y_3} = 0. \tag{12}$$

Points for which the conditions (12) hold are called *singular points*.

We may sum up as follows: *At every nonsingular point* $(y_1 : y_2 : y_3)$ *of a curve*
$$f(x_1, x_2, x_3) = 0$$
there is a definite tangent line given by the equation

$$x_1 \frac{\partial f}{\partial y_1} + x_2 \frac{\partial f}{\partial y_2} + x_3 \frac{\partial f}{\partial y_3} = 0.$$

Consider now any straight line determined by two fixed points y_i and z_i so that $y_i + \lambda z_i$ is any point of the line. The point $y_i + \lambda z_i$ lies on the curve (1) when λ has a value satisfying the equation

$$f(y_1 + \lambda z_1,\ y_2 + \lambda z_2,\ y_3 + \lambda z_3) = 0, \tag{13}$$

which expands by Taylor's theorem into

$$A_0 + A_1 \lambda + A_2 \lambda^2 + \cdots = 0, \tag{14}$$

where $A_0 = f(y_1, y_2, y_3)$ and $A_1 = \dfrac{\partial f}{\partial y_1} z_1 + \dfrac{\partial f}{\partial y_2} z_2 + \dfrac{\partial f}{\partial y_3} z_3$.

If y_i is on the curve (4), $A_0 = 0$ and one root of (14) is zero. If, in addition, $A_1 = 0$ and y_i is not a singular point, z_i lies on the tangent line to (4) and two roots of (14) are zero. If y_i is a singular point of the curve, $A_0 = 0$ and $A_1 = 0$ for all values of z; that is, *any line through a singular point of a curve intersects the curve in at least two coincident points.*

If $f(x_1, x_2, x_3)$ is a homogeneous polynomial of the nth degree, the locus of points satisfying (4) is defined as a *curve of the nth order*. Equation (14) is then an algebraic equation of the nth degree unless its left-hand member vanishes identically for all values of λ. Hence *any curve of the nth order is cut by any straight line in n points unless the straight line lies entirely on the curve.*

32. Curves in line coördinates. The equations

$$u_1 : u_2 : u_3 = \phi_1(t) : \phi_2(t) : \phi_3(t), \tag{1}$$

where t is an independent variable and the ratios of the functions $\phi_i(t)$ are not constant or indeterminate, define a one-dimensional extent of straight lines. We shall see that these lines determine a curve in the sense of § 31. Equations (1) are called the line equations of that curve.

Proceeding as in § 31 with the same hypotheses as to the nature of the functions $\phi_i(t)$, we may show that equations (1) are equivalent to the equation

$$\frac{u_1}{u_3} = \Phi\left(\frac{u_2}{u_3}\right).$$

Conversely, let there be given an equation

$$f(u_1, u_2, u_3) = 0, \tag{2}$$

where f is a homogeneous function in u_1, u_2, u_3; we may show, as in § 31, that equation (2) defines a one-dimensional extent of lines of the type (1).

The discussion now proceeds dualistically to that in § 31.

Let $p(v_1 : v_2 : v_3)$ and $q(v_1 + \Delta v_1 : v_2 + \Delta v_2 : v_3 + \Delta v_3)$ be two straight lines determined by placing $t = t_0$ and $t = t_0 + \Delta t$ in (1). These two lines determine a point K the coördinates of which satisfy the two equations

$$v_1 x_1 + v_2 x_2 + v_3 x_3 = 0,$$

$$(v_1 + \Delta v_1)x_1 + (v_2 + \Delta v_2)x_2 + (v_3 + \Delta v_3)x_3 = 0,$$

the solution of which is

$$x_1 : x_2 : x_3 = v_2 \Delta v_3 - v_3 \Delta v_2 : v_3 \Delta v_1 - v_1 \Delta v_3 : v_1 \Delta v_2 - v_2 \Delta v_1.$$

Now let Δt approach zero. The line q approaches the line p, the ratios $\Delta v_1 : \Delta v_2 : \Delta v_3$ approach the ratios $dv_1 : dv_2 : dv_3$, and the point K approaches the point L, of which the coördinates are

$$x_1 : x_2 : x_3 = v_2 dv_3 - v_3 dv_2 : v_3 dv_1 - v_1 dv_3 : v_1 dv_2 - v_2 dv_1. \tag{3}$$

By virtue of (3) and (1) the points L form in general a curve. An exception would occur when the right-hand ratios of (3) are independent of t. In that case the points L for all lines of (1) coincide.

If the extent of lines is defined by a single equation (2) the coördinates of L may be put in another form, as follows: Since f is a homogeneous function we have, by Euler's theorem,

$$\frac{\partial f}{\partial v_1} v_1 + \frac{\partial f}{\partial v_2} v_2 + \frac{\partial f}{\partial v_3} v_3 = nf = 0.$$

But $$df = \frac{\partial f}{\partial v_1} dv_1 + \frac{\partial f}{\partial v_2} dv_2 + \frac{\partial f}{\partial v_3} dv_3 = 0;$$

whence
$$v_2 dv_3 - v_3 dv_2 : v_3 dv_1 - v_1 dv_3 : v_1 dv_2 - v_2 dv_1 = \frac{\partial f}{\partial v_1} : \frac{\partial f}{\partial v_2} : \frac{\partial f}{\partial v_3}.$$

The coördinates of L are therefore

$$x_1 : x_2 : x_3 = \frac{\partial f}{\partial v_1} : \frac{\partial f}{\partial v_2} : \frac{\partial f}{\partial v_3}. \tag{4}$$

These equations determine a unique point on any line p unless p is such a line that

$$\frac{\partial f}{\partial v_1} = 0, \quad \frac{\partial f}{\partial v_2} = 0, \quad \frac{\partial f}{\partial v_3} = 0,$$

in which case p is called a *singular line*.

Equations (4) also show that the points L form a curve unless the ratios of the partial derivatives $\dfrac{\partial f}{\partial v_i}$ are constant in the neighborhood of v_i. This would happen, for example, if

$$f = (a_1 u_1 + a_2 u_2 + a_3 u_3)\, \phi\, (u_1,\, u_2,\, u_3)$$

and v_i is any point which makes the first factor vanish. The points L on all lines in the neighborhood of v_i are then all $a_1 : a_2 : a_3$.

Leaving the exceptional case aside we have the theorem:

On any nonsingular line of a one-dimensional extent of lines there lies a unique point, called a limit point, the locus of which is in general a curve. This curve is said to be defined in line coördinates by the equation of the line extent. In special cases the curve may reduce to a point or contain a number of points as parts of the curve.

In case we have a true curve of limit points it will be possible to solve equations (4) for $v_1 : v_2 : v_3$ and substitute in (2). This gives

$$f(v_1, v_2, v_3) = \phi(x_1, x_2, x_3) = 0, \tag{5}$$

which is the equation in point coördinates of the locus of L.

From (5),
$$\frac{\partial \phi}{\partial x_i} = \frac{\partial f}{\partial v_1} \frac{\partial v_1}{\partial x_i} + \frac{\partial f}{\partial v_2} \frac{\partial v_2}{\partial x_i} + \frac{\partial f}{\partial v_3} \frac{\partial v_3}{\partial x_i}$$

$$= \rho \left(x_1 \frac{\partial v_1}{\partial x_i} + x_2 \frac{\partial v_2}{\partial x_i} + x_3 \frac{\partial v_3}{\partial x_i} \right),$$

where ρ is a proportionality factor and the last reduction is made by means of (4). But since $v_1 x_1 + v_2 x_2 + v_3 x_3 = 0$ we have

$$x_1 \frac{\partial v_1}{\partial x_i} + x_2 \frac{\partial v_2}{\partial x_i} + x_3 \frac{\partial v_3}{\partial x_i} + v_i = 0.$$

Therefore
$$\frac{\partial \phi}{\partial x_i} = - \rho v_i.$$

This shows that the tangent line to the curve (5) at the point L is the line p. Hence we have the theorem:

Each line of a one-dimensional extent of lines is tangent at its limit point to the curve which is the locus of the limit points. The lines therefore envelop the curve.

Let us suppose now that in equation (2) f is an algebraic polynomial of the nth degree. Then the locus of the limit points L is called a *curve of the nth class*. We shall prove that *through any point of the plane go n lines tangent to a curve of the nth class.*

To do this we have to show that n lines satisfying equation (2) go through any point of the plane. Now any point is fixed by two lines v_i and w_i, and any line through that point has the coördinates $v_i + \lambda w_i$. This line satisfies (2) when λ satisfies the equation

$$f(v_1 + \lambda w_1, v_2 + \lambda w_2, v_3 + \lambda w_3) = 0.$$

This is an equation of the nth degree, and the theorem is proved.

We have shown in this section that a one-dimensional extent of lines are in general the tangent lines to a curve. Conversely, the tangent lines to any curve are easily shown to be a one-dimensional extent of lines. An exception occurs only when the curve consists of a number of straight lines.

The dualistic relation between point and line coördinates is exhibited in the following restatement, in parallel columns, of the results of §§ 31 and 32:

An equation $f(x_1, x_2, x_3) = 0$ is satisfied by a one-dimensional extent of points which lie on a curve. A line joining two consecutive points of the curve is tangent to the curve. Its line coördinates are $u_1 : u_2 : u_3 = \dfrac{\partial f}{\partial x_1} : \dfrac{\partial f}{\partial x_2} : \dfrac{\partial f}{\partial x_3}$. The elimination of $x_1 : x_2 : x_3$ between these equations and that of the curve gives the line equation of the curve.

The equation of the tangent line to the curve defined by the point extent is

$$\frac{\partial f}{\partial y_1} x_1 + \frac{\partial f}{\partial y_2} x_2 + \frac{\partial f}{\partial y_3} x_3 = 0.$$

If f is of the nth degree the curve is of the nth order.

On any line lie n points of the curve.

The curve of the first order is a straight line, the base of a pencil of points. It is of zero class and has no line equation.

An equation $f(u_1, u_2, u_3) = 0$ is satisfied by a one-dimensional extent of lines which are tangent to a curve. A point of intersection of two consecutive lines is a point on the curve. Its point coördinates are $x_1 : x_2 : x_3 = \dfrac{\partial f}{\partial u_1} : \dfrac{\partial f}{\partial u_2} : \dfrac{\partial f}{\partial u_3}$. The elimination of $u_1 : u_2 : u_3$ between these equations and that of the line extent gives the point equation of the curve.

The equation of a point on the curve enveloped by the line extent is

$$\frac{\partial f}{\partial v_1} u_1 + \frac{\partial f}{\partial v_2} u_2 + \frac{\partial f}{\partial v_3} u_3 = 0.$$

If f is of the nth degree the curve is of the nth class.

Through any point go n lines which are tangent to the curve.

The curve of the first class is a point, the vertex of a pencil of lines. It is of zero order and has no point equation.

EXERCISES

1. Find the singular point of $x_1^3 + x_1^2 x_3 - x_2^2 x_3 = 0$. Show that through the singular point go two real lines which meet the curve in three coincident points. Sketch the curve with special reference to its relation with the triangle of reference. Also sketch the curve interpreting the coördinates as Cartesian coördinates and taking $x_3 = 0$, $x_2 = 0$, $x_1 = 0$ successively as the line at infinity.

2. Find the singular point of $x_1^3 - x_2^2 x_3 = 0$. Show that through it go two coincident lines which meet the curve in three coincident points. Sketch the curve as in Ex. 1.

3. Find the singular point of the curve $x_1^3 + x_1^2 x_3 + x_2^2 x_3 = 0$. Show that through it go two imaginary lines which meet the curve in three coincident points. Sketch the curve as in Ex. 1.

4. Find the line equation of each of the curves in Exs 1–3.

5. Show that any point whose coördinates satisfy the three equations $\dfrac{\partial f}{\partial x_1} = 0$, $\dfrac{\partial f}{\partial x_2} = 0$, $\dfrac{\partial f}{\partial x_3} = 0$ lies on the curve $f = 0$ and is therefore a singular point.

6. Show that the singular points of a curve in nonhomogeneous Cartesian coördinates are given by $\dfrac{\partial f}{\partial x} = 0$, $\dfrac{\partial f}{\partial y} = 0$, provided the solutions of these equations also satisfy $f(x, y) = 0$. (Compare Ex. 5.) Apply to find the singular points of $x^2 + y^2 = a^2$ and $x^2 - y^2 = 0$.

7. Show that through any point on a singular line of a line extent go at least two coincident lines of the extent. Hence show that if the extent envelops a curve of the nth class, the singular lines are the locus of a point such that at least two of the n tangents to the curve from that point are coincident. Illustrate by considering the line extent $u_1^3 + u_2 u_3^2 = 0$.

8. If $f(x_1, x_2, x_3) = 0$ is the equation of a curve and $y_1 : y_2 : y_3$ is a fixed point, show that the equation

$$y_1 \frac{\partial f}{\partial x_1} + y_2 \frac{\partial f}{\partial x_2} + y_3 \frac{\partial f}{\partial x_3} = 0$$

represents a curve which passes through all the singular points of $f = 0$ and through all the points of tangency from y_i to $f = 0$, but intersects $f = 0$ in no other points.

9. Prove that a curve of the third order can have at most one singular point unless it consists of a straight line and a curve of second order, or entirely of straight lines.

CHAPTER V

CURVES OF SECOND ORDER AND SECOND CLASS

33. Singular points of a curve of second order. By § 31 a curve of second order is defined by the equation

$$a_{11}x_1^2 + a_{22}x_2^2 + a_{33}x_3^2 + 2a_{12}x_1x_2 + 2a_{23}x_2x_3 + 2a_{13}x_1x_3 = 0, \quad (1)$$

which can be more compactly written in the form

$$\sum a_{ik}x_ix_k = 0. \quad (a_{ki} = a_{ik})$$

By the last theorem of § 31 *any straight line cuts a curve of second order in two points or lies entirely on the curve.*

It follows immediately that if the curve has singular points it must consist of straight lines. For any line through a singular point meets the curve in two points coincident with the singular point, and if it passes through a third point of the curve it must lie entirely on the curve.

We proceed to examine the singular points more closely, as they are important in determining the nature of the curve.

By (12), § 31, the singular points are the solutions of the equations

$$a_{11}y_1 + a_{12}y_2 + a_{13}y_3 = 0,$$
$$a_{12}y_1 + a_{22}y_2 + a_{23}y_3 = 0, \quad (2)$$
$$a_{13}y_1 + a_{23}y_2 + a_{33}y_3 = 0.$$

Let D, called the *discriminant* of equation (1), be defined by

$$D = \begin{vmatrix} a_{11} & a_{12} & a_{13} \\ a_{12} & a_{22} & a_{23} \\ a_{13} & a_{23} & a_{33} \end{vmatrix}. \quad (3)$$

There are then three cases in the discussion of equations (2).

CASE I. $D \neq 0$. Equations (2) have no solution, and the curve has no singular point. This is the general case.

CASE II. $D = 0$, but not all the first minors of D are zero. Equations (2) have one solution, and the curve has one singular point. Let that point be taken by a change of coördinates as the point $0:0:1$. The degree of the equation will not be changed (§ 29), but in the new equation we shall have $a_{13}=0$, $a_{23}=0$, $a_{33}=0$. The equation therefore becomes

$$a_{11}x_1^2 + 2\,a_{12}x_1x_2 + a_{22}x_2^2 = 0,$$

which can be factored into two linear factors. These factors cannot be equal, for if they were we should have $a_{11}:a_{12}=a_{12}:a_{22}$, and equations (2), written for the new coördinates and new equation, would have more than one solution. Hence the locus of (1) consists of two intersecting straight lines.

CASE III. $D=0$, and all its first minors are zero. Any solution of one of the equations (2) is a solution of the others, and the curve has a line of singular points. If by a change of coördinates that line is taken as the line $x_1=0$, we shall have in the new equation $a_{12}=a_{13}=a_{22}=a_{23}=a_{33}=0$, and the equation becomes $x_1^2=0$. Hence in this case the curve consists of two coincident straight lines.

Summing up, we have the following theorem :

A curve of the second order has in general no singular point. If it has one singular point it consists of two straight lines intersecting in that point. If it has a line of singular points it consists of that line doubly reckoned.

The curves of second order in homogeneous coördinates are the same as the conics in Cartesian coördinates, for, as shown in § 29, the degree of an equation is not altered by a change of coördinates. We may on occasion distinguish between the conics without singular points and those which consist of two straight lines by calling the latter degenerate cases of the conic.

34. Poles and polars with respect to a curve of second order. By (11), § 31, if y_i is a point on the conic (1), § 33, the line coördinates of the tangent at y_i are

$$\begin{aligned}
\rho u_1 &= a_{11}y_1 + a_{12}y_2 + a_{13}y_3,\\
\rho u_2 &= a_{12}y_1 + a_{22}y_2 + a_{23}y_3,\\
\rho u_3 &= a_{13}y_1 + a_{23}y_2 + a_{33}y_3.
\end{aligned} \tag{1}$$

Let us now drop the condition that y_i is on the curve and consider y, as any point of the plane, whether on the curve or not.

Equations (1) then associate to any point y_i a definite line u_i. This line is called the *polar* of the point, and the point is called the *pole* of the line. The equation of the polar is

$$a_{11}y_1x_1 + a_{22}y_2x_2 + a_{33}y_3x_3 + a_{12}(y_1x_2 + y_2x_1) + a_{13}(y_1x_3 + y_3x_1)$$
$$+ a_{23}(x_2y_3 + x_3y_2) = 0,$$

or, more compactly,

$$\sum a_{ik}y_ix_k = 0. \qquad (a_{ik} = a_{ki}) \qquad (2)$$

If y_i is given, u_i is uniquely determined by (1); but if u_i is given, y_i is determined only when equations (1) can be solved, that is, when the discriminant D, § 33, does not vanish. Hence,

I. To any point of the plane corresponds always a unique polar; but to any line of the plane corresponds a unique pole when and only when the curve has no singular point.

The following theorems are now easily proved:

II. The polar of a point on the curve is the tangent line at that point and, conversely, the pole of any tangent to the curve is the point of contact of the tangent.

It is obvious that equation (2) reduces to the equation of the tangent when the point y_i is on the curve. Conversely, if equation (2) is that of a tangent to the curve, the solution of equations (1) will give the point of contact.

III. The polar of a point passes through the point when and only when the point is on the curve.

This follows from the fact that the substitution $x_i = y_i$ reduces equation (2) to the equation of the curve.

IV. The polar of any point passes through the singular points of the curve if such exist.

This follows from the fact that equation (2) can be written

$$y_1(a_{11}x_1 + a_{12}x_2 + a_{13}x_3) + y_2(a_{12}x_1 + a_{22}x_2 + a_{23}x_3) + y_3(a_{13}x_1 + a_{23}x_2 + a_{33}x_3) = 0.$$

V. If a point P lies on the polar of a point Q, then Q lies on the polar of P.

If P is the point y_i and Q is the point z_i, the polar of P is

$$\sum a_{ik} y_i x_k = 0, \qquad (a_{ki} = a_{ik})$$

and that of Q is

$$\sum a_{ik} z_i x_k = 0. \qquad (a_{ki} = a_{ik})$$

The condition that P should lie on the polar of Q is

$$\sum a_{ik} z_i y_k = 0,$$

which is just the condition that Q should lie on the polar of P.

VI. *If a curve of second order has no singular point, two tangents may be drawn to the curve from any point not on it, and the chord connecting the points of contact of these tangents is the polar of the point of intersection of the tangents.*

Let P (Fig. 15) be a point not on the curve. The polar of P, being a straight line, cuts the curve in two points T and S. These two points are distinct because by theorem II the polar is not tangent, since P, by hypothesis, is not on the curve.

Since by hypothesis the curve has no singular point, it has a unique tangent line at each of the points T and S. These tangents are the polars of their points of contact and hence by theorem V pass through P. The polar of P therefore passes through T and S (theorem V).

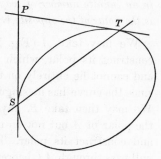

Fig. 15

There can be no more tangents from P to the curve, for if there were, the point of tangency would lie on TS by theorem V, and hence TS would intersect the curve in more than two points, which is impossible. The possibility that TS should lie entirely on the curve is ruled out by the fact that in that case the curve would consist of two straight lines and would have a singular point, which is contrary to hypothesis.

This theorem as proved takes no account of the reality of the lines and points concerned. In the case in which it is possible to draw real tangents from P, however, the theorem furnishes an easy method of sketching the polar of P.

When real tangents cannot be drawn from P, as in Fig. 16, the polar of P may be constructed as follows:

Through P draw two chords, one intersecting the curve in the points R and S and the other intersecting the curve in the points

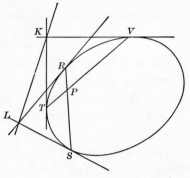

T and V. Draw the tangents at the points R, S, T, and V, and let the tangents at R and S intersect at L and let the tangents at T and V intersect at K. Then, by theorem VI, L is the pole of RS, and K is the pole of TV. Consequently the polar of P passes through L and K and is the line LK.

VII. *For a curve of second order without singular points it is possible*

Fig. 16

in an infinite number of ways to construct triangles in which each side is the polar of the opposite vertex. These are called self-polar triangles.

We may take A (Fig. 17), any point not on the curve, and construct its polar, which will not pass through A (theorem III)

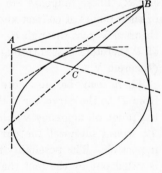

and cannot lie entirely on the curve, since the curve has no singular point. We may then take B, any point on the polar of A but not on the curve, and construct its polar. This polar will pass through A (theorem V) but not through B (theorem III). The two polars now found are distinct lines (theorem I) and will intersect in a point C. Draw AB. Then AB is the polar of C by theorem V. The triangle ABC is a self-polar triangle.

Fig. 17

VIII. *If any straight line m is passed through a point P, and R and S are the points of intersection of m with a curve of the second order, and Q is the point of intersection of m with the polar of P, then P and Q are harmonic conjugates with respect to R and S.*

Let P (Fig. 18) be any point with coördinates y_i, let p be the polar of P, and let m be any line through P cutting p in Q and the curve in R and S. Then, if z_i are the coördinates of Q, the coördinates of R and S are $y_i + \lambda_1 z_i$ and $y_i + \lambda_2 z_i$, where λ_1 and λ_2 are the roots of the equation

$$\sum a_{ik} y_i y_k + 2 \lambda \sum a_{ik} y_i z_k + \lambda^2 \sum a_{ik} z_i z_k = 0,$$

obtained by substituting $x_i = y_i + \lambda z_i$ in the equation of the curve.

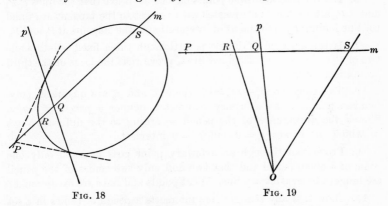

FIG. 18   FIG. 19

But since Q is on the polar of P, we have $\sum a_{ik} y_i z_k = 0$, and therefore $\lambda_1 = -\lambda_2$. By § 14 the theorem is proved.

This theorem gives a method of finding the polar of P when the curve of second order consists of two straight lines intersecting in a point O (Fig. 19). Draw through P any straight line m intersecting the curve in the points R and S, distinct from O, and find the point Q, the harmonic conjugate of P with respect to R and S. By theorem VIII, Q is on the polar of P, and by theorem IV the polar of P passes through O. Hence Q and O determine the required polar p.

EXERCISES

1. Prove that if a conic passes through the vertices of the triangle of reference its equation is $c_1 x_2 x_3 + c_2 x_3 x_1 + c_3 x_1 x_2 = 0$. Classify the conic according to the nature of the coefficients c_i.

2. Prove that if the triangle of reference is composed of two tangents to a conic and the chord of contact, the equation of the conic is $c_1 x_1 x_3 + c_2 x_2^2 = 0$. Classify the conic according to the nature of the coefficients c_i.

3. Prove that the triangle formed by the diagonals of any complete quadrangle whose vertices are in the conic is a self-polar triangle.

4. Prove that the triangle whose vertices are the diagonal points of a complete quadrilateral circumscribed about a conic is a self-polar triangle.

5. Prove that a range of points on any line is projective with the pencil of lines formed by the polars of the points with respect to any conic.

6. If P_1, P_2, P_3 are three points on a conic, prove that the lines P_2P_1 and P_2P_3 are harmonic conjugates with respect to the tangent at P_2 and the line joining F_2 to the point of intersection of the tangents at P_1 and P_3.

7. If the sides of a triangle pass through three fixed points while two of the vertices describe fixed lines, prove that the locus of the third vertex is a conic.

8. The equation $f_1 + \lambda f_2 = 0$, where f_1 and f_2 are quadratic polynomials and λ is an arbitrary parameter, defines a *pencil of conics*. Sketch the appearance of the pencil according to the different ways in which the conics $f_1 = 0$ and $f_2 = 0$ intersect.

9. Prove that through an arbitrary point goes one and only one conic of a given pencil and that two and only two conics of the pencil are tangent to an arbitrary line. What points and lines are exceptional?

10. Show that any straight line intersects a pencil of conics in a set of points in involution. What are the fixed points of the involution?

11. Prove that the polars of the same point with respect to the conics of a pencil form a pencil of lines.

12. If the point P describes a straight line, prove that the vertex of its polar pencil (Ex. 11) with respect to the conics of a pencil describes a conic.

13. Prove that the locus of the poles of a straight line with respect to the conics of a pencil is a conic.

14. Prove that the conics of a pencil of conics which intersect in four distinct points have one and only one common self-polar triangle.

15. Prove that the pole of the line at infinity is the center of the conic unless the conic is tangent to the line at infinity.

16. Prove that the tangents to a central conic at the extremities of a diameter are parallel.

17. Two lines are *conjugate* with respect to a conic if each passes through the pole of the other. Prove that each of two conjugate diameters is parallel to the tangents at the ends of the other. Prove also that a system of parallel chords are all conjugate to the same diameter and therefore bisected by it.

18. Consider a pencil of lines with its vertex at the center of a conic, and an involution in the pencil such that corresponding lines in the involution are conjugate diameters of the conic. Show that the fixed lines of the involution are the asymptotes.

19. The foci are defined as the finite intersections of the tangents from the circle points at infinity to any conic. Show that a real central conic has four foci, two real and two imaginary, and that the real foci are those considered in elementary analytic geometry.

35. Classification of curves of second order. We are now ready to find the simplest forms into which the equation

$$\sum a_{ik}x_ix_k = 0 \qquad (a_{ki} = a_{ik}) \tag{1}$$

can be put by a change of coördinates.

As before let us place

$$D = \begin{vmatrix} a_{11} & a_{12} & a_{13} \\ a_{12} & a_{22} & a_{23} \\ a_{13} & a_{23} & a_{33} \end{vmatrix}.$$

CASE I. $D \neq 0$. The curve has no singular points (§ 33), and there can be found an infinite number of self-polar triangles (VII, § 34). Let one such triangle be taken as the triangle of reference. Then, since the polar of $0:0:1$ is the line $x_3 = 0$, we shall have, in the new equation of the curve, $a_{13} = a_{23} = 0$. Since the polar of $0:1:0$ is $x_2 = 0$, we shall have $a_{12} = a_{23} = 0$. Since the polar of $1:0:0$ is $x_1 = 0$, we shall have $a_{12} = a_{13} = 0$. The equation of the curve is therefore

$$a_{11}x_1^2 + a_{22}x_2^2 + a_{33}x_3^2 = 0. \tag{2}$$

No one of the coefficients a_{11}, a_{22}, a_{33} can be zero, for if it were the curve would have a singular point.

If the coördinates of the original equation of the curve are real and the new coördinates are referred to a real self-polar triangle with a real unit point, the coefficients a_{11}, a_{22}, and a_{33} are real. We may then distinguish two cases according as all or two of the signs in (2) are alike. By replacing $\sqrt{|a_{ii}|}\,x_i$ by x_i we have then two types of equations,

$$x_1^2 + x_2^2 + x_3^2 = 0, \tag{3}$$

$$x_1^2 + x_2^2 - x_3^2 = 0. \tag{4}$$

The first equation represents a curve with no real points and the other represents one which has real points. It is obvious that no real substitution can reduce one equation to the other. Of course the second equation can be reduced to the first by placing $x_3 = i x_3$, which does not involve imaginary axes but an imaginary value of the constant k_3. Summing up, we have the theorem:

A curve of second order whose equation has real coefficients and which has no singular point is one of two types: an imaginary curve the equation of which can be reduced to the form (3), *and a real curve the equation of which can be reduced to the form* (4). *If no account is taken of imaginaries the equation of any curve of the second order with no singular point can be reduced to the form* (3).

CASE II. $D = 0$, but not all first minors of D are zero. The curve has then one and only one singular point (§ 33). This may be taken as the point $0:0:1$. Then $a_{13} = a_{23} = a_{33} = 0$. The points $0:1:0$ and $1:0:0$ may be taken in an infinite number of ways so that each is on the polar of the other. Each of these polars passes through $0:0:1$ (IV, § 34). Since $0:1:0$ is the pole of $x_2 = 0$ we have $a_{12} = 0$ in addition to $a_{23} = 0$, as already found, which is also the condition that $1:0:0$ is the pole of $x_1 = 0$. The equation of the curve is therefore

$$a_{11}x_1^2 + a_{22}x_2^2 = 0. \tag{5}$$

Neither of the coefficients a_{11} or a_{22} can be zero, for if it were, the curve would have more than one singular point.

Equation (5) may be reduced without the use of imaginary quantities to one of the types

$$x_1^2 + x_2^2 = 0, \tag{6}$$

$$x_1^2 - x_3^2 = 0. \tag{7}$$

Summing up, we have the theorem:

A curve of the second order whose equation has real coefficients and which has one singular point is one of two types: two imaginary straight lines represented by equation (6) *or two real straight lines represented by equation* (7). *If no account is taken of imaginaries a curve of second order with one singular point consists of two straight lines intersecting in that point, and its equation may be put in the form* (6).

CASE III. $D = 0$, and all its first minors are zero. The curve has then a line of singular points, and its equation may be reduced to $x_1^2 = 0$ (§ 33). *A curve of second order with a line of singular points consists of that line taken double.*

1. Apply the foregoing discussion to the classification of curves in Cartesian coördinates, using $x_3 = 0$ as the equation of the line at infinity. Where does the parabola occur in the discussion? (See Ex. 2, § 34.)

2. Show from the foregoing that if an ellipse or a hyperbola is referred to a pair of conjugate diameters, its equation is $\dfrac{x^2}{a^2} \pm \dfrac{y^2}{b^2} = 1$, and conversely.

3. Show from the foregoing that if a parabola is referred to a diameter * and a tangent at the end of the diameter, the equation of the parabola is $y^2 = ax$, and conversely.

4. Show that if a central conic does not pass through either of the circle points at infinity, it has one and only one pair of conjugate diameters which are orthogonal to each other.

5. Show that if a parabola does not pass through a circle point at infinity one and only one pair of axes described in Ex. 4 will be orthogonal. Write the equation of a parabola tangent to the line at infinity in a circle point.

36. Singular lines of a curve of second class. Consider the curve of second class defined by the equation in line coördinates

$$\sum A_{ik} u_i u_k = 0. \qquad (A_{ki} = A_{ik}) \qquad (1)$$

By § 32 the singular lines of this locus are defined by the equations

$$A_{11} u_1 + A_{12} u_2 + A_{13} u_3 = 0,$$
$$A_{12} u_1 + A_{22} u_2 + A_{23} u_3 = 0, \qquad (2)$$
$$A_{13} u_1 + A_{23} u_2 + A_{33} u_3 = 0.$$

Let Δ, called the *discriminant* of the curve (1), be defined by the equation

$$\Delta = \begin{vmatrix} A_{11} & A_{12} & A_{13} \\ A_{12} & A_{22} & A_{23} \\ A_{13} & A_{23} & A_{33} \end{vmatrix}.$$

There are then three cases in the discussion of equations (2).

CASE I. $\Delta \neq 0$. Equations (2) have no solution, and the curve has no singular line. This is the general case.

---

* A diameter of a parabola is defined as a straight line through the point of tangency of the parabola with the line at infinity.

CASE II. $\Delta = 0$, but not all the first minors of Δ are zero. Equations (2) have one solution, and the curve has one singular line. Let this line by a change of coördinates be taken as the line $0:0:1$. The degree of the equation will not be changed, but in the new equation we shall have $A_{13} = A_{23} = A_{33} = 0$. The equation therefore becomes

$$A_{11}u_1^2 + 2 A_{12}u_1u_2 + A_{22}u_2 = 0,$$

which can be factored into two linear factors. These factors cannot be equal, for if they were we should have $A_{11} : A_{12} = A_{12} : A_{22}$, and equations (2), written for the new equation, would have more than one solution. Each of the factors of (3) represents a pencil of lines the vertex of which lies on the line $x_3 = 0$; that is, on the singular line of the locus of (1). Equation (1) is the line equation of the two vertices of the pencils represented, and the singular line is the line connecting these two vertices.

CASE III. $\Delta = 0$, and all its first minors are zero. Any solution of one of the equations (2) is a solution of the others, and the curve has a pencil of singular lines. If by a change of coördinates that pencil is taken as the pencil $u_1 = 0$, we shall have in the new equation (1) $A_{12} = A_{13} = A_{22} = A_{23} = A_{33} = 0$, and the equation becomes $u_1^2 = 0$. Hence in this case equation (1) is the equation of two coincident points.

Summing up, we have the following theorem: *A curve of the second class has in general no singular line. If it has one singular line it consists of two distinct points lying on that line. If it has a pencil of singular lines it consists of the vertex of that pencil doubly reckoned.*

37. Classification of curves of second class. By § 32 the limit points of intersection of two lines of the locus

$$\sum A_{ik}u_iu_k = 0 \qquad (A_{ki} = A_{ik}) \tag{1}$$

are given by the equations

$$\begin{aligned}
\rho x_1 &= A_{11}u_1 + A_{12}u_2 + A_{13}u_3, \\
\rho x_2 &= A_{12}u_1 + A_{22}u_2 + A_{23}u_3, \\
\rho x_3 &= A_{13}u_1 + A_{23}u_2 + A_{33}u_3.
\end{aligned} \tag{2}$$

There are again three cases corresponding to the cases of the previous section.

CASE I. $\Delta \neq 0$. Equations (2) can be solved for u_1, u_2, and u_3, and the results substituted in (1). But by aid of equations (2), equation (1) can be replaced by the equation

$$u_1 x_1 + u_2 x_2 + u_3 x_3 = 0. \tag{3}$$

The result of the substitution is therefore

$$\begin{vmatrix} x_1 & A_{11} & A_{12} & A_{13} \\ x_2 & A_{12} & A_{22} & A_{23} \\ x_3 & A_{13} & A_{23} & A_{33} \\ 0 & x_1 & x_2 & x_3 \end{vmatrix} = 0, \tag{4}$$

which may be written $\qquad \sum_i a_{ik} x_i x_k = 0,$ $\qquad(5)$

where a_{ik} is the cofactor of A_{ik} in the expansion of the determinant Δ.

This is the curve of second class enveloped by the lines which satisfy equation (1). It appears that it is also a curve of second order. Let

$$D = \begin{vmatrix} a_{11} & a_{12} & a_{13} \\ a_{12} & a_{22} & a_{23} \\ a_{13} & a_{23} & a_{33} \end{vmatrix}$$

be the discriminant of (5). Then

$$D \cdot \Delta = \begin{vmatrix} \Delta & 0 & 0 \\ 0 & \Delta & 0 \\ 0 & 0 & \Delta \end{vmatrix} = \Delta^3$$

and $\qquad\qquad\qquad D = \Delta^2 \neq 0.$

We have therefore the following result: *A curve of second class with no singular line is also a curve of second order with no singular point.* The converse theorem is easily proved: *A curve of second order with no singular point is also a curve of second class with no singular line.*

Since the simplest equations of the curve of second order are

$$x_1^2 + x_2^2 + x_3^2 = 0,$$
$$x_1^2 + x_2^2 - x_3^2 = 0,$$

the simplest equations of the curve of second class are

$$u_1^2 + u_2^2 + u_3^2 = 0,$$
$$u_1^2 + u_2^2 - u_3^2 = 0.$$

CASE II. $\Delta = 0$, but not all its first minors are zero. Equations (2) have no solution, so that no point equation can be found for the locus of the limit points on the lines of equation (1). In fact, we have already seen that the limit points are two in number only, the vertices of the two pencils of lines defined by (1). The simplest forms into which equation (1) can be put without the use of imaginary coördinates are obviously

$$u_1^2 + u_2^2 = 0,$$

$$u_1^2 - u_2^2 = 0.$$

CASE III. $\Delta = 0$, and all first minors are equal to zero. We have already seen that the simplest form of the equation in this case is

$$u_1^2 = 0.$$

38. Poles and polars with respect to a curve of second class. Equations (2), § 37, can be used to establish a relation between any line u_i, whether or not it satisfies (1), § 37, and a point x_i defined by these equations. The point is called the *pole* of the line, and the line is called the *polar* of the point with respect to the curve of second class given by equation (1), § 37. The following theorem is then obvious:

To any line of the plane corresponds a distinct pole, but to any point corresponds a distinct polar when and only when the discriminant of the curve of second class does not vanish.

This relation is dualistic to that of § 34, and all theorems of that section can be read with a change of "point" to "line," "pole" to "polar," etc. We shall prove in fact that *in case of a curve of second order and second class without singular point or line the definitions of poles and polars in § 34 and § 38 coincide.*

This follows from the fact that the curve of second class defined by

$$\sum A_{ik} u_i u_k = 0$$

is, when $\Delta \neq 0$, the curve of second order

$$\sum a_{ik} x_i x_k = 0,$$

where a_{ik} is the cofactor of A_{ik} in Δ. Now, if equations (2), § 37, are solved for u_1, u_2, and u_3, there result the equations (1), § 34, and the theorem is proved.

In case a curve of second class consists of two points, by a theorem dualistic to IV, § 34, the pole of any line lies in the singular line, which is the line connecting the two points. It may be found by means of a theorem which is dualistic to VIII, § 34, and which may be worded as follows:

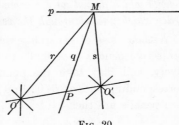

If any point M is taken on a line p, and r and s are the lines through M belonging to a curve of second class, and q is the line joining M to the pole of p, the lines p and q are harmonic conjugates with respect to r and s.

FIG. 20

This theorem is illustrated in Fig. 20, which also suggests the construction necessary to find P the pole of p, since P is the intersection of q and the line OO'.

EXERCISES

1. If the three vertices of a triangle move on three fixed lines and two of its sides pass through fixed points, the third side will envelop a conic.

2. A range of conics is defined by the equation $f_1 + \lambda f_2 = 0$, where $f_1 = 0$ and $f_2 = 0$ are the equations in line coördinates of two conics. Discuss the appearance of the range.

3. Prove that there is in general one and only one conic of a range which is tangent to a given line and two and only two conics of a range which pass through a given point. What are the exceptional lines and points?

4. Prove that for a given range all tangents through a fixed point form a pencil in involution with itself.

5. Prove that for a given range of conics the poles of a fixed straight line form a range of points.

6. If a straight line in Ex. 5 turns about a point, show that the base of the range of its polar points envelop a conic.

7. Prove that the centers of the conics of a range lie on a straight line.

8. Prove that the conics of a range with four distinct common tangents have one and only one self-polar triangle.

39. Projective properties of conics. We shall prove the following theorems which are connected with the curves of second order and involve projective pencils or ranges.

I. The points of intersection of corresponding lines of two projective pencils which do not have a common vertex generate a curve of second order which passes through the vertices of the pencils.

Without loss of generality we may take the vertices of the two projective pencils as $A(0:0:1)$ and $C(1:0:0)$ (Fig. 21) respectively, and may take the point of intersection of one pair of corresponding lines as $B(0:1:0)$. The two pencils are then

$$x_1 + \lambda x_2 = 0$$

and

$$x_2 + \lambda' x_3 = 0,$$

where $\lambda' = \dfrac{\alpha\lambda + \beta}{\gamma\lambda + \delta}$. The point B lies on the line of the first pencil, for which $\lambda = 0$, and on the line of the second pencil, for which $\lambda' = \infty$. Since these are corresponding lines in the projectivity, we have $\delta = 0$. Then β and γ cannot vanish, owing to the condition $\alpha\delta - \beta\gamma \neq 0$. Now, if $x_1 : x_2 : x_3$ is a point on two corresponding lines of the pencils, we have $\lambda = -\dfrac{x_1}{x_2}$, $\lambda' = -\dfrac{x_2}{x_3}$, and hence

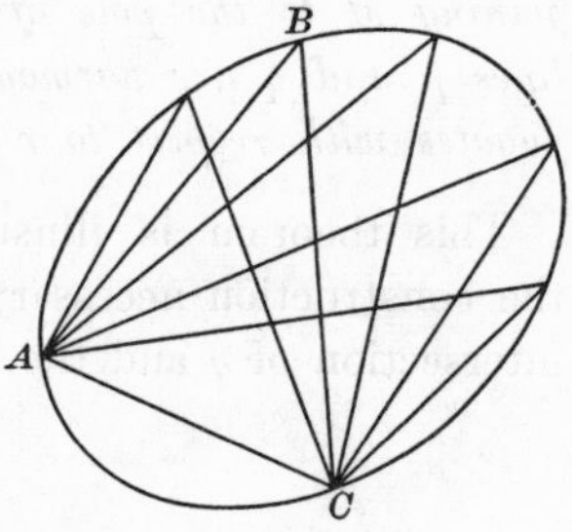

$$\gamma x_1 x_2 - \beta x_2 x_3 + \alpha x_3 x_1 = 0. \tag{1}$$

Fig. 21

The point $x_1 : x_2 : x_3$ therefore lies on a curve of second order.

Conversely, if $y_1 : y_2 : y_3$ is a point on this curve of second order,

we have

$$\frac{y_2}{y_3} = \frac{-\alpha + \beta\dfrac{y_2}{y_1}}{\gamma}.$$

But the line joining y_i to A has the parameter $\lambda = -\dfrac{y_1}{y_2}$, and the line joining y_i to B has the parameter $\lambda' = -\dfrac{y_2}{y_3}$, and consequently $\lambda' = \dfrac{\alpha\lambda + \beta}{\gamma\lambda}$. Hence the point y_i is the intersection of two corresponding lines of the two projective pencils.

That the curve of second order with the equation (1) passes through A and C is obvious. Hence the theorem is proved.

If $\alpha = 0$ the curve (1) reduces to the two straight lines $x_2 = 0$ and $\gamma x_1 - \beta x_3 = 0$, and the two pencils are in perspective (§ 16).

Equation (1) may be written in the more symmetrical form

$$c_1 x_2 x_3 + c_2 x_3 x_1 + c_3 x_1 x_2 = 0,$$

or
$$\frac{c_1}{x_1} + \frac{c_2}{x_2} + \frac{c_3}{x_3} = 0. \tag{2}$$

II. *The lines connecting corresponding points of two projective ranges which do not have the same base envelop a curve of second class which is tangent to the bases of the two ranges.*

This is dualistic to I. We may take the bases of the two ranges as $a(0:0:1)$ and $c(1:0:0)$ (Fig. 22) respectively, and a line connecting two pairs of corresponding points as $b(0:1:0)$. The line equations of points on the two ranges are then

$$u_1 + \lambda u_2 = 0$$

and
$$u_2 + \lambda' u_3 = 0,$$

where, as for I,

$$\lambda' = \frac{\alpha\lambda + \beta}{\gamma\lambda}.$$

The lines connecting corresponding points then satisfy an equation of the form

$$c_1 u_2 u_3 + c_2 u_3 u_1 + c_3 u_1 u_2 = 0,$$

or
$$\frac{c_1}{u_1} + \frac{c_2}{u_2} + \frac{c_3}{u_3} = 0. \tag{3}$$

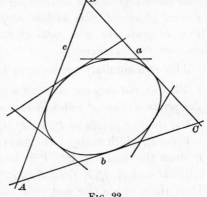

Fig. 22

Conversely, any line satisfying this equation is a line connecting corresponding points of the two ranges.

When $\alpha = 0$ the equation factors into $u_1 = 0$ and $\gamma u_1 - \beta u_3 = 0$, and the two ranges are in perspective.

III. *Any two points on a curve of second order without singular lines may be used as the vertices of two generating pencils.*

No three points of the curve lie in a straight line. Hence any three points on the curve may be taken as the vertices of the coördinate triangle ABC. The equation of the curve is then of the form
$$c_1 x_2 x_3 + c_2 x_3 x_1 + c_3 x_1 x_2 = 0, \tag{4}$$
where c_1, c_2, c_3 are not zero, since the curve has no singular point.

The equation of any line through A is $x_1 + \lambda x_2 = 0$ and that of any line through C is $x_2 + \lambda' x_3 = 0$. If these lines intersect on (4) we have

$$\lambda' = \frac{c_2 \lambda - c_1}{c_3 \lambda}.$$

The correspondence of lines of the pencil with vertex A and those of the pencil with vertex C is therefore projective. This proves the theorem.

IV. *Any two tangent lines to a curve of second class without singular points may be taken as the bases of two projective generating ranges.*

This is dualistic to theorem III.

V. *If any point of a curve of second order without singular points is connected with any four points on the curve, the cross ratio of the four connecting lines is constant for the curve. If any tangent line to a curve of second class without singular lines is intersected by any four tangents, the cross ratio of the four points of intersection is constant for the curve.*

This is a corollary to theorems III and IV.

VI. *One and only one curve of second order can be passed through five points, no four of which lie in a straight line.*

Let the five points be P_1, P_2, P_3, P_4, and P_5 (Fig. 23).

From P_1, which cannot be in the same straight line with P_2, P_3, and P_4, draw the lines P_1P_2, P_1P_3, P_1P_4; and from P_5, which also cannot be collinear with P_2, P_3, P_4, draw P_5P_2, P_5P_3, P_5P_4. Then there exists one and only one projectivity (I, § 13) between the pencil with vertex P_1 and that with vertex P_5 in which the line P_1P_2 corresponds to P_5P_2, the line P_1P_3 to P_5P_3, and the line P_1P_4 to P_5P_4. The intersection of corresponding lines of these projective pencils determine a curve of

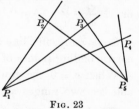

FIG. 23

second order through the five given points. Since any two points on the curve may be taken as the vertices of the generating pencils, only one curve can be passed through the points.

VII. *One and only one curve of second class can be constructed tangent to five lines no four of which meet in a point.*

This is dualistic to theorem VI.

VIII. _Pascal's theorem._ _If a hexagon is inscribed in a curve of second order, the points of intersection of opposite sides lie on a straight line._

By a hexagon is meant in this theorem the straight-line figure formed by connecting in order the six points P_1, P_2, P_3, P_4, P_5, P_6, taken anywhere on the curve of second order (Fig. 24). The opposite sides are then P_1P_2 and P_4P_5, P_2P and P_5P_6, P_3P_4 and P_6P_1 respectively.

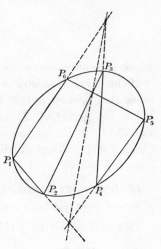

We shall first assume that the curve is without singular points. Then the points P_1, P_3, and P_5 do not lie on a straight line and may be taken as the vertices of the triangle of reference. Let P_1 be the point $(0:0:1)$, P_3 the point $(0:1:0)$, and P_5 the point $(1:0:0)$. Then the equation of the curve is, by (2),

$$\frac{c_1}{x_1} + \frac{c_2}{x_2} + \frac{c_3}{x_3} = 0. \qquad (5)$$

Let P_2 have the coördinates y_i, P_4 the coördinates z_i, and P_6 the

coördinates w_i. Then, since the three points P_2, P_4, and P_6 lie on the curve (4), we have

$$\begin{vmatrix} \dfrac{1}{y_1} & \dfrac{1}{y_2} & \dfrac{1}{y_3} \\[2mm] \dfrac{1}{z_1} & \dfrac{1}{z_2} & \dfrac{1}{z_3} \\[2mm] \dfrac{1}{w_1} & \dfrac{1}{w_2} & \dfrac{1}{w_3} \end{vmatrix} = 0. \qquad (6)$$

The equation of the line P_1P_2 is $y_2 x_1 - y_1 x_2 = 0$ and that of P_4P_5 is $z_3 x_2 - z_2 x_3$. They intersect in the point $\dfrac{y_1}{y_2} : 1 : \dfrac{z_3}{z_2}$. Similarly, the lines P_2P_3 and P_5P_6 intersect in the point $\dfrac{y_1}{y_3} : \dfrac{w_2}{w_3} : 1$ and the lines

P_3P_4 and P_6P_1 intersect in the point $1 : \dfrac{w_2}{w_1} : \dfrac{z_3}{z_1}$. The condition that these three points lie on a straight line is

$$\begin{vmatrix} 1 & \dfrac{w_2}{w_1} & \dfrac{z_3}{z_1} \\[2mm] \dfrac{y_1}{y_2} & 1 & \dfrac{z_3}{z_2} \\[2mm] \dfrac{y_1}{y_3} & \dfrac{w_2}{w_3} & 1 \end{vmatrix} = 0,$$

which is readily seen to be the same as equation (6).

If the curve of second order consists of two intersecting straight lines, the theorem is still true, but the proof needs modification. When the points P_1, P_3, and P_5 lie on one of the straight lines and P_2, P_4, P_6 lie on the other, we have the theorem of Pappus (VII, § 30). Other distributions of the points on the straight lines are trivial.

IX. Brianchon's theorem. *If a hexagon is circumscribed about a curve of second class, the lines connecting opposite vertices meet in a point.*

This is dualistic to VIII, and the proof is left to the student.

EXERCISES

1. Prove that the center of homology (see Ex. 9, § 30) of two projective pencils of lines is the intersection of the tangents at the vertices of the pencils to the conic generated by the pencils.

2. Prove that the axis of homology (see Ex. 10, § 30) of two projective ranges is the line joining the points of contact of the bases of the ranges with the conic generated by the ranges.

3. Show that the lines drawn through a fixed point intersect a conic in a set of points in involution, the fixed points of the involution being the points of contact of the tangents from the fixed point.

4. Prove that if two triangles are inscribed in the same conic they are circumscribed about another conic, and conversely.

5. Prove that if a pentagon is inscribed in a conic the intersections of two pairs of nonadjacent sides and the intersection of the fifth side and the tangent at the opposite vertex lie on a straight line.

6. State and prove the dualistic theorem to Ex. 5.

7. Prove that if a quadrilateral is inscribed in a conic the intersections of the opposite sides and of the tangents at the opposite vertices lie on a straight line.

8. State and prove the dualistic theorem to Ex. 6.

9. If a quadrilateral $ABCD$ is inscribed in a conic and L is the intersection of the tangent at A and the side BC, K is the intersection of the tangent at B and the side AD, and M is the intersection of the sides AB and CD, prove that L, K, and M lie on a straight line.

10. State and prove the dualistic theorem to Ex. 8.

11. If a triangle is inscribed in a conic, prove that the intersections of the tangents at the vertices with the opposite sides lie on a straight line.

12. State and prove the dualistic theorem to Ex. 12.

13. Prove that the complete quadrangle formed by four points of a conic has, as diagonal points, the points of intersection of the diagonal lines of the complete quadrilateral formed by the tangents at the vertices of the complete quadrangle.

CHAPTER VI

LINEAR TRANSFORMATIONS

40. Collineations. A collineation in a plane is a point transformation (§ 5) expressed by the equations

$$\rho x_1' = a_{11}x_1 + a_{12}x_2 + a_{13}x_3,$$
$$\rho x_2' = a_{21}x_1 + a_{22}x_2 + a_{23}x_3, \tag{1}$$
$$\rho x_3' = a_{31}x_1 + a_{32}x_2 + a_{33}x_3.$$

If the determinant $|a_{ik}|$ is not equal to zero, these equations can be solved for x_i, with the result

$$\sigma x_1 = A_{11}x_1' + A_{21}x_2' + A_{31}x_3',$$
$$\sigma x_2 = A_{12}x_1' + A_{22}x_2' + A_{32}x_3', \tag{2}$$
$$\sigma x_3 = A_{13}x_1' + A_{32}x_2' + A_{33}x_3',$$

where A_{ik} is the cofactor of a_{ik} in the expansion of $|a_{ik}|$ and where $|A_{ik}| \neq 0$.

If the determinant $|a_{ik}| = 0$, equations (2) cannot be obtained from (1). For this reason it is necessary to divide collineations into two classes:

1. Nonsingular collineations, for which $|a_{ik}| \neq 0$.
2. Singular collineations, for which $|a_{ik}| = 0$.

We shall consider only nonsingular collineations in this text, though some examples of singular collineations will be found in the exercises.

It is obvious that for a nonsingular collineation x_i cannot have such values in (1) that $x_1' = x_2' = x_3' = 0$. Hence by (1) any point x_i is transformed into a unique point x_i'. Similarly, from (2) any point x_i' is the transformed point of a unique point x_i.

Consider now a straight line with the equation

$$u_1x_1 + u_2x_2 + u_3x_3 = 0.$$

All points x_i, which satisfy this equation, will be transformed into points x_i', which satisfy the equation

$$u_1'x_1' + u_2'x_2' + u_3'x_3' = 0,$$

where, by (2),

$$\tau u_1' = A_{11}u_1 + A_{12}u_2 + A_{13}u_3,$$
$$\tau u_2' = A_{21}u_1 + A_{22}u_2 + A_{23}u_3, \tag{3}$$
$$\tau u_3' = A_{31}u_1 + A_{32}u_2 + A_{33}u_3.$$

It appears then that any straight line with coördinates u_i is transformed by (1) into a unique line with coördinates u_i'. Also, equations (3) may be solved for u_i with the result

$$\lambda u_1 = a_{11}u_1' + a_{21}u_2' + a_{31}u_3',$$
$$\lambda u_2 = a_{12}u_1' + a_{22}u_2' + a_{32}u_3', \tag{4}$$
$$\lambda u_3 = a_{13}u_1' + a_{23}u_2' + a_{33}u_3',$$

from which it appears that any line is the transformed line of a unique line.

Equations (3) express in line coördinates the same transformation that is expressed by equations (1) in point coördinates. For it is easy to see that by equations (3) any pencil of lines with the vertex x_i is transformed into a pencil of lines with the vertex x_i' and that the relation between x_i and x_i' is exactly that given by equations (1). Equations (3), therefore, which express a transformation of straight lines into straight lines, also afford a transformation of points into points in a sense dualistic to that in which equations (1) afford a transformation of straight lines into straight lines.

We will sum up the results thus far obtained in the following theorem:

I. By a nonsingular collineation in a plane every point is transformed into a unique point and every straight line into a unique straight line and, conversely, every point is the transformed point of a unique point and every straight line the transformed line of a unique straight line.

Consider now a collineation R_1 by which any point x_i is transformed into the point x_i', where

$$\rho x_i' = a_{i1}x_1 + a_{i2}x_2 + a_{i3}x_3,$$

and let R_2 be a collineation by which any point x_i' is transformed into x'', where

$$\sigma x_i'' = b_{i1}x_1' + b_{i2}x_2' + b_{i3}x_3'.$$

Then the product R_2R_1 is a substitution of the form

$$\tau x_i'' = c_{i1}x_1 + c_{i2}x_2 + c_{i3}x_3,$$

which is a collineation. Hence the product of two collineations is a collineation.

Moreover, if R_1 is as above and R_2 is of the form

$$\sigma x_i'' = A_{1i}x_1' + A_{2i}x_2' + A_{3i}x_3',$$

the product R_2R_1 is

$$\tau x_1'' = x_1, \quad \tau x_2'' = x_2, \quad \tau x_3'' = x_3,$$

which is the identical substitution. Hence in this case R_2 is the inverse substitution to R_1 and is denoted by R_1^{-1}. Our work shows that the inverse transformation to a collineation always exists and is itself a collineation.

These considerations prove the following theorem:

II. The totality of nonsingular collineations in a plane form a group.

We shall now prove the following theorems:

III. If P_1, P_2, P_3, P_4 are any four arbitrarily assumed points, no three of which are on the same straight line, and P_1', P_2', P_3', P_4' are also four arbitrarily assumed points, no three of which lie on a straight line, there exists one and only one collineation by means of which P_1 is transformed into P_1', P_2 into P_2', P_3 into P_3', and P_4 into P_4'.

To prove this we will first show that one and only one collineation exists which transforms the four fundamental points of the coördinate system, namely $A(0:0:1)$, $B(0:1:0)$, $C(1:0:0)$, and $I(1:1:1)$, respectively, into four arbitrary points P_1 $(\alpha_1:\alpha_2:\alpha_3)$, P_2 $(\beta_1:\beta_2:\beta_3)$, P_3 $(\gamma_1:\gamma_2:\gamma_3)$, and P_4 $(\delta_1:\delta_2:\delta_3)$, no three of which lie on a straight line. `

By substituting in equation (1) the coördinates of corresponding points, remembering that the factor ρ may have different values for different pairs of points, we have the following equations out of which to determine the coefficients a_{ik}:

$$\begin{aligned}
\rho_1\alpha_1 &= a_{13}, & \rho_2\beta_1 &= a_{12}, & \rho_3\gamma_1 &= a_{11}, \\
\rho_1\alpha_2 &= a_{23}, & \rho_2\beta_2 &= a_{22}, & \rho_3\gamma_2 &= a_{21}, \\
\rho_1\alpha_3 &= a_{33}, & \rho_2\beta_3 &= a_{32}, & \rho_3\gamma_3 &= a_{31},
\end{aligned} \tag{5}$$

$$\begin{aligned}
\rho_4\delta_1 &= a_{11} + a_{12} + a_{13}, \\
\rho_4\delta_2 &= a_{21} + a_{22} + a_{23}, \\
\rho_4\delta_3 &= a_{31} + a_{32} + a_{33}.
\end{aligned} \tag{6}$$

By substitution from equations (5) in equations (6) we have

$$\rho_1\alpha_1 + \rho_2\beta_1 + \rho_3\gamma_1 - \rho_4\delta_1 = 0,$$
$$\rho_1\alpha_2 + \rho_2\beta_2 + \rho_3\gamma_2 - \rho_4\delta_2 = 0,$$
$$\rho_1\alpha_3 + \rho_2\beta_3 + \rho_3\gamma_3 - \rho_4\delta_3 = 0,$$

which may be solved for $\rho_1 : \rho_2 : \rho_3 : \rho_4$. Since no three of the points P_1, P_2, P_3, P_4 lie on a straight line no determinant of the third order formed from the matrix

$$\begin{vmatrix} \alpha_1 & \beta_1 & \gamma_1 & \delta_1 \\ \alpha_2 & \beta_2 & \gamma_2 & \delta_2 \\ \alpha_3 & \beta_3 & \gamma_3 & \delta_3 \end{vmatrix}$$

can vanish, and hence no one of the factors ρ_i can be zero. The values of ρ_1, ρ_2, ρ_3, and ρ_4 having thus been determined except for a constant factor, the values of the coefficients a_{ik} can be found from (5) except for this same factor. Hence the collineation (1) is uniquely determined, since only the ratios of a_{ik} in (1) are essential.

Let it now be required to transform the four points P_1, P_2, P_3, P_4, no three of which are on a straight line, into the four points P_1', P_2', P_3', P_4', respectively, no three of which are on a straight line. As we have seen, there is a unique collineation R_1 which transforms A, B, C, I into P_1, P_2, P_3, P_4 respectively, and a unique collineation R_2 which transforms A, B, C, I into P_1', P_2', P_3', P_4' respectively. Then the collineation R_1^{-1} (theorem II) exists and transforms P_1, P_2, P_3, P_4 into A, B, C, I respectively. The product $R_2 R_1^{-1}$ is a collineation (theorem II) which transforms P_1, P_2, P_3, P_4 into P_1', P_2', P_3', P_4' respectively. Moreover, this is the only collineation which makes the desired transformation. For let R be a collineation which does so. Then $R_2^{-1}R$ transforms P_1, P_2, P_3, P_4 into A, B, C, I respectively. Hence

$$R_2^{-1}R = R_1^{-1};$$

whence $$R = R_2 R_1^{-1}.$$

This establishes the theorem. It is not necessary that all the points P_1, P_2, P_3, P_4 should be distinct from the points P_1', P_2', P_3', P_4'. In the special case in which P_1 is the same as P_1', P_2 the same as

P_2', P_3 the same as P_3', and P_4 the same as P_4', $R_1 = R_2$ and R is the identical substitution. Hence we have as a corollary to the above theorem:

IV. *Any collineation with four fixed points no three of which are in the same straight line is the identical substitution.*

V. *Any nonsingular collineation establishes a projectivity between the points of two corresponding ranges and the lines of two corresponding pencils, and any such projectivity may be established in an infinite number of ways by a nonsingular collineation.*

To prove the first part of the theorem let the point y_i be transformed into y_i' and the point z_i be transformed into z_i' by the collineation (1), so that

$$\rho_1 y_i' = a_{i1} y_1 + a_{i2} y_2 + a_{i3} y_3,$$
$$\rho_2 z_i' = a_{i1} z_1 + a_{i2} z_2 + a_{i3} z_3.$$

Then $y_i + \lambda z_i$ is transformed into ξ_i, where

$$\rho_3 \xi_1 = a_{i1}(y_1 + \lambda z_1) + a_{i2}(y_2 + \lambda z_2) + a_{i3}(y_3 + \lambda z_3)$$
$$= \rho_1 y_i' + \lambda \rho_2 z_i' ;$$

whence $$\sigma \xi_i = y_i' + \lambda' z_i$$

where $$\lambda' = \frac{\lambda \rho_2}{\rho_1}.$$

This establishes a projectivity between the points of the range $y_i + \lambda z_i$ and those of the range $y_i' + \lambda' z_i'$. By the use of line coördinates and equations (3) the proof may be repeated for the lines of a pencil.

To prove that there are an infinite number of nonsingular collineations which establish a given projectivity between the points of two ranges, it is only necessary to show that there are an infinite number of collineations which transform any three points P, Q, R lying on a straight line into any three points P', Q', R', also on a straight line, and apply III, § 15.

To prove this, draw through R any straight line and take S and T two points on it. Draw also through R' any straight line and take S' and T' any two points on it.

Then by theorem III there exists a collineation which transforms the four points P, Q, S, T into the four points P', Q', S', T', and this collineation transforms R into R'. Since S, T and S', T' are to a large extent arbitrary, there are an infinite number of required collineations.

If it is required to determine a collineation which establishes a projectivity between two given pencils of lines, this may be done by establishing a projectivity between two ranges, each of which is in perspective with one of the pencils. Since this may be done in an infinite number of ways, there are an infinite number of the required collineations.

41. Types of nonsingular collineations. A collineation has a *fixed point* when $x_i' = x_i$ in equations (1), §40. The fixed points are therefore given by the equations

$$(a_{11} - \rho) x_1 + a_{12} x_2 + a_{13} x_3 = 0,$$
$$a_{21} x_1 + (a_{22} - \rho) x_2 + a_{23} x_3 = 0, \tag{1}$$
$$a_{31} x_1 + a_{32} x_2 + (a_{33} - \rho) x_3 = 0.$$

The necessary and sufficient conditions that these equations have a solution is that ρ should satisfy the equation

$$\begin{vmatrix} a_{11} - \rho & a_{12} & a_{13} \\ a_{21} & a_{22} - \rho & a_{23} \\ a_{31} & a_{32} & a_{33} - \rho \end{vmatrix} = 0. \tag{2}$$

Similarly, the fixed lines of the collineation are given by the equations

$$(a_{11} - \rho) u_1 + a_{21} u_2 + a_{31} u_3 = 0,$$
$$a_{12} u_1 + (a_{22} - \rho) u_2 + a_{32} u_3 = 0, \tag{3}$$
$$a_{13} u_1 + a_{23} u_2 + (a_{33} - \rho) u_3 = 0,$$

and the necessary and sufficient condition that these equations have a solution is

$$\begin{vmatrix} a_{11} - \rho & a_{21} & a_{31} \\ a_{12} & a_{22} - \rho & a_{32} \\ a_{13} & a_{23} & a_{33} - \rho \end{vmatrix} = 0. \tag{4}$$

Equations (2) and (4) are the same and will be written

$$f(\rho) = 0. \tag{5}$$

Now let ρ_1 be a root of (5). Then ρ_1 cannot be zero, since by hypothesis $|a_{ik}| \neq 0$. The root ρ_1 is a double root when

$$f'(\rho_1) = -\begin{vmatrix} a_{22} - \rho_1 & a_{23} \\ a_{32} & a_{33} - \rho_1 \end{vmatrix} - \begin{vmatrix} a_{11} - \rho_1 & a_{13} \\ a_{31} & a_{33} - \rho_1 \end{vmatrix} - \begin{vmatrix} a_{11} - \rho_1 & a_{12} \\ a_{21} & a_{22} - \rho_1 \end{vmatrix} = 0, \tag{6}$$

and it is a triple root when

$$f''(\rho_1) = 2\left[(a_{11} - \rho_1) + (a_{22} - \rho_1) + (a_{33} - \rho_1)\right] = 0. \tag{7}$$

We may now distinguish three cases:

1. When all the first minors of the determinant $f(\rho_1)$ do not vanish. Equations (1) and (3) have each a single solution. The collineation has then a single fixed point and a single fixed line corresponding to the value ρ_1. The root ρ_1 may be a simple, a double, or a triple root of (5), according as equations (6) and (7) are or are not satisfied.

2. When all the first minors of $f(\rho_1)$ vanish, but not all the second minors vanish. Equations (1) and (3) contain then a single independent equation. The collineation has then a line of fixed points and a pencil of fixed lines corresponding to the value ρ_1.

The root ρ_1 is at least a double root of (5) since equation (6) is necessarily satisfied, and it may or may not be a triple root.

3. When all the second minors of $f(\rho_1)$ vanish. Equations (1) and (3) are satisfied by all values of x_i and u_i respectively, and the collineation leaves all points and lines fixed. The root ρ_1 is then a triple root of (5) since equations (6) and (7) are satisfied.

From this it follows that *a collineation has as many fixed lines as fixed points and as many pencils of fixed lines as lines of fixed points.*

From § 12 it follows also that *in every fixed line lies at least one fixed point and that through every fixed point goes at least one fixed line. The line connecting two fixed points is fixed and the point common to fixed lines is fixed.*

We are now prepared to classify collineations according to their fixed points and to give the simplest form to which the equations of each type may be reduced. We will first notice, however, that if the point $x_i = 0$, $x_j = 0$, $x_k = 1$ is fixed, then by (1), § 40, $a_{ik} = a_{jk} = 0$; and if the line $x_k = 0$ is fixed, then $a_{ki} = a_{kj} = 0$.

A. Collineations with at least three fixed points not in the same straight line. Take the fixed points as the vertices A, B, C of the triangle of reference. Then the collineation is

$$\rho x_1' = a_{11}x_1,$$
$$\rho x_2' = \quad\quad a_{22}x_2,$$
$$\rho x_3' = \quad\quad\quad\quad a_{33}x_3.$$

No one of the coefficients can be zero, since the collineation is nonsingular, but they may or may not be equal. We have then the following types, in writing which different letters are used to indicate quantities which are not equal.

TYPE I.
$$\rho x_1' = a x_1,$$
$$\rho x_2' = \quad b x_2,$$
$$\rho x_3' = \quad\quad c x_3.$$

The collineation has only the fixed points A, B, C and the fixed lines AB, BC, and CD.

TYPE II.
$$\rho x_1' = a x_1,$$
$$\rho x_2' = \quad a x_2,$$
$$\rho x_3' = \quad\quad c x_3.$$

The collineation has the fixed point A, the line of fixed points BC, the fixed line BC, and the pencil of fixed lines with vertex A. It is called a *homology*.

TYPE III.
$$\rho x_1' = x_1,$$
$$\rho x_2' = \quad x_2,$$
$$\rho x_3' = \quad\quad x_3.$$

All points and lines are fixed. It is the identical transformation.

B. Collineations with at least two distinct fixed points, but no others not in the same straight line. We will take the two fixed points as A $(0:0:1)$ and C $(1:0:0)$ of the triangle of reference. The collineation has at least two distinct fixed lines one of which is AC. The other must contain one of the fixed points, and we will take it as BC $(x_3 = 0)$. The collineation is then

$$\rho x_1' = a_{11} x_1 + a_{12} x_2,$$
$$\rho x_2' = \quad\quad a_{22} x_2,$$
$$\rho x_3' = \quad\quad\quad a_{33} x_3.$$

Here $a_{12} \neq 0$ or we should have case A. We shall place $a_{12} = 1$. The equation (5) is now $(a_{11} - \rho)(a_{22} - \rho)(a_{33} - \rho) = 0$. Placing $\rho = a_{22}$ we have as the equations to determine the corresponding fixed point

$$(a_{11} - a_{22}) x_1 + x_2 = 0,$$
$$(a_{33} - a_{22}) x_3 = 0.$$

Since by hypothesis every fixed point lies on $x_2 = 0$, we have $a_{11} = a_{22}$. It is left undetermined whether a_{33} is or is not equal to a_{22}. Hence we have two new types.

TYPE IV.
$$\rho x_1' = ax_1 + x_2,$$
$$\rho x_2' = \qquad ax_2,$$
$$\rho x_3' = \qquad\qquad bx_3.$$

The collineation has only the fixed points A and C and the fixed lines AC and BC.

TYPE V.
$$\rho x_1' = ax_1 + x_2,$$
$$\rho x_2' = \qquad ax_2,$$
$$\rho x_3' = \qquad\qquad ax_3.$$

The collineation has the line of fixed points AC and the pencil of fixed lines with its vertex at C.

In either Type IV or V the point B may be taken at pleasure on the line BC.

C. Collineations with only one fixed point. Take the fixed point as C $(1:0:0)$. The collineation has also a fixed line which must pass through C. Take it as BC $(x_3 = 0)$. The collineation is now

$$\rho x_1' = a_{11}x_1 + a_{12}x_2 + a_{13}x_3,$$
$$\rho x_2' = \qquad a_{22}x_2 + a_{23}x_3,$$
$$\rho x_3' = \qquad\qquad a_{33}x_3.$$

Equation (5) is now $(a_{11} - \rho)(a_{22} - \rho)(a_{33} - \rho) = 0$, and since by hypotheses C is the only fixed point, we have $a_{11} = a_{22} = a_{33}$. The point A $(0:0:1)$ taken at pleasure is transformed into A' $(a_{13} : a_{23} : a_{33})$, and if we take the line AA' as $x_1 = 0$, we have $a_{13} = 0$. The coefficients a_{12} and a_{23} cannot vanish or we have the previous cases. We may accordingly replace x_2 by $\dfrac{x_2}{a_{12}}$ and x_3 by $\dfrac{x_3}{a_{12}a_{23}}$ and have, finally,

TYPE VI.*
$$\rho x_1' = ax_1 + x_2,$$
$$\rho x_2' = \qquad ax_2 + x_3,$$
$$\rho x_3' = \qquad\qquad ax_3.$$

---

*The above classification has been made by means of geometric properties. The reader who is familiar with modern algebra should compare the classification by means of Weierstrass's elementary divisors. Cf. Bocher's "Higher Algebra," p. 292.

EXERCISES

1. Find the fixed points and determine the type of collineation to which each of the following transformations in Cartesian coördinates belong : (a) a translation, (b) a rotation about a fixed point, (c) a reflection on a straight line.

2. Determine the group of collineations in Cartesian coördinates which leaves the pair of straight lines $x^2 - y^2 = 0$ invariant and discuss the subgroups.

3. Are two collineations with the same fixed points always commutative? Answer for each type.

4. Consider the singular collineations. Prove that there is always a point or a line of points for which the transformed point is indeterminate. We shall call this the singular point or line. If there is a singular point, every other point is transformed into a point on a fixed line which may or may not pass through the singular point. If there is a singular line, every point not on the line is transformed into a fixed point which may or may not lie on the singular line. Prove these facts and from them show that the singular collineations consist of the following types:

I. One singular point P, a fixed line p not through P, two fixed points on p.

$$\rho x_1' = x_1,$$
$$\rho x_2' = \quad ax_2,$$
$$\rho x_3' = 0. \qquad (a \neq 1)$$

II. One singular point P, a fixed line not through P, one fixed point on p.

$$\rho x_1' = ax_1 + x_2,$$
$$\rho x_2' = \quad ax_2,$$
$$\rho x_3' = 0.$$

III. One singular point P, a singular line p not through P, all points of p fixed.

$$\rho x_1' = x_1,$$
$$\rho x_2' = \quad x_2,$$
$$\rho x_3' = 0.$$

IV. One singular point P, a fixed line p through P, one point of p fixed.

$$\rho x_1' = \quad x_3,$$
$$\rho x_2' = \quad x_2,$$
$$\rho x_3' = 0.$$

V. One singular point P, a fixed line p through P, no point of p fixed.

$$\rho x_1' = \quad x_2,$$
$$\rho x_2' = \quad x_3,$$
$$\rho x_3' = 0.$$

VI. A singular line p, a fixed point P on p.

$$\rho x_1' = \quad x_3,$$
$$\rho x_2' = 0,$$
$$\rho x_3' = 0.$$

VII. A singular line p, a fixed point P not on p.

$$\rho x_1' = x_1,$$
$$\rho x_2' = 0,$$
$$\rho x_3' = 0.$$

42. Correlations. The equations

$$\rho u_1' = a_{11}x_1 + a_{12}x_2 + a_{13}x_3,$$
$$\rho u_2' = a_{21}x_1 + a_{22}x_2 + a_{23}x_3, \tag{1}$$
$$\rho u_3' = a_{31}x_1 + a_{32}x_2 + a_{33}x_3,$$

where x_i are point coördinates and u' are line coördinates, define a transformation of a point into a line. Such a transformation is called a *correlation*. As in the case of collineations, we shall distinguish between nonsingular and singular correlations according as the determinant $|a_{ik}|$ does not or does vanish, and shall consider only nonsingular correlations. Equations (1) can then be solved for x, with the result

$$\sigma x_1 = A_{11}u_1' + A_{21}u_2' + A_{31}u_3',$$
$$\sigma x_2 = A_{12}u_1' + A_{22}u_2' + A_{32}u_3', \tag{2}$$
$$\sigma x_3 = A_{13}u_1' + A_{23}u_2' + A_{33}u_3',$$

where A_{ik} is the cofactor of a_{ik} in the determinant $|a_{ik}|$. Every straight line u_i' is therefore the transformed element of a point x_i'.

Consider now the points of a line given by the equation

$$u_1x_1 + u_2x_2 + u_3x_3 = 0,$$

where u_i are constants. By (2) these points go into a pencil of lines the vertex of which is the point x_i', where

$$\rho' x_1' = A_{11}u_1 + A_{12}u_2 + A_{13}u_3,$$
$$\rho' x_2' = A_{21}u_1 + A_{22}u_2 + A_{23}u_3, \tag{3}$$
$$\rho' x_3' = A_{31}u_1 + A_{32}u_2 + A_{33}u_3.$$

We may express this by saying that the line u_i is transformed into the point x_i'. Also, since equations (3) can be solved for u_i with the result

$$\sigma u_1 = a_{11}x_1' + a_{21}x_2' + a_{31}x_3',$$
$$\sigma u_2 = a_{12}x_1' + a_{22}x_2' + a_{32}x_3', \tag{4}$$
$$\sigma u_3 = a_{13}x_1' + a_{23}x_2' + a_{33}x_3',$$

every point is the transformed element of one and only one line.

Since equations (2), (3), and (4) are consequences of equations (1), we shall consider them as given with (1) and sum up our results in the following theorem:

I. A nonsingular correlation defined by equations (1) is a transformation by which each point is transformed into a straight line and each straight line into a point, in such a manner that points which lie on a straight line are transformed into straight lines which pass through a point, and lines which pass through a point are transformed into points which lie on a straight line. Each line or point is transformed into one point or line and is the transformed element of one line or point.

Consider now a correlation S_1 by which a point x_i is transformed into a line u_i', and let S_2 be a correlation by which the line u_i' is transformed into a point x_i''. It is clear that the product $S_2 S_1$ is a linear transformation by which the point x_i is transformed into the point x_i''; that is, a collineation. Therefore the correlations do not form a group. It is evident, however, that the inverse transformation of any correlation exists and is a correlation.

We can therefore prove the following theorems:

II. If P_1, P_2, P_3, P_4 are four arbitrary points, no three of which lie on a straight line, and if p_1, p_2, p_3, p_4 are four arbitrary lines, no three of which pass through a point, there exists one and only one correlation by means of which P_1 is transformed into p_1, P_2 into p_2, P_3 into p_3, and P_4 into p_4, and there exists also one and only one correlation by means of which p_1 is transformed into P_1, p_2 into P_2, p_3 into P_3, and p_4 into P_4.

III. Any nonsingular collineation establishes a projectivity between the points of a range and the lines of a corresponding pencil, and any such projectivity may be established in an infinite number of ways by a correlation.

The proofs of these theorems are the same as those of the corresponding theorems of § 40 and need not be repeated.

By equations (1) a point x_i lies on the line u_i', into which it is transformed when and only when

$$a_{11}x_1^2 + a_{22}x_2^2 + a_{33}x_3^2 + (a_{12}+a_{21})x_1x_2 + (a_{13}+a_{31})x_1x_3 \\ + (a_{23}+a_{32})x_2x_3 = 0. \tag{5}$$

That is, x_1 lies on a conic K_1.

Similarly, from equations (3) a line u_i passes through the point x_i, into which it is transformed when and only when

$$A_{11}u_1^2 + A_{22}u_2^2 + A_{33}u_3^2 + (A_{12}+A_{21})u_1u_2 + (A_{13}+A_{31})u_1u_3 \\ + (A_{23}+A_{32})u_2u_3 = 0. \tag{6}$$

That is, u_i envelops a conic K_2.

It is evident that the conics K_1 and K_2 are not in general the same. Their exact relations to each other will be determined later in this section. In the meantime we state the above result in the following theorem:

IV. *In the case of any nonsingular correlation the points which lie on their transformed lines are points of a certain conic, and the lines which pass through their transformed points envelop a certain conic, which, in general, is not the same as the first.*

Any point P of the plane may be considered in a twofold manner: as either an original point which is transformed by the correlation into a line or as a transformed point obtained from an original line. If P is an original point it corresponds to a line p' whose coördinates are given by (1). If P is a transformed point it corresponds to a line p whose coördinates are given by (4), in which we must replace x_i' by x_i, the coördinates of P.

The lines p and p' do not in general coincide. When they do the line p and the point P are called a *double pair* of the correlation. That P should be a point of a double pair it is necessary and sufficient that the coördinates u_i' and u_i of equations (1) and (4) should be proportional; that is, that the coördinates of P should satisfy the equations

$$(a_{11} - \rho a_{11})x_1 + (a_{12} - \rho a_{21})x_2 + (a_{13} - \rho a_{31})x_3 = 0,$$
$$(a_{21} - \rho a_{12})x_1 + (a_{22} - \rho a_{22})x_2 + (a_{23} - \rho a_{32})x_3 = 0, \tag{7}$$
$$(a_{31} - \rho a_{13})x_1 + (a_{32} - \rho a_{23})x_2 + (a_{33} - \rho a_{33})x_3 = 0,$$

where ρ is an unknown factor. For these equations to have a solution it is necessary and sufficient that ρ should satisfy the equation

$$\begin{vmatrix} a_{11} - \rho a_{11} & a_{12} - \rho a_{21} & a_{13} - \rho a_{31} \\ a_{21} - \rho a_{12} & a_{22} - \rho a_{22} & a_{23} - \rho a_{32} \\ a_{31} - \rho a_{13} & a_{32} - \rho a_{23} & a_{33} - \rho a_{33} \end{vmatrix} = 0. \tag{8}$$

The correlations may be classified into types according to the nature of the double pairs and of the conics K_1 and K_2. As a preliminary step we shall prove the theorem:

V. *If the point P and the line p form a double pair, then p is the polar of P with respect to the conic K_1.*

To prove this let the coördinates of P be y_i, where y_i is the solution of (7) for $\rho = \rho_1$, and let v_i be the coördinates of p. Then v_i is determined from (1) when x_i is replaced by y_i. Then from (1) and (7) we have

$$\rho v_i = a_{i1}y_1 + a_{i2}y_2 + a_{i3}y_3 = \rho_1(a_{1i}y_1 + a_{2i}y_2 + a_{3i}y_3);$$

whence

$$\left(\rho + \frac{1}{\rho_1}\right)v_i = (a_{i1} + a_{1i})y_1 + (a_{i2} + a_{2i})y_2 + (a_{3i} + a_{i3})y_3.$$

These last equations are exactly those which determine the polar of P with respect to K_1, and the theorem is proved.

We now proceed to the classification.

A. Let K_1 be a nondegenerate conic. By a proper choice of coördinates its equation can be put in the form

$$x_3^2 + (a_{12} + a_{21})x_1x_2 = 0, \tag{9}$$

so that $a_{11} = a_{22} = 0$, $a_{31} = -a_{13}$, $a_{32} = -a_{23}$, $a_{12} \neq -a_{21}$.

If there is at least one double pair of which the point is not on the conic, it may be taken as A $(0:0:1)$ without changing the form of equation (9). We shall then have $a_{13} = a_{23} = 0$. The correlation is now expressed by the equations

$$\rho u_1' = \qquad a_{12}x_2,$$
$$\rho u_2' = a_{21}x_1,$$
$$\rho u_3' = \qquad\qquad x_3.$$

Neither a_{12} nor a_{21} can be zero. There are then two types according as a_{12} and a_{21} are or are not equal:

TYPE I.
$$\rho u_1' = \qquad ax_2,$$
$$\rho u_2' = ax_1,$$
$$\rho u_3' = \qquad\qquad x_3.$$

The conic K_1 has now the equation $x_3^2 + 2\,ax_1x_2 = 0$, and the correlation is a polarity with respect to this conic. Conversely, any polarity with respect to a nondegenerate conic can be expressed in this form.

The equation (8) now becomes $a^2(1-\rho)^3 = 0$, and equations (7) are identically satisfied when $\rho = 1$. Hence *in a polarity every correlated point and line form a double pair*. The equation (6) now becomes $au_3^2 + 2\,u_1u_2 = 0$, which is the line equation of K_1. Hence *in a polarity the conics K_1 and K_2 coincide*.

TYPE II.
$$\rho u_1' = \qquad ax_2,$$
$$\rho u_2' = bx_1,$$
$$\rho u_3' = \qquad\quad x_3. \qquad (a \neq \pm\, b)$$

The conic K_2 has the line equation
$$(a+b)\,u_1u_2 + abu_3^2 = 0$$
or the point equation
$$4\,abx_1x_2 + (a+b)\,x_3^2 = 0,$$

and the relation of the two conics K_1 and K_2 is as in Fig. 25. Equation (8) becomes
$$(1-\rho)\,(a-b\rho)\,(b-a\rho) = 0,$$

which has three unequal roots. The correlation has accordingly three double pairs: namely, the point A and the line BC, the point B and the line AB, the point C and the line AC.

Types I and II arise from the assumption that there is a double pair of which the point lies outside the conic. If there is no such pair, there must be at least one of which the point lies on the conic. In this case take the point as $B\,(0:1:0)$ without changing

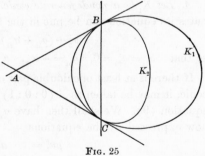

Fig. 25

the form of equation (9). By theorem V the line of the double pair which contains B is the tangent BA. Then, from (1), $a_{32} = 0$. We have before seen that $a_{23} = -\,a_{32}$, so that the correlation is now

$$\rho u_1' = \qquad a_{12}x_2 + a_{13}x_3,$$
$$\rho u_2' = \qquad a_{21}x_1,$$
$$\rho u_3' = -\,a_{13}x_1 \qquad\qquad +\, x_3.$$

The coefficient a_{13} cannot be zero or we should have the previous case. The equation (8) is now $(a_{12} - \rho a_{21})(a_{21} - \rho a_{12})(1 - \rho) = 0$, and the solution $\rho = 1$ would give a point not on K_1, contrary to hypothesis, unless $a_{21} = a_{12}$. We have, finally, for the equations of the correlation:

TYPE III.
$$\rho u_1' = \qquad ax_2 + bx_3,$$
$$\rho u_2' = \qquad ax_1,$$
$$\rho u_3' = -bx_1 \qquad + x_3,$$

where $a = b$ is not excluded. The line equation of K_2 is now
$$b^2 u_2^2 - a^2 u_3^2 - 2au_1u_2 = 0,$$

and the corresponding point equation is
$$b^2 x_1^2 + x_3^2 + 2ax_1x_2 = 0.$$

The two conics K_1 and K_2 lie therefore in the position of Fig. 26.

The equation (8) for ρ has the triple root $\rho = 1$, and the correlation has only one double pair consisting of the line point B and the line AB.

B. Let the conic K_1 degenerate into two intersecting straight lines. We may take the equations of the lines in the form
$$a_{11}x_1^2 + x_3^2 = 0;$$
whence
$$a_{22} = 0, \qquad a_{21} = -a_{12},$$
$$a_{32} = -a_{23}, \qquad a_{31} = -a_{13}.$$

The point B is again taken as the point of a double pair

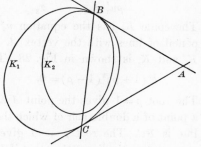

FIG. 26

and is therefore transformed into a line through B, and if we take that line as $x_1 = 0$ we have, from (1), $a_{32} = 0$. The equation (8) is now
$$a_{12}^2(1 + \rho)^2(1 - \rho) = 0,$$

where a_{12} cannot be zero since the correlation is nonsingular. The root $\rho = -1$ gives the point B as a point of a double pair. The root $\rho = 1$ gives the point $0 : -a_{13} : a_{12}$, and if this be taken as A we have $a_{13} = 0$.

We have then, finally,

TYPE IV.
$$\rho u_1' = \quad ax_1 + bx_2,$$
$$\rho u_2' = - bx_1,$$
$$\rho u' = \qquad\qquad x_3,$$

where the equality of the coefficients is not excluded.

The conic K_2 has now the equation

$$au_2^2 + b^2 u_3^2 = 0,$$

which is that of two pencils with their vertices on AB. The relation of K_1 and K_2 is shown in Fig. 27.

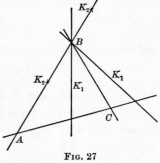

C. Let the conic K_1 degenerate into two coincident straight lines. Take the equation of K_1 as $\quad x_3^2 = 0.$

The discussion proceeds as in the previous case with the coefficient a placed equal to zero. We have, accordingly,

TYPE V.
$$\rho u_1 = \quad - bx_2,$$
$$\rho u_2' = bx_1,$$
$$\rho u_3' = \qquad x_3.$$

FIG. 27

The conic K_2 has the equation $u_3^2 = 0$, which is that of a double pencil of lines with the vertex A. The relation of the two conics K_1 and K_2 is shown in Fig. 28. The equation (8) now becomes

$$b^2 (1 + \rho)^2 (1 - \rho) = 0.$$

The root $\rho = 1$ gives the point A as a point of a double pair of which the line is BC. The root $\rho = -1$ gives any point on the line BC, so that if M is any point on BC it is a point of a double pair the line of which is AM.

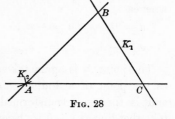

FIG. 28

EXERCISES

1. Find the square of each of the different types of correlations and determine the type of collineation to which it belongs.

2. Prove that if P is a point on K_1 the two tangents drawn from P to K_2 are the two lines to which P corresponds in the correlation according as P is considered as an original point or a transformed point.

3. Prove that if p is a tangent to K_2 the two points in which p intersects K_1 are the two points to which p corresponds in the correlation according as p is considered as an original line or a transformed line.

4. Take any point P. Show that the line into which P is transformed by a correlation of Types II, III, V is a line which connects two of the four points of intersection with K_1 of the two tangents drawn from P to K_2. Show also that the line which is transformed into P is another line connecting the same four points of intersection. Determine these two lines more exactly and explain the construction in Type IV.

5. Take any line p. Show that the point into which p is transformed by a correlation of Types II, III, V is one of the four points of intersection of the four tangents drawn to K_2 from the points in which p intersects K_1. Show also that another of these points of intersection is the point which is transformed into p. Determine these points more exactly and explain the construction in Type IV.

6. Show that if every point lies in the line into which it is transformed by a correlation, the correlation is a singular one of the form

$$\rho u_1' = \qquad\qquad a_{12}x_2 + a_{13}x_3,$$
$$\rho u_2 = - a_{12}x_1 \qquad\quad + a_{23}x_3,$$
$$\rho u_3' = - a_{13}x_1 - a_{23}x_2.$$

Study the correlation.

43. Pairs of conics. The preceding results may be given an interesting application in studying the relation of two conics to each other, especially with reference to points and lines which are the poles and polars of each other with respect to both the conics.

Let $$\sum a_{ik}x_i x_k = 0 \tag{1}$$

and $$\sum b_{ik}x_i x_k = 0 \tag{2}$$

be two conics without singular points. The product of a polarity with respect to (1) and a polarity with respect to (2) is a nonsingular collineation which may be expressed by the equations

$$\rho\,(b_{11}x_1' + b_{12}x_2' + b_{13}x_3') = a_{11}x_1 + a_{12}x_2 + a_{13}x_3,$$
$$\rho\,(b_{12}x_1' + b_{22}x_2' + b_{23}x_3') = a_{12}x_1 + a_{22}x_2 + a_{23}x_3, \tag{3}$$
$$\rho\,(b_{13}x_1' + b_{23}x_2' + b_{33}x_3') = a_{13}x_1 + a_{23}x_2 + a_{33}x_3.$$

The fixed points of the collineation (3) are identical with the points which have the same polars with respect to both (1) and (2), and the fixed lines of (3) are identical with the lines which have the same poles with respect to (1) and (2). Each fixed point of (3) will be paired with some fixed line of (3) as pole and polar. These points and lines we shall refer to briefly as common polar elements.

We shall have as many arrangements of common polar elements as there are arrangements of fixed points of (3) and may classify them into the types given in § 41.

TYPE I. There are three and only three common poles A, B, C (Fig. 29) and three common polars AB, BC, CA. To pair these off we notice first that no point can be the pole of a line through it.

For if B were the pole of AB, for example, C would be the pole of either AC or BC, say AC. The lines AB and AC would be tangent to each of the conics (1) and (2) and A would be the pole of BC. Then if D were any point whatever on BC, and E its harmonic conjugate with respect to B and C, the line EA would be the polar of D with respect to both (1)

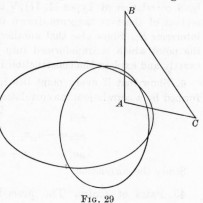

FIG. 29

and (2). Hence the conics would have more than three common polars, and the collineation (3) would not be of Type I, § 41.

Therefore the triangle is a self-polar triangle with respect to both (1) and (2). By taking this triangle as the coördinate triangle, the equations of the conics reduce to the forms

$$x_1^2 + x_2^2 + x_3^2 = 0, \qquad (4)$$

$$a_1 x_1^2 + a_2 x_2^2 + a_3 x_3^2 = 0, \qquad (5)$$

and the collineation (3) becomes

$$\rho x_1' = a_1 x_1,$$
$$\rho x_2' = \qquad a_2 x_2, \qquad (6)$$
$$\rho x_3' = \qquad\qquad a_3 x_3,$$

where, by § 41, $a_1 \neq a_2 \neq a_3$.

The two conics (4) and (5) intersect in four distinct points, as is easily proved.

TYPE II. There are two common poles A and C (Fig. 30) and two common polars AC and BC. The point C must be the pole of one of the lines AC and BC which pass through it, and hence C lies on the two conics. But C cannot be the pole of BC, for, if it were, A would be the pole of AC, and the line AC would be tangent to the conics at A and intersecting them again at C, which is impossible. Therefore C is the pole of AC and A of BC. If we take the axes of coördinates as in

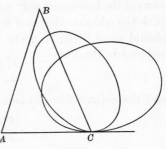

Fig. 30

Type IV, § 41, the equation of each of the conics is of the form

$$a_1 x_2^2 + a_2 x_3^2 + 2\,a_3 x_1 x_2 = 0. \tag{7}$$

Without changing the position of the axes we may take one of the conics as

$$x_2^2 + x_3^2 + 2\,x_1 x_2 = 0, \tag{8}$$

leaving the equation of the other in the general form (7). The collineation (3) is then

$$\rho x_2' = a_3 x_2,$$
$$\rho\,(x_1' + x_2') = a_3 x_1 + a_1 x_2,$$
$$\rho x_3' = a_2 x_3,$$

or

$$\rho x_1' = a_3 x_1 + (a_1 - a_3)\,x_2,$$
$$\rho x_2' = \qquad\qquad a_3 x_2, \tag{9}$$
$$\rho x_3' = \qquad\qquad a_2 x_3.$$

That this should be of Type IV, § 41, we must have $a_1 \neq a_3$, $a_2 \neq a_3$.

The conics (1) and (2) are tangent at C and intersect in two other points, as is easily proved. The conics have no common self-polar triangle since there are not three fixed points in the collineation (9).

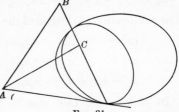

Fig. 31

TYPE III. There is a line BC (Fig. 31) each point of which is a common pole and another common pole A not on BC. The common polars consist of the line BC and all lines through A. It is evident that A is the common pole of BC, and hence BC is not tangent to the conics. Take as B any point of BC and take C as the pole of AB. Then ABC is a common self-polar triangle. The equations of the two conics may now be written as in Type I, (4) and (5), with the addition that now $a_1 = a_2$, in order that the collineation (6) should be of Type II, § 41. Hence the equations of the conics are reduced to the forms

$$x_1^2 + x_2^2 + x_3^2 = 0, \tag{10}$$
$$x_1^2 + x_2^2 + ax_3^2 = 0, \tag{11}$$

and the collineation (3) becomes

$$\begin{aligned} \rho x_1' &= x_1, \\ \rho x_2' &= x_2, \\ \rho x_3' &= ax_3. \end{aligned} \tag{12}$$

The two conics are tangent at two points, namely the points in which the line BC meets the conics. This is easily seen from the equations. We may also argue that if BC meets (10) in L, the point L is a common pole of the line AL. Hence AL is tangent to both conics. Similarly, if M is the other point of intersection of BC and (10), AM is a common tangent to the conics.

TYPE IV. There is one common pole C (Fig. 32) and one common polar BC. Hence the two conics are tangent to BC at C and tangent at no other point. Take any point on the conic (1) as A, and the tangent to (1) at A as AB.
The equation of (1) then is

$$x_2^2 + 2\,x_1x_3 = 0,$$

while that of (2), since it is known only to be tangent to BC at C, is

$$a_1x_2^2 + a_2x_3^2 + 2\,a_3x_2x_3 + 2\,a_4x_3x_1 = 0.$$

The collineation (3) is then of the type

$$\begin{aligned} \rho x_3' &= a_4x_3, \\ \rho x_2' &= a_1x_2 + a_3x_3, \\ \rho x_1' &= a_4x_1 + a_3x_2 + a_2x_3. \end{aligned}$$

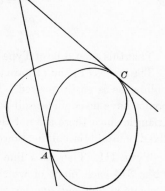

FIG. 32

In order that this should have only one fixed point it is necessary and sufficient that $a_1 = a_4$, $a_3 \neq 0$. The two conics, besides being tangent at C, intersect in the point $x_1 : x_2 : x_3 = a_2^2 : 4\,a_3a_2 : -8\,a_3^2$.

If this point is taken as the point A in the coördinate triangle, we have $a_2 = 0$. The equations of the conics are then

$$x_2^2 + 2 x_1 x_3 = 0, \tag{13}$$

$$x_2^2 + 2 a_3 x_2 x_3 + 2 x_1 x_3 = 0, \tag{14}$$

and the collineation (3) is

$$\begin{aligned}
\rho x_1' &= x_1 + a_3 x_2 = a x_1 + x_2, \\
\rho x_2' &= x_2 + a_3 x_3 = a x_2 + x_3, \\
\rho x_3' &= x_3 = a x_3,
\end{aligned} \tag{15}$$

which is of Type VI, § 41.

As noted, the two conics are tangent at one point and intersect in another point.

TYPE V. There is a line BC (Fig. 33) of common poles and a pencil, with vertex C on BC, of common polars. Every point on BC is therefore the common pole of some line through C, and hence C is the common pole of BC. Hence the two conics are tangent to BC at C. We proceed as in Type IV, but we now find that in order that all points on $x_3 = 0$ should be fixed points of the collineation we must have $a_1 = a_4$, $a_3 = 0$. The equations of the conics therefore reduce to

$$x_2^2 + 2 x_1 x_3 = 0, \tag{16}$$

$$x_2^2 + a_2 x_3^2 + 2 x_1 x_3 = 0, \tag{17}$$

and the collineation (3) becomes

$$\begin{aligned}
\rho x_1' &= x_1 + a x_3, \\
\rho x_2' &= x_2, \\
\rho x_3' &= x_3,
\end{aligned} \tag{18}$$

which is of Type V, § 41.

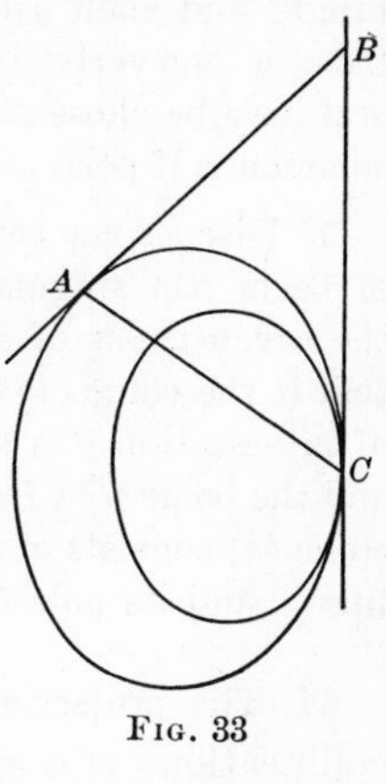

FIG. 33

The two conics are tangent at one point and have no other point of intersection.

TYPE VI. Every point of the plane is a common pole with respect to the two conics. The two conics are obviously identical.

To each type of the arrangements of the common polar elements corresponds a distinct kind of intersection of the two conics. Conversely, the nature of the common polar elements is determined by the nature of the intersections, as is easily proved.

It is sometimes important to find, if possible, a self-polar triangle common to two conics. The foregoing discussion leads to the following theorem:

If two conics intersect in four distinct points they have one and only one common self-polar triangle. If they are tangent in two points they have an infinite number of common self-polar triangles, one vertex of which is at the intersection of the common tangents. In all other cases two distinct conics have no common self-polar triangle.

It is only when two conics have a common self-polar triangle that their equations can be reduced each to the sum of squares as in Types I and III.

EXERCISES

1. Prove that the diagonal triangle of a complete quadrangle whose vertices are on a conic, or of a complete quadrilateral whose sides are tangent to a conic, is self-polar with respect to the conic; and, conversely, every self-polar triangle is the diagonal triangle of such a quadrangle and such a quadrilateral. Corresponding to a given self-polar triangle one vertex or one side of such a quadrangle or such a quadrilateral may be chosen arbitrarily. Apply this theorem to determining the common self-polar triangle of two conics in the position of Type I.

2. Discuss the common polar elements of a pair of conics when one of them has singular points, obtaining seven types corresponding to the seven types of singular collineations given in Ex. 4, § 41. (Notice that if the conic (1) consists of two intersecting straight lines, the point of intersection P is the singular point of the corresponding collineation, and the polar p of P with respect to the conic (2) is the fixed line. If the conic (1) consists of a straight line taken double, that line is the singular line p, and its pole P with respect to the conic (2) is the fixed point.)

44. The projective group. As we have seen, the product of two collineations is a collineation, and the product of two correlations is a collineation. It is not difficult to show that the product of a collineation and a correlation in either order is a correlation. The inverse transformation of either a collineation or a correlation always exists and is a collineation or a correlation respectively. Hence we have the theorem:

The totality of nonsingular collineations and nonsingular correlations in a plane form a group, of which the collineations form a subgroup.

This group is called the *projective group*, and *projective geometry* consists of the study of properties which are invariant under this group.

It is evident then that projective geometry will include the study of straight-line figures with reference to the manner in which lines intersect in points or points lie on straight lines. Such theorems have been illustrated in § 30. Lengths of lines are not in general invariant under the projective group, and projective geometry is not therefore concerned with the metrical properties of figures. The cross ratio of four elements is, however, an invariant of the projective group, and hence the cross ratio is of importance in projective geometry.

By means of a collineation any conic without singular points may be transformed into the conic

$$x_1^2 + x_2^2 + x_3^2 = 0.$$

This was virtually proved in § 35 when we showed that any equation of the second order with discriminant not zero may be reduced to the above form. But any transformation of coördinates is expressed by a linear substitution of the variables, and this substitution may be interpreted as a collineation, the coördinate system being unchanged. Hence any conic without singular points can be transformed into any other conic without singular points by a collineation. Similarly, any conic with one singular point may be transformed into any other conic with one singular point, and any conic with an infinite number of singular points may be transformed into any other which also has an infinite number of singular points. Hence projective geometry recognizes only three types of conics and studies the properties which are common to all conics which belong to each of the types. Such properties are illustrated in the theorems of § 39, where the distinction between ellipse, hyperbola, and parabola is not made.

In projective geometry it is convenient sometimes to consider the properties invariant under the subgroup of collineations. The correlations may be implicitly employed by use of the dualistic property.

45. The metrical group. We shall proceed to study the collineations which leave all distance invariant or multiply all distances by the same constant k. For that purpose it is convenient to use

Cartesian coördinates. Since it is evident that all points at infinity remain at infinity, the transformations must be of the form

$$\rho x' = a_1 x + a_2 y + a_3 t,$$
$$\rho y' = b_1 x + b_2 y + b_3 t, \tag{1}$$
$$\rho t' = t,$$

or in nonhomogeneous form

$$x' = a_1 x + a_2 y + a_3,$$
$$y' = b_1 x + b_2 y + b_3. \tag{2}$$

Transformations of this type are called *affine*, since any point in the finite part of the plane is transformed into a similar point. We proceed to find the conditions under which an affine transformation will have the properties required above.

If (x_1, y_1) and (x_2, y_2) are any two points which are transformed respectively into (x_1', y_1') and (x_2', y_2'), then, by hypothesis,

$$(x_2' - x_1')^2 + (y_2' - y_1')^2 = k^2 [(x_2 - x_1)^2 + (y_2 - y_1)^2],$$

from which we obtain

$$(a_1^2 + b_1^2)(x_2 - x_1)^2 + (a_2^2 + b_2^2)(y_2 - y_1)^2 + 2(a_1 a_2 + b_1 b_2)(x_2 - x_1)(y_2 - y_1)$$
$$= k^2 [(x_2 - x_1)^2 + (y_2 - y_1)^2].$$

Since this must be true for all values of the variables, we have

$$a_1^2 + b_1^2 = k^2,$$
$$a_2^2 + b_2^2 = k^2,$$
$$a_1 a_2 + b_1 b_2 = 0.$$

From this follows algebraically $b_2 = \pm a_1$, $b_1 = \mp a_2$. Also an angle can always be found such that $a_1 = k \cos \phi$, $b_1 = k \sin \phi$. Equations (2) can then be written

$$x' = k (x \cos \phi - y \sin \phi) + a,$$
$$y' = \pm k (x \sin \phi + y \cos \phi) + b. \tag{3}$$

The product of any two transformations of the form (3) is also of the form (3). This can be shown by direct substitution, or follows geometrically, since (3) is the most general collineation which multiplies distances by a constant. It is also evident that the inverse transformation of (3) exists and is of the same form. Hence the following theorem:

I. Transformations of the form (3) *form a group called the metrical group of collineations.*

To this we add the following theorem:

II. By the metrical group of collineations the circle points at infinity are either fixed or interchanged with each other. Conversely, any collineation which leaves the circle points fixed or interchanges them belongs to the metrical group.

This follows from the fact that minimum lines (§ 19) must be transformed into minimum lines. Since the line at infinity is fixed, the points where the minimum lines intersect the line at infinity must be fixed or interchanged. Theorem II may therefore be restated as follows:

III. The metrical group leaves invariant the curve of second class consisting of the two circle points at infinity.

We shall now enumerate certain special types of the transformation (3).

I. *Translation.*

$$T \begin{cases} x' = x + a, \\ y' = y + b. \end{cases}$$

This is of Type V, § 41, the line of fixed points being the line at infinity, and the pencil of fixed lines being the parallel lines intersecting in $a : b : 0$.

The translations evidently form a subgroup of the metrical group.

II. *Rotation about a fixed point.*

If the fixed point is the origin, we have the transformation

$$R \begin{cases} x' = x \cos \phi - y \sin \phi, \\ y' = x \sin \phi + y \cos \phi. \end{cases}$$

This is of Type I, § 41, the fixed points being the origin and the two circle points at infinity.

A rotation about any other point is the transform (§ 5) of R by T. Thus, if R' is a rotation about (a, b), $R' = TRT^{-1}$, where R' is the transformation

$$R' \begin{cases} x' - a = (x - a) \cos \phi - (y - b) \sin \phi, \\ y' - b = (x - a) \sin \phi + (y - b) \cos \phi. \end{cases}$$

The substitutions R and R' form each a subgroup of the metrical group.

III. *Magnification.*

$$M \begin{cases} x' = kx, \\ y' = ky. \end{cases}$$

This is of Type II, § 41, the fixed point being the origin, and the line of fixed points being the line at infinity. The pencil of fixed lines is the pencil with its vertex at $(0, 0)$.

A magnification M' with the fixed point (a, b) is the transform of M by T; thus, $M' = TMT^{-1}$, where M' is the transformation

$$M' \begin{cases} x' - a = k(x - a), \\ y' - b = k(y - b). \end{cases}$$

The transformations M and M' form each a subgroup of the metrical group.

IV. *Reflection on a straight line.*

If the straight line is the axis of x, the transformation is

$$S \begin{cases} x' = x, \\ y' = -y. \end{cases}$$

This is of Type II, § 41, the line of fixed points being $y = 0$, and the distinct fixed point being $0 : 1 : 0$. The fixed pencil of lines consists of the parallel lines through $0 : 1 : 0$.

If, now, U is a transformation of the metrical group (3), it is not difficult to show that it is the product of transformations of the types we have enumerated. There are, in fact, two main divisions of the metrical transformations, namely,

CLASS I. *Metrical transformations not involving a reflection.*

Consider $U_1 = TMR$. It is evident that U_1 is given by the equations

$$U_1 \begin{cases} x' = k(x \cos \phi - y \sin \phi) + a, \\ y' = k(x \sin \phi + y \cos \phi) + b, \end{cases}$$

and that, conversely, any transformation of this type can be expressed as the product TMR.

CLASS II. *Metrical transformations involving a reflection.*

Consider $U_2 = TSMR$. It is evident that U is of the type

$$U_2 \begin{cases} x' = k(x \cos \phi - y \sin \phi) + a, \\ y' = -k(x \sin \phi + y \cos \phi) + b, \end{cases}$$

which can also be written

$$U_2 \begin{cases} x' = k(x \cos \phi + y \sin \phi) + a, \\ y' = k(x \sin \phi - y \cos \phi) + b \end{cases}$$

by replacing ϕ by $-\phi$, an allowable change, since ϕ is any angle.

Conversely, any transformation of type U_2 can be expressed as the product $TSMR$.

The transformations U_1 form a subgroup of the metrical group. The transformations U_2, however, do not form a group, since the product of two such transformations is one of the form U_1.

46. Angle and the circle points at infinity. By the metrical group angles are left unchanged. This is evident from the fact that any triangle is transformed into a similar triangle. Also the cross ratio of any two lines and the minimum lines through their point of intersection is equal to the cross ratio of the transformed lines and the minimum lines through the transformed point of intersection, since minimum lines are transformed into minimum lines. This suggests a connection between this cross ratio and the angle between the two lines. We shall proceed to find this connection.

Let the two lines be l_1 with line coördinates v_i, and l_2 with line coördinates w_i. The coördinates of any line through the point of intersection of l_1 and l_2 are $u_i = v_i + \lambda w_i$, and this is a minimum line when u_i satisfies the line equation of the circle points at infinity, namely,

$$u_1^2 + u_2^2 = 0.$$

This gives for λ the equation

$$A\lambda^2 + 2B\lambda + C = 0,$$

where $\quad A = w_1^2 + w_2^2, \quad B = w_1 v_1 + v_2 w_2, \quad C = v_1^2 + v_2^2.$

Let us place $\quad \lambda_1 = \dfrac{-B + i\sqrt{AC - B^2}}{A},$

$$\lambda_2 = \dfrac{-B - i\sqrt{AC - B^2}}{A}$$

and call m_1 the minimum line corresponding to λ_1, and m_2 the minimum line corresponding to λ_2. Then (§ 13)

$$(l_1 l_2,\ m_1 m_2) = \frac{\lambda_1}{\lambda_2} = \frac{-B + i\sqrt{AC - B^2}}{-B - i\sqrt{AC - B^2}}.$$

Now the point equations of l_1 and l_2 are respectively

$$v_1 x + v_2 y + v_3 t = 0,$$
$$w_1 x + w_2 y + w_3 t = 0,$$

and if ϕ is the angle between them,

$$\cos \phi = \frac{v_1 w_1 + v_2 w_2}{\sqrt{v_1^2 + v_2^2}\sqrt{w_1^2 + w_2^2}} = \frac{B}{\sqrt{AC}},$$

$$\sin \phi = \frac{\pm\sqrt{AC - B^2}}{\sqrt{AC}}.$$

Therefore
$$\frac{\lambda_1}{\lambda_2} = \frac{-\cos \phi \pm i \sin \phi}{-\cos \phi \mp i \sin \phi} = \frac{e^{\mp i\phi}}{e^{\pm i\phi}}$$

$$= e^{\mp 2 i\phi};$$

whence
$$\phi = \pm \frac{i}{2} \log \frac{\lambda_1}{\lambda_2}.$$

The ambiguity of sign is natural, since an interchange of λ_1 and λ_2 would change the sign of ϕ. We have, therefore,

$$\phi = \pm \frac{i}{2} \log (l_1 l_2,\ m_1 m_2).$$

The angle between two lines is therefore equal to $\dfrac{i}{2}$ times the logarithm of the cross ratio of the two lines and the minimum lines through their point of intersection.

If $\phi = \dfrac{\pi}{2}$, $\dfrac{\lambda_1}{\lambda_2} = -1$, and, conversely, if $\dfrac{\lambda_1}{\lambda_2} = -1$, $\phi = \dfrac{\pi}{2} + k\pi$. Hence

Perpendicular lines may be defined as lines which are harmonic conjugates with respect to the minimum lines through their point of intersection.

CHAPTER VII

PROJECTIVE MEASUREMENT

47. General principles. The results of the last section suggest a generalization, to be made by replacing the circle points at infinity by the general curve of the second class,

$$\sum A_{ik}u_iu_k = 0, \qquad (A_{ki} = A_{ik}) \tag{1}$$

which we shall call the *fundamental conic*. Let l_1 and l_2 (Fig. 34) be any two lines, and let t_1 and t_2 be the two tangents which can be drawn to the fundamental conic from the point of intersection of l_1 and l_2. Then the projective angle between l_1 and l_2 is defined by the equation

$$\angle(l_1l_2) = M \log(l_1l_2, t_1t_2), \tag{2}$$

where M is a constant to be determined more exactly later.

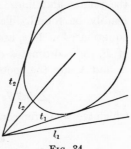

Fig. 34

This satisfies the fundamental requirements for the measurement of an angle, since it attaches to every angle a definite numerical measure such that the sum of the measures of the parts of a whole is equal to the measure of the whole. To prove the latter statement, notice that

$$\angle(l_1l_2) + \angle(l_2l_3) = M \log(l_1l_2, t_1t_2)(l_2l_3, t_1t_2).$$

Now, if l_1, l_2, and l_3 are three lines of the same pencil, with coördinates λ_1, λ_2, λ_3 respectively, and the coördinates of the lines t_1 and t_2 of the same pencil are taken as 0 and ∞, we have

$$(l_1l_2, t_1t_2) = \frac{\lambda_1}{\lambda_2},$$

$$(l_2l_3, t_1t_2) = \frac{\lambda_2}{\lambda_3},$$

$$(l_1l_2, t_1t_2)(l_2l_3, t_1t_2) = \frac{\lambda_1}{\lambda_3} = (l_1l_3, t_1t_2).$$

Hence
$$\angle(l_1l_2) + \angle(l_2l_3) = \angle(l_1l_3).$$

107

Dualistically, if the fundamental conic does not reduce to two points its equation can be expressed in point coördinates as

$$\sum a_{ik}x_ix_k = 0. \qquad (a_{ki} = a_{ik}) \tag{3}$$

Then, if P_1 and P_2 (Fig. 35) are two points, and T_1 and T_2 are the two points in which the line P_1P_2 cuts the conic, the projective distance P_1P_2 is defined by the equation

$$\text{dist. } (P_1P_2) = K \log (P_1P_2,\ T_1T_2), \tag{4}$$

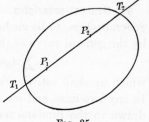

where K is to be determined later. It is shown, as in the case of angles, that dist. (P_1P_2) + dist. (P_2P_3) = dist. (P_1P_3).

The analytic expression for distance and angle in terms of the coördinates of the points and lines, respectively, may readily be found. Take, for example,

FIG. 35

equation (4). If y_i are the coördinates of P_1, and z_i the coördinates of P_2, the coördinates of T_1 and T_2 are $y_i - \lambda_1 z_i$ and $y_i - \lambda_2 z_i$, where λ_1 and λ_2 are the roots of the quadratic equation

$$\sum a_{ik}y_iy_k - 2\lambda \sum a_{ik}y_iz_k + \lambda^2 \sum a_{ik}z_iz_k = 0,$$

which we write for convenience in the form

$$\omega_{yy} - 2\lambda\omega_{yz} + \lambda^2\omega_{zz} = 0.$$

We will take $\quad \lambda_1 = \dfrac{\omega_{yz} + \sqrt{\omega_{yz}^2 - \omega_{yy}\omega_{zz}}}{\omega_{zz}},$

and $\quad \lambda_2 = \dfrac{\omega_{yz} - \sqrt{\omega_{yz}^2 - \omega_{yy}\omega_{zz}}}{\omega_{zz}}.$

Then, by the definition (2) and theorem III, § 13, we have

$$\text{dist. } (y_iz_i) = K \log \frac{\lambda_1}{\lambda_2}. \tag{5}$$

But $\quad \dfrac{\lambda_1}{\lambda_2} = \dfrac{\omega_{yz} + \sqrt{\omega_{yz}^2 - \omega_{yy}\omega_{zz}}}{\omega_{yz} - \sqrt{\omega_{yz}^2 - \omega_{yy}\omega_{zz}}} = \dfrac{\left[\omega_{yz} + \sqrt{\omega_{yz}^2 - \omega_{yy}\omega_{zz}}\right]^2}{\omega_{yy}\omega_{zz}},$

and therefore we have, as the final form,

$$\text{dist. } (y_iz_i) = 2\,K \log \frac{\omega_{yz} + \sqrt{\omega_{yz}^2 - \omega_{yy}\omega_{zz}}}{\sqrt{\omega_{yy}\omega_{zz}}}. \tag{6}$$

There is of course free choice as to which of the two values of λ is taken as λ_1. To interchange λ_1 and λ_2 is simply to change the positive direction on the line.

The distance between two points is zero when the two points are coincident or when the line connecting them is tangent to the fundamental conic, since in the latter case $\lambda_1 = \lambda_2$. The tangents to the conic are therefore analogous in the projective measurement to the minimum lines in ordinary measurement.

The distance between two points is infinite when λ_1 or λ_2 is zero or infinity. This happens only when P_1 or P_2 is on the fundamental conic. That is, *points on the fundamental conic are at an infinite distance from all other points.*

Similarly, consider equation (2). If v_i and w_i are the coördinates of l_1 and l_2 respectively, the coördinates of t_1 and t_2 are $v_i - \lambda_1 w_i$ and $v_i - \lambda_2 w_i$, where λ_1 and λ_2 are the roots of the equation

$$\sum_i A_{ik} v_i v_k - 2\lambda \sum_i A_{ik} v_i w_k + \lambda^2 \sum_i A_{ik} w_i w_k = 0,$$

which may be written

$$\Omega_{vv} - 2\lambda \Omega_{vw} + \lambda^2 \Omega_{ww} = 0.$$

If we take

$$\lambda_1 = \frac{\Omega_{vw} + \sqrt{\Omega_{vw}^2 - \Omega_{vv}\Omega_{ww}}}{\Omega_{vv}},$$

$$\lambda_2 = \frac{\Omega_{vw} - \sqrt{\Omega_{vw}^2 - \Omega_{vv}\Omega_{ww}}}{\Omega_{vv}},$$

we have, by (2),

$$\measuredangle(v_i w_i) = M \log \frac{\lambda_1}{\lambda_2} = 2 M \log \frac{\Omega_{vw} + \sqrt{\Omega_{vw}^2 - \Omega_{vv}\Omega_{ww}}}{\sqrt{\Omega_{vv}\Omega_{ww}}}. \tag{7}$$

An angle is zero if l_1 and l_2 coincide or if l_1 and l_2 intersect on the fundamental conic, for in the latter case $\lambda_1 = \lambda_2$. That is, *all lines which intersect at an infinite distance make a zero angle with each other.* They are therefore analogous to parallel lines in Euclidean measurement.

The angle between two lines is infinite if either line is tangent to the fundamental conic.

From the definitions we have the following theorem:

Projective distance and angle are unchanged by the group of collineations which leave the fundamental conic invariant.

We shall now proceed to discuss more in detail three cases, according to the nature of the fundamental conic.

48. The hyperbolic case. We assume that the fundamental conic is real. It may then be brought by proper choice of coördinate axes to the form

$$\omega_{xx} = x_1^2 + x_2^2 - x_3^2 = 0 \qquad (1)$$

in point coördinates and to the form

$$\Omega_{uu} = u_1^2 + u_2^2 - u_3^2 = 0 \qquad (2)$$

in line coördinates.

The conic divides the plane into two portions, one of which we call the *inside* of the conic and which is characterized by the fact that the tangents to the curve from any point of the region are imaginary. The *outside* of the conic is the region characterized by the fact that from every point of it two real tangents can be drawn. We shall consider the inside of the conic.

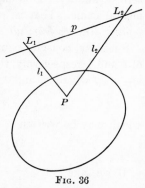

If l_1 and l_2 (Fig. 36) are two real lines intersecting in a point inside the conic, λ_1 and λ_2 of equation (7), § 47, are conjugate imaginary. Let us place $\lambda_1 = re^{i\phi}$, where

FIG. 36

$$\cos \phi = \frac{\Omega_{vw}}{\sqrt{\Omega_{vv}\Omega_{ww}}}, \qquad \sin \phi = \frac{\sqrt{\Omega_{vv}\Omega_{ww} - \Omega_{vw}^2}}{\sqrt{\Omega_{vv}\Omega_{ww}}}. \qquad (2)$$

Then $\lambda_2 = re^{-i\phi}$ and

$$\measuredangle (l_1 l_2) = M \log e^{2i\phi} = M(2\phi + 2n\pi) i.$$

Since it is desirable that the angles which a line makes with another should differ by multiples of π, we shall place $M = -\dfrac{i}{2}$, and have, as the complete definition of the angle θ between the lines l_1 and l_2, $\qquad \theta = \phi + n\pi \,;$

whence $\qquad\qquad \cos \theta = \pm \dfrac{\Omega_{vw}}{\sqrt{\Omega_{vv}\Omega_{ww}}}. \qquad (3)$

Two lines are perpendicular to each other when $\theta = (2n+1)\dfrac{\pi}{2}.$ For that it is necessary and sufficient that $\dfrac{\lambda_1}{\lambda_2} = -1$. The two lines are then harmonic conjugates with respect to t_1 and t_2. This has a geometric meaning, as follows: Let P (Fig. 36) be the point of intersection of l_1 and l_2, p the polar of P, L_1 and L_2 the intersections of p with l_1 and l_2 respectively, and T_1 and T_2 the intersections of the conic with t_1 and t_2 respectively. T_1, T_2, t_1, t_2, being imaginary, are not shown in the figure. Then by VI, § 34, T_1 and T_2 lie on p, and by I, § 16, $(L_1L_2, T_1T_2) = (l_1l_2, t_1t_2)$. Hence, in order that the two lines l_1 and l_2 should be perpendicular it is necessary and sufficient that L_1 and L_2 should be harmonic conjugates to T_1 and T_2, and hence (VIII, § 34) L_1 must lie on the polar of L_2, and L_2 must lie on the polar of L_1. But the polars of L_1 and L_2 pass through P by V, § 34, and therefore l_1 is the polar of L_2, and l_2 is the polar of L_1. Hence *for two lines to be perpendicular it is necessary and sufficient that each should pass through the pole of the other.*

Consider now the distance between two points P_1 and P_2 (Fig. 36) inside the conic. Then λ_1 and λ_2 of (5), § 47, are both real, and hence if the distance P_1P_2 is to be real we must take K as a real quantity. Let us place $K = \dfrac{k}{2}$, where k is real. We have, for the distance,

$$\text{dist.} (y_i \, z_i) = \frac{k}{2} \log \frac{\lambda_1}{\lambda_2} = k \log \frac{\omega_{yz} + \sqrt{\omega_{yz}^2 - \omega_{yy}\omega_{zz}}}{\sqrt{\omega_{yy}\omega_{zz}}}. \tag{4}$$

If we write d for dist. $(y_i \, z_i)$ we have, from (4),

$$e^{\frac{d}{k}} = \frac{\omega_{yz} + \sqrt{\omega_{yz}^2 - \omega_{yy}\omega_{zz}}}{\sqrt{\omega_{yy}\omega_{zz}}},$$

$$e^{-\frac{d}{k}} = \frac{\omega_{yz} - \sqrt{\omega_{yz}^2 - \omega_{yy}\omega_{zz}}}{\sqrt{\omega_{yy}\omega_{zz}}};$$

whence

$$\cosh \frac{d}{k} = \frac{\omega_{yz}}{\sqrt{\omega_{yy}\omega_{zz}}},$$

$$\sinh \frac{d}{k} = \frac{\sqrt{\omega_{yz}^2 - \omega_{yy}\omega_{zz}}}{\sqrt{\omega_{yy}\omega_{zz}}}. \tag{5}$$

We have already noted that if P_1 is inside the conic and P_2 on the conic, the distance P_1P_2 becomes infinite. If P_1 is inside the conic and P_2 outside of it, λ_1 and λ_2 in equation (4) have opposite signs, and the distance P_1P_2 becomes imaginary. If, then, we can imagine a being living inside the conic and measuring distance and angle by the formulas (5) and (3), the conic would lie for him at an infinite distance, and the region outside would be simply nonexistent, a mere analytic conception in which a point means simply a pair of coördinate values. Such a being would have a *non-Euclidean geometry* of the type named Lobachevskian.

We have, of course, based all our discussion on the assumption of the Euclidean axioms, and the inside of our fundamental conic is simply a portion of the Euclidean plane. It lies outside the scope of this book to show that by a choice of axioms, differing from those of Euclid only in the parallel axiom, it is possible to arrive at a geometry which for the entire plane has properties which are exactly those of the interior of our fundamental conic, with the projective measurement here defined. Such a discussion may be found in treatises on non-Euclidean geometry. The inside of the fundamental conic is a picture in the Euclidean plane of the non-Euclidean geometry. We shall proceed to notice some of the most striking properties.

We first notice that if LK (Fig. 37) is a straight line and P a point not on it, there go through P two kinds of lines, those which intersect LK and those which do not. The latter lines are those which in the entire plane intersect LK in points outside the conic, but from the standpoint of the interior of the conic they must be considered as not intersecting LK. The two classes of lines, the intersecting and the nonintersecting, are separated from each other by two

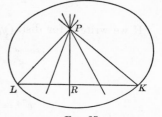

FIG. 37

lines PL and PK, which intersect LK on the conic; that is, at infinity. These lines we call *parallel* lines, and say that *through a point not on a straight line can be drawn two lines parallel to that straight line.*

The angle which a line parallel to LK through P makes with the perpendicular to LK is called the *angle of parallelism*, and is a function of the length of the perpendicular. To compute it, let us take LK as $x_1 = 0$, the point P as y_i, and the equation of the conic as $x_1^2 + x_2^2 - x_3^2 = 0$. The pole of LK is $(1:0:0)$. The line PR is perpendicular to LK when it passes through the pole of LK. Its equation is therefore $y_3 x_2 - y_2 x_3 = 0$, and it intersects LK in R $(0:y_2:y_3)$.

Hence, if p is the length of PR we have, from (5),

$$\cosh\frac{p}{k} = \frac{\sqrt{y_3^2 - y_2^2}}{\sqrt{y_3^2 - y_1^2 - y_2^2}}, \qquad \sinh\frac{p}{k} = \frac{y_1}{\sqrt{y_3^2 - y_1^2 - y_2^2}}. \qquad (6)$$

The point K is the point $(0:1:1)$, and the equation of PK is $(y_2 - y_3)x_1 - y_1 x_2 + y_1 x_3 = 0$. Hence to find the angle between PK and PR we have to place in (3)

$$v_1 = 0, \quad v_2 = y_3, \quad v_3 = -y_2,$$

$$w_1 = y_2 - y_3, \quad w_2 = -y_1, \quad w_3 = y_1.$$

There results, with the aid of (6),

$$\cos\theta = \frac{y_1}{\sqrt{y_3^2 - y_2^2}} = \tanh\frac{p}{k}.$$

It appears, then, that the angle θ is a function of p. We shall place, following Lobachevsky's notation,

$$\theta = \pi(p).$$

Our last equation then leads with little work to the final result:

$$\tan\tfrac{1}{2}\pi(p) = e^{-\frac{p}{k}}. \qquad (7)$$

This result is independent of the fact that it has been obtained for the special line $x_1 = 0$ and the special form of the equation of the conic since no transformation of coördinates alters the projective angles or distances.

If in formula (5) we consider y_i as a fixed point C and replace z_i by a variable point x_i, at the same time holding the distance d constant, we have

$$\omega_{yx}^2 + c\omega_{xx} = 0 \qquad (8)$$

as the equation of the locus of a point at a constant distance from a fixed point. This locus is called a pseudo circle. From the form of (8) it is obvious that the pseudo circle is tangent to the fundamental conic $\omega_{xx} = 0$ at the points in which the latter is cut by the polar $\omega_{yx} = 0$ of the point y_i. There are three cases:

I. The point C lies inside the conic (Fig. 38). The pseudo circles with the center y_i are then closed curves intersecting the conic in imaginary points.

II. The point C lies on the conic (Fig. 39), and the distance of each point from y_i is infinite. The pseudo circles are tangent to the

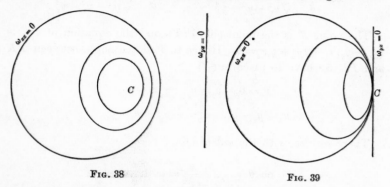

Fig. 38   Fig. 39

conic. They are the limiting cases of the pseudo circles of Case I when the center recedes to infinity and the radius becomes infinite, and are called in non-Euclidean geometry limit circles or horicycles.

III. The point C is outside the conic (Fig. 40), and the radius is imaginary so that points of (8) lie inside the conic. The straight line $\omega_{yx} = 0$ is one of these pseudo circles, and the others are the loci of points equidistant from this line. To prove the latter statement draw any straight line through C. It intersects the polar of C at R and the pseudo circle in two points one of which is Q. Then CR and CQ are constant, and hence RQ is constant. In this geometry,

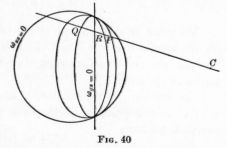

Fig. 40

then, the locus of points equally distant from a straight line is not a straight line, but a pseudo circle with imaginary center and imaginary radius. It is called a hypocycle.

EXERCISES

1. Consider angle and distance for points outside the fundamental conic, especially with reference to real and imaginary values.

2. Construct a triangle all of whose angles are zero.

3. Compute the angle between two lines of zero length and between any line and a line of zero length.

4. Prove that the sum of the angles of a triangle is less than two right angles.

49. The elliptic case. We assume that the fundamental conic is imaginary. It may be reduced by proper choice of coördinates to the form

$$\omega_{xx} = x_1^2 + x_2^2 + x_3^2 = 0 \tag{1}$$

in point coördinates and to the form

$$\Omega_{uu} = u_1^2 + u_2^2 + u_3^2 = 0 \tag{2}$$

in line coördinates.

Since the tangents from any point to the fundamental conic are imaginary, the problem of determination of angle is the same here as in the hyperbolic case, and we have

$$\cos \theta = \frac{\Omega_{vw}}{\sqrt{\Omega_{vv}\Omega_{ww}}}. \tag{3}$$

Any straight line connecting the two points P_1 and P_2 meets the conic in imaginary points, and if P_1 and P_2 are real points, the quantities λ_1 and λ_2 in (5), § 47, are conjugate imaginary. Hence, if the distance between two real points is to be real, we must take K as pure imaginary. We will place $K = \dfrac{ik}{2}$, where k is real.

Placing $\lambda_1 = re^{i\phi}$, where

$$\cos \phi = \frac{\omega_{yz}}{\sqrt{\omega_{yy}\omega_{zz}}}, \qquad \sin \phi = \frac{\sqrt{\omega_{yy}\omega_{zz} - \omega_{yz}^2}}{\sqrt{\omega_{yy}\omega_{zz}}},$$

and representing the distance $(y_i z_i)$ by d, we may reduce formula (5), § 47, to the form

$$\cos \frac{d}{k} = \frac{\omega_{yz}}{\sqrt{\omega_{yy}\omega_{zz}}}. \tag{4}$$

Two real points are always at a finite distance from each other, since, as shown in § 47, an infinite distance only results when one of the points is on the fundamental conic.

Consider the change in d as z_i moves along a straight line, y_i being fixed. In the beginning of the motion, when z_i coincides with y_i, $\cos \dfrac{d}{k} = \dfrac{\omega_{yy}}{\sqrt{\omega_{yy}\omega_{yy}}}$, and the sign of the radical must be taken

so that $\cos \dfrac{d}{k} = 1$ and $d = 0$. As z_i moves away from y_i the signs of the quantities on the right-hand side of equation (4) remain positive and d increases until z_i reaches a point on the line $\omega_{yx} = 0$, (Fig. 41), the polar of y_i. Then

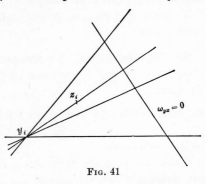

FIG. 41

$\cos \dfrac{d}{k} = 0$ and $d = \dfrac{\pi}{2} k$. This is true of all lines through y_i and for either direction on any such line. Hence the straight line $\omega_{yx} = 0$, which, by § 48, is perpendicular to all lines through y_i, is at a constant distance $\dfrac{\pi k}{2}$ from y_i in all directions.

Consequently, if we start from y_i and traverse a distance πk on any line through y_i and in either direction, we return to y_i. There are two cases of importance to be distinguished:

CASE I. All straight lines may be considered of length πk. The coördinates y_i always refer, then, to a single point. All straight lines intersect in one and only one point, there are no parallel lines, and two lines always bound a portion of the plane. This is the *Riemannian geometry*. It may be visualized by drawing straight lines from a point outside the plane and considering each point of the plane as represented by one and only one of these lines.

CASE II. All straight lines may be considered of length $2\pi k$. When we traverse the distance πk on a line from y_i and return to y_i, we shall consider that we are on the opposite side of the plane and need to repeat the journey to return to our starting point. Any coördinates y_i, then, are the coördinates of two points lying on opposite sides of the plane. Two straight lines intersect in two points, there are no parallel lines, and two lines inclose two portions of the plane. We call this *spherical geometry*, since it is exactly that on the surface of a sphere. It is also the geometry of the half-lines or rays drawn to the plane from a point outside of it.

1. Construct a triangle all of whose angles are right angles.

2. Prove that the sum of the angles of a triangle is greater than two right angles.

50. The parabolic case. We may consider that the fundamental conic is one which contains singular points or singular lines. There are, then, the two possibilities of the point equation representing two straight lines or of the line equation representing two points. The former possibility has little interest, and we shall consider only the case in which the line equation represents two points. There are two cases to distinguish:

CASE I. *The two points are imaginary.* We may take them as the two points $1 : \pm i : 0$, and the line equation of the fundamental conic is then

$$\Omega_{uu} = u_1^2 + u_2^2 = 0. \tag{1}$$

The formula for angle may be modified as in § 48, with the result that

$$\cos \theta = \frac{v_1 w_1 + v_2 w_2}{\sqrt{v_1^2 + v_2^2} \sqrt{w_1^2 + w_2^2}}. \tag{2}$$

The point equation of the fundamental conic does not exist and the distance formula (6), § 47, cannot be immediately applied. We may proceed, however, by a method of limits. In place of (1) we will write

$$\Omega_{uu} = u_1^2 + u_2^2 + \epsilon u_3^2 = 0, \tag{3}$$

which goes over into (1) when $\epsilon = 0$. The point equation corresponding to (3) is

$$\omega_{xx} = \epsilon (x_1^2 + x_2^2) + x_3^2 = 0, \tag{4}$$

and from this we find, as in § 48,

$$\sinh \frac{d}{k} = i \frac{\sqrt{\epsilon (y_1 z_3 - y_3 z_1)^2 + \epsilon (y_2 z_3 - y_3 z_2)^2 + \epsilon^2 (y_1 z_2 - y_2 z_1)^2}}{\sqrt{\epsilon (y_1^2 + y_2^2) + y_3^2} \sqrt{\epsilon (z_1^2 + z_2^2) + z_3^2}}.$$

Since the quantity on the right hand of this equation is infinitesimal, we may replace $\sinh \frac{d}{k}$ by $\frac{d}{k}$ and then pass to the limit, as $\epsilon \doteq 0$ and $k = \infty$ in such a manner that $\operatorname{Lim} ik \sqrt{\epsilon} = 1$. We have

$$d = \frac{\sqrt{(y_1 z_3 - y_3 z_1)^2 + (y_2 z_3 - y_3 z_2)^2}}{y_3 z_3}. \tag{5}$$

If we take $x_3 = 0$ as the line at infinity, the points $1 : \pm i : 0$ become the circle points, and the formula (2) for angle and (5) for distance become the usual Cartesian formulas. The geometry is Euclidean. We have this result:

Euclidean measurement is a special case of projective measurement.

CASE II. *The fundamental points are real.* We may take them as $1 : \pm 1 : 0$. The line equation of the fundamental conic is then

$$\Omega_{uu} = u_1^2 - u_2^2 = 0. \tag{6}$$

Since through every real point there go two lines of the pencils defined by (6), it is necessary to take the constant K of § 47 as real if real lines are to make real angles with each other. We will take $K = \frac{1}{2}$ and find, by a discussion analogous to that used in § 48 for finding d,

$$\cosh \theta = \frac{v_1 w_1 - v_2 w_2}{\sqrt{v_1^2 - v_2^2} \sqrt{w_1^2 - w_2^2}}. \tag{7}$$

The formula for distance may be found as in Case I, with the result

$$d = \frac{\sqrt{(y_1 z_3 - y_3 z_1)^2 - (y_2 z_3 - y_3 z_2)^2}}{y_3 z_3}. \tag{8}$$

If we take $x_3 = 0$ as the line at infinity and use nonhomogeneous Cartesian coördinates, we have, for the distance between two points (x, y) and (x', y'),

$$d = \sqrt{(x - x')^2 - (y - y')^2}, \tag{9}$$

and for the angle between the two lines $ax + by + c = 0$ and $a'x + b'y + c' = 0$,

$$\cosh \theta = \frac{aa' - bb'}{\sqrt{a^2 - b^2} \sqrt{a'^2 - b'^2}}.$$

Consider now any fixed point in the plane. For convenience let it be the origin O. Through O go two lines of the pencils defined by the fundamental conic; that is, two lines drawn to the fundamental points at infinity. The equations of these lines are $x \pm y = 0$ (Fig. 42). They divide the plane into two regions, which we may mark as shaded and unshaded. If a point (x, y) lies in the unshaded region, $x^2 - y^2 > 0$; and if it lies in the shaded region, $x^2 - y^2 < 0$. Consequently, distances measured from O are imaginary in the shaded region and real in the unshaded region. The boundaries between the two regions are lines of length zero. The locus of points equidistant from O are equilateral hyperbolas $x^2 - y^2 = k$.

A line $ax + by = 0$, passing through O, is in the unshaded region if $a^2 - b^2 < 0$ and in the shaded region if $a^2 - b^2 > 0$. Hence an angle with its vertex at O is real if both sides are in the shaded region or both sides in the unshaded region, and is imaginary if one side is in the shaded region and one side in the unshaded region. A line through O which is not a line of zero length makes an infinite angle with each of the lines of zero length. The two lines of zero length make an inde-

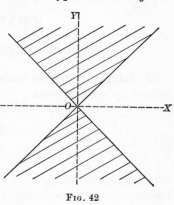

Fig. 42

terminate angle with each other. In this respect as in other ways they are analogous to the minimum lines in a Euclidean plane.

These properties are of course the same at all points of the plane. They make a geometry which differs widely from the geometry of actual physical experience.*

* This geometry has recently gained new interest because of its occurrence in the theory of relativity. Cf. Wilson and Lewis, " The Space-Time Manifold of Relativity," *Proceedings of the American Academy of Arts and Sciences* (1912), Vol. XLVIII, No. 11.

CHAPTER VIII

CONTACT TRANSFORMATIONS IN THE PLANE

51. Point-point transformations. Consider now the transformation defined by the equations

$$\rho x_1' = f_1(x_1, x_2, x_3),$$
$$\rho x_2' = f_2(x_1, x_2, x_3), \tag{1}$$
$$\rho x_3' = f_3(x_1, x_2, x_3),$$

where x_1, x_2, x_3 and x_1', x_2', x_3' are point coördinates and f_1, f_2, f_3 are homogeneous functions which are continuous and possess derivatives and for which the Jacobian

$$\begin{vmatrix} \dfrac{\partial f_1}{\partial x_1} & \dfrac{\partial f_1}{\partial x_2} & \dfrac{\partial f_1}{\partial x_3} \\ \dfrac{\partial f_2}{\partial x_1} & \dfrac{\partial f_2}{\partial x_2} & \dfrac{\partial f_2}{\partial x_3} \\ \dfrac{\partial f_3}{\partial x_1} & \dfrac{\partial f_3}{\partial x_2} & \dfrac{\partial f_3}{\partial x_3} \end{vmatrix}$$

does not identically vanish.

By the transformation (1) a point x_i is transformed into one or more points x_i', with possible exceptional points. Owing to the hypothesis as to the Jacobian, equations (1) can in general be solved for x_i, and any point x_i' is therefore the transformed point of one or more points x_i, with possible exceptional points.

Consider now a point M and its transformed point M'. If there is more than one transformed point, we will fix our attention on one only. If M describes a curve c defined by the equations

$$x_1 = \phi_1(t), \quad x_2 = \phi_2(t), \quad x_3 = \phi_3(t), \tag{2}$$

the point M' describes a curve c', the equations of which may be found by substituting from (2) into (1). The direction of c at M is determined by x_1, x_2, x_3 and dx_1, dx_2, dx_3, as shown in (4), § 31. The direction of c' at M' is determined in the same manner by x_1', x_2', x_3' and dx_1', dx_2', dx_3'. These latter six quantities are determined by the former six, and hence the direction of c' at a point M' is determined by the direction of c at M. From this follows the theorem

If two curves c_1 and c_2 are tangent at a point M, the transformed curves c_1' and c_2' are tangent at the transformed point M'.

For this reason the transformation (1) is called a *contact transformation*.

If the transformation (1) is expressed in nonhomogeneous Cartesian coördinates, it becomes

$$x' = f_1(x, y),$$
$$y' = f_2(x, y).$$

Now let p be the direction $\dfrac{dy}{dx}$ of a curve traversed by the point (x, y) and let p' be the direction $\dfrac{dy'}{dx'}$ of the transformed curve. We have, evidently,

$$p' = \frac{\dfrac{\partial f_2}{\partial x} + p \dfrac{\partial f_2}{\partial y}}{\dfrac{\partial f_1}{\partial x} + p \dfrac{\partial f_1}{\partial y}}.$$

The three equations

$$x' = f_1(x, y),$$
$$y' = f_2(x, y), \tag{3}$$
$$p' = \frac{\dfrac{\partial f_2}{\partial x} + p \dfrac{\partial f_2}{\partial y}}{\dfrac{\partial f_1}{\partial x} + p \dfrac{\partial f_1}{\partial y}},$$

are called an enlarged point transformation. They bring into clear evidence that two curves with a common point and a common direction are transformed into two curves which have also a common point and a common direction.

52. Quadric inversion. An example of a point-point transformation as defined by (1), § 51, has already been met in the case of the collineations.

As another example consider the transformation

$$\rho x_1' = x_1 x_3,$$
$$\rho x_2' = x_2 x_3,$$
$$\rho x_3' = x_1 x_2.$$

(1)

These equations can be solved when neither x_1, x_2, nor x_3 are zero into the equivalent equations

$$\sigma x_1 = x_1' x_3',$$
$$\sigma x_2 = x_2' x_3',$$
$$\sigma x_3 = x_1' x_2'.$$

(2)

The transformation establishes, therefore, a one-to-one relation between the points x_i and the points x_i' with the possible exception of points on the triangle of reference ABC. To examine these points let A be as usual the point $0 : 0 : 1$, B the point $0 : 1 : 0$, and C the point $1 : 0 : 0$, so that the equation of AB is $x_1 = 0$, that of AC is $x_2 = 0$, and that of BC is $x_3 = 0$. Then from (1) any point on the line AB is transformed into B, any point on the line AC is transformed into C, and any point on the line BC is transformed into A. The coördinates of either A, B, or C, if substituted in (1), give the indeterminate expression $0 : 0 : 0$, but if we enlarge the definition of the transformation by assuming that (2) holds for all points, including those on AB, AC, and BC, it follows that B is transformed into the entire line AB, C is transformed into the entire line AC, and A is transformed into the entire line BC.

Consider any straight line with the equation

$$a_1 x_1 + a_2 x_2 + a_3 x_3 = 0.$$

It is transformed into the curve

$$a_1 x_1' x_3' + a_2 x_2' x_3' + a_3 x_1' x_2' = 0,$$

which is a conic through the points A, B, and C. In fact, the point in which the line meets AB is transformed into B, the point in which the line meets AC is transformed into C, and the point in which the line meets BC is transformed into A.

If the straight line passes through one of the points A, B, or C, the conic into which it is transformed splits up into two straight lines, one of which is a side of the coördinate triangle and the other of which passes through the vertex opposite that side. In particular, consider a line $x_1 + \lambda x_2 = 0$ through A. The first two of equations (1) give $x_1' + \lambda x_2' = 0$ for all points except the point A; that is, any point except A on a line through A gives a definite point on the same line. The point A, however, goes over into the entire line $x_3 = 0$.

In a similar manner a conic is transformed into a curve of fourth order, which passes twice through each of the points A, B, C, since the conic cuts each of the lines AB, BC, CA in two points. If, however, the conic passes through one of the points A, B, C, that point is transformed into a side of the coördinate triangle, and the curve of fourth order must consist of that side and a curve of third order.

In particular, a conic through A but not through B or C is transformed into the line BC and a curve of third order through B and C. A nondegenerate conic through B and C and not through A is transformed into two lines AB and AC and a conic through B and C, but not through A. Finally, a nondegenerate conic through the three points A, B, C is transformed into the three sides of the triangle of reference and a straight line not through its vertices. These results may all be seen directly or verified analytically.

By placing $x_i' = x_i$ in equations (1) the locus of fixed points of the transformation is found to be the conic

$$x_1 x_2 - x_3^2 = 0,$$

which passes through B and C and is tangent to AB and AC.

It is not difficult to show that each point P of the plane is transformed into a point P' in which the line AP cuts the polar of P with respect to the fixed conic.

This transformation is called a *quadric inversion* to distinguish it from the circular inversion, or simply inversion, discussed in the next section.

EXERCISES

1. Prove the statement in the text that the point P is transformed into the point in which AP cuts the polar of P with respect to the fixed conic. Hence show that P and P' are harmonic conjugates to the points in which PP' cuts the conic.

2. Prove that the cross ratio of four points on a straight line p is equal to the cross ratio of the corresponding four points on the conic into which p is transformed.

3. Study the transformations

$$(1) \quad \rho x_1' = \frac{1}{x_1},$$

$$\rho x_2' = \frac{1}{x_2},$$

$$\rho x_3' = \frac{1}{x_3}.$$

$$(2) \quad \rho x_1' = x_1 x_3,$$

$$\rho x_2' = x_2 x_3,$$

$$\rho x_3' = x_1^2.$$

$$(3) \quad \rho x_1' = x_1^2,$$

$$\rho x_2' = x_1 x_2,$$

$$\rho x_3' = x_2^2 - x_1 x_3.$$

53. Inversion. The transformation (1) of § 52 has particular interest and importance when the points B and C are the circle points at infinity. We may then place $x_3 = t$, $x_1 = x + iy$, $x_2 = x - iy$ and, using Cartesian coördinates, write the transformation in the form

$$\rho (x' + iy') = (x + iy)t;$$

$$\rho (x' - iy') = (x - iy)t, \qquad (1)$$

$$\rho t' = x^2 + y^2,$$

or, what is the same thing in nonhomogeneous form,

$$x' = \frac{x}{x^2 + y^2}.$$

$$y' = \frac{y}{x^2 + y^2}, \qquad (2)$$

$$x'^2 + y'^2 = \frac{1}{x^2 + y^2}.$$

By this transformation a one-to-one relation is established between the points (x, y) and (x', y'), with the exceptions that the origin corresponds to the line at infinity, and conversely, and that each of the circle points at infinity corresponds to the minimum line joining it to the origin, and conversely. The circle $x^2 + y^2 = 1$ is fixed. Any point of the fixed circle is transformed into a point inside that circle, and, conversely, in such a way that if O is the origin, P any point, and P' the transformed point, $OP \cdot OP' = 1$. The transformation is called an *inversion* with respect to the unit circle, or a transformation by *reciprocal radius* with respect to that circle. The origin is called the *center of inversion*, and the fixed circle the *circle of inversion*.

Remembering that a circle is a conic through the circle points and applying the results of the previous section, we have the following theorems:

I. *A straight line not through the center of inversion is transformed into a circle through the center of inversion.*

II. *A straight line through the center of inversion is transformed into itself (and the line at infinity).*

III. *A circle not through the center of inversion is transformed into a circle not through the center of inversion (and the two minimum lines through the center of inversion).*

IV. *A circle through the center of inversion is transformed into a straight line not through the center of inversion (and the two minimum lines through the center of inversion and the line at infinity).*

V. *A conic is transformed in general into a curve of fourth order through the circle points at infinity.*

VI. *A conic through the center of inversion is transformed into a curve of third order through the circle points (and the line at infinity).*

If we take the nonhomogeneous form (2) of the transformation and apply it to the equations

$$ax + by + c = 0,$$
$$a(x^2 + y^2) + bx + cy + f = 0$$

we readily get theorems I–IV without the clauses in parentheses. It is in this simplified form that the theorems are often given, but they then fail to tell the whole story.

Let us denote by I the transformation (1) and by M the transformation III, § 45. Then M^{-1} transforms the circle $x^2 + y^2 = k^2$ into the unit circle, I carries out an inversion with respect to the unit circle, and M carries the unit circle back into the circle $x^2 + y^2 = k^2$. The product of these three, namely MIM^{-1}, which is the transform of I by M, is an inversion with respect to the circle $x^2 + y^2 = k^2$ and is represented by the equations

$$x' = \frac{k^2 x}{x^2 + y^2},$$

$$y' = \frac{k^2 y}{x^2 + y^2},\tag{3}$$

$$x'^2 + y'^2 = \frac{k^4}{x^2 + y^2}.$$

It is evident that a point P is transformed into a point P', where $OP \cdot OP' = k^2$, and that theorems I–VI still hold.

If we desire an inversion with respect to a circle with center (a, b) and radius k, we may transform (3) by means of a transformation which carries O into (a, b). The result is

$$x' - a = \frac{k^2 (x - a)}{(x - a)^2 + (y - b)^2},$$

$$y' - b = \frac{k^2 (y - b)}{(x - a)^2 + (y - b)^2},$$

$$(x' - a)^2 + (y - b)^2 = \frac{k^4}{(x - a)^2 + (y - b)^2}.$$

Obviously theorems I–VI hold for (5).

If the inversion (2) is written as an enlarged point-point transformation of the form (3), § 51, we have

$$x' = \frac{x}{x^2 + y^2},$$

$$y' = \frac{y}{x^2 + y^2},$$

$$p' = \frac{2 xy + (y^2 - x^2) p}{x^2 - y^2 + 2 pxy}.$$

From this it is easy to compute that if p_1 and p_2 are the slopes of two curves through the same point, and if p_1' and p_2' are the slopes of the two transformed curves through the transformed point, then

$$\frac{p_1 - p_2'}{1 + p_1' p_2'} = \frac{p_1 - p_2}{1 + p_1 p_2}.$$

This shows that the angle between two curves is preserved by the transformation. A transformation which preserves angles is said to be *conformal*. Hence *an inversion is a conformal transformation*.

EXERCISES

1. Show that any circle through a point P and its inverse point P' is orthogonal to the circle of inversion.

2. Show that a pencil of straight lines is transformed by inversion into a pencil of circles consisting of circles through two fixed points. Study the configuration formed by the inversion of a series of concentric circles and the straight lines through their common center.

3. Show that parallel lines invert into circles which are tangent at the center of inversion.

4. Show that the cross ratio of four points collinear with the center of inversion is equal to that of the transformed points.

5. Show that a point P and its inverse point P' are harmonic conjugates with respect to the intersections of the line PP' and the circle of inversion.

6. If a circle is inverted into a straight line, show that two points which are inverse with respect to the circle go into two points which are symmetrical with respect to the line.

7. Study the real properties of an inversion with respect to the imaginary circle $x^2 + y^2 = -1$.

8. Show that an inversion is completely determined by two pairs of inverse points.

9. From the theorem "four circles can be drawn tangent to three given lines" prove by inversion the theorem "four circles can be drawn tangent to three given circles which pass through a fixed point."

10. From the theorem "two circles have four common tangent lines" prove by inversion the theorem "through a given point four circles can be drawn tangent to two given circles."

54. Point-curve transformations. Consider now a transformation defined by the equation

$$F(x_1, x_2, x_3, x_1', x_2', x_3') = 0, \tag{1}$$

where x_i and x_i' are point coördinates and F is a function homogeneous in both x_i and x_i', continuous in both sets of these variables, and possessing derivatives with respect to both.

Let M be a point with the coördinates y_i. If these coördinates are substituted for x_i in (1) and held fixed, the resulting equation is that of a curve which we call an m'-curve, the equation being

$$F(y_1, y_2, y_3, x_1', x_2', x_3') = 0, \tag{2}$$

and we say that *the point M is transformed into the m'-curve.*

We shall make the hypothesis that these m'-curves form a two-parameter family of curves such that one curve of this family goes through any given point in any given direction.

Let K' be a point with the coördinates z'_i. This point will lie on the m'-curve (2) if

$$F(y_1, y_2, y_3, z'_1, z'_2, z'_3) = 0,\qquad(3)$$

and all values of the ratios $y_1 : y_2 : y_3$ which can be determined from equation (3) will, if used in (2), determine an m'-curve through K'. These values of y_i, however, are given by any point M which lies on the curve

$$F(x_1, x_2, x_3, z'_1, z'_2, z'_3) = 0.\qquad(4)$$

Call any curve defined by equation (4) a k-curve. We have, then, the following result:

Fig. 43

All points M which lie on a k-curve are transformed into m'-curves which pass through a point K' (Fig. 43).

We can say, then, that *the k-curve is transformed into a point K'.* In fact, the equation of a k-curve is found by holding x'_i constant in (1), just as the equation of an m'-curve is found by holding x_i constant in the same equation.

It is further evident that *all k-curves which pass through a point M are transformed into points K' which lie on the curve m'.*

If any proof of this is necessary, it may be supplied by noticing that equation (3) is the condition that M should lie on k and that K' should lie on m'.

Consider now any curve c, not a k-curve, defined by the equations

$$x_1 = \phi_1(\lambda),$$
$$x_2 = \phi_2(\lambda),\qquad(5)$$
$$x_3 = \phi_3(\lambda).$$

The m'-curves corresponding to points M on c form a one-parameter family of curves which in general have an envelope c', and the *curve c is said to be transformed into the curve c'.*

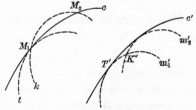

Fig. 44

To follow this analytically let $M_1(x_1, x_2, x_3)$ (Fig. 44) be the point on c corresponding to the value λ_1 of λ, and let M_2 be the point corresponding to the value $\lambda + \Delta\lambda$, the coördinates of M_2 being $x_1 + \Delta x_1$, $x_2 + \Delta x_2$, $x_3 + \Delta x_3$. The two points M_1 and M_2 are transformed into m_1' and m_2', which intersect in a point K', the coördinates of which are given by the equations

$$F(x_1, x_2, x_3, x_1', x_2', x_3') = 0,$$

$$\left(\frac{\partial F}{\partial x_1} + \epsilon_1\right)\Delta x_1 + \left(\frac{\partial F}{\partial x_2} + \epsilon_2\right)\Delta x_2 + \left(\frac{\partial F}{\partial x_3} + \epsilon_3\right)\Delta x_3 = 0, \qquad (6)$$

where the values of x_i and Δx_i are to be taken from (5). The point K' corresponds to a k-curve through M_1 and M_2.

Now let M_2 approach M_1. The curve m_2' approaches the curve m_1', and the point K' approaches a limiting point T' the coördinates of which are given by

$$F(x_1, x_2, x_3, x_1', x_2', x_3') = 0,$$

$$\frac{\partial F}{\partial x_1}dx_1 + \frac{\partial F}{\partial x_2}dx_2 + \frac{\partial F}{\partial x_3}dx_3 = 0, \qquad (7)$$

where the values of x_i and dx_i are to be taken from (5).

The point T' is obviously the transformed point of t, a k-curve tangent to c at M_1. The locus of T' is the curve c', which corresponds to c.

Equations (7) furnish a proof that c' is tangent to m' at T'. For, by differentiating the first of these equations and taking account of the second, we have

$$\frac{\partial F}{\partial x_1'}dx_1' + \frac{\partial F}{\partial x_2'}dx_2' + \frac{\partial F}{\partial x_3'}dx_3' = 0, \qquad (8)$$

which, as in § 31, determines the direction of c'. But this is just the equation which determines the direction of m_1'. The direction of c' is thus determined at the point T' by the direction of m_1'. It is therefore determined by the point M_1 and the curve t, the latter being determined by the direction of c. Hence *two curves c which are tangent are transformed into two curves c' which are tangent*. The transformation is therefore called a *contact transformation*.

Suppose now that the transformation (1) is expressed in non-homogeneous Cartesian coördinates by the equation

$$F(x, y, x', y') = 0,$$

and let p be the slope $\dfrac{dy}{dx}$ of any curve c, and p' the slope $\dfrac{dy'}{dx'}$ of the transformed curve c'. Then equations (6) and (8) are replaced in the present coördinates by

$$\frac{\partial F}{\partial x} + p \frac{\partial F}{\partial y} = 0,$$

$$\frac{\partial F}{\partial x'} + p' \frac{\partial F}{\partial y'} = 0,$$

which enable us to determine p and p' when x, y, x', and y' are known. The last three equations, written together,

$$F(x,\, y,\, x',\, y') = 0,$$

$$\frac{\partial F}{\partial x} + p \frac{\partial F}{\partial y} = 0, \tag{9}$$

$$\frac{\partial F}{\partial x'} + p' \frac{\partial F}{\partial y'} = 0,$$

are called an enlarged point-curve contact transformation. If solved for x', y', and p' they may be written in the form

$$x' = f_1(x,\, y,\, p),$$

$$y' = f_2(x,\, y,\, p), \tag{10}$$

$$p' = f_3(x,\, y,\, p).$$

If, then, the point (x, y) describes the curve $x = f_1(\lambda)$, $y = f_2(\lambda)$, we have $p = \dfrac{f_2'(\lambda)}{f_1'(\lambda)}$, and equations (10) give the transformed curve expressed in terms of the parameter λ.

An example of a point-curve transformation is found in the correlations already discussed, since the equations (1), § 42, may be written in the form

$$(a_{11}x_1 + a_{12}x_2 + a_{13}x_3)\,x_1' + (a_{21}x_1 + a_{22}x_2 + a_{23}x_3)x_2'$$
$$+ (a_{31}x_1 + a_{32}x_2 + a_{33}x_3)\,x' = 0.$$

Here the m'-curves and the k-curves are straight lines. If x_i describes a curve c, the straight line m' envelops the transformed curve c'. If the correlation is expressed in Cartesian coördinates, it is readily put into the form (10).

1. Express the general correlation in the form of equations (10).

2. Place in the form of equations (10) the polarity by which a point is transformed into its polar line with respect to the circle $x^2 + y^2 = 1$.

3. Find the curve into which the parabola $y^2 = ax$ is transformed by the polarity of Ex. 2.

4. Show that the curve into which the circle $(x - h)^2 + (y - k)^2 = r^2$ is transformed by the polarity of Ex. 2 is a conic, and state the conditions under which it is an ellipse, a parabola, or a hyperbola. Find the focus and directrix of the conic.

5. Prove that by any polarity the order and the class of the transformed curve is equal to the class and the order, respectively, of the original curve.

6. Study the transformation

$$x' = \frac{y}{p} - x,$$

$$y' = \frac{2}{p},$$

$$p' = \frac{2}{y},$$

and find the curve into which the circle $x^2 + y^2 = 1$ is transformed by it.

7. Express in the form of equations (10) each of the types of correlations given in § 42 and study them from this standpoint.

55. The pedal transformation. As another example of a point-curve transformation we shall use homogeneous Cartesian coördinates and take the equation

$$(x'^2 + y'^2)t - x't'x - y't'y = 0. \tag{1}$$

If we take M as any point $(x : y : t)$, the corresponding m'-curve is in general a circle constructed on the line OM as a diameter. Exceptional points are the origin and the points at infinity. If M is the origin, the circle becomes the two minimum lines through the origin. If M is a point at infinity, not a circle point, the circle m' splits up into the line at infinity and a straight line through O perpendicular to OM. If M is a circle point I, the circle m' splits up into the line at infinity and the minimum line OI.

The k-curve corresponding to a point K' is in general a straight line through K' and perpendicular to OK'. Exceptions occur when K' is the origin or one of the circle points at infinity, in which cases the k-curve is indeterminate. If K' is any point on the line at infinity but not a circle point, the k-curve is the line at infinity. If K' is on a minimum line through O, but not at infinity, the k-curve is the other minimum line through O. A k-line does not in general pass through O or the circle points at infinity.

Conversely, any straight line which does not pass through the origin, and is neither the line at infinity nor a minimum line, is a k-line, the point K' being the point in which the normal from O meets the line. This may be seen by comparing the equation $ax + by + ct = 0$ with (1), thus determining $x' : y' : t' = -ac : -bc : a^2 + b^2$, which is the foot of the normal from O to the line.

Take any curve c. The tangent k-curve at any point M is the tangent line t, and the point T' is the foot of the perpendicular from O on T. Therefore *the transformed curve c' of any curve c is the locus of the feet of the perpendiculars drawn from the origin to the tangent lines of c*. The transformation is called the *pedal transformation*, and the point O is the *origin* of the transformation.

If the pedal transformation is expressed in Cartesian coördinates as an enlarged point-curve transformation of the form (9), § 54, it becomes

$$x'^2 + y'^2 - x'x - y'y = 0,$$

$$p = -\frac{x'}{y'}, \tag{2}$$

$$p' = -\frac{2\,x' - x}{2\,y' - y},$$

and these equations can be solved for x', y', and p', giving

$$x' = -\frac{(y - px)p}{1 + p^2},$$

$$y' = \frac{y - px}{1 + p^2}, \tag{3}$$

$$p' = \frac{xp^2 - x - 2\,yp}{yp^2 - y + 2\,xp}.$$

EXERCISES

1. If Q is the pedal transformation with the origin O, P a polarity with respect to any circle with the center O, and R an inversion with respect to the same circle, prove the relations $Q = RP$, $P = RQ$, $R = QP$.

2. Show that by a pedal transformation a parabola with its focus at the origin of the transformation is transformed into the tangent line at the vertex of the parabola.

3. Show that by a pedal transformation an ellipse with its focus at the origin of the transformation is transformed into a circle with its diameter coinciding with the major diameter of the ellipse. State and prove the corresponding theorem for the hyperbola.

4. Find the curve into which the ellipse $\dfrac{x^2}{a^2} + \dfrac{y^2}{b^2} = 1$ is transformed by a pedal transformation with its origin at the center of the ellipse.

56. The line element. With the use of Cartesian coördinates the contact transformations may be looked at from a new viewpoint by the aid of the concept of the *line element*. A line element may be defined as a point with an associated direction. More precisely let there be given three numbers (x, y, p), where the numbers x and y are to be interpreted as the usual Cartesian coördinates of a point in the plane and p is to be interpreted as the slope or direction of a line through the point. Then the three quantities taken together define a line element. A line element may be roughly represented by plotting a point M and drawing a short line through M in the direction p, but this line must be considered as having no length just as the dot which represents M must be considered as without magnitude. There are ∞^3 line elements in the plane out of which we may form a one-dimensional extent of line elements by taking x, y, and p as functions of a single parameter; thus,

$$x = f_1(\lambda), \quad y = f_2(\lambda), \quad p = f_3(\lambda). \tag{1}$$

There are two types of one-dimensional extents:

TYPE I. The functions $f_1(\lambda)$ and $f_2(\lambda)$ may reduce to constants. In this case the one-dimensional extent consists of a fixed point with all possible directions associated with it.

Type II. The point (x, y) may describe a curve the equations of which are the first two of (1). Then the third equation of (1) associates with every point of that curve a certain direction.

It is obviously convenient that the direction associated with each point of the curve should be that of the tangent to the curve. The necessary and sufficient condition for this is that by virtue of (1) we should have $dx - pdy = 0$.

A one-dimensional extent of line elements defined by equation (1) shall be called a *union* of line elements when it satisfies the condition $dx - pdy = 0$. It is evident that the first type of extents always satisfies this condition and that the second type satisfies the condition when the direction of each element is that of the curve on which the point of the element lies.

Two unions of line elements have *contact* with each other if they have a line element in common. Two unions of the first type have contact, therefore, when they coincide; one of the first type has contact with one of the second when the point of the first lies on the curve of the second; and two elements of the second type have contact when their curves are tangent in the ordinary sense.

Any transformation of line elements defined by the equations

$$x' = f_1(x, y, p),$$
$$y' = f_2(x, y, p), \qquad\qquad (2)$$
$$p' = f_3(x, y, p),$$

where the functions are bound by the condition

$$dy' - p'dx' = \rho(dy - pdx), \qquad\qquad (3)$$

where ρ is not identically zero, is called a *contact transformation*.

It is clear that by such a transformation a union of line elements is transformed into a union of line elements and that two unions which are in contact are transformed into two which are in contact.

The enlarged point-point transformation (3), § 51, and the enlarged point-curve transformation (9), § 54, are cases of the general contact transformation (2). In fact, any contact transformation may be reduced to one of these cases. To show this let us proceed to deduce from (2) equations which are free from p and p'. Two cases only can occur.

CASE I. The first two equations in (2) may each be free from p. Then equation (3) gives the condition

$$\frac{\partial f_2}{\partial x}\,dx + \frac{\partial f_2}{\partial y}\,dy - p'\frac{\partial f_1}{\partial x}\,dx - p'\frac{\partial f_1}{\partial y}\,dy = \rho\,(dy - p\,dx),$$

which must be true for all values of the ratios $dx : dy$. Hence we have

$$\frac{\partial f_2}{\partial y} - p'\frac{\partial f_1}{\partial y} = \rho,$$

$$\frac{\partial f_2}{\partial x} - p'\frac{\partial f_1}{\partial x} = -\rho p,$$

whence, by eliminating ρ and solving for p', we have the result that the contact transformation (2) is in this case of the form

$$\begin{aligned}
x' &= f_1(x, y),\\
y' &= f_2(x, y),\\
p' &= \frac{\dfrac{\partial f_2}{\partial x} + p\dfrac{\partial f_2}{\partial y}}{\dfrac{\partial f_1}{\partial x} + p\dfrac{\partial f_1}{\partial y}},
\end{aligned} \qquad (4)$$

which is exactly that of (3), § 51.

By this transformation any one-dimensional extent of line elements which form a union of the first type is transformed into a union of the first type, and any union of the second type is transformed into a union of the second type.

CASE II. At least one of the first two equations in (2) contains p. It is then possible to find one, but only one, equation free from p and p'. Let that equation be

$$F(x, y, x', y') = 0.$$

From this equation we find

$$\frac{\partial F}{\partial x}\,dx + \frac{\partial F}{\partial y}\,dy + \frac{\partial F}{\partial x'}\,dx' + \frac{\partial F}{\partial y'}\,dy' = 0,$$

which must be identical with (3). By comparison we find

$$\frac{\dfrac{\partial F}{\partial x}}{\rho p} = \frac{\dfrac{\partial F}{\partial y}}{-\rho} = \frac{\dfrac{\partial F}{\partial x'}}{-p'} = \frac{\dfrac{\partial F}{\partial y'}}{1},$$

from which p and p' can be found, with the result that the contact transformation (2) can in this case be put into the form

$$F(x, y, x', y') = 0,$$
$$\frac{\partial F}{\partial x} + p\,\frac{\partial F}{\partial y} = 0, \qquad (5)$$
$$\frac{\partial F}{\partial x'} + p'\,\frac{\partial F}{\partial y'} = 0,$$

which is exactly that of (9), § 54.

By this transformation any union of the first type is transformed into a union of the second type, each element of the former being transformed into an element of the latter.

As an example consider the transformation

$$x' = x \mp \frac{kp}{\sqrt{1+p^2}},$$
$$y' = y \pm \frac{k}{\sqrt{1+p^2}},$$
$$p' = p.$$

If written in the form (5) this becomes

$$(x' - x)^2 + (y' - y)^2 = k^2,$$
$$x' - x + p\,(y' - y) = 0,$$
$$x' - x + p'\,(y' - y) = 0.$$

The geometrical meaning of these equations is simple. Any line element (x, y, p) is transformed into a line element (x', y', p') so placed that the point (x', y') is at a distance k from the point (x', y'), and the line joining (x', y') to (x, y) is perpendicular to the line element. A transformed line element is parallel to the original element. Otherwise stated, each line element is moved parallel to itself through a distance k in a direction perpendicular to the direction of the element. Each line element is therefore transformed into two line elements. A union of the first type, consisting of line elements through the same point, is transformed into a union consisting of the line elements of a circle with that point as a center and a radius k. Any curve c is transformed into two curves parallel to c at a normal distance k from c.

This transformation is sometimes called a *dilation*, suggesting that each point of the plane is dilated into a circle.

1. Show that the transformation

$$x' = p,$$
$$y' = xp - y,$$
$$p' = x,$$

is a contact transformation and study its properties.

2. Show that the transformation

$$x' = x + 2\,p,$$
$$y' = y + p^2,$$
$$p' = p,$$

is a contact transformation and study its properties.

3. Show that any differential equation of the form $f\left(x,\, y,\, \dfrac{dy}{dx}\right) = 0$ may be written in the form $f(x,\, y,\, p) = 0$ and considered as defining a doubly infinite extent of line elements. To solve the equation is to arrange the elements into unions of line elements. In general, the solution consists of a family of curves. Any union formed by taking one element from each curve of a family is a singular solution. Note that an equation $f(x,\, y) = 0$ can also be interpreted in this way, and that the family of solutions consists of points on the curve $f(x,\, y) = 0$ with all the line elements through each, while the singular solution is the curve $f(x,\, y) = 0$ with its tangent elements.

4. Study the differential equation $y - px = 0$ in the light of Ex. 3. Show that the singular solution is the one-dimensional extent of line elements which consists of all elements through the origin.

5. Apply to Ex. 4 the dilation $x' = x - \dfrac{p}{\sqrt{1 + p^2}},\ y' = y + \dfrac{1}{\sqrt{1 + p^2}},$ $p = p'$. Show that the differential equation becomes $y' - p'x' - \sqrt{1 + p'^2} = 0$. What becomes of the singular solution and the family of solutions?

6. Study Clairaut's equation, $y = px + f(p)$, by the method of Ex. 3 and show geometrically that the family of solutions consists of the straight lines $y = cx + f(c)$. What is the singular solution? Apply to the variables in the equation the transformation $xx' + yy' = 1$ and determine the effect on the equation and its solutions.

CHAPTER IX

TETRACYCLICAL COÖRDINATES

57. Special tetracyclical coördinates. We shall discuss in this chapter a system of coördinates especially useful for the treatment of the circle. These coördinates are not dependent upon the Cartesian coördinates, though they are often so presented. On the contrary they may be set up independently by elementary geometry for real points and then extended to imaginary and infinite points in the usual manner. It is therefore not to be expected that the geometry in the imaginary domain and at infinity should agree in all respects with that obtained by the use of Cartesian coördinates.

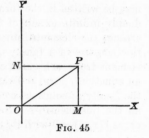

The coördinates we are to discuss are called tetracyclical coördinates, and we begin, for convenience, with a special type.

Let OX and OY (Fig. 45) be two straight lines of reference intersecting at

FIG. 45

right angles at O, and let P be any real point of the plane. Let MP and NP be the distances of P from OX and OY, respectively, taken with the usual convention as to signs, and let OP be the distance of P from O, taken always positive. Then the special tetracyclical coördinates of P are the ratios

$$x_1 : x_2 : x_3 : x_4 = \overline{OP}^2 : NP : MP : 1, \tag{1}$$

from which it follows that the quantities x are connected by the fundamental relation

$$\omega(x) = x_2^2 + x_3^2 - x_1 x_4 = 0. \tag{2}$$

It is obvious that to any real point corresponds one set of coördinates and, conversely, to any real set of the ratios $x_1 : x_2 : x_3 : x_4$ which satisfy the relation (2), and for which $x_4 \neq 0$, corresponds one real point P. We extend the coördinate system in the usual

138

manner by the convention that any set of ratios satisfying (2) shall define a real or an imaginary point of the plane, the ratios $0:0:0:0$ being of course unallowed.

As the real point P recedes from O, the ratios approach a limiting set of values $1:0:0:0$. To see this we write equation (1) in the form

$$x_1:x_2:x_3:x_4 = 1:\frac{NP}{\overline{OP}^2}:\frac{MP}{\overline{OP}^2}:\frac{1}{\overline{OP}^2}$$

$$= 1:\frac{\cos\theta}{OP}:\frac{\sin\theta}{OP}:\frac{1}{\overline{OP}^2},$$

where $\theta =$ the angle MOP. The limit of the ratios of x_i is therefore $1:0:0:0$. Hence we say that *by the use of the special tetracyclical coördinates the plane is regarded as having a single real point at infinity*. This point, however, is not the only one which must be considered at infinity, as will appear later.

58. Distance between two points. Let C $(y_1:y_2:y_3:y_4)$ and P $(x_1:x_2:x_3:x_4)$ (Fig. 46) be two real points, and let $d = CP$, the distance between them. Then, by trigonometry,

$$d^2 = \overline{OP}^2 + \overline{OC}^2 - 2\,OP\cdot OC \cos(\theta_1 - \theta_2),$$

where $\theta_1 =$ the angle XOP and $\theta_2 =$ the angle XOC. But from the definition of the coördinates and from the relations

$$OP \cos\theta_1 = \frac{x_2}{x_4}, \quad OP \sin\theta_1 = \frac{x_3}{x_4},$$

$$OC \cos\theta_2 = \frac{y_2}{y_4}, \quad OC \sin\theta_2 = \frac{y_3}{y_4},$$

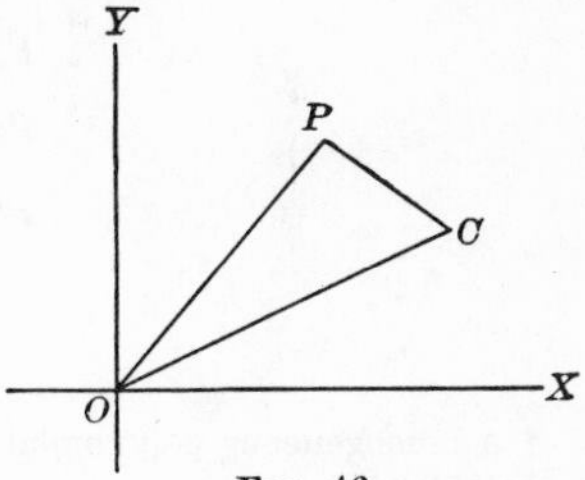

the above equation can be written

FIG. 46

$$d^2 = \frac{y_4 x_1 - 2\,y_2 x_2 - 2\,y_3 x_3 + y_1 x_4}{y_4 x_4}. \tag{1}$$

This equation, obtained by the use of real points, is now taken as the definition of the distance between imaginary points.

Equation (1) can be written

$$d = -\frac{2\,\omega(x,\,y)}{x_4 y_4}, \tag{2}$$

where in accordance with the usual notation $\omega(x, y)$ denotes the polar * of the form $\omega(x)$.

From (3) it appears that $d = \infty$ when $y_4 = 0$ or when $x_4 = 0$. Hence *the locus of the points at infinity is defined by the equation* $x_4 = 0$.

Since always $\omega(x) = 0$, the points at infinity satisfy also the condition $x_2^2 + x_3^2 = 0$, from which it appears that the point $1 : 0 : 0 : 0$ is the only real point at infinity, as we have already seen. The nature of the locus at infinity will appear later.

59. The circle. If we take the usual definition of a circle, the equation of a circle with center y_i and radius r can be written from (1), § 58, as

$$y_4 x_1 - 2 y_2 x_2 - 2 y_3 x_3 + (y_1 - r^2 y_4) x_4 = 0. \tag{1}$$

This is of the type

$$a_1 x_1 + a_2 x_2 + a_3 x_3 + a_4 x_4 = 0, \tag{2}$$

and the relations between the coefficients a_i and the center and radius of the circle are readily found. For we have by direct comparison of (1) and (2)

$$\rho a_1 = y_4, \quad \rho a_2 = -2 y_2, \quad \rho a_3 = -2 y_3, \quad \rho a_4 = y_1 - r^2 y_4.$$

From these and the fundamental relation $y_2^2 + y_3^2 - y_1 y_4 = 0$ we easily compute the following values:

$$\begin{aligned}
\rho y_1 &= a_2^2 + a_3^2, \\
\rho y_2 &= -2 a_1 a_2, \\
\rho y_3 &= -2 a_1 a_3, \\
\rho y_4 &= 4 a_1^2, \\
r^2 &= \frac{a_2^2 + a_3^2 - 4 a_1 a_4}{4 a_1^2},
\end{aligned} \tag{3}$$

---

* A homogeneous polynomial is called a *form*. The general quadratic form in n variables is

$$\sum_1^n a_{ik} x_i x_k, \tag{1}$$

and the bilinear form

$$\sum_1^n a_{ik} x_i y_k$$

is called the polar form of (1). If by a linear transformation of the variables x_i the form (1) is transformed into

$$\sum A_{ik} x_i' x_k',$$

its polar is transformed into

$$\sum A_{ik} x_i' y_k'.$$

which give the coördinates of the center and the radius of the circle in terms of the coefficients a_i of equation (2).

These results, obtained primarily for real circles, are now generalized *by definition* as follows:

Every linear equation of the form (2) *represents a circle, the center and the radius of which are given by equations* (3).

We may classify circles by means of the expression for the radius. For that purpose let us denote the numerator of r^2 in (3) by $\eta(a)$; that is,
$$\eta(a) = a_2^2 + a_3^2 - 4\,a_1 a_4. \tag{4}$$

We make, then, the following cases:

CASE I. $\eta(a) \neq 0$. *Nonspecial circles.*

Subcase 1. $a_1 \neq 0$. *Proper circles.* Equation (2) is reducible to (1) and represents the locus of a point at a constant distance from a fixed point. Neither center nor radius is necessarily real, but the center is not at infinity and the radius is finite. The circle does not contain the real point at infinity, since $1 : 0 : 0 : 0$ will not satisfy equation (2).

Subcase 2. $a_1 = 0$. *Ordinary straight lines.* The radius becomes infinite and the center is the real point at infinity. The equation may be written, by § 57, in the form
$$a_2 \overline{NP} + a_3 \overline{MP} + a_4 = 0, \qquad (a_2^2 + a_3^2 \neq 0)$$
which, as in Cartesian geometry, is a straight line. This line passes through the real point at infinity. In fact, the necessary and sufficient condition that equation (2) should be satisfied by the coördinates of the real point at infinity is that $a_1 = 0$. Hence *an ordinary straight line may be defined as a nonspecial circle which passes through the real point at infinity.*

CASE II. $\eta(a) = 0$. *Special circles.*

Since $a_2^2 + a_3^2 = 4\,a_1 a_4$, the coördinates of the center may be written
$$y_1 : y_2 : y_3 : y_4 = -2\,a_4 : a_2 : a_3 : -2\,a_1. \tag{5}$$

Subcase 1. $a_1 \neq 0$. *Point circles.* The radius is zero and the coördinates of the center are those of a point not at infinity. The center may be any finite point. It is obvious that if the center is real, it is the only real point on the circle, and hence the name "point circle." The point circles do not pass through the real point at infinity.

By (2), § 58, the equation of a point circle may be written
$$\omega(x, y) = 0,$$
where $\omega(y) = 0$. Comparing with (4), we see how the equation $\eta(a) = 0$ may be deduced from $\omega(y) = 0$.

Subcase 2. $a_1 = 0$. *Special straight lines.* The radius becomes indeterminate, and the center, given by (4), becomes $-2 a_4 : a_2 : a_3 = 0$, which is a point at infinity. The special straight lines pass through the real point at infinity. In fact, *a special straight line may be defined as a special circle which passes through the real point at infinity.*

We have seen that the locus of all points at infinity is $x_4 = 0$, which is the equation of a circle belonging to the case now being considered, and with its center at $1 : 0 : 0 : 0$. Hence we say:

The locus at infinity is a special straight line whose center is the real point at infinity.

EXERCISES

1. Consider the point circle $x_1 = 0$. Show that it is made up of two one-dimensional extents ("threads") expressed by the equations $x_1 : x_2 : x_3 : x_4 = 0 : 1 : \pm i : \lambda$, where λ is an arbitrary parameter. Show that these threads have the one point $0 : 0 : 0 : 1$ in common, but that neither can be expressed by a single equation in tetracyclical coördinates. Hence note the difference between this locus and that expressed by $x^2 + y^2 = 0$ in Cartesian coördinates.

2. As in Ex. 1, show that the special circle $x_4 = 0$ is composed of two threads having the real point at infinity in common.

3. Examine the special circles $x_2 + ix_3 = 0$ and $x_2 - ix_3 = 0$ and show that these two and the two in Exs. 1 and 2 are made up of different combinations of the same four threads.

4. Show that any special circle is made up as is the circle in Ex. 1.

60. Relation between tetracyclical and Cartesian coördinates.
If we introduce Cartesian coördinates, by which, in Fig. 45,
$$x : y : t = OM : MP : 1,$$
there exists for any real point of the plane the following relation between the special tetracyclical coördinates and the Cartesian coördinates:
$$\rho x_1 = x^2 + y^2,$$
$$\rho x_2 = xt,$$
$$\rho x_3 = yt,$$
$$\rho x_4 = t^2.$$

These equations, derived for real points of the plane at a finite distance from O, can now be used to define the relation between the imaginary and infinite points introduced into each system of coördinates.

There appear, then, exceptional points. In the 'first place, we notice that the tetracyclical coördinates take the unallowed values $0:0:0:0$ when $x^2 + y^2 = 0$, $t = 0$. That is, the circle points at infinity necessary in the Cartesian geometry have no place in the tetracyclical geometry. Furthermore, any point on the line at infinity $t = 0$, other than a circle point, corresponds to the real point at infinity $1:0:0:0$ in the tetracyclical coördinates.

If the tetracyclical coördinates are given, the Cartesian coördinates are obtained through the equations $xt : yt : t^2 = x_2 : x_3 : x_4$. These equations will determine a single point on the Cartesian plane unless $x_2 = x_3 = x_4 = 0$. In this case $t = 0$ and the ratio $x : y$ is indeterminate. That is, the real point at infinity in tetracyclical coördinates corresponds to the entire line at infinity in Cartesian coördinates. Any other point on the tetracyclical locus at infinity $x_4 = 0$ has coördinates of the form $x_1 : 1 : \pm i : 0$, and no Cartesian coördinates can be found corresponding to these values.

Hence, *in Cartesian coördinates we find certain points, the circle points at infinity, which do not exist in tetracyclical coördinates, and in tetracyclical coördinates we find certain points, the imaginary points at infinity, which do not exist in the Cartesian coördinates. We also find that the real point at infinity in tetracyclical coördinates corresponds to the entire line at infinity in Cartesian coördinates, and, conversely, that any point at infinity in Cartesian coördinates corresponds to the real point at infinity in tetracyclical coördinates.* With these exceptions the relation between the coördinates is one to one.

The exceptional cases bear out the statements in §§ 3 and 4 as to the artificial nature of the conventions as to imaginary points and points at infinity. Since the Cartesian coördinates are more common, there is some danger of thinking that the conventions there made are in some way essential. The discussion of this text shows, however, that the tetracyclical conventions may be made independently of the Cartesian ones, and the geometry thus deduced is equally as valid as the Cartesian. As long as either set of coördinates is used by itself, the difference in the conventions is unnoticeable. It is only when we wish to pass from one set of coördinates to the other that we need to consider this difference.

61. Orthogonal circles. Consider two proper circles with real centers C_a and C_b and real radii r_a and r_b, intersecting in a real point P. Then, if (r_a, r_b) is the angle between the radii C_aP and C_bP, and d is the length of the line C_aC_b, we have, from trigonometry,

$$\cos(r_a, r_b) = \frac{r_a^2 + r_b^2 - d^2}{2\, r_a r_b}.$$

But the angle between the circles is either equal or supplementary to the angle between their radii. Hence, if we call θ the angle between the circles we have

$$\cos\theta = \pm\, \frac{r_a^2 + r_b^2 - d^2}{2\, r_a r_b}.$$

If the equations of the two circles are

$$a_1x_1 + a_2x_2 + a_3x_3 + a_4x_4 = 0 \tag{1}$$

and $$b_1x_1 + b_2x_2 + b_3x_3 + b_4x_4 = 0 \tag{2}$$

respectively, the formula for the angle may be reduced by (3), § 59, and (4), § 59, to the form

$$\cos\theta = \pm\, \frac{-\,2\,a_4b_1 + a_2b_2 + a_3b_3 - 2\,a_1b_4}{\sqrt{a_2^2 + a_3^2 - 4\,a_1a_4}\,\sqrt{b_2^2 + b_3^2 - 4\,b_1b_4}},$$

or, more compactly,

$$\cos\theta = \pm\, \frac{\eta(a,\, b)}{\sqrt{\eta(a)}\,\sqrt{\eta(b)}}, \tag{3}$$

where $\eta(a,\, b)$ is the polar of $\eta(a)$.

This formula, which has been obtained for two real proper circles intersecting in a real point, is now taken as the *definition* of the angle between any two circles of any types whose equations are given by (1) and (2). We leave it for the reader to show that if one or both of the circles is a real straight line, the definition agrees with the usual definition.

The condition that two circles should be orthogonal is then

$$\eta(a,\, b) = 0. \tag{4}$$

If the circle (1) is a special circle, the coördinates of its center have been shown to be $-\,2\,a_4 : a_2 : a_3 : -\,2\,a_1$, and equation (4) is the condition that this center should lie on (2). Hence *a special circle, whether a point circle or a special straight line, is orthogonal to another circle when and only when the center of the special circle lies on the other circle.*

We might equally well say that a special circle makes any angle with a circle on which its center lies, since in such a case $\cos \theta$ in (3) is indeterminate.

It is possible in an infinity of ways to find four circles which are mutually orthogonal. For if

$$\sum a_i x_i = 0 \qquad (5)$$

is any circle, the circle

$$\sum b_i x_i = 0 \qquad (6)$$

may be found in ∞^2 ways orthogonal to (5), since the ratios b_i have to satisfy only one linear equation of the form (4). Circles (5) and (6) being fixed, the circle

$$\sum c_i x_i = 0 \qquad (7)$$

may be found in an infinite number of ways orthogonal to (5) and (6), since the ratios c_i have to satisfy only two linear equations. Finally, the circle

$$\sum e_i x_i = 0$$

may be found orthogonal to (5), (6), and (7) by solving three linear equations for e_i.

It is geometrically evident that at least one of these circles is imaginary.

EXERCISES

1. Prove, as stated in the text, that formula (3) gives the ordinary angle in the cases in which one or both of the circles is a straight line.

2. Prove that a special circle is orthogonal to itself.

3. What is the angle between a special circle and another circle not through its center?

4. Prove that the circles $x_1 - x_4 = 0$, $x_2 = 0$, $x_3 = 0$ are mutually orthogonal and find a fourth circle orthogonal to them.

5. Prove that $x_1 = 0$, $x_2 = 0$, $x_3 = 0$ are mutually orthogonal. Can a fourth circle be found orthogonal to them? Explain.

6. Find all circles orthogonal to the circle at infinity $x_4 = 0$.

7. Find the equations of all circles orthogonal to the point circle $x_1 = 0$. How do they lie in the plane ?

8. Find the equations of all circles orthogonal to the real proper circle $x_1 - x_4 = 0$.

9. Show that all circles whose coefficients a_i satisfy a linear equation

$$c_1 a_1 + c_2 a_2 + c_3 a_3 + c_4 a_4 = 0$$

are in general orthogonal to a fixed circle and find that circle.

62. Pencils of circles. Consider two circles

$$a_1 x_1 + a_2 x_2 + a_3 x_3 + a_4 x_4 = 0, \tag{1}$$

$$b_1 x_1 + b_2 x_2 + b_3 x_3 + b_4 x_4 = 0. \tag{2}$$

With reference to them we shall prove first the following theorem :

I. Any two circles intersect in two and only two points. These points may be coincident, in which case the circles are said to be tangent.

To prove this we note that if equations (1) and (2) are independent, at least one of the determinants, $a_i b_j - a_j b_i$, must be different from zero. Hence we can solve for one pair of variables, x_i and x_j, in terms of the other two. For example, we may find from (1) and (2) $x_1 = c_1 x_3 + c_2 x_4$, $x_2 = c_3 x_3 + c_4 x_4$. If these values are substituted in the fundamental relation $\omega(x) = 0$, there results a quadratic equation in x_3 and x_4. This determines two values of $x_3 : x_4$, and from each of these the ratios $x_1 : x_2$ are determined. This proves the theorem.

It is evident that the circle points at infinity which are introduced as a convenient fiction in Cartesian geometry do not appear here. In Cartesian geometry it is found that there are always two sets of coördinates which satisfy the equation of any circle, and we are consequently led to declare that all circles pass through the same two imaginary points at infinity. By the use of tetracyclical coördinates there are no two points at infinity common to all circles. In fact the circle (1) meets the locus at infinity $x_4 = 0$ in the two points $- a_2 \mp a_3 i : a_1 : \pm i a_1 : 0$, which are not the same for all circles.

Theorem I holds of course for the case in which the circles are straight lines, one of the points of intersection being always the real point at infinity. Two straight lines which are tangent at the real point at infinity are parallel lines in the Cartesian geometry.

Consider now the equation

$$\sum_1^4 (a_i + \lambda b_i) x_i = 0, \tag{3}$$

where λ is an arbitrary parameter. For any value of λ (3) defines a circle which passes through the points common to (1) and (2) and intersects (1) and (2) in no other point. The totality of the circles corresponding to all values of λ forms a *pencil of circles.*

If (1) and (2) are real circles, the pencil (3) may be of one of the following types:

(1) proper circles intersecting in the same two real points;
(2) proper circles intersecting in the same two imaginary points;
(3) proper circles tangent in the same point;
(4) proper concentric circles;
(5) a pencil of intersecting straight lines;
(6) a pencil of parallel straight lines.

II. In any pencil of circles there is one and only one straight line, unless the pencil consists entirely of straight lines.

The condition that (3) should represent a straight line is

$$a_1 + \lambda b_1 = 0,$$

which determines one and only one value of λ unless both a_1 and b_1 are zero. In the latter case all circles defined by (3) are straight lines. This proves the theorem.

The straight line of the pencil is called the *radical axis* of any two circles of the pencil. Its equation is

$$(a_2 b_1 - a_1 b_2)x_2 + (a_3 b_1 - a_1 b_3)x_3 + (a_4 b_1 - a_1 b_4)x_4 = 0.$$

This is a special line when

$$(a_2 b_1 - a_1 b_2)^2 + (a_3 b_1 - a_1 b_3)^2 = 0.$$

If the circles (1) and (2) are real and proper, the last equation can be satisfied only when

$$\frac{b_1}{a_1} = \frac{b_2}{a_2} = \frac{b_3}{a_3}$$

and the equations (1), (2), and (3) represent concentric circles, and the radical axis is the line at infinity $x_4 = 0$.

In all other cases the radical axis of two real circles is a real straight line.

III. *In any pencil of circles there are two and only two (distinct or imaginary) special circles, unless the pencil consists entirely of special circles.*

By § 59 the condition that (3) should be a special circle is

$$\eta(a + \lambda b) = 0,$$

or $$\eta(a) + 2\lambda\eta(a, b) + \lambda^2\eta(b) = 0.$$

This equation determines two distinct or equal values of λ unless it is identically satisfied. Hence the theorem is proved.

If the pencil is defined by two real proper circles, the special circles are point circles, since by II there is only one straight line in the pencil and that is real and nonspecial. It is not difficult to show that if the circles of the pencil intersect in real points, the special circles have imaginary centers; if the circles of the pencil intersect in imaginary points, the special circles have real centers; and if the circles of the pencil are tangent, the centers of the special circles coincide at the point of tangency.

IV. *A circle orthogonal to two circles of a pencil is orthogonal to all circles of the pencil.*

Let $\sum c_i x_i = 0$ be orthogonal to (1) and (2). Then

$$\eta(c, a) = 0, \quad \eta(c, b) = 0;$$

whence $$\eta(c, a + \lambda b) = \eta(c, a) + \lambda\eta(c, b) = 0$$

for all values of λ. This proves the theorem.

It follows from this and § 61 that a circle orthogonal to all circles of a pencil passes through the centers of the special circles of the pencil, and, conversely, a circle through the centers of the special circles is orthogonal to all circles of the pencil. If the pencil has only one special circle, the orthogonal circles can be determined as circles which pass through the center of the special circle and are orthogonal to one other circle of the pencil, say the radical axis.

These considerations lead to the following theorem:

V. *For any pencil of circles there exists another pencil such that all circles of either pencil are orthogonal to all circles of the other, and any circle which is orthogonal to all circles of one pencil belongs to the other. The points common to the circles of one pencil are the centers of the special circles of the other.*

Fig. 47 shows such mutually orthogonal pencils.

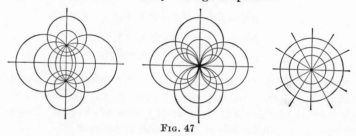

FIG. 47

EXERCISES

1. Show that two real circles intersect in two real distinct points, are tangent, or intersect in two conjugate imaginary points according as $[\eta(a, b)]^2 - \eta(a)\eta(b) \lesseqgtr 0$.

2. Show that the point circles in a pencil of real circles have real and distinct, conjugate imaginary, or coincident centers, according as the circles of the pencil intersect in conjugate imaginary, real and distinct, or coincident points. In the last case show that the centers of the point circles coincide with the point of tangency of the circles of the pencil.

3. Show that circles which intersect in the same two points at infinity are concentric.

4. Prove that the radical axis of a pencil of circles passes through the centers of the circles of the orthogonal pencil.

5. Prove that the radical axes of three circles not belonging to the same pencil meet in a point.

6. Take $\sum a_i x_i = 0$, $\sum b_i x_i = 0$, $\sum c_i x_i = 0$, any three circles not belonging to the same pencil, and show that $\sum (a_i + \lambda b_i + \mu c_i) x_i = 0$ defines a two-dimensional extent of circles (a *circle complex*) consisting of circles orthogonal to a fixed circle. Discuss the number and position of the point circles, the straight lines, and the special lines of a complex.

7. Show that the totality of straight lines form a complex. To what circle are they orthogonal?

8. Show that circles common to two complexes form a pencil.

63. The general tetracyclical coördinates. Let us take as circles of reference any four circles not intersecting in the same point and the equations of which, in the special tetracyclical coördinates thus far used, are

$$\sum \alpha_i x_i = 0, \quad \sum \beta_i x_i = 0, \quad \sum \gamma_i x_i = 0, \quad \sum \delta_i x_i = 0,$$

and let us place

$$\begin{aligned}
\rho X_1 &= \alpha_1 x_1 + \alpha_2 x_2 + \alpha_3 x_3 + \alpha_4 x_4, \\
\rho X_2 &= \beta_1 x_1 + \beta_2 x_2 + \beta_3 x_3 + \beta_4 x_4, \\
\rho X_3 &= \gamma_1 x_1 + \gamma_2 x_2 + \gamma_3 x_3 + \gamma_4 x_4, \\
\rho X_4 &= \delta_1 x_1 + \delta_2 x_2 + \delta_3 x_3 + \delta_4 x_4.
\end{aligned} \tag{1}$$

Since the four circles do not meet in a point their equations cannot be satisfied by the same values of x_i, and therefore the determinant of the coefficients in (1) does not vanish. Therefore the equations can be solved for x_i with the result

$$\begin{aligned}
\sigma x_1 &= A_1 X_1 + B_1 X_2 + \Gamma_1 X_3 + \Delta_1 X_4, \\
\sigma x_2 &= A_2 X_1 + B_2 X_2 + \Gamma_2 X_3 + \Delta_2 X_4, \\
\sigma x_3 &= A_3 X_1 + B_3 X_2 + \Gamma_3 X_3 + \Delta_3 X_4, \\
\sigma x_4 &= A_4 X_1 + B_4 X_2 + \Gamma_4 X_3 + \Delta_4 X_4,
\end{aligned} \tag{2}$$

where A_i is the cofactor of α_i in the determinant of the coefficients of (1), B_i the cofactor of β_i, etc.

The relation between the ratios $x_1 : x_2 : x_3 : x_4$ and $X_1 : X_2 : X_3 : X_4$ is therefore one to one, and the latter ratios may be taken as the coördinates of any point. These are the most general tetracyclical coördinates.

A geometric meaning may be given to these coördinates as follows:

If the circle with the Cartesian equation

$$a(x^2 + y^2) + bx + cy + d = 0$$

is a real proper circle, and the point $P(x, y)$ is a real point outside of it, then the expression

$$a(x^2 + y^2) + bx + cy + d$$

is proportional to the *power* of P with respect to the circle; that is, to the length of the square of the tangent from P to the circle. If

P is a real point inside the circle, the power may be defined as the product of the lengths of the segments of any chord through P. Also, if

$$bx + cy + d = 0$$

is a real straight line, the expression

$$bx + cy + d$$

is proportional to the length of the perpendicular from any real point to the line.

By virtue of § 60 these relations hold for a linear equation in tetracyclical coördinates. Of course if the points, circles, or lines involved are imaginary, the phraseology is largely a matter of definition. We may say, then:

The most general tetracyclical coördinates of a point consist of the ratios of four quantities each of which is equal to a constant times the power of the point with reference to a circle of reference, or, in case the circle of reference is a straight line, to a constant times the length of the perpendicular from the point to the line.[*]

By means of (1) the fundamental relation $\omega(x) = 0$ goes over into the new fundamental relation

$$\Omega(x) = \sum' a_{ik} X_i X_k = 0, \tag{3}$$

and the polar equation $\omega(x, y) = 0$ becomes

$$\Omega(X, Y) = \sum' a_{ik} X_i Y_k = 0, \tag{4}$$

where the determinant $|a_{ik}|$ does not vanish.

The real point at infinity has now the coördinates $X_1 : X_2 : X_3 : X_4 = \alpha_1 : \beta_1 : \gamma_1 : \delta_1$, and hence by a proper choice of the circles of reference may be given any desired coördinates. The locus at infinity has the equation

$$A_4 X_1 + B_4 X_2 + \Gamma_4 X_3 + \Delta_4 X_4 = 0.$$

[*] Some authors prefer to define the coördinate as the quotient of the power of the point divided by the radius, since this quotient goes over into twice the length of the perpendicular from the point to a straight line when the radius of the circle becomes infinite. This definition fails if the circle of reference is a point circle when the corresponding coördinate is the square of the distance of the point from the center of the circle. Since the constant which may multiply each coördinate is arbitrary, we prefer the definition in the text.

A circle with the equation

$$a_1x_1 + a_2x_2 + a_3x_3 + a_4x_4 = 0$$

has in the new coördinates the equation

$$A_1X_1 + A_2X_2 + A_3X_3 + A_4X_4 = 0,$$

where
$$\begin{aligned}
\rho a_1 &= \alpha_1 A_1 + \beta_1 A_2 + \gamma_1 A_3 + \delta_1 A_4, \\
\rho a_2 &= \alpha_2 A_1 + \beta_2 A_2 + \gamma_2 A_3 + \delta_2 A_4, \\
\rho a_3 &= \alpha_3 A_1 + \beta_3 A_2 + \gamma_3 A_3 + \delta_3 A_4, \\
\rho a_4 &= \alpha_4 A_1 + \beta_4 A_2 + \gamma_4 A_3 + \delta_4 A_4.
\end{aligned} \tag{5}$$

By virtue of these relations the condition for a special circle $\eta(a) = 0$ becomes a new relation

$$\mathrm{H}(A) = \sum b_{ik} \mathrm{A}_i \mathrm{A}_k = 0, \tag{6}$$

and the condition $\eta(a, b) = 0$ for orthogonal circles becomes

$$\mathrm{H}(A, B) = \sum b_{ik} \mathrm{A}_i \mathrm{B}_k = 0. \tag{7}$$

The form $\mathrm{H}(A)$ may be computed directly from $\Omega(X)$ as follows: By formulas (4) and (2), § 58, the equation of a point circle with the center Y_i is

$$\Omega(X, Y) = 0.$$

Hence, if
$$A_1X_1 + A_2X_2 + A_3X_3 + A_4X_4 = 0$$

is a point circle, we must have

$$\rho A_i = a_{i1} Y_1 + a_{i2} Y_2 + a_{i3} Y_3 + a_{i4} Y_4. \tag{8}$$

These equations can be solved for Y_i since the determinant $|a_{ik}|$ does not vanish. But Y_i being the coördinates of a point must satisfy the fundamental relation (3). Substituting, we obtain a relation between the A's to be satisfied by any point circle. This can be nothing else than the condition

$$\mathrm{H}(A) = 0.$$

By virtue of (8) we have, accordingly,

$$\mathrm{H}(A) \equiv k\Omega(Y).$$

But (8) can be written
$$\sigma A_i = \frac{\partial \Omega}{\partial Y_i}.$$

Hence we have
$$\mathrm{H}\left(\frac{\partial \Omega}{\partial Y}\right) \equiv K\Omega(Y). \tag{9}$$

Also the form $\Omega(X)$ may be computed from the form $H(A)$ as follows: If A is a point circle, equation (7) expresses the condition that the center of A should lie on a circle B. But if X_i are the coördinates of the center of A, this condition is

$$B_1 X_1 + B_2 X_2 + B_3 X_3 + B_4 X_4 = 0.$$

Hence, by comparison with (7),

$$\rho X_i = b_{i1} A_1 + b_{i2} A_2 + b_{i3} A_3 + b_{i4} A_4. \tag{10}$$

Since A is a point circle its coefficients A_i satisfy (6). Therefore, if equations (10) are solved for A_i and the result substituted in (6), we have a relation satisfied by the coördinates of any point. This can only be

$$\Omega(X) = 0.$$

By virtue of (10) we have, accordingly,

$$\Omega(X) \equiv k H(A).$$

But (10) can be written $\quad \sigma X_i = \dfrac{\partial H}{\partial A_i}.$

Hence we have $\qquad \Omega\left(\dfrac{\partial H}{\partial A}\right) \equiv K H(A). \tag{11}$

64. Orthogonal coördinates. Particular interest attaches to the case in which the four circles of reference are mutually orthogonal. If the circle $X_i = 0$ is orthogonal to the circle $X_k = 0$, we have, from (7), § 63, $b_{ik} = 0$. Therefore, for an orthogonal system of coördinates we have

$$H(A) = k_1 A_1^2 + k_2 A_2^2 + k_3 A_3^2 + k_4 A_4^2.$$

Equations (10), § 63, give

$$\rho X_i = k_i A_i,$$

whence the fundamental relation for the point coördinates is

$$\Omega(X) = \frac{X_1^2}{k_1^2} + \frac{X_2^2}{k_2^2} + \frac{X_3^2}{k_3^2} + \frac{X_4^2}{k_4^2} = 0.$$

Without changing the coördinate circles it is obviously possible to change the coefficients in (1), § 63, so that $k_i = 1$. Then we have

$$\Omega(X) = X_1^2 + X_2^2 + X_3^2 + X_4^2,$$
$$H(A) = A_1^2 + A_2^2 + A_3^2 + A_4^2.$$

A special case is obtained by placing

$$\rho X_1 = x_1 - x_4,$$
$$\rho X_2 = 2\, x_2,$$
$$\rho X_3 = 2\, x_3,$$
$$\rho X_4 = -i\,(x_1 + x_4),$$

where x_i are the special coördinates of § 57. The four circles of reference are a real circle with center at O and radius 1, two perpendicular straight lines through O, and an imaginary circle with center at O and radius i.

65. The linear transformation. Let x_i be any set (special or general) of tetracyclical coördinates where $\omega(x) = 0$ is the fundamental relation, and consider the transformation defined by the equations

$$
\begin{aligned}
\rho x_1' &= \alpha_{11}x_1 + \alpha_{12}x_2 + \alpha_{13}x_3 + \alpha_{14}x_4, \\
\rho x_2' &= \alpha_{21}x_1 + \alpha_{22}x_2 + \alpha_{23}x_3 + \alpha_{24}x_4, \\
\rho x_3' &= \alpha_{31}x_1 + \alpha_{32}x_2 + \alpha_{33}x_3 + \alpha_{34}x_4, \\
\rho x_4' &= \alpha_{41}x_1 + \alpha_{42}x_2 + \alpha_{43}x_3 + \alpha_{44}x_4,
\end{aligned}
\tag{1}
$$

where the determinant of the coefficients $|\alpha_{ik}|$ does not vanish and where x_i' satisfies the same fundamental relation as x_i.

By means of (1) any point x_i is transformed into a point x_i', and since the equations can be solved for x_i, the relation between a point and its transformed point is one to one.

By means of (1), also, any circle

$$a_1 x_1 + a_2 x_2 + a_3 x_3 + a_4 x_4 = 0$$

is transformed into the circle

$$a_1' x_1' + a_2' x_2' + a_3' x_3' + a_4' x_4' = 0,$$

where $$\rho a_i' = A_{i1} a_1 + A_{i2} a_2 + A_{i3} a_3 + A_{i4} a_4.$$

Now, if y_i is a fixed point, x_i a variable point, and y_i' and x_i' the transformed points respectively, the equation

$$\omega(x,\, y) = 0$$

is transformed into the equation

$$\omega(x',\, y') = 0,$$

since the equation $\omega(x) = 0$ is transformed into $\omega(x') = 0$.

That is, *by the transformation* (1) *special circles are transformed into special circles, the center of each special circle being transformed into the center of the transformed circle.*

It follows from the above that *nonspecial circles are transformed into nonspecial circles*, for if a nonspecial circle were transformed into a special circle, the inverse transformation would transform a special circle into a nonspecial circle, and since the inverse transformation is also of the form (1), this is impossible.

We may accordingly infer that by the transformation (1) the equation $\eta(a) = 0$ is transformed into itself.

We may distinguish between two main classes of transformations of the form (1) according as the real point at infinity is invariant or not. The truth of the following theorem is evident:

If a linear transformation leaves the real point at infinity invariant, every straight line is transformed into a straight line and every proper circle into a proper circle. If a linear transformation transforms the real point at infinity into a point O and transforms a point O' into the real point at infinity, any straight line is transformed into a circle through O, and any circle through O' is transformed into a straight line.

Since, as we have seen, the equation $\eta(a) = 0$ is transformed into itself, we may write $\eta(a') = k\eta(a)$, the value of k depending on the factor ρ in (1). With the same factor we have $\eta(b') = k\eta(b)$ and $\eta(a', b') = k\eta(a, b)$. Hence by (3), § 61, the angle between two circles is equal to the angle between the two transformed circles. *The linear transformation is therefore conformal.*

66. The metrical transformation. We shall prove first that *any transformation of the metrical group can be expressed as a linear transformation of tetracyclical coördinates.*

We have seen in § 45 that a transformation of the metrical group is a linear transformation of the Cartesian coördinates x and y together with the condition $(x'^2 + y'^2) = k^2(x^2 + y^2)$. It follows from this that the transformation can be expressed as a linear transformation of the special coördinates of § 57. But the general tetracyclical coördinates are linear combinations of the special ones. Hence the theorem is proved.

Since a metrical transformation transforms straight lines into straight lines, it must leave the real point at infinity invariant.

Conversely, *any linear transformation of tetracyclical coördinates which leaves the real point at infinity invariant is a transformation of the metrical group.* This may be shown as follows:

If the real point at infinity is invariant, the locus at infinity is transformed into itself, since it is a special circle with its center at the real point at infinity. Therefore any linear transformation of general tetracyclical coördinates which leaves the real point at infinity invariant is equivalent to a transformation of the special coördinates of § 57, which leaves the point $1 : 0 : 0 : 0$ invariant and transforms the locus $x_4 = 0$ into itself; that is, to a transformation of the form

$$
\begin{aligned}
\rho x_1' &= \alpha_{11}x_1 + \alpha_{12}x_2 + \alpha_{13}x_3 + \alpha_{14}x_4, \\
\rho x_2' &= \qquad\quad \alpha_{22}x_2 + \alpha_{23}x_3 + \alpha_{24}x_4, \\
\rho x_3' &= \qquad\quad \alpha_{32}x_2 + \alpha_{33}x_3 + \alpha_{34}x_4, \\
\rho x_4' &= \qquad\qquad\qquad\qquad\qquad x_4.
\end{aligned}
\tag{1}
$$

Since $\qquad x_2'^2 + x_3'^2 - x_1'x_4' = k^2(x_2^2 + x_3^2 - x_1x_4),$ (2)

we have, for the coefficients, the conditions

$$
\begin{aligned}
\alpha_{22}^2 + \alpha_{32}^2 &= \alpha_{23}^2 + \alpha_{33}^2 = \alpha_{11} = \frac{k^2}{\rho^2}, \\
\alpha_{22}\alpha_{23} + \alpha_{32}\alpha_{33} &= 0, \\
\alpha_{12} - 2(\alpha_{22}\alpha_{24} + \alpha_{32}\alpha_{34}) &= 0, \\
\alpha_{13} - 2(\alpha_{23}\alpha_{24} + \alpha_{33}\alpha_{34}) &= 0.
\end{aligned}
\tag{3}
$$

Now the last three equations of (1) are equivalent to the equations in Cartesian coördinates

$$
\begin{aligned}
x' &= \alpha_{22}x + \alpha_{23}y + \alpha_{24}, \\
y' &= \alpha_{32}x + \alpha_{33}y + \alpha_{34},
\end{aligned}
$$

and the conditions imposed on the coefficients are exactly those necessary to make this a metrical transformation. The first equation in (1) is a consequence of the last three equations in (1) and the condition (2). In fact, the coefficients α_{22}, α_{23}, α_{32}, and α_{33} may first be determined to satisfy equations (3), the coefficients α_{24} and α_{34} may be assumed arbitrarily, and the coefficients α_{11}, α_{12}, α_{13}, and α_{14} are then determined by (3). This proves the theorem.

67. Inversion. Two points P and P' are *inverse* with respect to a nonspecial circle C if every circle through P and P' is orthogonal to C. From this it follows that if C is a straight line two inverse points are symmetrical with respect to that line ; that is, the straight line PP' is perpendicular to C and bisected by it. By a limit process it is natural to define the inverse of a point on the straight line C as the point itself.

If C is a proper circle with radius r and center A (Fig. 48), the inverse of A is the real point at infinity, since the circles which pass through A and the real point at infinity are straight lines perpendicular to C. If P is not at A nor on C, the straight line PP' must pass through A, since that line is a circle through P and P' which by definition must be orthogonal to C. Take now the point M midway between P and P' so that

$$AM = \tfrac{1}{2}(AP + AP'),$$

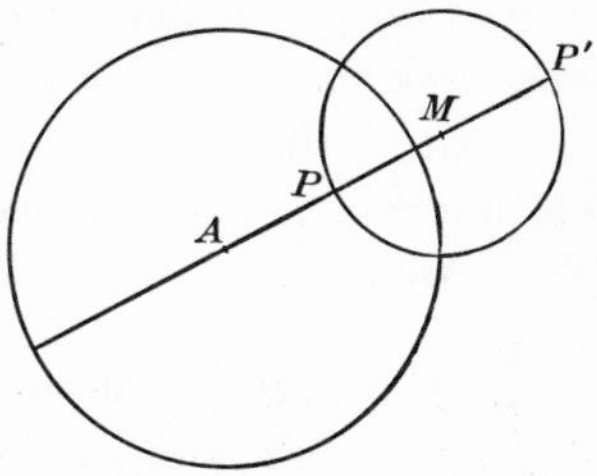

and with M as a center construct a

Fig. 48

circle through P and P'. If R is the radius of this circle,

$$R = \tfrac{1}{2}(AP' - AP).$$

By squaring the last two equations and subtracting one from the other, we have

$$\overline{AM}^2 - \overline{R}^2 = AP \cdot AP'.$$

But the condition for orthogonal circles gives

$$R^2 + r^2 - \overline{AM}^2 = 0.$$

Hence we have as the condition satisfied by two inverse points with respect to a circle with radius r and center A

$$AP \cdot AP' = r^2. \tag{1}$$

Conversely, if P and P' are two points so placed that the line PP' passes through A and the condition (1) is satisfied, the line PP' and the circle described on PP' as a diameter are easily proved to be orthogonal to C. Then any circle through P and P' is orthogonal to C by theorem IV, § 62. Hence P and P' are inverse points.

The condition (1) shows that if one of the points P and P' is inside of the circle, the other is outside of it. The condition holds also for the point A, since if $AP = 0$, $AP' = \infty$. By a natural extension of the definition of inverse points, condition (1) can also be taken to hold for a point on the circle C, so that we may say that any point on the circle C is its own inverse.

It is to be noticed that inverse points as here defined are also inverse in the sense of § 53 if the circle C is a proper circle, but the definition given in this section is wider than that in § 53; since it holds when the circle becomes a straight line.

An *inversion* with respect to a nonspecial circle C is defined as a point transformation by which each point of the plane is transformed into its inverse point with respect to that circle. We shall proceed to prove that *any inversion can be represented by a linear transformation of tetracyclical coördinates.* It is first of all to be noticed that by an inversion each point of the circle C is left unchanged by the inversion. This condition is met by the transformation

$$\rho x_i' = \lambda x_i + a_i \sum c_k x_k, \tag{2}$$

where $\sum c_k x_k = 0$ is the equation of C. Now let $\sum b_i x_i = 0$ be any circle through x_i and its transformed point x_i'. Since $\sum b_i x_i = 0$ and $\sum b_i x_i' = 0$, we have, from (2),

$$a_1 b_1 + a_2 b_2 + a_3 b_3 + a_4 b_4 = 0. \tag{3}$$

If $\sum b_i x_i = 0$ is orthogonal to C, we have

$$\eta(b, c) = \frac{1}{2}\left[b_1 \frac{\partial \eta}{\partial c_1} + b_2 \frac{\partial \eta}{\partial c_2} + b_3 \frac{\partial \eta}{\partial c_3} + b_4 \frac{\partial \eta}{\partial c_4} \right] = 0, \tag{4}$$

and therefore if (4) is satisfied by all values of b_i which satisfy (3), we may place

$$a_i = \frac{\partial \eta}{\partial c_i}.$$

It remains to determine λ. For that purpose we use the condition that $\omega(x) = 0$ and $\omega(x') = 0$, and for convenience writing A in place of the symbol $\sum c_k x_k$, we have

$$\omega(\lambda x + aA) = 2\lambda A \omega(x, a) + A^2 \omega(a) = 0. \tag{5}$$

But $\omega(a) = \omega\left(\frac{\partial \eta}{\partial c}\right)$ and, by (11), § 63,

$$\omega\left(\frac{\partial \eta}{\partial c}\right) = k\eta(c) = \frac{1}{2} k\left[c_1 \frac{\partial \eta}{\partial c_1} + c_2 \frac{\partial \eta}{\partial c_2} + c_3 \frac{\partial \eta}{\partial c_3} + c_4 \frac{\partial \eta}{\partial c_4} \right].$$

Hence

$$\omega(a) = \tfrac{1}{2} k\left[a_1 c_1 + a_2 c_2 + a_3 c_3 + a_4 c_4 \right],$$

and since

$$\omega(a) = \frac{1}{2} \sum a_i \frac{\partial \omega}{\partial a_i},$$

we have

$$\frac{\partial \omega}{\partial a_i} = k c_i.$$

Therefore $\quad \omega(x, a) = \dfrac{1}{2} \sum x_i \dfrac{\partial \omega}{\partial a_i} = \dfrac{k}{2} \sum c_i x_i = \dfrac{k}{2} A,$

and, from (5), $\qquad \lambda = -\dfrac{1}{k}\, \omega(a) = -\,\eta(c).$

We have consequently built up the transformation

$$\rho x_i' = x_i \eta(c) - \dfrac{\partial \eta}{\partial c_i} \sum c_k x_k, \tag{6}$$

which is an inverse transformation, since it transforms any point x_i into a point x_i' such that any circle through x_i and x_i' is orthogonal to C. The theorem is therefore proved. It is to be noticed that the transformation is completely determined when the circle C is known.

68. The linear group. We are now prepared to prove the following proposition:

Any linear transformation by which the real point at infinity is invariant or is transformed into a point not at infinity is the product of an inversion and a metrical transformation.

To prove this let T be a transformation of the form

$$\rho x_i' = \alpha_{i1} x_1 + \alpha_{i2} x_2 + \alpha_{i3} x_3 + \alpha_{i4} x_4,$$

by means of which the relation $\omega(x) = 0$ is transformed into itself.

If the real point at infinity is invariant, the transformation is metrical (§ 66). If the real point at infinity is transformed into a finite point A, let A be taken as the center of a circle C with respect to which an inversion I is carried out. By I the point A goes into the real point at infinity. Hence the product IT leaves the point at infinity invariant and is therefore a metrical transformation. Call it M. Then $\qquad IT = M;$

whence $\qquad\qquad T = I^{-1}M = IM.$

We have written $I^{-1} = I$ because an inversion repeated gives the identical transformation, and hence an inversion is its own inverse.

The tetracyclical coördinates are adapted to the study of the properties of figures which are not altered by this group of linear transformations. In the geometry of these properties the straight line is not to be distinguished from a circle, since any point of the plane may be transformed into the real point at infinity, and thereby any circle may be transformed into a straight line and vice versa. Any pencil of circles may in this way be transformed into a pencil of straight lines and many properties of pencils of circles obtained from the more evident properties of pencils of straight lines.

The distinction between special and nonspecial circles is, however, fundamental, since a circle of one of these classes is transformed into a circle of the same class.

EXERCISES

1. Write formulas (6), § 67, for the special coördinates of § 57 and for the orthogonal coördinates of § 64.

2. From (6), § 67, obtain in the coördinates of § 57 the formulas for inversion on the circle of unit radius with its center at the origin, and check by changing to Cartesian coördinates.

3. Show from (6), § 67, that inversion on a fundamental circle of a system of orthogonal coördinates is expressed by changing the sign of the corresponding coördinate and leaving the other coördinates unchanged.

4. Prove that a plane figure is unchanged by four inversions on four orthogonal circles.

5. Show that three inversions on orthogonal circles have the same effect as an inversion on a fourth circle orthogonal to the three.

6. Prove that the product of two inversions is commutative when and only when they take place with reference to orthogonal circles.

7. Show that the product of two inversions on two straight lines is a rotation about the point of intersections of the two lines.

8. By Ex. 7 show that the product of two inversions on the circles C_1 and C_2 can be replaced by the product of the inversions on two circles C_1' and C_2' if C_1' and C_2' pass through an intersection of C_1 and C_2 and make the same angle with each other.

9. Consider the curve defined by the quadratic equation

$$\sum a_{ik}x_i x_k = 0.$$

Show that any circle or straight line intersects the curve in four points. If the coördinates are the special coördinates of § 57, classify the curve according as (1) it does not pass through the real point at infinity, (2) it passes once through the real point at infinity, (3) it passes twice through the real point at infinity. Obtain the Cartesian equation for each of the classes and note the relation of the curve to the circular points at infinity. Note that the above classification is unessential from the standpoint of the linear group of tetracyclical transformations.

69. Duals of tetracyclical coördinates. By anticipating a little of the discussion of space geometry, to be given later, we may obtain duals to the tetracyclical coördinates. The student to whom space geometry is unknown may postpone the reading of this section.

If we interpret the ratios $x_1 : x_2 : x_3 : x_4$ as quadriplanar point coördinates in space of three dimensions, then

$$\omega(x) = 0 \tag{1}$$

is a surface of second order, and the geometry on this surface is dualistic with the geometry in the plane obtained by the use of tetracyclical coördinates.

The linear equation $\sum a_i x_i = 0$ represents the plane section of the surface (1), and these sections are the duals of the circles in the plane. The point at infinity is a point on (1) not necessarily geometrically peculiar, and the straight lines in the tetracyclical plane are duals to the plane sections of (1) through this point.

More specifically let us consider the specialized coördinates of § 57 and place in space $x_1 : x_2 : x_3 : x_4 = z : x : y : t$, the usual homogeneous Cartesian coördinates. The fundamental equation is now the equation $x^2 + y^2 - zt = 0,$

which, in space, represents an elliptic paraboloid. We have, then, the following dualistic properties:

The tetracyclical plane	*The elliptic paraboloid*
The real point at infinity.	The point at infinity on OZ.
Any circle.	Any plane section.
Any proper circle.	An elliptic section made by a plane not parallel to OZ.
Any straight line.	A parabolic section made by a plane parallel to OZ.
A special circle.	A section made by a tangent plane.
A point circle.	A section made by a tangent plane not parallel to OZ.
The center of a point circle.	The point of tangency.
A special straight line.	A section made by a tangent plane parallel to OZ (a minimum plane).
The special line at infinity.	The section made by the plane at infinity.

Again, if we have tetracyclical coördinates for which the fundamental equation is
$$x_1^2 + x_2^2 + x_3^2 - x_4^2 = 0,$$

which can be obtained from the special orthogonal system given in § 64 by multiplying x_4 by i, the geometry obtained thereby is dualistic with the geometry on the surface of the sphere

$$x^2 + y^2 + z^2 = 1.$$

In this case the tetracyclical point at infinity is dualistic to the point N, where the sphere is cut by OZ. Circles on the tetracyclical plane are dualistic to circles on the sphere, the straight lines on the plane corresponding to circles through the point N on the sphere. This brings into clear light the absolute equivalence of a straight line and circle by the use of tetracyclical coördinates. In fact, the plane geometry on the tetracyclical plane is the stereographic projection of the spherical geometry.

To see this take the sphere whose equation is

$$x^2 + y^2 + z^2 = 1,$$

and let $N(0, 0, 1)$ be a fixed point on it and $P(\xi, \eta, \zeta)$ any point on it. The equation of the straight line NP is

$$\frac{x}{\xi} = \frac{y}{\eta} = \frac{z-1}{\zeta-1},$$

and this line intersects the plane $z = 0$ in a point Q with the coördinates

$$x = \frac{\xi}{1-\zeta}, \qquad y = \frac{\eta}{1-\zeta}.$$

From these equations and the equation $\xi^2 + \eta^2 + \zeta^2 = 1$, which expresses the fact that P is on the sphere, we may compute

$$\xi = \frac{2x}{x^2 + y^2 + 1}, \qquad \eta = \frac{2y}{x^2 + y^2 + 1}, \qquad \zeta = \frac{x^2 + y^2 - 1}{x^2 + y^2 + 1},$$

from which, by placing

$$\xi = \frac{x_2}{x_4}, \qquad \eta = \frac{x_3}{x_4}, \qquad \zeta = \frac{x_1}{x_4},$$

we have

$$\rho x_1 = x^2 + y^2 - 1,$$
$$\rho x_2 = 2x,$$
$$\rho x_3 = 2y,$$
$$\rho x_4 = x^2 + y^2 + 1.$$

Now, on the one hand, $x_1 : x_2 : x_3 : x_4$ are homogeneous Cartesian coördinates of a point on the sphere, and, on the other hand, they are tetracyclical coördinates of a point on the plane, being connected with the specialized coördinates of § 57 by the equations

$$\rho x_1 = x_1' - x_4', \quad \rho x_2 = 2\,x_3', \quad \rho x_3 = 2\,x_3', \quad \rho x_4 = x_4 + x_4',$$

where $x_1' : x_2' : x_3' : x_4'$ are the special coördinates.

From this relation we may read off the following dualistic properties:

Plane	Sphere
Any point of the plane.	Any point on the sphere.
The point at infinity.	The point N.
Any circle.	A circle (any plane section).
A straight line.	A circle through N.
A special circle.	A section made by a tangent plane.
A point circle.	A section made by a tangent plane not passing through N.
The center of a point circle.	The point of tangency of the tangent plane.
A special straight line.	A tangent plane passing through N.
The center of a special straight line.	A point on the plane $z = 1$ not coincident with N.
The special line at infinity.	The section made by the plane $z = 1$ (a tangent plane).
Parallel lines.	Circles tangent to each other at N.

CHAPTER X

A SPECIAL SYSTEM OF COÖRDINATES

70. The coördinate system. Each of the two coördinates x and y in a Cartesian system is of the type described in § 7 for the coördinate of a point on a line. An interesting example of a more general type of coördinates may be obtained by taking each of the coördinates in the manner described in § 8. We shall develop a little of the geometry obtained. The results will be of importance chiefly as showing that much of the ordinary conventions as to points at infinity and the ordinary classification of curves is dependent on the choice of the coördinate system. This fact has already come to light in the use of tetracyclical coördinates. The present chapter emphasizes the fact.

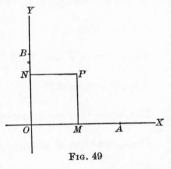

Fig. 49

To obtain our system of coördinates take two axes OX and OY (Fig. 49) intersecting in O at right angles, and on each axis take besides O another point of reference, A on OX and B on OY. Then, if P is any point of the plane, to obtain the coördinates of P draw through P a parallel to OY meeting OX in M, and a parallel to OX meeting OY in N. Let the coördinates of M be defined as in § 8 by

$$\lambda = \frac{k_1 \cdot OM}{k_2 \cdot AM} = \frac{x_1}{x_2},$$

and those of N by $\qquad \mu = \frac{k_3 \cdot ON}{k_4 \cdot BN} = \frac{y_1}{y_2}.$

The coördinates of P may then be taken as (λ, μ) or otherwise written as $(x_1 : x_2, y_1 : y_2)$. It is clear from § 8 that the ordinary Cartesian coördinates are a limiting case of these coördinates as A and B recede to infinity.

The coördinates being thus defined for real points the usual extension is made to imaginary points as defined by imaginary values of the coördinates. To consider the locus at infinity let P recede indefinitely from O. This may happen in three ways:

1. P may move on a straight line parallel to OX. Then the ratio $x_1 : x_2$ approaches the limiting ratio $k_1 : k_2$, and the ratio $y_1 : y_2$ has the constant value determined by any point on the straight line.

2. P may move on a straight line parallel to OY. Then $x_1 : x_2$ has the constant value determined by a point on that line, and $y_1 : y_2$ approaches the limiting value $k_3 : k_4$.

3. P may move on a straight line not parallel to OX or OY. Then M and N each approaches the point at infinity on its respective axis, and therefore the ratio $x_1 : x_2$ approaches $k_1 : k_2$ and the ratio $y_1 : y_2$ approaches $k_3 : k_4$.

These are the only points which we recognize as at infinity. In other words, if P recedes indefinitely from O it will not be considered as approaching a definite point at infinity unless the point on the curve approaches as a limit a point on a straight line. We have, then, the proposition

All points at infinity have coördinates which satisfy the equation

$$(k_2x_1 - k_1x_2)(k_4y_1 - k_3y_2) = 0. \tag{1}$$

To define the nature of the locus at infinity we note first that an equation of the type

$$a_1x_1 + a_2x_2 = 0, \tag{2}$$

if satisfied by real points, represents a straight line parallel to OX; and the equation

$$a_1y_1 + a_2y_2 = 0, \tag{3}$$

if satisfied by real points, represents a line parallel to OY. With the usual extension of theorems in analytic geometry we say that these equations always represent lines parallel respectively to OX and OY. We must therefore say that equation (1) represents two straight lines which have the point $(k_1 : k_2, k_3 : k_4)$ in common. We have, then, the proposition

The locus at infinity consists of two straight lines having in common a point called the double point at infinity.

The foregoing discussion shows that an important distinction between lines which are parallel ʻeither to OX or to OY and lines which are not so parallel. The straight lines which are parallel to OX or OY we shall call *special* lines and divide them into two families of parallel lines. Lines which are not special we shall call *ordinary* lines. We have already seen that a special line has a point at infinity which is peculiar to itself and that all ordinary lines have the same point at infinity; namely, the double point at infinity. We may accordingly state the following theorems, the proofs of which are obvious:

I. Two special lines of the same family have no point in common.

II. Two special lines of different families, or a special line and an ordinary line, have only one point in common which lies in the finite region of the plane.

III. Two nonparallel ordinary lines have always the double point at infinity and one other finite point in common.

IV. Two parallel ordinary lines have only the double point at infinity in common.

71. The straight line and the equilateral hyperbola. From the equations

$$\rho x_1 = k_1 \cdot OM,$$
$$\rho x_2 = k_2 \cdot AM,$$

which define the coördinates, we may obtain

$$\rho (k_2 x_1 - k_1 x_2) = k_1 k_2 \cdot OA = k_1 k_2 a;$$

whence

$$OM = \frac{a k_2 x_1}{k_2 x_1 - k_1 x_2}.$$

Similarly, $ON = \dfrac{b k_4 y_1}{k_4 y_1 - k_3 y_2}.$

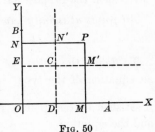

Fig. 50

Now let C (Fig. 50) be a fixed point with coördinates $(\alpha_1 : \alpha_2,\ \beta_1 : \beta_2)$, let CD be the line through C parallel to OY, and let CE be the line through C parallel to OX. Then, if the line PM meets CE in M' and the line PN meets CD in N', we have

$$CM' = OM - OD = \frac{a k_2 x_1}{k_2 x_1 - k_1 x_2} - \frac{a k_2 \alpha_1}{k_2 \alpha_1 - k_1 \alpha_2} = c_1 \frac{\alpha_2 x_1 - \alpha_1 x_2}{k_2 x_1 - k_1 x_2},$$

$$CN' = ON - OE = \frac{b k_4 y_1}{k_4 y_1 - k_3 y_2} - \frac{b k_4 \beta_1}{k_4 \beta_1 - k_3 \beta_2} = c_2 \frac{\beta_2 y_1 - \beta_1 y_2}{k_4 y_1 - k_3 y_2},$$

where c_1 and c_2 are constants dependent upon the position of C.

Consider now a locus defined by the condition

$$\frac{CM'}{CN'} = \text{const.}$$

This locus is obviously a straight line through C, and its equation is of the form

$$(\alpha_2 x_1 - \alpha_1 x_2)(k_4 y_1 - k_3 y_2) - a(\beta_2 y_1 - \beta_1 y_2)(k_2 x_1 - k_1 x_2) = 0, \quad (1)$$

where a is a constant.

Conversely, any equation of the form (1) in which a is not zero or infinity, and $\dfrac{\alpha_2}{\alpha_1} \neq \dfrac{k_2}{k_1}$, $\dfrac{\beta_2}{\beta_1} \neq \dfrac{k_4}{k_3}$, represents an ordinary straight line. For $(\alpha_2 : \alpha_1, \beta_2 : \beta_1)$ fixes a point C, and the equation is equivalent to $\dfrac{CM'}{CN'} = \text{const.}$ If a is zero, or infinity, or $\dfrac{\alpha_2}{\alpha_1} = \dfrac{k_2}{k_1}$, or $\dfrac{\beta_2}{\beta_1} = \dfrac{k_4}{k_3}$, the equation is factorable and represents two special lines, one at least of which is at infinity.

Again, consider the locus of P defined by the equation

$$CM' \cdot CN' = \text{const.}$$

This locus is an equilateral hyperbola with two special lines as asymptotes. We shall call it a *special* hyperbola. Its equation is

$$(\alpha_2 x_1 - \alpha_1 x_2)(\beta_2 y_1 - \beta_1 y_2) - a(k_2 x_1 - k_1 x_2)(k_4 y_1 - k_3 y_2) = 0. \quad (2)$$

Conversely, any equation of the form (2) in which a is not zero or infinity, and $\dfrac{\alpha_2}{\alpha_1} \neq \dfrac{k_2}{k_1}$, $\dfrac{\beta_2}{\beta_1} \neq \dfrac{k_4}{k_3}$, represents a special hyperbola. For $(\alpha_2 : \alpha_1, \beta_2 : \beta_1)$ fixes a point C, and the equation is equivalent to $CM' \cdot CN' = \text{const.}$ If a is zero, or infinity, or $\dfrac{\alpha_2}{\alpha_1} = \dfrac{k_2}{k_1}$, or $\dfrac{\beta_2}{\beta_1} = \dfrac{k_4}{k_3}$, equation (2) can be factored and represents two special lines.

It is to be noticed that equation (1) is satisfied by the coördinates of the double point at infinity and that equation (2) is not.

72. The bilinear equation. Equations (1) and (2) of § 71 are of the form

$$A x_1 y_1 + B x_1 y_2 + C x_2 y_1 + D x_2 y_2 = 0, \tag{1}$$

which is a bilinear equation in $x_1 : x_2$ and $y_1 : y_2$.

We shall now assume equation (1) and examine it in order to see if it is always of one of the types of § 71.

In the first place it is easy to show that the necessary and sufficient condition that (1) should factor into the form

$$(ax_1 + bx_2)(ey_1 + fy_2) = 0$$

is that $AD - BC = 0$. Furthermore, the necessary and sufficient condition that (1) should be satisfied by the coördinates of the double point at infinity is

$$Ak_1k_3 + Bk_1k_4 + Ck_2k_3 + Dk_2k_4 = 0.$$

We shall denote the left-hand member of this equation by K and make four cases according to the vanishing or nonvanishing of the two quantities K and $AD - BC$.

CASE I. $AD - BC \neq 0$, $K \neq 0$. The equation cannot be factored and the locus does not pass through the double point at infinity. Therefore it cannot be of the type (1), § 71. It will be of the form (2), § 71, however, if we can find α_1, α_2, β_1, β_2, and a to satisfy the equations

$$\alpha_2\beta_2 - ak_2k_4 = \rho A,$$
$$-\alpha_2\beta_1 + ak_2k_3 = \rho B,$$
$$-\alpha_1\beta_2 + ak_1k_4 = \rho C,$$
$$\alpha_1\beta_1 - ak_1k_3 = \rho D.$$

These equations can be solved by taking

$$\alpha_1 = Ck_3 + Dk_4,$$
$$\alpha_2 = -(Ak_3 + Bk_4),$$
$$\beta_1 = Bk_1 + Dk_2,$$
$$\beta_2 = -(Ak_1 + Ck_2),$$
$$a = BC - AD.$$

Hence equation (1) represents a special hyperbola.

CASE II. $AD - BC \neq 0$, $K = 0$. The equation cannot be factored and the locus passes through the double point at infinity. We shall compare the equation with (1), § 71. The locus of the equation under consideration intersects OX in the point $(D : -B, 0 : 1)$, which we will take as $(\alpha_1 : \alpha_2, \beta_1 : \beta_2)$. Using these values in (1), § 71, and comparing with (1) of this section, we have

$$-Bk_4 - ak_2 = \rho A,$$
$$Bk_3 = \rho B,$$
$$-Dk_4 + ak_1 = \rho C,$$
$$Dk_3 = \rho D,$$

whence $a = \dfrac{Bk_4 + Ak_3}{-k_2} = \dfrac{Dk_4 + Ck_3}{k_1}$, these values agreeing, since $K = 0$. Since $AD - BC \neq 0$, a cannot be zero.

Therefore the locus represents an ordinary straight line.

CASE III. $AD - BC = 0$, $K \neq 0$. The equation is factorable into the equations of two special lines, one of each family. Neither line can be at infinity since the locus does not pass through the double point at infinity.

CASE IV. $AD - BC = 0$, $K = 0$. The equation is factorable into the equations of two special lines, one of each family. At least one of these lines must be at infinity since the locus passes through the double point at infinity.

If we call a singular bilinear locus one defined by the equation (1) when $AD - BC = 0$, and a nonsingular bilinear locus one defined by (1) when $AD - BC \neq 0$, we have the following result:

A nonsingular bilinear locus is a special hyperbola or an ordinary straight line according as it does not or does pass through the double point at infinity.

A singular bilinear locus consists of two special lines, one of each family, where one or both of the lines may be a line at infinity.

73. The bilinear transformation. Consider the transformation

$$\rho x_1' = \alpha_1 x_1 + \beta_1 x_2,$$
$$\rho x_2' = \gamma_1 x_1 + \delta_1 x_2, \qquad (\alpha_1 \delta_1 - \beta_1 \gamma_1 \neq 0)$$
$$\sigma y_1' = \alpha_2 y_1 + \beta_2 y_2,$$
$$\sigma y_2' = \gamma_2 y_1 + \delta_2 y_2. \qquad (\alpha_2 \delta_2 - \beta_2 \gamma_2 \neq 0)$$

This defines a one-to-one relation between the points $(x_1 : x_2, \; y_1 : y_2)$ and the points $(x_1' : x_2', \; y_1' : y_2')$. The following properties are evident:

I. Any special line is transformed into a special line of the same family and any singular bilinear locus into a singular bilinear locus.

II. The lines at infinity may remain fixed or be transformed into any two special lines.

III. The point at infinity may be fixed or be transformed into any other point either at infinity or in the finite part of the plane.

IV. If the double point at infinity is fixed, ordinary straight lines are transformed into ordinary straight lines and special hyperbolas into special hyperbolas.

V. If the double point at infinity is transformed into a finite point A and the finite point B is transformed into the double point at infinity, any ordinary line is transformed into a special hyperbola through A, and any special hyperbola through B is transformed into an ordinary straight line. The line AB is transformed into itself.

EXERCISES

1. Show that the cross ratio of the four points in which a special line meets four special lines of the other family is unaltered by the bilinear transformation.

2. Study the transformation $\rho x_1' = y_1$, $\rho x_2' = y_2$, $\sigma y_1' = x_1$, $\sigma y_2' = x_2$, and also the transformation obtained as the product of this and the bilinear transformation of the text.

3. Given in space the hyperboloid $x^2 + y^2 - z^2 = 1$ and λ and μ defined by the equations

$$\lambda = \frac{x - z}{1 - y} = \frac{1 + y}{x + z}, \quad \mu = \frac{x - z}{1 + y} = \frac{1 - y}{x + z}.$$

Note that (λ, μ) are coördinates of a point on the hyperboloid and name the essential features of a geometry on the hyperboloid which is dualistic to the geometry in the plane discussed in this chapter. Generalize by replacing the hyperboloid by any quadric surface.

REFERENCES

For the benefit of students who may wish to read more on the subjects treated in the foregoing text the following references are given. No attempt has been made to make the list complete or to include journal articles, and preference has been given to books which are easily accessible.

General treatises:
DARBOUX, Principes de géométrie analytique. Gauthier-Villars.
KLEIN, Höhere Geometrie. Lithographed Lectures. Göttingen.
SALMON, Conic Sections. Longmans, Green & Co.
SCOTT, Modern Analytical Geometry. The Macmillan Company.

Projective geometry:
EMCH, Introduction to Projective Geometry and its Applications. John Wylie & Sons, Inc.
MILNE, Cross Ratio Geometry. Cambridge University Press.
VEBLEN and YOUNG, Projective Geometry, Vol. I. Ginn and Company.

Projective measurement and non-Euclidean geometry:
CARSLAW, Non-Euclidean Geometry and Trigonometry. Longmans, Green & Co.
COOLIDGE, Non-Euclidean Geometry. Clarendon Press.
MANNING, Non-Euclidean Geometry. Ginn and Company.
WOODS, "Non-Euclidean Geometry" (in Young's Monographs on Modern Mathematics). Longmans, Green & Co.

PART III. THREE-DIMENSIONAL GEOMETRY

CHAPTER XI

CIRCLE COÖRDINATES

74. Elementary circle coördinates. As the first example of a geometric element determined by three coördinates, thus leading to a three-dimensional geometry, we will take the circle. If we consider a real proper circle with the radius r and with its center at the point (h, k) in Cartesian coördinates, we might take the three quantities (h, k, r) as the coördinates of the circle. It is more general, however, to take the Cartesian equation

$$a_1(x^2+y^2) + a_2 x + a_3 y + a_4 = 0 \tag{1}$$

as the definition of the circle and to take the ratios $a_1 : a_2 : a_3 : a_4$ as its coördinates. The circle may then be of any of the types specified in § 59. If it is a real proper circle the coördinates are essentially the same as (h, k, r).

We may also take the equation in tetracyclical coördinates x_i,

$$u_1 x_1 + u_2 x_2 + u_3 x_3 + u_4 x_4 = 0, \tag{2}$$

and take the ratios $u_1 : u_2 : u_3 : u_4$ as the coördinates of the circle. If the point coördinates x_i are the special coördinates of § 57, the circle coördinates u_i obtained from equation (2) are the same as the coördinates a_i obtained from equation (1), but in general no simplification is introduced by the use of the special coördinates. In fact, it is in many cases simpler to assume that the point coördinates x_i in equation (2) are orthogonal.

Unless it is otherwise explicitly stated we shall assume in the following that x_i are orthogonal tetracyclical point coördinates connected by the relation:

$$\omega(x) = x_1^2 + x_2^2 + x_3^2 + x_4^2 = 0. \tag{3}$$

Then the condition that equation (2) shall represent a special circle is

$$\eta(u) = u_1^2 + u_2^2 + u_3^2 + u_4^2 = 0. \tag{4}$$

As shown in § 63 the equation of a special circle with the center y_i is
$$\omega(y,\ x) = y_1 x_1 + y_2 x_2 + y_3 x_3 + y_4 x_4 = 0, \tag{5}$$
where, of course, y_i satisfy the fundamental relation (3).

Hence, if (2) is a special circle the coefficients u_i are exactly the coördinates of its center. Because of the importance of this result we repeat it in a theorem:

I. If x_i are orthogonal tetracyclical point coördinates and u_i are circle coördinates based upon them, then the circle coördinates of a special circle are the point coördinates of the center of the circle.

Two circles with the coördinates v_i and w_i are orthogonal when
$$\eta(v,\ w) = v_1 w_1 + v_2 w_2 + v_3 w_3 + v_4 w_4 = 0. \tag{6}$$
From this we may deduce the following theorems:

II. A linear equation
$$a_1 u_1 + a_2 u_2 + a_3 u_3 + a_4 u_4 = 0 \tag{7}$$
in circle coördinates defines a linear circle complex which is composed of all circles orthogonal to a base circle $a_1 : a_2 : a_3 : a_4$.

For equation (7) is simply equation (6) with v_i replaced by the constants a_i and with w_i replaced by the variables u_i.

The complex contains special circles whose centers are the points of the base circle.

When the base circle is a special circle the complex is called a *special* complex. It consists of all circles through the center of the base circle, and the condition for it is
$$a_1^2 + a_2^2 + a_3^2 + a_4^2 = 0.$$

If a_i are the coördinates of the real point at infinity, equation (7) defines a special complex consisting of all the straight lines of the plane.

III. If two circles belong to a linear complex, all circles of the pencil defined by the two belong to the complex.

The proof of this theorem is left to the student.

IV. Two simultaneous linear equations
$$a_1 u_1 + a_2 u_2 + a_3 u_3 + a_4 u_4 = 0,$$
$$b_1 u_1 + b_2 u_2 + b_3 u_3 + b_4 u_4 = 0$$
define a linear congruence, which consists of a pencil of circles.

To prove this, note that the congruence consists of all circles which belong to the two complexes $\sum a_i u_i = 0$ and $\sum b_i u_i = 0$. These circles are also common to all complexes of the pencil of complexes

$$\sum (a_i + \lambda b_i)\, u_i = 0, \tag{8}$$

and is defined by any two complexes of this pencil. But the pencil (8) contains two special complexes given by the values of λ which satisfy the equation

$$(a_1 + \lambda b_1)^2 + (a_2 + \lambda b_2)^2 + (a_3 + \lambda b_3)^2 + (a_4 + \lambda b_4)^2 = 0. \tag{9}$$

If the bases of the two special complexes are distinct, the congruence consists of all circles through two points and is therefore a pencil of circles.

If the bases of the two special complexes coincide, equation (9) has equal roots. We may without loss of generality assume $\sum a_i u_i = 0$ to be the special complex of the pencil. Then $\sum a_i^2 = 0$, and since (9) has equal roots $\sum a_i b_i = 0$; that is, the point a_i is on the circle b_i. Hence the congruence consists of all circles which pass through a fixed point on a circle and are orthogonal to that circle. They accordingly form a pencil of tangent circles.

75. The quadratic circle complex. The equation

$$\sum a_{ik} u_i u_k = 0 \qquad (a_{ki} = a_{ik}) \tag{1}$$

defines a quadratic circle complex.

Let v_i and w_i be any two circles. Then $\rho u_i = v_i + \lambda w_i$ is any circle of the pencil defined by v_i and w_i, and belongs to the complex (1) when λ satisfies the equation

$$\sum a_{ik} v_i v_k + 2\,\lambda \sum a_{ik} v_i w_k + \lambda^2 \sum a_{ik} w_i w_k = 0. \tag{2}$$

Hence we have the following theorem:

I. The quadratic complex contains two distinct or coincident circles from any pencil of circles unless all circles of the pencil belong to the complex.

Now let v_i be a circle of the complex (1). Then one root of (2) is zero, and two roots will be zero when

$$\sum a_{ik} v_i w_k = 0. \tag{3}$$

Equation (3) will be satisfied by all values of w_i when v_i satisfies the equations

$$a_{11}v_1 + a_{12}v_2 + a_{13}v_3 + a_{14}v_4 = 0,$$
$$a_{12}v_1 + a_{22}v_2 + a_{23}v_3 + a_{24}v_4 = 0,$$
$$a_{13}v_1 + a_{23}v_2 + a_{33}v_3 + a_{34}v_4 = 0, \tag{4}$$
$$a_{14}v_1 + a_{24}v_2 + a_{34}v_3 + a_{44}v_4 = 0,$$

and any v_i which satisfy these equations will also satisfy (1) and hence be the coördinates of a circle of the complex. Therefore

II. Any circle whose coördinates v_i satisfy equations (4) will be a circle of the complex such that any pencil of circles which contains v_i and does not lie entirely on the complex will have only v_i in common with the complex.

Such a circle is called a *double* circle of the complex. A double circle does not always exist in a given complex, however, for the necessary and sufficient condition that equations (4) should have a solution is that the determinant of the coefficients should vanish. A complex that contains a double circle is called a *singular* complex.

If in equation (2) v_i is the double circle of a singular complex and w_i any other circle of the complex, the equation is identically satisfied. Hence we have the following theorem:

III. In a singular complex the pencil of circles defined by the double circle and any other pencil of the complex lies entirely in the complex.

We shall now proceed to find the locus of the centers of the special circles of the quadratic complex. The special circles have coördinates u_i which satisfy simultaneously equation (1) and also the equation for a special circle

$$u_1^2 + u_2^2 + u_3^2 + u_4^2 = 0. \tag{5}$$

The circle coördinates are also (theorem I, § 74) the point coördinates of the centers of the special circles. These coördinates define a one-dimensional extent. Therefore the locus of the centers of the special circles of the complex is a curve, which is called a *cyclic* or a *bicircular curve* (see Ex. 9, § 68).

The coördinates u_i which satisfy simultaneously (1) and (5) will also satisfy the equation

$$\sum a_{ik}u_iu_k + \lambda(u_1^2 + u_2^2 + u_3^2 + u_4^2) = 0 \tag{6}$$

for all values of λ, and any equation of the form (6) may replace (1) in the definition of the locus sought. But among the complexes defined by (6) there are in general four singular complexes corresponding to the values of λ defined by the equation

$$\begin{vmatrix} a_{11} - \lambda & a_{12} & a_{13} & a_{14} \\ a_{12} & a_{22} - \lambda & a_{23} & a_{24} \\ a_{13} & a_{23} & a_{33} - \lambda & a_{34} \\ a_{14} & a_{24} & a_{34} & a_{44} - \lambda \end{vmatrix} = 0.$$

Hence we have the following theorem:

IV. The cyclic is in general the locus of the centers of the special circles of any one of four singular complexes.

Take C, any one of these singular complexes, and consider the straight lines belonging to the complex C. Their coördinates satisfy a linear equation

$$c_1 u_1 + c_2 u_2 + c_3 u_3 + c_4 u_4 = 0,$$

where c_i are the coördinates of the real point at infinity. Consequently the straight lines form a one-dimensional extent, and by theorem I any pencil of straight lines contains two of the lines of this extent. Consequently the lines of the complex C envelop a conic, which we shall call Γ.

Now let D be the double circle of C, and T any straight line of C; that is, any tangent line to Γ. The pencil defined by D and T belongs entirely to C, and consequently the two centers of the two point circles of this pencil are points of the cyclic. Furthermore, all points of the cyclic can be obtained in this way, since a point of the cyclic and the circle D will determine a pencil of circles belonging to C and containing a line T. Hence we may say:

V. A cyclic can be defined (and in general in four ways) as the locus of the centers of the point circles of the pencils of circles defined by a fixed circle D and the tangent lines to a fixed conic Γ.

Take P_1 and P_2, two points on the conic Γ, and with P_1 and P_2 as centers construct two circles c and c' orthogonal to D. The circles c and c' determine a pencil of circles orthogonal to D and to the chord $P_1 P_2$. Hence, by theorem V, § 62, if A and A' are the points of intersection of c and c', A and A' are the centers of the point circles of the pencil of circles defined by D and the chord $P_1 P_2$.

Now let P_1 approach P_2 as a limit. The points A and A' approach M and M' respectively, two points on the envelope of the circles c. At the same time A and A' approach as limits the centers of the point circles in the pencil of circles defined by D and the tangent to the conic Γ. Hence we have the following theorem:

VI. *A cyclic can be generated as the envelope of a family of circles whose centers are on a given conic Γ and which are orthogonal to a given circle D. Each circle of the family is doubly tangent to the cyclic.*

This generation of the cyclic can in general be made in four ways, since, as we have seen, the cyclic can be obtained from the point circles of four singular complexes. The cyclic curves have been exhaustively studied both with the use of Cartesian coördinates and with the use of tetracyclical coördinates, but a further discussion of their properties would require too much space for this book.

EXERCISES

1. Given the equation $\sum a_{ik}u_iu_k = 0$, consider the polar equation $\sum a_{ik}v_iu_k = 0$. This assigns to any circle a definite linear complex. Discuss this on the analogy of polar lines with respect to a curve of second order in the plane, defining tangent complexes, self-polar systems of complexes, and the reduction of the original equation to a standard form.

2. Prove that if a quadratic complex contains more than one double circle it contains at least a pencil of double circles and degenerates into two linear complexes or a single linear complex taken double. In the former case show that each circle of the pencil common to the two complexes is a double circle of the quadratic complex.

3. If a quadratic complex degenerates into two linear complexes, show that the cyclic defined by it degenerates into two circles.

4. Show that any circle in a nonsingular quadratic complex belongs to two pencils which lie entirely in the complex. Hence show that any quadratic complex is made up of two families of pencils such that any circle of the complex belongs to one of each of the families. Show that two pencils of the same families never have a circle in common and that any pencil of one family contains one circle of each pencil of the other family.

5. Show that the following curves are special cases of cyclics: the ovals of Descartes, the ovals of Cassini, the cissoid, the lemniscate, the inverse and the pedal curves of conics.

76. Higher circle coördinates. In addition to the four quantities u_1, u_2, u_3, u_4 used in the foregoing sections, we shall now introduce a fifth quantity u_5, defined by the relation

$$u_1^2 + u_2^2 + u_3^2 + u_4^2 + u_5^2 = 0. \tag{1}$$

If the point coördinates x_i used in defining the elementary circle coördinates u_i were not orthogonal, we should define u_5 by the equation
$$\eta(u) + u_5^2 = 0,$$
of which (1) is a special case. We may also, if we wish, replace the five quantities u_i by five independent linear combinations of them, by virtue of which equation (1) would be transformed into a more general quadratic equation, so that we may say *the higher circle coördinates in their most general form consist of the ratios of five variables connected by a fundamental quadratic relation*

$$\xi(u) = \sum a_{ik} u_i u_k = 0.$$

We shall continue to use the orthogonal form for simplicity of treatment.

As shown in § 59 the vanishing of the coördinate u_5 is the necessary and sufficient condition that the circle should be special. In this case the circle is completely determined by the four coördinates u_1, u_2, u_3, u_4. So, in general, the center and the radius of a circle are fully determined by means of the first four coördinates, u_1, u_2, u_3, u_4; that is, the circle is completely determined in the elementary sense. The absolute value of u_5 is then determined, but its sign is not fixed.

It is necessary, then, to distinguish between two circles which are alike in the elementary sense but differ in the sign of the coördinate u_5. This may be done by noting that any nonspecial circle, whether a proper circle or a straight line, divides the plane into two portions, and by considering a circle with a fixed u_5 as the boundary of one of these portions and the circle with a coördinate u_5 of opposite sign as the boundary of the other portion. The same result may be obtained by considering the circle described in opposite directions, with the agreement, perhaps, that the circle shall be considered as bounding that portion of the plane which lies on the left hand in describing the circle.

If x_i are the orthogonal coördinates described in detail in § 64, that is, if we introduce Cartesian coördinates so that

$$\rho x_1 = x^2 + y^2 - 1, \quad \rho x_2 = 2\,x, \quad \rho x_3 = 2\,y, \quad \rho x_4 = -i\,(x^2 + y^2 + 1),$$

it is easy to compute that the radius of the circle u_i is equal to $\dfrac{iu_5}{u_1 - iu_4}$. Hence to fix a sign of u_5 is equivalent to fixing the sign of the radius. We may agree that the sign of the radius is to be considered positive when the center of the circle lies in the area bounded by the circle and that the sign of the radius is to be taken as negative when the center lies in the part of the plane not bounded by the circle.

The angle between two circles u_i and v_i is now defined without ambiguity by the formula

$$\cos \theta = -\frac{u_1 v_1 + u_2 v_2 + u_3 v_3 + u_4 v_4}{u_5 v_5}$$

or
$$u_1 v_1 + u_2 v_2 + u_3 v_3 + u_4 v_4 + u_5 v_5 \cos \theta = 0. \tag{2}$$

To change the sign of u_5 but not of v_5 is to change the angle θ into its supplementary angle.

If the circles u_i and v_i are real and the coördinates are those of § 64, it is not difficult to see that the angle θ is the angle between the two normals drawn each into the region of the plane which each circle bounds.

If either of the two circles is special, θ is either infinite or indeterminant. In particular, if v_i is a special circle and u_i is not, we have $\cos \theta = \infty$ when the center of v_i does not lie on u_i, and $\cos \theta = \dfrac{0}{0}$ when the center of v_i lies on u_i. Hence we may say:

A special circle makes any angle with a circle on which its center lies.

Two circles are orthogonal when $\theta = (2\,k+1)\dfrac{\pi}{2}$. The necessary and sufficient condition for this is

$$u_1 v_1 + u_2 v_2 + u_3 v_3 + u_4 v_4 = 0. \tag{3}$$

Two circles are tangent when $\theta = 0$. The necessary and sufficient condition for this is

$$u_1 v_1 + u_2 v_2 + u_3 v_3 + u_4 v_4 + u_5 v_5 = 0. \tag{4}$$

It is to be noted that two circles are not defined as tangent when $\theta = \pi$. If the circles are real proper circles they are tangent only when they are tangent in the elementary sense and the interior of one lies in the interior of the other.

Consider the equation

$$a_1u_1 + a_2u_2 + a_3u_3 + a_4u_4 + a_5u_5 = 0 \qquad (5)$$

in the higher circle coördinates. This is equivalent to equation (2) if we place

$$a_1 = v_1, \quad a_2 = v_2, \quad a_3 = v_3, \quad a_4 = v_4, \quad a_5 = v_5 \cos \theta,$$

together with the condition

$$v_1^2 + v_2^2 + v_3^2 + v_4^2 + v_5^2 = 0.$$

These equations are just sufficient to determine v_i and $\cos \theta$. Hence *the higher circle complex consists of circles cutting a fixed circle under a fixed angle.*

If $a_5 = 0$ the higher circle complex becomes the elementary complex consisting of circles orthogonal to a base circle.

The circle complex (5) is called a special complex when

$$a_1^2 + a_2^2 + a_3^2 + a_4^2 + a_5^2 = 0.$$

In that case $\theta = 0$ and the equation may be identified with (4). Hence *a special complex in the higher coördinates consists of circles tangent to a fixed circle.*

Two simultaneous equations

$$a_1u_1 + a_2u_2 + a_3u_3 + a_4u_4 + a_5u_5 = 0,$$
$$b_1u_1 + b_2u_2 + b_3u_3 + b_4u_4 + b_5u_5 = 0$$

define a higher circle *congruence.* Circles which satisfy these two equations also satisfy any equation of the form

$$\sum (a_i + \lambda b_i)u_i = 0,$$

but among the complexes defined by this last equation are two special complexes. Hence *a higher circle congruence consists of all circles tangent to two fixed circles.*

EXERCISES

1. What is the configuration of the higher circle congruence if the two special complexes coincide?

2. Show that if x_i are orthogonal tetracyclical coördinates, the circle coördinates u_1, u_2, u_3, u_4 are proportional to the cosines of the angles which the circle u_i makes with the coördinate circles.

3. Describe the complexes defined by each of the equations $u_i = 0$.

CHAPTER XII

POINT AND PLANE COÖRDINATES

77. Cartesian point coördinates. Let OX, OY, OZ (Fig. 51) be three axes of coördinates, which we take for convenience as mutually orthogonal. Then, if P is any point in space, and PL, PM, PN are the perpendiculars to the three planes determined by the axes, the lengths of these perpendiculars with a proper convention as to signs are the rectangular Cartesian coördinates of P. That is, we place

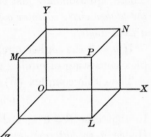

FIG. 51

$$x = MP, \quad y = LP, \quad z = NP, \quad (1)$$

where MP, LP, and NP are positive if measured in the directions OX, OY, and OZ respectively, and negative if measured in the opposite directions.

The coördinates may be made homogeneous by placing

$$MP = \frac{x}{t}, \quad LP = \frac{y}{t}, \quad NP = \frac{z}{t} \qquad (2)$$

and taking the ratios $x : y : z : t$ as the coördinates of P.

To any point P corresponds then a real set of ratios, and to any set of real ratios in which t is not zero corresponds a real point P. The relation between point and coördinates is then made one to one by the following conventions: (1) the ratios $0 : 0 : 0 : 0$ are not allowable; (2) complex values of the ratios define an imaginary point; (3) ratios in which $t = 0$ but $x : y : z$ are determinate define a point at infinity. In fact, as t approaches zero P recedes indefinitely from O.

If a point is not at infinity we may, if we choose, place $t = 1$ in (2), thus reducing the homogeneous coördinates to the nonhomogeneous ones. Again, nonhomogeneous coördinates are easily made homogeneous by dividing by t. Accordingly we shall use the two kinds side by side, passing from one to the other as convenience dictates.

A more general system of Cartesian coördinates may be defined by dropping the assumption that the axes OX, OY, OZ (Fig. 51) are mutually orthogonal, and drawing the lines MP, LP, NP parallel to the axes. The coördinates are then called *oblique*. They may be made homogeneous by the same device as that used in the case of rectangular coördinates.

Throughout this book the axes will be assumed as rectangular unless the contrary is explicitly stated.

78. Distance. Let P_1 and P_2 be two real points with the coördinates (x_1, y_1, z_1) and (x_2, y_2, z_2) respectively, and let a rectangular parallelepiped be constructed on P_1P_2 as a diagonal, with its edges parallel to the coördinate axes. Then, if P_1R, RS, and SP_2 are three consecutive edges of the parallelepiped, it is evident that

$$P_1R = x_2 - x_1, \quad RS = y_2 - y_1, \quad SP_2 = z_2 - z_1. \tag{1}$$

Hence the distance P_1P_2 is given by the equation

$$P_1P_2 = \sqrt{(x_2 - x_1)^2 + (y_2 - y_1)^2 + (z_2 - z_1)^2}, \tag{2}$$

or, written in homogeneous coördinates,

$$P_1P_2 = \frac{\sqrt{(x_2t_1 - x_1t_2)^2 + (y_2t_1 - y_1t_2)^2 + (z_2t_1 - z_1t_2)^2}}{t_1t_2}. \tag{3}$$

This formula has been proved for real points only. It is now taken as the definition of the distance between all points of whatever nature. From the definition we obtain at once the following propositions:

I. The distance between two points neither of which is at infinity is finite.

II. The distance between a point at infinity and a point not at infinity is infinite, unless the point at infinity has coördinates which satisfy the conditions

$$x^2 + y^2 + z^2 = 0, \quad t = 0. \tag{4}$$

In the latter case the distance between the point at infinity and any point not at infinity is indeterminate.

The points whose coördinates satisfy equations (4) form a one-dimensional extent called *the circle at infinity*. The reason for the use of the word "circle" will appear later.

If in equation (2) we replace the coördinates of P_1 by those of a fixed point C (x_0, y_0, z_0) and the coördinates of P_1 by those of a variable point P (x, y, z), while keeping CP equal to a constant r, we obtain

$$(x - x_0)^2 + (y - y_0)^2 + (z - z_0)^2 = r^2, \qquad (5)$$

which defines the locus of a point at a constant distance from a fixed point. This locus is by definition *a sphere.*

Equation (5) may be written in the form

$$A(x^2 + y^2 + z^2) + Bxt + Cyt + Dzt + Et^2 = 0, \qquad (6)$$

where

$$x_0 : y_0 : z_0 : t_0 = B : C : D : -2A, \quad r^2 = \frac{B^2 + C^2 + D^2 - 4AE}{4A^2}. \qquad (7)$$

If the center C and the radius r are finite, the coefficient A is not zero. Conversely, any equation of the form (6) in which A is not zero defines a sphere, the radius and the center of which are given by (7). More generally it is possible to define a sphere as the locus of any equation of the form (6). In case $A = 0$ the center is at infinity, the radius is infinite or indeterminate, and the equation splits into the two equations $t = 0$ and $Bx + Cy + Dz + Et = 0$. These cases of the sphere will be discussed in detail in § 118. In the present section we shall consider only the case in which $A \neq 0$ and the sphere conforms more nearly to the elementary definition, and its equation may then be put in the form (5).

The radius, however, may be real, imaginary, or zero. If the radius is zero, the equation takes the form

$$(x - x_0)^2 + (y - y_0)^2 + (z - z_0)^2 = 0, \qquad (8)$$

and the sphere is called a *null sphere* or a *point sphere.*

It is obvious that if (x_0, y_0, z_0) is a real point, equation (8) is satisfied by the coördinates of no other real point. There exist, however, a doubly infinite set of imaginary points which satisfy equation (8).

79. The straight line. A straight line is by definition the one-dimensional extent of points whose coördinates satisfy equations of the form

$$\begin{aligned}
\rho x &= x_1 + \lambda x_2, \\
\rho y &= y_1 + \lambda y_2, \\
\rho z &= z_1 + \lambda z_2, \\
\rho t &= t_1 + \lambda t_2,
\end{aligned} \qquad (1)$$

where $(x_1 : y_1 : z_1 : t_1)$ and $(x_2 : y_2 : z_2 : t_2)$ are the coördinates of two fixed points and λ is a variable parameter.

From the definition we may draw the following conclusions:

I. Any two distinct points determine a straight line, and any two distinct points on the line may be used to determine it.

The first part of this theorem is obvious. To prove the second part let P_1 be a point on the line (1) determined by $\lambda = \lambda_1$ and let P_2 be another point on the line determined by $\lambda = \lambda_2$. Let σ be a quantity defined by the relation $\dfrac{\lambda_1 + \sigma \lambda_2}{1 + \sigma} = \lambda$. Then the first equation in (1) may be written

$$\rho x = \frac{x_1 + \lambda_1 x_2 + \sigma (x_1 + \lambda_2 x_2)}{1 + \sigma}$$

or $$\tau x = x_1 + \lambda_1 x_2 + \sigma (x_1 + \lambda_2 x_2),$$

and similar equations can be found for y, z, and t. But these are the equations of a straight line defined by P_1 and P_2, which is thus shown to be identical to that defined by $(x_1 : y_1 : z_1 : t_1)$ and $(x_2 : y_2 : z_2 : t_2)$.

II. A straight line contains a single point at infinity unless it lies entirely at infinity.

If, in equations (1), $t_1 = 0$ and $t_2 = 0$, then $t = 0$ for all values of λ. Otherwise $t = 0$ only when $\lambda = -\dfrac{t_1}{t_2}$, which determines on the line the single point at infinity $(x_1 t_2 - x_2 t_1 : y_1 t_2 - y_2 t_1 : z_1 t_2 - z_2 t_1 : 0)$. This proves the theorem. Straight lines which lie at infinity are sometimes called *improper straight lines*; other lines are called *proper straight lines.*

III. If two points of a straight line are real, the line contains an infinity of real points.

This follows from the fact that if the two real points are used to determine the equations (1), any real value of λ gives a real point on the line. Such lines are called *real lines*, although it should not be forgotten that they contain an infinity of imaginary points also.

If a real line is also a proper line we may put t_1, t_2, and t equal to unity in equations (1) and write the equations of the line in the form

$$\frac{x - x_1}{x_2 - x_1} = \frac{y - y_1}{y_2 - y_1} = \frac{z - z_1}{z_2 - z_1}. \tag{2}$$

From this and equations (1), § 78, it is not difficult to show that the real points of a real proper line form a straight line in the elementary sense.

IV. An imaginary straight line may contain one real point or no real point.

To prove this it is only necessary to give an example of each kind. The line defined by the two points $(1:1:1:1)$ and $(1:0:i:1)$ contains the first point and no other real point, while the line defined by $(1:i:i:1)$ and $(1:0:i:1)$ contains no real point. These statements may be verified by using the given points in equations (1) and examining the values of λ necessary to give a real point on the line.

An imaginary line which contains no real point may be called *completely imaginary*, one with a single real point *incompletely imaginary*.

V. If the distance between two points on a straight line is zero, the distance between any other two points of the line is zero.

To prove this we may use the coördinates of the points between which the distance is zero for the fixed points in equation (1). Then, if P_1 and P_2 are two points determined by $\lambda = \lambda_1$ and $\lambda = \lambda_2$ respectively, we may compute the distance $\overline{P_1 P_2}^2$ by formula (3), § 78. There results

$$\overline{P_1 P_2}^2 = \frac{(\lambda_2 - \lambda_1)^2}{(t_1 + \lambda_1 t_2)^2 (t_1 + \lambda_2 t_2)^2}[(x_2 t_1 - x_1 t_2)^2 + (y_2 t_1 - y_1 t_2)^2 + (z_2 t_1 - z_1 t_2)^2] = 0.$$

A straight line with the above property is called a *minimum line*. Such lines have already been met in the plane geometry. Concerning the minimum lines in space we have the following theorems:

VI. A minimum line meets the plane at infinity in the circle at infinity, and, conversely, any line not at infinity which intersects the circle at infinity is a minimum line.

From the proof of theorem II the necessary and sufficient condition that a line meet the circle at infinity is

$$(x_2 t_1 - x_1 t_2)^2 + (y_2 t_1 - y_1 t_2)^2 + (z_2 t_1 - z_1 t_2)^2 = 0,$$

which is also the necessary and sufficient condition that the two points $(x_1 : y_1 : z_1 : t_1)$ and $(x_2 : y_2 : z_2 : t_2)$ should be at a zero distance apart. By theorem V the line is then a minimum line.

VII. *Through any point of space goes a cone of minimum lines which is also a point sphere.*

Any point in space may be joined to the points of the circle at infinity. We have then a one-dimensional extent of lines through a common point, and such lines form a cone by definition. Also if $(x_0 : y_0 : z_0 : t_0)$ is the fixed point and $(x : y : z : t)$ is any point on a minimum line through it, the coördinates of $(x : y : z : t)$ will satisfy the equation

$$(xt_0 - x_0t)^2 + (yt_0 - y_0t)^2 + (zt_0 - z_0t)^2 = 0, \qquad (3)$$

and, conversely, any point whose coördinates satisfy this equation lies by theorem VI on a minimum line through $(x_0 : y_0 : z_0 : t_0)$.

Equation (3) is, however, the equation of a point sphere in homogeneous form. Hence the minimum cone is identical with the point sphere.

80. The plane. A plane is defined as the two-dimensional extent of points whose coördinates satisfy an equation of the form

$$Ax + By + Cz + Dt = 0. \qquad (1)$$

From the definition we deduce the following propositions:

I. *If two points lie on a plane, the straight line connecting them lies entirely on the plane.*

This follows immediately from the fact that if $(x_1 : y_1 : z_1 : t_1)$ and $(x_2 : y_2 : z_2 : t_2)$ satisfy (1), then $(x_1 + \lambda x_2 : y_1 + \lambda y_2 : z_1 + \lambda z_2 : t_1 + \lambda t_2)$ does also.

II. *A plane is uniquely determined by any three points not on the same straight line.*

If $(x_1 : y_1 : z_1 : t_1)$, $(x_2 : y_2 : z_2 : t_2)$, and $(x_3 : y_3 : z_3 : t_3)$ are any three points, the coefficients A, B, C, and D may be so determined that

$$Ax_1 + By_1 + Cz_1 + Dt_1 = 0,$$
$$Ax_2 + By_2 + Cz_2 + Dt_2 = 0, \qquad (2)$$
$$Ax_3 + By_3 + Cz_3 + Dt_3 = 0,$$

unless there exist relations of the form

$$\lambda_1 x_1 + \lambda_2 x_2 + \lambda_3 x_3 = 0,$$
$$\lambda_1 y_1 + \lambda_2 y_2 + \lambda_3 y_3 = 0,$$
$$\lambda_1 z_1 + \lambda_2 z_2 + \lambda_3 z_3 = 0,$$
$$\lambda_1 t_1 + \lambda_2 t_2 + \lambda_3 t_3 = 0;$$

that is, unless the three points taken lie on a straight line.

It follows from theorems I and II that any plane in the elementary sense may be represented by an equation in the form (1). The general definition of a plane extends the concept of the plane in the usual way.

III. *Points at infinity lie in a plane called the plane at infinity.*

This is a result of the definition, since the equation of points at infinity is $t = 0$.

On the plane $x = 0$ the coördinates $y : z : t$ are homogeneous coördinates of the type of § 18. Similarly, on the plane $y = 0$ we have the Cartesian coördinates $x : z : t$ and on the plane $z = 0$ the Cartesian coördinates $x : y : t$. On the plane $t = 0$ we may define $x : y : z$ as trilinear coördinates of the type in § 22.

IV. *If three points of a plane are real, the plane contains a doubly infinite number of real points.*

From equations (2) the values of A, B, C, and D are real if the coördinates of the points involved are real. Then in equations (1) real values may be assumed for two of the ratios $x : y : z : t$, and the third is determined as real.

Such a plane is called a *real plane*, although it contains, of course, an infinity of imaginary points.

V. *Any two distinct planes intersect in a straight line, and any straight line may be defined as the intersection of two planes.*

Consider the two planes

$$A_1 x + B_1 y + C_1 z + D_1 t = 0,$$
$$A_2 x + B_2 y + C_2 z + D_2 t = 0.$$

These equations are satisfied by an infinite number of values of the coördinates. Let $(x_1 : y_1 : z_1 : t_1)$ and $(x_2 : y_2 : z_2 : t_2)$ be two such values. Then the values $(x_1 + \lambda x_2 : y_1 + \lambda y_2 : z_1 + \lambda z_2 : t_1 + \lambda t_2)$ also satisfy the two equations so that the two planes have certainly a line in common. They cannot have in common any point not on this line if the two planes are distinct, since three points completely determine a plane (theorem II).

Again, a plane (by theorem II) may be passed through two points on a given line and a third point not on the line, and two such planes will determine the line.

VI. *Any plane except the plane at infinity contains a single line at infinity, and any two planes intersecting in the same line at infinity are parallel.*

The first part of this theorem is a corollary of theorem V. The second part is a definition of parallel planes. The definition agrees with the elementary definition since, by theorem V, parallel planes in this sense have no finite point in common.

VII. *An imaginary plane contains one and only one real straight line.*

Since an imaginary plane has one or more of the coefficients in its equation complex, we may write the equations as

$$(\alpha_1 + i\alpha_2)x + (\beta_1 + i\beta_2)y + (\gamma_1 + i\gamma_2)z + (\delta_1 + i\delta_2)t = 0.$$

This can be satisfied by real values $(x:y:z:t)$ when and only when

$$\alpha_1 x + \beta_1 y + \gamma_1 z + \delta_1 t = 0,$$
$$\alpha_2 x + \beta_2 y + \gamma_2 z + \delta_2 t = 0 ;$$

that is, when $(x:y:z:t)$ lie on a real straight line (theorem V). That the line is real follows from theorem III, § 79, since the above equations are evidently satisfied by two real points.

The real line on an imaginary plane may lie at infinity. In that case the plane is said to be *imaginary of higher order*. If the real line is not at infinity, the plane is said to be *imaginary of lower order*.

VIII. *Any plane intersects a sphere in a circle.*

Consider the intersection of the plane

$$Ax + By + Cz + Dt = 0 \tag{3}$$

and the sphere

$$a(x^2 + y^2 + z^2) + bx + cy + dz + et = 0. \tag{4}$$

Any point on the intersection of these two surfaces also lies on the intersection of (3) and

$$a(x^2 + y^2 + z^2) + (b + \lambda A)x + (c + \lambda B)y + (d + \lambda C)z$$
$$+ (e + \lambda D)t = 0, \tag{5}$$

where λ is any multiplier. Equation (5) represents a sphere with the center

$$[(b + \lambda A):(c + \lambda B):(d + \lambda C):-2a],$$

which will lie in the plane (3) when

$$bA + cB + dC - 2aD + (A^2 + B^2 + C^2)\lambda = 0.$$

The points of the intersection of (3) and (4) are therefore shown to lie at a constant distance from a fixed point of the plane, and hence the intersection satisfies the usual definition of the circle.

The above discussion fails if the coefficients of the plane satisfy the condition $A^2 + B^2 + C^2 = 0.$

This happens for the plane at infinity and for other planes called *minimum planes*. In these two cases the truth of theorem VIII is maintained by taking it as the definition of a circle. This justifies the expression "circle at infinity," which we have already used, and shows that there is no other circle at infinity. The case of a minimum plane needs further discussion.

IX. Any plane not a minimum plane intersects the circle at infinity in two points, which are the circle points of that plane. A minimum plane is tangent to the circle at infinity. Through any point in a plane which is not a minimum plane go two minimum lines. Through any point in a minimum plane goes only one minimum line.

The plane (3) intersects the plane at infinity in the line $Ax + By + Cz = 0$, $t = 0$, and this line intersects the circle at infinity in two points unless $A^2 + B^2 + C^2 = 0$, when it is tangent to that circle. In the latter case the plane is by definition a minimum plane.

It is easy to see that in a plane which is not a minimum plane its intersections with the circle at infinity have all the properties of the circle points discussed in § 20 and that the metrical geometry on such a plane is that of §§ 45 and 46. The latter parts of the theorem follow from theorem VI, § 79.

The minimum planes are fundamentally different from other planes in that a minimum plane contains only one circle point at infinity. The geometry on a minimum plane presents, therefore, many peculiarities, some of which will be mentioned in the next section.

81. Direction and angle. We define the *direction* of a straight line as the coördinates of the point in which it meets the plane at infinity. This definition is justified by the facts that the lines through a point are distinguished one from another by their direction in accordance with theorem I, § 79, and that a line can be drawn through the point with any given direction by the same theorem.

We shall denote the direction of a line by the ratios $l : m : n$. Then we have, by theorem II, § 79,

$$l : m : n = x_2 t_1 - x_1 t_2 : y_2 t_1 - y_1 t_2 : z_2 t_1 - z_1 t_2,$$

where $(x_1 : y_1 : z_1 : t_1)$ and $(x_2 : y_2 : z_2 : t_2)$ are the coördinates of any two points of the line. If neither of these points is at infinity, we may write

$$l : m : n = x_2 - x_1 : y_2 - y_1 : z_2 - z_1,$$

which is in accordance with the more elementary definition of direction.

From the definition we have the following consequences:

I. Two noncoincident lines with the same direction are parallel.

Such lines lie in the plane determined by their common point at infinity and two distinct points one on each line (theorem II, § 80), and they can intersect at no point except the common point at infinity. Hence they are parallel.

II. The necessary and sufficient condition that a line should be a minimum line is that its direction should satisfy the condition

$$l^2 + m^2 + n^2 = 0.$$

This follows from (3), § 79.

In § 46 we have defined the angle between two intersecting lines l_1 and l_2 by the equation

$$\phi = \frac{i}{2} \log (l_1 l_2, \, m_1 m_2),$$

where m_1 and m_2 are the two minimum lines through the intersection of l_1 and l_2 and in their plane. We shall continue to use this definition.

Now, if the lines $l_1, l_2, m_1,$ and m_2 intersect the plane at infinity in the points $L_1, L_2, M_1,$ and M_2 respectively, we have, by theorem I, § 16,

$$\phi = \frac{i}{2} \log (L_1 L_2, \, M_1 M_2).$$

From this we have the following theorem, in which the condition that l_1 and l_2 should be intersecting lines may be dropped:

III. The angle between two lines is equal to the projective distance between the points in which they intersect the plane at infinity, the circle at infinity being taken as the fundamental conic and the constant K of (4), § 47, being equal to $\dfrac{i}{2}$.

The cross ratio $(L_1 L_2, M_1 M_2)$ is unity when and only when M_1 and M_2 coincide or L_1 and L_2 coincide, it being assumed that neither L_1 nor L_2 lies on the circle at infinity. In the former case the lines l_1 and l_2 are parallel; in the latter case they lie in the same minimum plane. Hence follows the theorem:

IV. If two nonminimum lines are parallel or if they lie in the same minimum plane, they make a zero angle with each other, and, conversely, if two nonminimum lines make a zero angle with each other, they are either parallel or lie in the same minimum plane.

Let us suppose that l_1 and l_2 are nonminimum and distinct and that their directions are $A_1 : B_1 : C_1$ and $A_2 : B_2 : C_2$ respectively. Then, as in (4), § 49,

$$\cos \phi = \frac{A_1 A_2 + B_1 B_2 + C_1 C_2}{\sqrt{A_1^2 + B_1^2 + C_1^2} \sqrt{A_2^2 + B_2^2 + C_2^2}}. \tag{1}$$

From this we obtain the following result:

V. Two nonminimum lines are perpendicular to each other when their directions satisfy the condition

$$A_1 A_2 + B_1 B_2 + C_1 C_2 = 0. \tag{2}$$

Interpreted on the plane at infinity this means that the two points $(A_1 : B_1 : C_1)$ and $(A_2 : B_2 : C_2)$ lie each on the polar of the other.

VI. If $Ax + By + Cz + Dt = 0$ is not a minimum plane, any line with the direction $A : B : C$ does not lie in the plane and is perpendicular to every line in the plane.

The plane mentioned meets the plane at infinity in the line $Ax + By + Cz = 0$, and any line with the direction $A : B : C$ meets the plane at infinity in the point $(A : B : C)$, which is the pole of the line $Ax + By + Cz = 0$ with respect to the circle at infinity. Hence the point $(A : B : C)$ will not lie in the line $Ax + By + Cz = 0$ unless the latter is tangent to the circle at infinity. This proves the theorem.

Any line with the direction $A : B : C$ is said to be *normal* to the plane $Ax + By + Cz + Dt = 0$, and this designation is used sometimes even for minimum planes. The above discussion, however, establishes the following theorem:

VII. The normals to a minimum plane lie in the plane and are the minimum lines in the plane.

By (1) a line with the direction $l : m : n$ makes with the axes of coördinates the angles α, β, γ, where

$$\cos \alpha = \frac{l}{\sqrt{l^2 + m^2 + n^2}}, \quad \cos \beta = \frac{m}{\sqrt{l^2 + m^2 + n^2}}, \quad \cos \gamma = \frac{n}{\sqrt{l^2 + m^2 + n^2}}.$$

These quantities are called the *direction cosines* of the line. With their use equations (2) of § 79 may be put in the form

$$x = x_1 + r \cos \alpha,$$
$$y = y_1 + r \cos \beta,$$
$$z = z_1 + r \cos \gamma,$$

where it is easy to show that r is the distance of the variable point (x, y, z) from the fixed point (x_1, y_1, z_1). It is obvious that these equations do not hold for a minimum line.

EXERCISES

1. Show that through any imaginary point in space there goes a pencil of real planes having a real line as axis.

2. Show that the equation of any imaginary plane of lower order may be written $ax + by + cz + dt = 0$, where a, b, and c are real and d is complex.

3. Show that any imaginary straight line either lies in one real plane and contains one real point, or lies in no real plane and contains no real point. The last kind of lines is called *completely imaginary* and the former kind *incompletely imaginary*.

4. Show that the necessary and sufficient condition that two points should determine an incompletely imaginary straight line is that the two points lie in the same plane with their conjugate imaginary points, but not on the same straight line.

5. Show that two conjugate imaginary points determine a real straight line and that if an imaginary point lies on a real straight line its conjugate imaginary point does also.

6. Show that a minimum line makes an infinite angle with any other line not in the same minimum plane with it and makes an indeterminate angle with any line in the same minimum plane with it.

7. If (2) is taken as the definition of perpendicular lines, show that a minimum line is perpendicular to itself and that a line in a minimum plane is perpendicular to every minimum line in the plane.

8. If the angle between two planes is the angle between their normals, show that two nonminimum planes make a zero angle when they are parallel or intersect in a minimum line.

9. Show that any minimum plane makes an infinite angle with any plane not intersecting it in a minimum line and makes an indeterminate angle with any plane intersecting it in a minimum line.

10. Show that the coördinates of a point on the circle at infinity can be written $x : y : z = 1 - s^2 : i(1 + s^2) : 2 s$, where s is an arbitrary parameter. Hence show that the equations of a minimum line may be written

$$x = x_1 + (1 - s^2)\, r,$$
$$y = y_1 + i(1 + s^2)\, r,$$
$$z = z_1 + 2\, sr,$$

where s is fixed for the line and r is variable.

11. Show that the equations

$$x = \int (1 - s^2)\, F(s)\, ds,$$

$$y = \int i\,(1 + s^2)\, F(s)\, ds,$$

$$z = \int 2\, s\, F(s)\, ds,$$

where $F(s)$ is an arbitrary function, represent a minimum curve; that is, a curve such that the length between any two points is zero and the tangent line at any point is a minimum line.

12. Show that a minimum plane through the center of a sphere intersects the latter in two minimum lines intersecting at infinity.

13. If a line is defined by the two equations

$$A_1 x + B_1 y + C_1 z + D_1 t = 0,$$
$$A_2 x + B_2 y + C_2 z + D_2 t = 0,$$

show that its direction is $B_1 C_2 - B_2 C_1 : C_1 A_2 - C_2 A_1 : A_1 B_2 - A_2 B_1$.

14. Show by reference to the plane at infinity that the necessary and sufficient condition that the plane $Ax + By + Cz + Dt = 0$ should be parallel to a line with direction $l : m : n$ is $Al + Bm + Cn = 0$.

15. Show that the equation of a plane through the point $(x_1 : y_1 : z_1 : t_1)$ and parallel to the two lines with the directions $l_1 : m_1 : n_1$ and $l_2 : m_2 : n_2$, respectively, is

$$\begin{vmatrix} x & y & z & t \\ x_1 & y_1 & z_1 & t_1 \\ l_1 & m_1 & n_1 & 0 \\ l_2 & m_2 & n_2 & 0 \end{vmatrix} = 0.$$

82. Quadriplanar point coördinates. Let us assume four planes of reference ABC, ABD, ADC, and BCD (Fig. 52), not intersecting in a point, and four arbitrary constants k_1, k_2, k_3, k_4. Let p_1, p_2, p_3, p_4 be the lengths of the perpendiculars from any point P to the four planes in the order named, the sign of each perpendicular being positive or negative according as P lies on one or the other (arbitrarily chosen) side of the corresponding plane. Then the ratios

$$x_1 : x_2 : x_3 : x_4 = k_1 p_1 : k_2 p_2 : k_3 p_3 : k_4 p_4$$

are the coördinates of the point P.

It is evident that if P is given as a real point its coördinates are uniquely determined. Conversely, let a set of real ratios $x_1 : x_2 : x_3 : x_4$ be given, no one of which is zero. The ratio $x_1 : x_4$ is one of the coördinates of any point in a definite plane through BC, and the ratio $x_2 : x_4$ is one of the coördinates of any point on a definite plane through BD. The two ratios are part of the coördinates of any point on a definite line through B and of no point not on this line. Call this line l. The ratio $x_3 : x_4$ is one of the coördinates of any point on a definite plane through

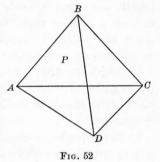

Fig. 52

CD. Call this plane m. If the plane m and the line l meet in a point P, the ratios $x_1 : x_2 : x_3 : x_4$ have fixed a definite point. If the line l and the plane m do not intersect, we shall say that the ratios define a point at infinity.

Complex values of the ratios define imaginary points, and the ratios $0 : 0 : 0 : 0$ are excluded.

If one of the coördinates is zero, the other three are trilinear coördinates on one of the planes of reference. For example, if $x_1 = 0$ the ratios $x_2 : x_3 : x_4$ are trilinear coördinates in the plane ABC, since the distance of a point in the plane ABC from the line AC is equal to its distance from the plane ACD multiplied by the cosecant of the angle between the planes ABC and ABD, and, similarly, for the distances from AB and BC.

Hence all values of the ratios $x_1 : x_2 : x_3 : x_4$, except the unallowable ratios $0 : 0 : 0 : 0$, determine a unique point.

Referring to the figure, we note that $x_1 = 0$ on the plane ABC; $x_2 = 0$ on the plane ABD; $x_3 = 0$ on the plane ADC; and $x_4 = 0$ on the plane DBC.

The point A has the coördinates $0 : 0 : 0 : 1$, the point B the coördinates $0 : 0 : 1 : 0$, the point C the coördinates $0 : 1 : 0 : 0$, the point D the coördinates $1 : 0 : 0 : 0$. The ratios $k_1 : k_2 : k_3 : k_4$ are determined by the position of the point I, for which the coördinates are $1 : 1 : 1 : 1$, and this point can be taken at pleasure.

Quadriplanar coördinates include Cartesian coördinates as a special or limiting case in which the plane $x_4 = 0$ is taken as the plane at infinity. For if the plane BCD recedes indefinitely from A, and the point P is not in BCD, the perpendicular p_4 becomes infinite in length, but k_4 can be made to approach zero at the same time and in such a manner that $\lim k_4 p_4 = 1$. Finally, if the planes ABC, ABD, and ACD are mutually orthogonal and $k_1 = k_2 = k_3 = 1$, the coördinates are rectangular Cartesian coördinates.

If the planes ABC, ABD, and ACD are not mutually orthogonal, we may place $k_1 = \csc \alpha_1$, where α_1 is the angle between AB and the plane ACD, and take similar values for k_2 and k_3. We then have oblique Cartesian coördinates.

In using quadriplanar coördinates it is not convenient or necessary to specify the coördinates of a point at infinity. In fact, such points are not to be considered as essentially different from other points. Distance and all metrical properties of figures are not conveniently expressed in terms of quadriplanar coördinates and should be handled by Cartesian coördinates. We may, however, pass from the general quadriplanar coördinates to Cartesian coördinates by simply interpreting one of the coördinate planes as the plane at infinity.

83. Straight line and plane. We shall prove the following theorems :

I. If $y_1 : y_2 : y_3 : y_4$ and $z_1 : z_2 : z_3 : z_4$ are two fixed points, the coördinates of any point on the straight line joining them are

$$\begin{aligned}
\rho x_1 &= y_1 + \lambda z_1, \\
\rho x_2 &= y_2 + \lambda z_2, \\
\rho x_3 &= y_3 + \lambda z_3, \\
\rho x_4 &= y_4 + \lambda z_4,
\end{aligned} \tag{1}$$

and any point with these coördinates lies on that line.

This is the definition of a straight line for imaginary points. If, however, the points y_i and z_i are real, the points given by real values of λ are real points which lie on a real straight line in the elementary sense. This is easily verified by the student in using a construction and argument similar to that used in § 23 for the straight line in the plane.

II. Any homogeneous linear equation of the form

$$a_1 x_1 + a_2 x_2 + a_3 x_3 + a_4 x_4 = 0 \tag{2}$$

represents a plane.

This is the definition of a plane. If y_i and z_i are any two points satisfying the equation of a plane, the coördinates of any point on the line joining y_i and z_i also satisfy the equation; that is, the line which joins any two points of a plane lies entirely in the plane. Hence, if the plane contains real points it coincides with a plane in the elementary sense.

III. Three points not in the same straight line determine one and only one plane.

The proof is as in § 80. If y_i, z_i, t_i are the three points, the equation of the plane is

$$\begin{vmatrix} x_1 & x_2 & x_3 & x_4 \\ y_1 & y_2 & y_3 & y_4 \\ z_1 & z_2 & z_3 & z_4 \\ t_1 & t_2 & t_3 & t_4 \end{vmatrix} = 0. \tag{3}$$

IV. If y_i, z_i, and t_i are any three points not on the same straight line, the coördinates of any point on the plane through them may be written

$$\begin{aligned} \rho x_1 &= y_1 + \lambda z_1 + \mu t_1, \\ \rho x_2 &= y_2 + \lambda z_2 + \mu t_2, \\ \rho x_3 &= y_3 + \lambda z_3 + \mu t_3, \\ \rho x_4 &= y_4 + \lambda z_4 + \mu t_4, \end{aligned} \tag{4}$$

and any point with these coördinates lies in the plane.

This follows immediately from the fact that the elimination of ρ, λ, and μ from equations (4) gives equation (3), and, conversely, from (3) the existence of (4) may be deduced.

V. *Any two distinct planes intersect in a straight line.*

The proof is the same as that of theorem V, § 80. A line can therefore be defined by two simultaneous equations of the form

$$a_1x_1 + a_2x_2 + a_3x_3 + a_4x_4 = 0,$$
$$b_1x_1 + b_2x_2 + b_3x_3 + b_4x_4 = 0.$$

VI. *If* $\sum a_ix_i = 0$ *and* $\sum b_ix_i = 0$ *are the equations of any two planes, then*

$$\sum a_ix_i + \lambda \sum b_ix_i = 0$$

is, for any value of λ, *the equation of a plane through the line of intersection of the first two planes. As* λ *takes all values, all planes of the pencil may be obtained.*

VII. *Any three planes not belonging to the same pencil intersect in a point.*

To prove this consider the three equations

$$a_1x_1 + a_2x_2 + a_3x_3 + a_4x_4 = 0,$$
$$b_1x_1 + b_2x_2 + b_3x_3 + b_4x_4 = 0,$$
$$c_1x_1 + c_2x_2 + c_3x_3 + c_4x_4 = 0.$$

These have the unique solution

$$x_1 : x_2 : x_3 : x_4 = \begin{vmatrix} a_2 & a_3 & a_4 \\ b_2 & b_3 & b_4 \\ c_2 & c_3 & c_4 \end{vmatrix} : - \begin{vmatrix} a_3 & a_4 & a_1 \\ b_3 & b_4 & b_1 \\ c_3 & c_4 & c_1 \end{vmatrix} : \begin{vmatrix} a_4 & a_1 & a_2 \\ b_4 & b_1 & b_2 \\ c_4 & c_1 & c_2 \end{vmatrix} : - \begin{vmatrix} a_1 & a_2 & a_3 \\ b_1 & b_2 & b_3 \\ c_1 & c_2 & c_3 \end{vmatrix},$$

unless the determinants involved are all zero. But in the latter case there must exist multipliers λ, μ, ρ such that

$$\rho c_i = \lambda a_i + \mu b_i,$$

and hence the three planes belong to the same pencil by theorem VI.

VIII. *If* $\sum a_ix_i = 0$, $\sum b_ix_i = 0$, $\sum c_ix_i = 0$ *are the equations of three planes not belonging to the same pencil, then*

$$\sum a_ix_i + \lambda \sum b_ix_i + \mu \sum c_ix_i = 0$$

is the equation of a plane through their point of intersection. As λ *and* μ *take all values, all planes through a common point can be found. Such planes form a bundle.*

The proof is obvious.

84. Plane coördinates. The ratios of the coefficients in the equation of the plane are sufficient to fix the plane and may be taken as the *coördinates of the plane*. We shall denote them by u_i and say that $u_1 : u_2 : u_3 : u_4$ are the plane coördinates of the plane whose point equation is

$$u_1 x_1 + u_2 x_2 + u_3 x_3 + u_4 x_4 = 0. \tag{1}$$

No difference is made in this definition if the point coördinates are Cartesian. Equation (1) is the condition that the plane u_i and the point x_i should be in *united position*; that is, that the plane should pass through the point or that the point should lie on the plane.

We have the following theorems, which are readily proved by means of those of § 83:

I. If $v_1 : v_2 : v_3 : v_4$ and $w_1 : w_2 : w_3 : w_4$ are the coördinates of two fixed planes, the coördinates of any plane through their line of intersection are

$$\rho u_1 = v_1 + \lambda w_1,$$
$$\rho u_2 = v_2 + \lambda w_2,$$
$$\rho u_3 = v_3 + \lambda w_3, \tag{2}$$
$$\rho u_4 = v_4 + \lambda w_4,$$

and any plane with these coördinates passes through this line.

The proof is obvious. Equations (2) are the equations of a pencil of planes. They are also called the *plane equations of a straight line*, the axis of the pencil. In this method of speaking the straight line is thought of as carrying the planes of the pencil in the same sense as that in which by the use of equations (1), § 83, the straight line is thought of as carrying the points of a range.

II. Any homogeneous linear equation of the form

$$a_1 u_1 + a_2 u_2 + a_3 u_3 + a_4 u_4 = 0 \tag{3}$$

is satisfied by the coördinates of all planes through a fixed point.

It follows from (1) that all planes whose coördinates satisfy (3) are united with the point $a_1 : a_2 : a_3 : a_4$. Equation (3) is therefore called the plane equation of the point $a_1 : a_2 : a_3 : a_4$, in the same sense in which equation (2), § 83, is the point equation of the plane $a_1 : a_2 : a_3 : a_4$.

III. Three planes not belonging to the same pencil determine a point.

This is, of course, the same theorem as VII, § 83, but in plane coördinates we prove it by noticing that three values of u_i, say v_i, w_i, s_i, which satisfy (3) are sufficient to determine the coefficients of (3) unless $\rho s_i = \lambda v_i + \mu w_i$. The equation of the point determined by the three planes is, then,

$$\begin{vmatrix} u_1 & u_2 & u_3 & u_4 \\ v_1 & v_2 & v_3 & v_4 \\ w_1 & w_2 & w_3 & w_4 \\ s_1 & s_2 & s_3 & s_4 \end{vmatrix} = 0. \tag{4}$$

IV. If v_i, w_i, and s_i are any three planes not belonging to the same pencil, the coördinates of any plane through their common point are

$$\rho u_i = v_i + \lambda w_i + \mu s_i,$$

and any plane with these coördinates passes through this point.

The proof is obvious. These planes form a *bundle*.

V. Two linear equations which are distinct are satisfied by the coördinates of planes which pass through a straight line.

This follows from the fact that each equation is satisfied by planes which pass through a fixed point. Simultaneously, therefore, the equations are satisfied by planes which have two points in common, and these points are distinct if the equations are distinct. The planes, therefore, have in common the line connecting the two points. The equation of a straight line can therefore be written in plane coördinates as the two simultaneous equations

$$a_1 u_1 + a_2 u_2 + a_3 u_3 + a_4 u_4 = 0,$$
$$b_1 u_1 + b_2 u_2 + b_3 u_3 + b_4 u_4 = 0.$$

VI. If $\sum a_i u_i = 0$ and $\sum b_i u_i = 0$ are the plane equations of two points not coincident, then $\sum a_i u_i + \lambda \sum b_i u_i = 0$ is the plane equation of any point on the line connecting the first two points. As λ takes all values, all points of a range can be thus obtained.

VII. If $\sum a_i u_i = 0$, $\sum b_i u_i = 0$, and $\sum c_i u_i = 0$ are the plane equations of three points not in the same plane, then $\sum a_i u_i + \lambda \sum b_i u_i + \mu \sum c_i u_i = 0$ is the plane equation of any point on the plane determined by the first three points. As λ and μ take all values, all points on the plane can be found.

The proofs of the last two theorems follow closely from theorems I and II of § 83.

The theorems of this section are plainly dualistic to the theorems of the previous section. We exhibit in parallel columns the fundamental dualistic objects:

Point	*Plane*
Points in a plane.	Planes through a point.
Points in two planes.	Planes through two points.
A straight line.	A straight line.
Points of a range.	Planes of a pencil.
Planes of a bundle.	Points of a plane.

EXERCISES

1. Write the equations, both in point and in plane coördinates, of the vertices, the faces, and the edges of the coördinate tetrahedron.

2. If a line is defined by the two points $(y_1 : y_2 : y_3 : y_4)$ and $(z_1 : z_2 : z_3 : z_4)$, show that its equations in plane coördinates are

$$u_1 y_1 + u_2 y_2 + u_3 y_3 + u_4 y_4 = 0,$$
$$u_1 z_1 + u_2 z_2 + u_3 z_3 + u_4 z_4 = 0;$$

and if a line is defined by the two planes $(v_1 : v_2 : v_3 : v_4)$ and $(w_1 : w_2 : w_3 : w_4)$, show that its equations in point coördinates are

$$v_1 x_1 + v_2 x_2 + v_3 x_3 + v_4 x_4 = 0,$$
$$w_1 x_1 + w_2 x_2 + w_3 x_3 + w_4 x_4 = 0.$$

3. Show that the condition that two lines defined by the planes $(a_1 : a_2 : a_3 : a_4)$, $(b_1 : b_2 : b_3 : b_4)$ and $(c_1 : c_2 : c_3 : c_4)$, $(d_1 : d_2 : d_3 : d_4)$, respectively, should intersect is

$$\begin{vmatrix} a_1 & a_2 & a_3 & a_4 \\ b_1 & b_2 & b_3 & b_4 \\ c_1 & c_2 & c_3 & c_4 \\ d_1 & d_2 & d_3 & d_4 \end{vmatrix} = 0,$$

and write the similar condition for two lines, each defined by two points.

4. Two conjugate imaginary lines being defined as lines such that each contains the conjugate imaginary point of any point of the other, show that if two conjugate imaginary lines intersect, the point of intersection and the plane of the two lines are real. Hence show that conjugate imaginary lines cannot lie on an imaginary plane.

5. Show that if a plane contains two pairs of conjugate imaginary points which are not on the same straight line the plane is real.

6. Two conjugate imaginary planes being defined as planes such that each contains the conjugate imaginary point of any point of the other, show that the plane coördinates of the planes are conjugate imaginary quantities, and conversely. Prove that two conjugate imaginary planes intersect in a real straight line.

85. One-dimensional extents of points. Consider the equations

$$\rho x_1 = f_1(t),$$
$$\rho x_2 = f_2(t),$$
$$\rho x_3 = f_3(t),$$
$$\rho x_4 = f_4(t),$$
$$\quad (1)$$

where t is an independent variable and $f_i(t)$ are functions which are continuous and possess derivatives of at least the first two orders. We shall also assume that the ratios of the four functions $f_i(t)$ are not independent of t. Then, to any value of t corresponds one or more points $x_1 : x_2 : x_3 : x_4$, and as t varies these points describe a one-dimensional extent of points, which, by definition, is a *curve*. It is evident that because of the factor ρ the form of the functions $f_i(t)$ may be varied without changing the curve, but there is no loss of generality if we assume a definite form for $f_i(t)$ and take $\rho = 1$.

Let y_i be a point P obtained by putting $t = t_1$ in (1), and let Q be a point obtained by putting $t = t_1 + \Delta t$. Then the coördinates of Q are $y_i + \Delta y_i$, and the points P and Q determine a straight line with the equations

$$\rho x_i = y_i + \mu (y_i + \Delta y_i)$$

or
$$\sigma x_i = y_i + \lambda \Delta y_i, \quad (2)$$

where the ratios of Δy_i and not the separate values of these quantities are essential. As Δt approaches zero the ratios $\Delta y_1 : \Delta y_2 : \Delta y_3 : \Delta y_4$ approach limiting ratios $dy_1 : dy_2 : dy_3 : dy_4 = f_1'(t_1) : f_2'(t_1) : f_3'(t_1) : f_4'(t_1)$, and the line (2) approaches as a limit the line

$$\rho x_i = y_i + \lambda dy_i = f_i(t_1) + \lambda f_i'(t_1), \quad (3)$$

which is called the *tangent line* to the curve. *At every point of the curve at which the four derivatives $f_i'(t)$ do not vanish, there is a definite tangent line.*

The points y_i and $y_i + dy_i$, which suffice to fix the tangent line, are often called *consecutive points* of the curve, but the exact meaning of this expression must be taken from the foregoing discussion.

We shall now show that *the tangent lines to a curve in the neighborhood of a fixed point of the curve form a point extent of two dimensions, unless in the neighborhood of the point in question the curve is a straight line.*

This follows in general from the fact that equations (3) involve two independent variables t_1 and λ. To examine the exceptional case we notice that at least two of the functions $f_i(t)$ cannot be identically zero if equations (1) do not represent a point. We shall also consider the neighborhood of a value t_1 in which $f_i'(t)$ are one-valued, and shall take $f_3(t)$ and $f_4(t)$ as the two functions which do not vanish identically. We may then place $\frac{f_3(t)}{f_4(t)} = \tau$ and replace equations (1) by the equivalent equations

$$\begin{aligned}
\rho x_1 &= F_1(\tau), \\
\rho x_2 &= F_2(\tau), \\
\rho x_3 &= \tau, \\
\rho x_4 &= 1,
\end{aligned} \qquad (4)$$

where $F_1(\tau)$ and $F_2(\tau)$ are one-valued in the neighborhood considered.

The equations of the tangent line are then

$$\begin{aligned}
\rho x_1 &= F_1(\tau_1) + \lambda F_1'(\tau_1), \\
\rho x_2 &= F_2(\tau_1) + \lambda F_2'(\tau_1), \\
\rho x_3 &= \tau_1 + \lambda, \\
\rho x_4 &= 1,
\end{aligned}$$

and the points on these lines form a two-dimensional extent unless

$$F_i(\tau_1) + \lambda F_i'(\tau_1) = \phi_i(\tau_1 + \lambda). \qquad (i = 1, 2) \qquad (5)$$

From this follows, by differentiating (5) with respect to λ,

$$F_i'(\tau_1) = \phi_i'(\tau_1 + \lambda), \qquad (6)$$

and by differentiating (5) with respect to τ_1,

$$F_i'(\tau_1) + \lambda F_i''(\tau_1) = \phi_i'(\tau_1 + \lambda), \qquad (7)$$

and from (6) and (7) we have $F_i''(\tau_1) = 0$; whence $F_i(\tau_1) = c_{i1}\tau + c_{i2}$.

Equations (4) then reduce to

$$\rho x_1 = c_{11}\tau + c_{12},$$
$$\rho x_2 = c_{21}\tau + c_{22},$$
$$\rho x_3 = \tau,$$
$$\rho x_4 = 1.$$

These are the equations of a straight line and the theorem is proved.

Consider now three points, P, Q, R, on the curve (1) with the coördinates y_i, $y_i + \Delta y_i$, and $y_i + \Delta y_i + \Delta(y_i + \Delta y_i)$, the increments corresponding to the increment Δt; that is,

$$y_i = f_i(t_1), \; y_i + \Delta y_i = f_i(t_1 + \Delta t), \; y_i + \Delta y_i + \Delta(y_i + \Delta y_i) = f_i(t_1 + 2\Delta t).$$

Then by the theorem of the mean,

$$\Delta y = f_i(t_1 + \Delta t) - f_i(t_1) = (f_i'(t_1) + \epsilon_1)\Delta t,$$

and by expansion into Maclaurin's series,

$$\Delta^2 y = f_i(t_1 + 2\Delta t) - 2f_i(t_1 + \Delta t) + f_i(t_1)$$
$$= (f_i''(t_1) + \epsilon_2)\Delta t^2.$$

The three points P, Q, and R determine a plane whose coördinates u_i satisfy the three equations

$$u_1 y_1 + u_2 y_2 + u_3 y_3 + u_4 y_4 = 0,$$
$$u_1 \Delta y_1 + u_2 \Delta y_2 + u_3 \Delta y_3 + u_4 \Delta y_4 = 0, \qquad (8)$$
$$u_1 \Delta^2 y_1 + u_2 \Delta^2 y_2 + u_3 \Delta^2 y_3 + u_4 \Delta^2 y_4 = 0.$$

As Δt approaches zero the three points P, Q, and R approach coincidence, and the plane (8) approaches as a limit the plane whose coördinates satisfy the three equations

$$u_1 y_1 + u_2 y_2 + u_3 y_3 + u_4 y_4 = 0,$$
$$u_1 dy_1 + u_2 dy_2 + u_3 dy_3 + u_4 dy_4 = 0, \qquad (9)$$
$$u_1 d^2 y_1 + u_2 d^2 y_2 + u_3 d^2 y_3 + u_4 d^2 y_4 = 0.$$

This plane is called the *osculating plane* at the point P. It is evident that *at any point P there is in general a definite osculating plane.* The only exceptions occur when the point P is such that the solution of the equations (9) is indeterminate. Writing these equations with derivatives in place of differentials we have

$$u_1 f_1(t_1) + u_2 f_2(t_1) + u_3 f_3(t_1) + u_4 f_4(t_1) = 0,$$
$$u_1 f_1'(t_1) + u_2 f_2'(t_1) + u_3 f_3'(t_1) + u_4 f_4'(t_1) = 0, \qquad (10)$$
$$u_1 f_1''(t_1) + u_2 f_2''(t_1) + u_3 f_3''(t_1) + u_4 f_4''(t_1) = 0,$$

and in order that the solution of these equations should be indeterminant it is necessary and sufficient that t_1 should satisfy the
equations formed by equating to zero all determinants of the third
order formed from the matrix

$$\begin{Vmatrix} f_1(t_1) & f_2(t_1) & f_3(t_1) & f_4(t_1) \\ f_1'(t_1) & f_2'(t_1) & f_3'(t_1) & f_4'(t_1) \\ f_1''(t_1) & f_2''(t_1) & f_3''(t_1) & f_4''(t_1) \end{Vmatrix}.$$

If these equations have solutions they will be in general discrete
values of t_1 which give discrete points on the curve at which the
osculating plane is indeterminate. To examine the character of a
curve for which the osculating plane is everywhere indeterminate,
it is convenient to take the equations of the curve in the form (4).
Equations (10) then take the form

$$u_1 F_1(\tau) + u_2 F_2(\tau) + u_3 \tau + u_4 = 0,$$
$$u_1 F_1'(\tau) + u_2 F_2'(\tau) + u_3 = 0, \tag{11}$$
$$u_1 F_1''(\tau) + u_2 F_2''(\tau) = 0,$$

and these have an indeterminate solution when and only when

$$F_1''(\tau) = 0, \quad F_2''(\tau) = 0. \tag{12}$$

If equations (9) are true for all values of τ, the curve is a
straight line, as has already been shown.

Equations (10) determine u_i as functions of the parameter t_1.
Therefore *the osculating planes of a curve form in general a one-
dimensional extent of planes.* An exception can occur only when
the ratios of u_i determined by (10) are constant. To examine this
case take again the special form (4) of the equations of the curve
and consider equations (11). If the ratios u_i determined by (11)
are constant, it is first of all necessary that

$$F_2''(\tau) = c_1 F_1''(\tau);$$

whence $\qquad F_2(\tau) = c_1 F_1(\tau) + c_2 \tau + c_3.$

Equations (4) then become

$$\rho x_1 = F_1(\tau),$$
$$\rho x_2 = c_1 F_1(\tau) + c_2 \tau + c_3,$$
$$\rho x_3 = \tau,$$
$$\rho x_4 = 1,$$

and any point whose coördinates satisfy these equations lies in the plane
$$c_1x_1 - x_2 + c_2x_3 + c_3x_4 = 0.$$

It is evident from the definition that this plane is the osculating plane at every point of the curve, and this can be verified from equations (11). We may accordingly make more precise the theorem already stated by saying that *the osculating planes of a curve in the neighborhood of a fixed point of the curve form a one-dimensional extent of planes unless the curve is a plane curve in the neighborhood considered.*

If from equations (1) the parameter t is eliminated in two ways, there results two equations of the form

$$\begin{aligned} f(x_1, x_2, x_3, x_4) &= 0, \\ g(x_1, x_2, x_3, x_4) &= 0. \end{aligned} \tag{13}$$

Conversely, any equations of form (13) may in general be replaced by equivalent equations of form (1).

EXERCISES

1. Show that in nonhomogeneous coördinates the equations of the tangent line and the osculating plane are, respectively,

$$\frac{X-x}{dx} = \frac{Y-y}{dy} = \frac{Z-z}{dz}$$

and
$$\begin{vmatrix} X-x & Y-y & Z-z \\ dx & dy & dz \\ d^2x & d^2y & d^2z \end{vmatrix} = 0.$$

2. Find the tangent line and osculating plane to the following curves:

(1) The cubic, $\quad\quad x = t^3, y = t^2, z = t.$

(2) The helix, $\quad\quad x = a\cos\theta, y = a\sin\theta, z = k\theta.$

(3) The conical helix, $\quad x = t\cos t, y = t\sin t, z = kt.$

3. Show that the osculating plane may be defined as the plane approached as a limit by a plane through the tangent line to the curve at a point P and through any other point P', as P' approaches P.

4. Show that the osculating plane may also be defined as the plane approached as a limit by a plane through a tangent line at P and parallel to a tangent line at P', the limit being taken as P' approaches P.

5. The principal normal to a curve is the line in the osculating plane perpendicular to the tangent at the point of contact; the binormal is the line perpendicular to the tangent and to the principal normal. Find the equations of these normals.

86. Locus of an equation in point coördinates. Consider the equation

$$f(x_1, x_2, x_3, x_4) = 0, \tag{1}$$

where f is a homogeneous function of x_1, x_2, x_3, and x_4, which is continuous and has derivatives of at least the first two orders. Two of the ratios $x_1 : x_2 : x_3 : x_4$ can be assumed arbitrarily, and the third determined from the equation. The equation therefore defines a two-dimensional extent of points which by definition is called a *surface*.

If f is an algebraic polynomial of degree n, the surface is called a surface of the *nth order*. *Any straight line meets a surface of the nth order in n points or lies entirely on the surface.* To prove this notice that a straight line is represented by equations of the form

$$\rho x_i = y_i + \lambda z_i,$$

where y_i and z_i are fixed points, and that these values of x_i substituted in (1) give an equation of the nth order in λ unless (1) is satisfied identically.

A *tangent line* to a surface is defined as the limit line approached by the secant through two points of the surface as the two points approach coincidence. Let y_i be the coördinates of a point P on the surface and $y_i + \Delta y_i$ those of a neighboring point Q also on the surface. The points P and Q determine a secant line, the equations of which are

$$\rho x_i = y_i + \lambda (y_i + \Delta y_i),$$

which can also be written

$$\rho x_i = y_i + \mu \Delta y_i, \tag{2}$$

where the ratios of Δy_i and not their individual values are essential. Now let the point Q approach the point P, moving on the surface, so that the ratios $\Delta y_1 : \Delta y_2 : \Delta y_3 : \Delta y_4$ approach definite limiting ratios $dy_1 : dy_2 : dy_3 : dy_4$. Then the line (2) approaches the limiting line

$$\rho x_i = y_i + \mu dy_i, \tag{3}$$

which is a tangent line to the surface at the point P.

If the four derivatives $\dfrac{\partial f}{\partial y_1}$, $\dfrac{\partial f}{\partial y_2}$, $\dfrac{\partial f}{\partial y_3}$, $\dfrac{\partial f}{\partial y_4}$ do not all vanish, the ratios $dy_1 : dy_2 : dy_3 : dy_4$ are bound only by the condition

$$\frac{\partial f}{\partial y_1} dy_1 + \frac{\partial f}{\partial y_2} dy_2 + \frac{\partial f}{\partial y_3} dy_3 + \frac{\partial f}{\partial y_4} dy_4 = 0. \tag{4}$$

By Euler's theorem for homogeneous functions we have, since y_i satisfies equation (1),

$$y_1 \frac{\partial f}{\partial y_1} + y_2 \frac{\partial f}{\partial y_2} + y_3 \frac{\partial f}{\partial y_3} + y_4 \frac{\partial f}{\partial y_4} = 0. \tag{5}$$

By virtue of (4) and (5) any point x_i of (3) satisfies the equation

$$x_1 \frac{\partial f}{\partial y_1} + x_2 \frac{\partial f}{\partial y_2} + x_3 \frac{\partial f}{\partial y_3} + x_4 \frac{\partial f}{\partial y_4} = 0. \tag{6}$$

This is the equation of a plane, and its coefficients depend only upon the coördinates of P and not on the ratios $dy_1 : dy_2 : dy_3 : dy_4$.

Hence all points on all tangent lines to the surface satisfy the equation (6). Equation (6), however, becomes illusive, and the discussion which led to it is impossible when P is such a point that

$$\frac{\partial f}{\partial y_1} = 0, \quad \frac{\partial f}{\partial y_2} = 0, \quad \frac{\partial f}{\partial y_3} = 0, \quad \frac{\partial f}{\partial y_4} = 0.$$

Points which satisfy these equations are called *singular points*, and other points are called *regular points*. We have, then, the following theorem:

All tangent lines to a surface at a regular point lie in a plane called the tangent plane, the equation of which is (6).

In the equation (6) the point y_i is called the point of tangency. Conversely, *any line drawn in the tangent plane through the point of tangency is a tangent line.* To prove this take z_i, any point in the plane (6). Then

$$z_1 \frac{\partial f}{\partial y_1} + z_2 \frac{\partial f}{\partial y_2} + z_3 \frac{\partial f}{\partial y_3} + z_4 \frac{\partial f}{\partial y_4} = 0,$$

and the equations of the line through y_i and z_i are

$$\rho x_i = y_i + \lambda z_i.$$

But a point Q on the surface may be made to approach P in such a way that $dy_1 : dy_2 : dy_3 : dy_4 = z_1 : z_2 : z_3 : z_4$, since the only restriction on dy_i is given by (4), which is satisfied by z_i. Hence the line determined by y_i and z_i has equations of the form (3) and is therefore a tangent line, and the theorem is proved.

The plane coördinates of the tangent plane to the surface (1) are, from (6),

$$\rho u_i = \frac{\partial f}{\partial y_i}. \qquad (i = 1, 2, 3, 4) \qquad (7)$$

The coördinates y_i can be eliminated between these equations, and the equation

$$f(y_1, y_2, y_3, y_4) = 0 \qquad (8)$$

found by substituting y_i for x_i in (1). There are three possible results:

1. There may be a single equation of the form

$$\phi(u_1, u_2, u_3, u_4) = 0. \qquad (9)$$

This is the general case, in which the equations (7) can be solved and the results substituted in (8).

The condition for this is that the Jacobian

$$\begin{vmatrix} \dfrac{\partial u_1}{\partial x_1} & \dfrac{\partial u_1}{\partial x_2} & \dfrac{\partial u_1}{\partial x_3} & \dfrac{\partial u_1}{\partial x_4} \\[2mm] \dfrac{\partial u_2}{\partial x_1} & \dfrac{\partial u_2}{\partial x_2} & \dfrac{\partial u_2}{\partial x_3} & \dfrac{\partial u_2}{\partial x_4} \\[2mm] \dfrac{\partial u_3}{\partial x_1} & \dfrac{\partial u_3}{\partial x_2} & \dfrac{\partial u_3}{\partial x_3} & \dfrac{\partial u_3}{\partial x_4} \\[2mm] \dfrac{\partial u_4}{\partial x_1} & \dfrac{\partial u_4}{\partial x_2} & \dfrac{\partial u_4}{\partial x_3} & \dfrac{\partial u_4}{\partial x_4} \end{vmatrix} \equiv \begin{vmatrix} \dfrac{\partial^2 f}{\partial x_1^2} & \dfrac{\partial^2 f}{\partial x_1 \partial x_2} & \dfrac{\partial^2 f}{\partial x_1 \partial x_3} & \dfrac{\partial^2 f}{\partial x_1 \partial x_4} \\[2mm] \dfrac{\partial^2 f}{\partial x_1 \partial x_2} & \dfrac{\partial^2 f}{\partial x_2^2} & \dfrac{\partial^2 f}{\partial x_2 \partial x_3} & \dfrac{\partial^2 f}{\partial x_2 \partial x_4} \\[2mm] \dfrac{\partial^2 f}{\partial x_1 \partial x_3} & \dfrac{\partial^2 f}{\partial x_2 \partial x_3} & \dfrac{\partial^2 f}{\partial x_3^2} & \dfrac{\partial^2 f}{\partial x_3 \partial x_4} \\[2mm] \dfrac{\partial^2 f}{\partial x_1 \partial x_4} & \dfrac{\partial^2 f}{\partial x_2 \partial x_4} & \dfrac{\partial^2 f}{\partial x_3 \partial x_4} & \dfrac{\partial^2 f}{\partial x_4^2} \end{vmatrix}$$

shall not vanish. In this case the tangent planes to (1) form a two-dimensional extent and their coördinates satisfy (9).

If $\phi(u_1, u_2, u_3, u_4)$ is an algebraic polynomial of the mth degree, the surface (1) is said to be of the mth class. *Through any straight line m planes can be passed, tangent to a surface of the mth class.* To prove this notice that a plane through any straight line has the coördinates

$$\rho u_i = v_i + \lambda w_i,$$

where v_i and w_i are fixed coördinates. These values of u_i substituted in (9) give an equation of the mth degree in λ. This proves the theorem.

For example, consider the surface

$$a_1 x_1^2 + a_2 x_2^2 + a_3 x_3^2 + a_4 x_4^2 = 0.$$

The coördinates of its tangent plane are

$$\rho u_i = a_i y_i,$$

and these values substituted in

$$a_1 y_1^2 + a_2 y_2^2 + a_3 y_3^2 + a_4 y_4^2 = 0$$

give

$$\frac{u_1^2}{a_1} + \frac{u_2^2}{a_2} + \frac{u_3^2}{a_3} + \frac{u_4^2}{a_4} = 0.$$

The order and class of this surface are both 2, but the class of a surface is not in general equal to its order.

2. There may be two equations of the form

$$\phi(u_1, u_2, u_3, u_4) = 0,$$

$$\psi(u_1, u_2, u_3, u_4) = 0.$$

In this case the tangent planes to (1) form a one-dimensional extent. The surface is called a *developable surface*.

For example, consider the surface

$$x_1^2 + x_2^2 - x_3^2 + 2\,x_3 x_4 - x_4^2 = 0.$$

The coördinates of a tangent plane at y_i are

$$\rho u_1 = y_1,$$

$$\rho u_2 = y_2,$$

$$\rho u_3 = -y_3 + y_4,$$

$$\rho u_4 = y_3 - y_4.$$

The elimination of y_i from these equations and the equation

$$y_1^2 + y_2^2 - y_3^2 + 2\,y_3 y_4 - y_4^2 = 0$$

gives the two equations $\qquad u_3 + u_4 = 0,$

$$u_1^2 + u_2^2 - u_3^2 = 0.$$

3. There may be three equations of the form

$$\phi(u_1, u_2, u_3, u_4) = 0,$$

$$\psi(u_1, u_2, u_3, u_4) = 0,$$

$$\chi(u_1, u_2, u_3, u_4) = 0.$$

These equations can be solved for u_i. Hence in this case the tangent planes form a discrete system.

For example, consider the surface

$$x_1 x_4 + x_2 x_4 + x_3 x_4 = 0.$$

The tangent planes have the coördinates

$$\rho u_1 = x_4,$$
$$\rho u_2 = x_4,$$
$$\rho u_3 = x_4,$$
$$\rho u_4 = x_1 + x_2 + x_3.$$

These lead to the equations

$$u_1 = u_2,$$
$$u_2 = u_3,$$
$$u_1 u_4 = 0.$$

The tangent planes are the two planes $x_4 = 0$ and $x_1 + x_2 + x_3 = 0$. In fact the surface consists of these two planes.

EXERCISES

1. Show that the section of a surface made by a tangent plane is a curve which has a singular point at the point of contact of the plane.

2. Show that the section of a surface of the nth order made by any plane is a curve of the nth order.

3. Show that any tangent plane to a surface of second order intersects the surface in two straight lines, and in particular that the tangent plane to a sphere intersects the sphere in two minimum lines.

4. Show that through the point of contact of a surface and a tangent plane there go in general two lines lying in the plane and having three coincident points in common with the surface.

5. Show that the equation $f(x_1, x_2, x_3) = 0$, where the function f is homogeneous in x_1, x_2, x_3 and the coördinate x_4 is missing, represents a cone, by showing that it is the locus of lines through the point $0:0:0:1$.

6. Show that the tangent plane to a cone contains the element of the cone through the point of contact.

7. From Ex. 5 show that in nonhomogeneous Cartesian coördinates the equation $f(x, y, z) = 0$, where f is homogeneous, represents a cone with its vertex at the origin and that $f(x, y) = 0$ represents a cylinder with its elements parallel to OZ.

8. Show that through a singular point of a surface there goes in general a cone of lines each of which has three coincident points in common with the surface.

9. Find the equation or equations satisfied by the coördinates of the tangent planes of each of the following surfaces:

$$(1)\ 2\,ax_1x_2 + bx_3^2 + cx_4^2 = 0,$$
$$(2)\ 2\,ax_1x_2 + bx_2^2 + cx_4^2 = 0,$$
$$(3)\ 2\,ax_1x_2 + bx_1^2 + cx_2^2 = 0.$$

10. Show that the tangent planes of a cone or a cylinder form a one-dimensional extent.

11. If the equation of a surface is written in the nonhomogeneous form $z = f(x, y)$, show that its tangent planes form a two-dimensional extent unless $rt - s^2 = 0$, where $r = \dfrac{\partial^2 f}{\partial x^2}$, $s = \dfrac{\partial^2 f}{\partial x \partial y}$, $t = \dfrac{\partial^2 f}{\partial y^2}$.

12. Show that two simultaneous equations $\phi_1(x_1, x_2, x_3, x_4) = 0$ and $\phi_2(x_1, x_2, x_3, x_4) = 0$ define a curve, and that if the tangent planes to the curve are defined as the planes through the tangent lines to the curve, they form a two-dimensional extent given by the equations $\rho u_i = \dfrac{\partial \phi_1}{\partial x_i} + \lambda \dfrac{\partial \phi_2}{\partial x_i}$ together with the equations of the curve.

87. One-dimensional extents of planes. Consider the equations

$$\begin{aligned}
\rho u_1 &= f_1(t), \\
\rho u_2 &= f_2(t), \\
\rho u_3 &= f_3(t), \\
\rho u_4 &= f_4(t),
\end{aligned} \tag{1}$$

where u_i are plane coördinates, t an independent variable, and $f_i(t)$ functions of t which are continuous and possess derivatives of at least the first two orders. We shall also assume that the ratios of the four functions $f_i(t)$ are not independent of t. The equations then define a one-dimensional extent of planes. Let v be the coördinates of a plane p (Fig. 53) obtained by placing $t = t_1$ in (1) and let $v_i + \Delta v_i$ be the coördinates of a plane q found by placing $t = t_1 + \Delta t$. Then p and q determine a straight line m, the equations of which are

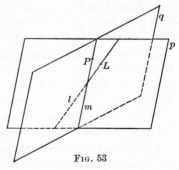

Fig. 53

$$\rho u_i = v_i + \mu\,(v_i + \Delta v_i)$$

or

$$\sigma u_i = v_i + \lambda \Delta v_i.$$

As Δt approaches zero the line m approaches a limiting line l, of which the equations are

$$\rho u_i = v_i + \lambda dv_i = f_i(t_1) + \lambda f_i'(t_1). \qquad (2)$$

This line is called a *characteristic* of the extent defined by (1). It is evident that *in any plane of the extent for which the four derivatives $f_i'(t)$ do not vanish there is a definite characteristic.*

We shall now prove the proposition

The characteristics form in general a surface to which each plane of the defining plane extent is tangent along the entire characteristic in that plane.

To prove this we notice that any point x_i which lies in a characteristic satisfies the two equations

$$\begin{aligned}
x_1 f_1(t) + x_2 f_2(t) + x_3 f_3(t) + x_4 f_4(t) = 0, \\
x_1 f_1'(t) + x_2 f_2'(t) + x_3 f_3'(t) + x_4 f_4'(t) = 0,
\end{aligned} \qquad (3)$$

and that in general t may be eliminated from these equations with a result of the form

$$\phi(x_1, x_2, x_3, x_4) = 0. \qquad (4)$$

This proves that any point on any characteristic lies on the surface with the equation (4).

By virtue of the manner in which (4) was derived we may write

$$\phi(x_1, x_2, x_3, x_4) = \sum x_i f_i(t),$$

where t is to be determined as a function of x_i from the second of equations (3). Therefore

$$\frac{\partial \phi}{\partial x_i} = f_i(t) + \left[\sum x_k f_k'(t) \right] \frac{\partial t}{\partial x_i} = f_i(t) = \rho u_i.$$

This shows that the tangent plane of (4) is the plane u_i of the extent (1) and that the same tangent plane is found for all points for which t has the same value; that is, for all points on the same characteristic. The proposition is then proved.

Consider now three planes, v_i, $v_i + \Delta v_i$, $v_i + \Delta v_i + \Delta(v_i + \Delta v_i)$. They determine a point P the coördinates of which satisfy the three equations

$$\begin{aligned}
x_1 v_1 + x_2 v_2 + x_3 v_3 + x_4 v_4 = 0, \\
x_1 \Delta v_1 + x_2 \Delta v_2 + x_3 \Delta v_3 + x_4 \Delta v_4 = 0, \\
x_1 \Delta^2 v_1 + x_2 \Delta^2 v_2 + x_3 \Delta^2 v_3 + x_4 \Delta^2 v_4 = 0,
\end{aligned} \qquad (5)$$

and as Δt approaches zero the point P approaches as a limit a point L the coördinates of which satisfy the equations

$$x_1 v_1 + x_2 v_2 + x_3 v_3 + x_4 v_4 = 0,$$
$$x_1 dv_1 + x_2 dv_2 + x_3 dv_3 + x_4 dv_4 = 0, \qquad (6)$$
$$x_1 d^2 v_1 + x_2 d^2 v_2 + x_3 d^2 v_3 + x_4 d^2 v_4 = 0,$$

or, what is the same thing, the equations

$$x_1 f_1(t) + x_2 f_2(t) + x_3 f_3(t) + x_4 f_4(t) = 0,$$
$$x_1 f_1'(t) + x_2 f_2'(t) + x_3 f_3'(t) + x_4 f_4'(t) = 0, \qquad (7)$$
$$x_1 f_1''(t) + x_2 f_2''(t) + x_3 f_3''(t) + x_4 f_4''(t) = 0.$$

The point L we shall call the *limit* point in the plane v_i and shall prove the following proposition:

The locus of the limit points is in general a curve, called the cuspidal edge, to which the characteristics are tangent.

The first part of the proposition follows from the fact that equations (6) can in general be solved for x_i as functions of t.

To prove the second part of the proposition note that by differentiating the first two equations of (7) on the hypothesis that x_1, x_2, x_3, x_4 and t vary, and reducing the results by aid of the three equations (7), we have

$$\sum dx_i f_i(t) = 0, \qquad \sum dx_i f_i'(t) = 0. \qquad (8)$$

Now from (3), § 86, the tangent line to the cuspidal edge at a point (x_1, x_2, x_3, x_4) given by a value t has the equations

$$\rho X_i = x_i + \lambda dx_i,$$

and from (7) and (8) any values of the coördinates X_i which satisfy these equations satisfy also

$$\sum X_i f_i(t) = 0, \qquad \sum X_i f_i'(t) = 0;$$

that is, the point X_i lies on the characteristic (3).

To complete the general discussion we shall now prove the proposition

The osculating planes of the cuspidal edge are the planes of the defining plane extent.

By differentiating the first of equations (7) and reducing by the aid of the second equation, we have $\sum dx_i f_i(t) = 0$. Therefore by selecting the proper equations from (3) and (8) and replacing $f_i(t)$ by v_i, we have the equations

$$\sum v_i x_i = 0, \quad \sum v_i dx_i = 0, \quad \sum v_i d^2 x_i = 0.$$

But from (9), § 85, these equations define v_i as the osculating plane of the cuspidal edge. This proves the proposition.

In the foregoing discussion we have considered what happens in general. To examine the exceptional cases we may, as in § 85, write the equations (1) in the form

$$\begin{aligned}
\rho u_1 &= F_1(\tau), \\
\rho u_2 &= F_2(\tau), \\
\rho u_3 &= \tau, \\
\rho u_4 &= 1.
\end{aligned} \tag{9}$$

The equations (3) for the characteristics now become

$$\begin{aligned}
x_1 F_1(\tau) + x_2 F_2(\tau) + \tau x_3 + x_4 &= 0, \\
x_1 F_1'(\tau) + x_2 F_2'(\tau) + x_3 &= 0,
\end{aligned} \tag{10}$$

and the equations (7) for the limit points become

$$\begin{aligned}
x_1 F_1(\tau) + x_2 F(\tau) + x_3 \tau + x_4 &= 0, \\
x_1 F_1'(\tau) + x_2 F'(\tau) + x_3 &= 0, \\
x_1 F_1''(\tau) + x_2 F''(\tau) &= 0.
\end{aligned} \tag{11}$$

The second of the equations (10) can be solved for τ unless

$$F_1'(\tau) = c_1, \qquad F_2'(\tau) = c_2;$$

whence

$$F(\tau) = c_1 \tau + c_3, \qquad F_2(\tau) = c_2 \tau + c_4,$$

and

$$F_1''(\tau) = 0, \qquad F_2''(\tau) = 0.$$

In this case equations (10) become

$$\begin{aligned}
c_1 x_1 + c_2 x_2 + x_3 &= 0, \\
c_3 x_1 + c_4 x_2 + x_4 &= 0,
\end{aligned} \tag{12}$$

so that all characteristics are the same straight line. At the same time equations (9) become

$$\begin{aligned}
\rho u_1 &= c_1 \tau + c_3, \\
\rho u_2 &= c_2 \tau + c_4, \\
\rho u_3 &= \tau, \\
\rho u_4 &= 1,
\end{aligned}$$

which are of the type (2), § 84, and represent a pencil of planes determined by the two planes $(c_3 : c_4 : 0 : 1)$ and $(c_1 : c_2 : 1 : 0)$. The axis of the pencil is the straight line (12) with which the characteristics coincide.

Turning now to equations (11) we see that the last one determines $x_1 : x_2$ and the others determine x_3 and x_4, unless $F_1''(\tau) = 0$ and $F_2''(\tau) = 0$. This is the same exceptional case just considered. The equations for the limit points become equations (12), so that the limit point in each plane is indeterminate but lies on the axis of the pencil of planes.

Another exceptional case appears here also when the solutions of (11) do not involve τ. This happens when

$$F_2''(\tau) = c_1 F_1''(\tau);$$

whence $\qquad F_2(\tau) = c_1 F_1(\tau) + c_2\tau + c_3.$

Equations (11) then have the solution

$$x_1 : x_2 : x_3 : x_4 = c_1 : -1 : c_2 : c_3. \tag{13}$$

At the same time equations (9) are

$$\rho u_1 = F_1(\tau),$$
$$\rho u_2 = c_1 F_1(\tau) + c_2\tau + c_3,$$
$$\rho u_3 = \tau,$$
$$\rho u_4 = 1.$$

All planes which satisfy these equations pass through the point (13).

The surface of the characteristics is in this case a *cone*, since it is made up of lines through a common point. The cuspidal edge reduces to the vertex of the cone.

In § 86 we have shown that the tangent planes to a surface may, under certain conditions, form a one-dimensional extent of planes, and have called such surfaces *developable surfaces*. We may now state the following theorem, which is in a sense the converse of the above:

Any one-dimensional extent of planes is composed of planes which are tangent to a developable surface, where, in the neighborhood of each point, the surface may be one of the following three kinds:

1. *It may be composed of tangent lines to a space curve.*
2. *It may be a cone. (If the vertex is at infinity, the cone is a cylinder.)*
3. *It may degenerate into the axis of a pencil of planes.*

In the above theorem the nature of the surface has been described only for each portion of it, since the foregoing discussion is based on the nature of the functions $f_i(t)$ in the neighborhood of a value of t, which fixes a definite plane, a definite characteristic, and a definite point on the cuspidal edge. In the simplest case the developable surface will have throughout one of the forms given above. Next in simplicity would be the case in which the surface is composed of two or more surfaces, each of which is one of the above kinds. It is of course possible to define surfaces which have different natures in different portions, but the character of each portion must be as above if the functions $f_i(t)$ satisfy the conditions given.

The planes of the extent are said in each case to *envelop* the developable surface.

88. Locus of an equation in plane coördinates. Consider an equation

$$f(u_1, u_2, u_3, u_4) = 0, \tag{1}$$

where f is a homogeneous function of the plane coördinates u_i. We shall consider only functions which are continuous and have derivatives of at least the first two orders. Two of the ratios $u_1 : u_2 : u_3 : u_4$ can be assumed arbitrarily, and the third determined from the equation. Hence *the equation represents an extent of two dimensions.*

If f is a polynomial of the nth degree, then n planes belonging to the extent (1) pass through any general line in space. The proof is as in § 86. In this case the extent is said to be of the nth class.

We shall not restrict ourselves, however, to polynomials in the following discussion, but shall proceed to find some of the general properties of the extent (1).

Let v_i be the coördinates of a plane p (Fig. 54) of the configuration defined by (1), and $v_i + \Delta v_i$ those of another plane q, also of the configuration. The two planes p and q determine a line m whose equations in plane coördinates (theorem I, § 84) are

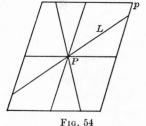

Fig. 54

$$\rho u_i = v_i + \lambda(v_i + \Delta v_i),$$

or, otherwise written, $\sigma u_i = v_i + \mu \Delta v_i,$

where the ratios only of Δv_i are essential.

Now let q approach coincidence with p in such a way that the ratios $\Delta v_1 : \Delta v_2 : \Delta v_3 : \Delta v_4$ approach limiting ratios $dv_1 : dv_2 : dv_3 : dv_4$. The line m approaches a limiting line L whose equations in plane coördinates are
$$\sigma u_i = v_i + \mu dv_i.$$

The differentials dv are bound only by the condition
$$df = \frac{\partial f}{\partial v_1} dv_1 + \frac{\partial f}{\partial v_2} dv_2 + \frac{\partial f}{\partial v_3} dv_3 + \frac{\partial f}{\partial v_4} dv_4 = 0, \tag{2}$$

so that the planes with coördinates $dv_1 : dv_2 : dv_3 : dv_4$ form a linear one-dimensional extent which by theorem II, § 84, consists of all planes through the point P, whose coördinates are
$$x_1 : x_2 : x_3 : x_4 = \frac{\partial f}{\partial v_1} : \frac{\partial f}{\partial v_2} : \frac{\partial f}{\partial v_3} : \frac{\partial f}{\partial v_4}. \tag{3}$$

This point lies in the plane v_i since, by Euler's theorem for homogeneous functions,
$$v_1 \frac{\partial f}{\partial v_1} + v_2 \frac{\partial f}{\partial v_2} + v_3 \frac{\partial f}{\partial v_3} + v_4 \frac{\partial f}{\partial v_4} = 0, \tag{4}$$

which is the condition (1), § 84, for united position.

A line L is the intersection of any one of the planes $dv_1 : dv_2 : dv_3 : dv_4$ with the plane $v_1 : v_2 : v_3 : v_4$. Hence the lines L form a pencil of lines through P.

The point P is not determined by equations (3) if
$$\frac{\partial f}{\partial v_1} = 0, \quad \frac{\partial f}{\partial v_2} = 0, \quad \frac{\partial f}{\partial v_3} = 0, \quad \frac{\partial f}{\partial v_4} = 0. \tag{5}$$

A plane for which these conditions is met is called a *singular plane* of the extent (1). Other planes are called *regular planes*.

We sum up our results in the following theorem:

In any regular plane p of the extent (1) *there lies a definite point P whose coördinates are given by* (3) *and which has the property that any line of the pencil with the vertex P and in the plane p is the limit of the intersection of p and a neighboring plane.*

The point P may be called the *limit point* in the plane p.

The elimination of v_i from equations (3) and equation (1), written in v_i, will give the locus of the points P. There are three cases:

I. The elimination may give one and only one equation of the form
$$\phi(x_1,\, x_2,\, x_3,\, x_4) = 0. \tag{6}$$

The locus of p is then a surface. If the extent (1) is of the nth class, the surface (6) is also called a surface of the nth class.

II. There may be two equations of the form

$$\phi_1(x_1, x_2, x_3, x_4) = 0,$$
$$\phi_2(x_1, x_2, x_3, x_4) = 0. \tag{7}$$

The locus of P is then a curve.

III. There may be three equations connecting x_1, x_2, x_3, x_4. The points P are then discrete points.

We shall now show that the planes of (1) are tangent to the locus of P in such a manner that P is the point of tangency of the plane p, in which it lies.

To prove this write equation (4) in the form

$$v_1 x_1 + v_2 x_2 + v_3 x_3 + v_4 x_4 = 0$$

and differentiate. We have

$$\sum v_i dx_i + \sum x_i dv_i = 0,$$

which, by aid of (2) and (3), is

$$v_1 dx_1 + v_2 dx_2 + v_3 dx_3 + v_4 dx_4 = 0. \tag{8}$$

Consider now in order the previous cases.

I. If x_i satisfy a single equation (6), we have

$$\frac{\partial \phi}{\partial x_1} dx_1 + \frac{\partial \phi}{\partial x_2} dx_2 + \frac{\partial \phi}{\partial x_3} dx_3 + \frac{\partial \phi}{\partial x_4} dx_4 = 0. \tag{9}$$

By comparison of (8) and (9) we have $\rho v_i = \dfrac{\partial \phi}{\partial x_i}$, which shows that v_i are the coördinates of the tangent to $\phi = 0$ at the point x_i.

II. If x_i satisfy the two equations (7), we have

$$\frac{\partial \phi_1}{\partial x_1} dx_1 + \frac{\partial \phi_1}{\partial x_2} dx_2 + \frac{\partial \phi_1}{\partial x_3} dx_3 + \frac{\partial \phi_1}{\partial x_4} dx_4 = 0,$$

$$\frac{\partial \phi_2}{\partial x_1} dx_1 + \frac{\partial \phi_2}{\partial x_2} dx_2 + \frac{\partial \phi_2}{\partial x_3} dx_3 + \frac{\partial \phi_2}{\partial x_4} dx_4 = 0.$$

A comparison with (8) gives $\rho v_i = \dfrac{\partial \phi_1}{\partial x_i} + \lambda \dfrac{\partial \phi_2}{\partial x_i}$, which shows that v_i passes through the line of intersection of the tangent planes to $\phi_1 = 0$ and $\phi_2 = 0$ and hence is tangent to the curve defined by the two surfaces.

III. If the points x_i are discrete points, we may say that each plane of the extent is tangent to the point, through which it passes, thus extending the use of the word "tangent" in a manner which will be useful later. Summing up, we say:

A two-dimensional extent of planes consists of planes which are tangent either to a surface or to a curve or to a point.

The theorem has reference, of course, only to the neighborhood of a plane of the extent. The entire extent may have the same nature throughout or different natures in different portions.

89. Change of coördinates. A tetrahedron of reference and a set of coördinates x_i having been chosen, consider any four planes not meeting in a point the equations of which are

$$\begin{aligned}
a_{11}x_1 + a_{12}x_2 + a_{13}x_3 + a_{14}x_4 &= 0, \\
a_{21}x_1 + a_{22}x_2 + a_{23}x_3 + a_{24}x_4 &= 0, \\
a_{31}x_1 + a_{32}x_2 + a_{33}x_3 + a_{34}x_4 &= 0, \\
a_{41}x_1 + a_{42}x_2 + a_{43}x_3 + a_{44}x_4 &= 0,
\end{aligned} \tag{1}$$

the coefficients being subject to the single condition that their determinant $|a_{ik}|$ shall not vanish. We assert that if we place

$$\rho x_i' = a_{i1}x_1 + a_{i2}x_2 + a_{i3}x_3 + a_{i4}x_4, \tag{2}$$

then x_i' are the coördinates of the point x_i referred to the tetrahedron formed by the four planes (1). The proof runs along the same lines as that of the corresponding theorem in the plane (§ 29) and will accordingly not be given.

It is also easy to show that by the same change of the tetrahedron of reference, the coördinates u_i become u_i', where

$$\rho u_i' = a_{1i}u_1 + a_{2i}u_2 + a_{3i}u_3 + a_{4i}u_4. \tag{3}$$

The change from one set of Cartesian coördinates to another is effected by means of formulas which are special cases of (2). If $(x:y:z:t)$ are rectangular Cartesian coördinates and

$$\begin{aligned}
a_1 x + b_1 y + c_1 z + e_1 t &= 0, \\
a_2 x + b_2 y + c_2 z + e_2 t &= 0, \\
a_3 x + b_3 y + c_3 z + e_3 t &= 0
\end{aligned} \tag{4}$$

are any three nonparallel planes, and we place

$$\begin{aligned}
\rho x' &= k_1(a_1 x + b_1 y + c_1 z + e_1 t), \\
\rho y' &= k_2(a_2 x + b_2 y + c_2 z + e_2 t), \\
\rho z' &= k_3(a_3 x_3 + b_3 y_3 + c_3 z_3 + e_3 t), \\
\rho t' &= t,
\end{aligned} \tag{5}$$

the quantities x', y', z', t' are proportional to the perpendiculars on the three planes, and it is possible to adjust the factors k_i so that $x' : y' : z' : t'$ may be exactly the Cartesian coördinates referred to the planes (4) as coördinate planes, the coördinates being rectangular or oblique according to the relative position of the planes (4).

The equations (5) represent a change from a rectangular set of coördinates to another set which may or may not be rectangular, and conversely. A change from an oblique system to another is represented by formulas of the same type, since the change may be brought about as the result of two transformations of this type.

EXERCISES

1. Find the characteristics, characteristic surface, and cuspidal edge of each of the following extent of planes:

(1) $\rho u_1 = 1$, $\rho u_2 = 3\,t$, $\rho u_3 = 3\,t^2$, $\rho u_4 = t^3$.

(2) $\rho u_1 = ak \sin t$, $\rho u_2 = -ak \cos t$, $\rho u_3 = a^2$, $\rho u_4 = -a^2 kt$.

(3) $\rho u_1 = 1 - t^2$, $\rho u_2 = 2\,t$, $\rho u_3 = -(1 + t^2)$, $\rho u_4 = 1 + t^2$.

(4) $\rho u_1 = 2\,t$, $\rho u_2 = t^2 - 1$, $\rho u_3 = t^2 + 1$, $\rho u_4 = 1$.

2. If a minimum developable is defined as a one-dimensional extent of minimum planes, show that the characteristics are minimum lines and the cuspidal edge is a minimum curve unless the developable is a cone.

3. Show that the necessary and sufficient condition that the surface $z = f(x, y)$ should be a minimum developable is that $p^2 + q^2 + 1 = 0$, where $p = \dfrac{\partial f}{\partial x}$, $q = \dfrac{\partial f}{\partial y}$. (Compare Ex. 11, § 86.)

4. Prove that planes which are tangent at the same time to two given surfaces, two given curves, or a given surface and a given curve define developable surfaces.

5. Find the envelope of each of the following one-dimensional extent of planes:

(1) $2\,u_1^2 + 3\,u_2^2 + 4\,u_3^2 - 24\,u_4^2 = 0$.

(2) $3\,u_1 u_2 u_3 - u_4^3 = 0$.

(3) $u_1^2 + u_2^2 - u_4^2 = 0$.

(4) $u_1^2 + u_2^2 + 2\,u_3^2 - 2\,u_1 u_2 + 2\,u_1 u_3 - 2\,u_2 u_3 - u_4^2 = 0$.

6. Show that the minimum planes form a two-dimensional extent and find its equation.

7. Show that $\rho x_i = f_i(t) + s f_i'(t)$ $(i = 1, 2, 3, 4)$ defines a developable surface and, conversely, that any developable surface which is not a cone or the axis of a pencil of planes may be expressed in this way.

CHAPTER XIII

SURFACES OF SECOND ORDER AND OF SECOND CLASS

90. Surfaces of second order. Consider the equation

$$\sum a_{ik}x_ix_k = 0, \qquad (a_{ki} = a_{ik}) \tag{1}$$

which defines a surface of second order (§ 86). The Jacobian of § 86 becomes, except for a factor 2, the determinant

$$\Delta = \begin{vmatrix} a_{11} & a_{12} & a_{13} & a_{14} \\ a_{12} & a_{22} & a_{23} & a_{24} \\ a_{13} & a_{23} & a_{33} & a_{34} \\ a_{14} & a_{24} & a_{34} & a_{44} \end{vmatrix},$$

called the *discriminant* of the equation. We may make the following preliminary classification:

I. $\Delta \neq 0$. The surface has a doubly infinite set of tangent planes. The plane equation of the surface may be found by eliminating u_i from the equations

$$\begin{aligned}
\rho u_1 &= a_{11}x_1 + a_{12}x_2 + a_{13}x_3 + a_{14}x_4, \\
\rho u_2 &= a_{12}x_1 + a_{22}x_2 + a_{23}x_3 + a_{24}x_4, \\
\rho u_3 &= a_{13}x_1 + a_{23}x_2 + a_{33}x_3 + a_{34}x_4, \\
\rho u_4 &= a_{14}x_1 + a_{24}x_2 + a_{34}x_3 + a_{44}x_4,
\end{aligned} \tag{2}$$

and equation (1). But a combination of (2) and (1) gives readily

$$u_1x_1 + u_2x_2 + u_3x_3 + u_4x_4 = 0,$$

and the elimination of x_i from this equation and the set (2) gives

$$\begin{vmatrix} a_{11} & a_{12} & a_{13} & a_{14} & u_1 \\ a_{12} & a_{22} & a_{23} & a_{24} & u_2 \\ a_{13} & a_{23} & a_{33} & a_{34} & u_3 \\ a_{14} & a_{24} & a_{34} & a_{44} & u_4 \\ u_1 & u_2 & u_3 & u_4 & 0 \end{vmatrix} = 0. \tag{3}$$

This is an equation of the second degree in u_i. Hence *a surface of the second order for which the discriminant is not zero is also a surface of the second class* (§ 88).

It is not difficult to show that the discriminant of (3) is not equal to zero.

II. $\Delta = 0$. The tangent planes either form a one-dimensional extent of planes or consist of discrete planes. These cases will be examined later.

91. Singular points. By § 86 singular points on the surface (1), § 90, are given by the equations

$$
\begin{aligned}
a_{11}x_1 + a_{12}x_2 + a_{13}x_3 + a_{14}x_4 &= 0, \\
a_{12}x_1 + a_{22}x_2 + a_{23}x_3 + a_{24}x_4 &= 0, \\
a_{13}x_1 + a_{23}x_2 + a_{33}x_3 + a_{34}x_4 &= 0, \\
a_{14}x_1 + a_{24}x_2 + a_{34}x_3 + a_{44}x_4 &= 0.
\end{aligned}
\tag{1}
$$

There are four cases:

I. $\Delta \neq 0$. Equations (1) have no solution, and the surface has no singular points. This is the general case.

II. $\Delta = 0$, but not all its first minors are zero. The surface has one and only one singular point. Let y_i be the coördinates of the singular point and z_i the coördinates of any other point in space, and consider the straight line

$$
\rho x_i = y_i + \lambda z_i.
\tag{2}
$$

To find the points in which the line (2) meets the surface substitute in equation (1), § 90. Since the coördinates y_i satisfy the equation of the surface and also the equations (1), the result is

$$
\lambda^2 \sum a_{ik} z_i z_k = 0.
\tag{3}
$$

This shows that any line through a singular point meets the surface only at that point ($\lambda = 0$), and there with a doubly counted point of intersection. An exception occurs when z_i is taken on the surface. Then equation (3) is identically satisfied, and the line yz lies entirely on the surface. Hence *the surface is a cone with the singular point as the vertex.* There is no plane equation of the surface. In fact the tangent planes form a singly infinite extent of planes, and their coördinates are subject to two conditions.

III. $\Delta = 0$, all its first minors are zero, but not all its second minors are zero. Equations (1) contain two and only two independent equations and hence the surface has a line of singular points. If this line is taken as the line $x_1 = 0$, $x_2 = 0$ in the coördinate system, equations (1) show that we shall have $a_{13} = a_{14} = a_{23} = a_{24} = a_{33} = a_{34} = a_{44} = 0$, and the equation of the surface becomes $a_{11}x_1^2 + 2\,a_{12}x_1x_2 + a_{22}x_2^2 = 0$. At least two of the coefficients in the last equation cannot vanish, since the surface has only the line $x_1 = 0$ and $x_2 = 0$ of singular points. Therefore the left-hand member of the equation of the surface factors into two linear factors. Hence *the surface consists of two distinct planes intersecting in the line of singular points.*

IV. $\Delta = 0$, all its first and second minors are zero, but not all the third minors are zero. Equations (1) contain one and only one independent equation, and hence the surface has a plane of singular points. If this plane is taken as $x_1 = 0$, the equation of the surface becomes $x_1^2 = 0$. Hence *the surface consists of the plane of singular points doubly reckoned.*

92. Poles and polars. The *polar plane* of a point y_i (the *pole*) with respect to a surface of the second order whose equation is (1), § 90, is defined as the plane whose coördinates are

$$\rho u_i = a_{i1}y_1 + a_{i2}y_2 + a_{i3}y_3 + a_{i4}y_4. \tag{1}$$

The following theorems are obvious or may be proved as are the similar theorems of § 34:

I. If the pole is on the surface, the polar plane is a tangent plane, the pole being the point of contact.

II. To every point not a singular point of the surface corresponds a unique polar plane.

III. To every plane corresponds a unique pole when and only when the discriminant of the surface does not vanish.

IV. A polar plane contains its pole when and only when the pole is on the surface.

V. All polar planes pass through all the singular points of the surface when such exist.

VI. If a point P lies on the polar plane of a point Q, then Q lies on the polar plane of P.

VII. All tangent planes through a point P touch the surface in a curve which lies in the polar plane of P.

VIII. *For a surface of second order without singular points it is possible in an infinite number of ways to construct a tetrahedron in which each face is the polar plane of the opposite vertex.*

These are *self-polar tetrahedrons.*

IX. *If any straight line m is passed through a point P, and R and S are the points in which m intersects a surface of second order and Q is the point of intersection of m and the polar plane of P, then P and Q are harmonic conjugates with respect to R and S.*

In addition to these theorems we will state and prove the following, which have no counterparts in § 34:

X. *The polar planes of points on a range form a pencil of planes the axis of which is called the conjugate polar line of the base of the range. Reciprocally the polar planes of points on the axis of this pencil form another pencil the axis of which is the base of the original range.*

Consider any range two of whose points are P and Q (Fig. 55). Let the polar planes of P and Q intersect in LK, and let A be any point of LK. The polar plane of A must contain both P and Q (theorem VI) and hence the entire line PQ. Now let R be any point on PQ. Its polar plane must contain A (theorem VI). But A is any point of LK. Therefore the polar plane of R contains LK. This proves the theorem. It is to be noted that the opposite edges of a self-polar tetrahedron are conjugate polar lines.

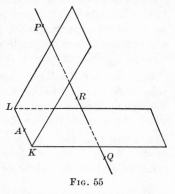

Fig. 55

XI. *If two conjugate polar lines intersect, each is tangent to the surface at their point of intersection.*

Let two conjugate polar lines, PQ and LK, intersect at R. Since R lies in each of the lines PQ and LK its polar plane must contain each of these lines by the definition of conjugate polar lines. Hence the polar plane of R contains R and is therefore (theorems IV and I) the tangent plane at R. The two lines LK and PQ lying in the tangent plane and passing through R are tangent to the surface at R.

EXERCISES

1. Show that any chord drawn through a fixed point P, intersecting at infinity the polar plane of P with respect to a quadric, is bisected by P. Hence show that if a quadric is not tangent to the plane at infinity there is a point such that all chords through it are bisected by it. This is the *center* of the quadric.

2. Show that the locus of the middle points of a system of parallel chords is a plane which is the polar plane of the point in which the parallel chords meet the plane at infinity. This is a *diametral plane* conjugate to the direction of the parallel chords. Show that a diametral plane passes through the center of the quadric, if there is one, and through the point of contact with the plane at infinity if the surface is tangent to the plane at infinity.

3. Prove that all points on a straight line which passes through the vertex of a cone have the same polar plane; namely, the diametral plane conjugate to the direction of the line.

4. Show that if a plane conjugate to a given direction is parallel to a second given line, the plane conjugate to the latter line is parallel to the first. Three diametral planes are said to be *conjugate* when each is conjugate to the intersection of the other two. Show that the intersections of three conjugate diametral planes with the plane at infinity form a triangle which is self polar with respect to the curve of intersection of the quadric and the plane at infinity. Discuss the existence and number of such conjugate planes in the two cases of central quadrics and quadrics tangent to the plane at infinity.

5. Show that if a line is tangent to a quadric surface its conjugate polar is also tangent to the surface at the same point, and that the two conjugate polars are harmonic conjugates with respect to the two lines in which the tangent plane at their point of intersection cuts the surface.

6. Show that the conjugate polars of all lines in a pencil form a pencil. When do the two pencils coincide? Show that the conjugate polars of all lines in a plane form a bundle of lines, and conversely.

93. Classification of surfaces of second order. With the aid of the results of the last two sections it is now possible to obtain the simplest equations of the various types of surfaces of the second order which have already been arranged in classes in § 91.

I. *The general surface.* $\Delta \neq 0$. The surface has no singular point (§ 91) and there can be found self-polar tetrahedrons (§ 92). Let one such tetrahedron be taken as the tetrahedron of reference in the coördinate system. Then the equation of the surface must be such that the polar of $0:0:0:1$ is $x_4 = 0$, that of $0:0:1:0$ is $x_3 = 0$, that of $0:1:0:0$ is $x_2 = 0$, and that of $1:0:0:0$ is $x_1 = 0$. The equation is then

$$a_{11}x_1^2 + a_{22}x_2^2 + a_{33}x_3^2 + a_{44}x_4^2 = 0, \qquad (2)$$

where no one of the coefficients can be zero, for, if it were, the surface would contain a singular point.

It is obvious that if the original tetrahedron of reference were real and if the coefficients in the original equation of the surface were real, the new tetrahedron of reference and the new coefficients are also real. We may now replace x_i in the last equation by $|a_{ii}|x_i$ and have three types according to the signs of the terms resulting.

1. *The imaginary type,* $x_1^2 + x_2^2 + x_3^2 + x_4^2 = 0.$ $\qquad$ (3)

This equation is satisfied by no real points.

2. *The oval type,* $\qquad$ $x_1^2 + x_2^2 + x_3^2 - x_4^2 = 0.$ $\qquad$ (4)

No real straight line can meet this surface in more than two real points. If it did, it would lie entirely on the surface (§ 86), and hence the point in which it met the plane $x_4 = 0$ would be a real point of the surface. But the plane $x_4 = 0$ meets the surface in the curve $x_1^2 + x_2^2 + x_3^2 = 0$, which has no real point. Hence, as was said, no real straight line can meet the surface in more than two real points. The surface, however, contains imaginary straight lines as will be seen later.

3. *The saddle type,* $\qquad$ $x_1^2 + x_2^2 - x_3^2 - x_4^2 = 0.$ $\qquad$ (4)

Through every point of this surface go two real straight lines which lie entirely on the surface. This follows from the fact that whatever be the values of λ and μ, the two lines

$$x_1 - x_3 - \lambda(x_2 - x_4) = 0, \qquad x_2 + x_4 + \lambda(x_1 + x_3) = 0$$
and $\quad x_1 - x_3 - \mu(x_2 + x_4) = 0, \qquad x_2 - x_4 + \mu(x_1 + x_3) = 0$

lie entirely on the surface. Moreover, values of λ and μ may be easily found so that one of each of these straight lines may pass through any point of the surface. This matter will be discussed in detail in § 96.

As the three types of surfaces here named are distinguished by properties which are essentially different in the domain of reality, the corresponding equations can evidently not be reduced to each other by any real change of coördinates. However, if no distinction is made between reals and imaginaries, all surfaces of the three types may be represented by the single equation

$$x_1^2 + x_2^2 + x_3^2 + x_4^2 = 0. \tag{5}$$

II. *The cones.* $\Delta = 0$, but not all the first minors are zero. The surface has one singular point (§ 91) and is a cone with the singular point as the vertex. Let the vertex be taken as A $(0:0:0:1)$. Then in the equation of the surface $a_{14} = a_{24} = a_{34} = a_{44} = 0$. Take now as B $(0:0:1:0)$ any point not on the surface. Its polar plane contains A (theorem V, § 92) but not B (theorem IV, § 92). Take as C $(0:1:0:0)$ any point in this plane but not on the surface. Such points exist unless the polar plane of B lies entirely on the surface, which is impossible since B was taken as not on the surface. The polar plane of C contains A and B and intersects the polar plane of B in a line through A. Take D $(1:0:0:0)$ as any point on this line. We have now fixed the tetrahedron of reference so that $0:0:0:1$ is a singular point, the polar plane of $0:0:1:0$ is $x_3 = 0$, the polar plane of $0:1:0:0$ is $x_2 = 0$, and the polar plane of $1:0:0:0$ is $x_1 = 0$. Therefore the equation of the surface is

$$a_{11}x_1^2 + a_{22}x_2^2 + a_{33}x_3^2 = 0,$$

where no one of the three coefficients can vanish, since the surface has only one singular point. By a real transformation of coördinates this equation reduces to two types:

1. *The imaginary cone,* $x_1^2 + x_2^2 + x_3^2 = 0$.
2. *The real cone,* $x_1^2 + x_2^2 - x_3^2 = 0$.

III. *Two intersecting planes.* $\Delta = 0$, all the first minors are zero, but not all the second minors are zero. This has been sufficiently discussed (§ 91). There are obviously two types in the domain of reals; namely:

1. *Imaginary planes,* $x_1^2 + x_2^2 = 0$.
2. *Real planes,* $x_1^2 - x_2^2 = 0$.

IV. *Two coincident planes.* $\Delta = 0$, all the first and all the second minors are equal to zero. Evidently the equation in this case is reducible to the form

$$x_1^2 = 0,$$

but the plane $x_1 = 0$ is not necessarily real. In fact the condition that all the second minors of Δ vanish is the condition that the left-hand member of equation (1), § 90, should be a perfect square, as is easily verified by the student.

94. Surfaces of second order in Cartesian coördinates. As we have seen (§ 82), we obtain Cartesian coördinates from general quadriplanar coördinates by taking one of the coördinate planes as the plane at infinity and giving special values to the constants k_i. This being done, the general equation of the second degree will be written

$$ax^2 + by^2 + cz^2 + 2fyz + 2gzx + 2hxy + 2lxt + 2myt + 2nzt + dt^2 = 0, \quad (1)$$

which reduces to the usual nonhomogeneous form when t is placed equal to 1.

For equation (1) the results of §§ 90-93 remain unchanged except for a slight change of notation. We will refer to the equations of these sections by number and make the necessary change in notation without further remark. Assuming that $\Delta \neq 0$ we may find the pole of the plane at infinity, for example, by placing u_i in equations (1), § 92, equal to the coördinates $0:0:0:1$ of the plane at infinity. There result the equations

$$
\begin{aligned}
ax + hy + gz + lt &= 0, \\
hx + by + fz + mt &= 0, \\
gx + fy + cz + nt &= 0, \\
lx + my + nz + dt &= \rho,
\end{aligned}
\quad (2)
$$

the solution of which is the coördinates of the pole required. This pole is therefore a finite point when the determinant

$$
D = \begin{vmatrix} a & h & g \\ h & b & f \\ g & f & c \end{vmatrix}
$$

is not zero and is a point at infinity when $D = 0$.

In the latter case, by theorems IV and I, § 92, the surface is tangent to the plane at infinity. In the former case, if the pole of the plane at infinity is taken as $0:0:0:1$, then $l = m = n = 0$, and consequently it appears that if $x_1 : y_1 : z_1 : t_1$ is a point on the surface, $-x_1 : -y_1 : -z_1 : t_1$ is also on the surface. The point is therefore called the *center* of the surface, and the surface is called a *central surface.* Conversely, if a surface without singular points has a center (that is, if there exists a point which is the middle point of all chords through it), that point is the pole of the plane at infinity. This follows from theorem IX, § 92, or may be shown by assuming the center as the origin of coördinates and reversing the argument just made.

We have reached the following result:

A surface of second order with the equation (1) *is a central surface or a noncentral surface according as the determinant D is not or is equal to zero. A noncentral surface is tangent to the plane at infinity.*

Holding now to the significance of the determinant Δ as given in § 90 we may proceed to find the simplest forms of the equations of the surface in Cartesian coördinates. There will be this difference from the work of § 93 that now the plane $t = 0$ plays a unique rôle and must always remain as one of the coördinate planes. The other three coördinate planes, however, may be taken at pleasure, and we shall not at present restrict ourselves to rectangular coördinates.

1. *Central surfaces without singular points.* As in § 93, by referring the surface to a self-polar tetrahedron one of whose faces is the plane at infinity its equation becomes

$$ax^2 + by^2 + cz^2 + dt^2 = 0.$$

According to the signs of the coefficients this gives the following types in nonhomogeneous form:

1. *The oval type:*

    (*a*) The imaginary ellipsoid, $\dfrac{x^2}{a^2} + \dfrac{y^2}{b^2} + \dfrac{z^2}{c^2} = -1.$

    (*b*) The real ellipsoid, $\dfrac{x^2}{a^2} + \dfrac{y^2}{b^2} + \dfrac{z^2}{c^2} = 1.$

    (*c*) The hyperboloid of two sheets, $\dfrac{x^2}{a^2} - \dfrac{y^2}{b^2} - \dfrac{z^2}{c^2} = 1.$

2. *The saddle type:*

    The hyperboloid of one sheet, $\dfrac{x^2}{a^2} + \dfrac{y^2}{b^2} - \dfrac{z^2}{c^2} = 1.$

II. *Noncentral surfaces without singular points.* Since the plane at infinity can no longer be a face of a self-polar tetrahedron, we cannot use the method of § 93. We will take the point of tangency in the plane at infinity as B $(0:0:1:0)$. Then $g = f = c = 0$ and $n \neq 0$. Take an arbitrary line through B. It meets the surface in one other point A, which we take as $0:0:0:1$. We then take the tangent plane at A as $z = 0$. Then $l = m = d = 0$, and the equation of the surface is

$$ax^2 + 2\,hxy + by^2 + ct^2 = 0.$$

The tangent plane at A meets the plane at infinity in a line $(z = 0,\ t = 0)$, which is the conjugate polar to the line AB $(x = 0, y = 0)$. The points C $(0:1:0:0)$ and D $(1:0:0:0)$ may be taken as any two points on this line such that each lies in the polar plane of the other. Then $h = 0$, and the equation of the surface is reduced to

$$ax^2 + by^2 + nz = 0.$$

According to the signs which occur we have two types:

1. *The oval type:*

The elliptic paraboloid, $\quad \dfrac{x^2}{a^2} + \dfrac{y^2}{b^2} = nz.$

2. *The saddle type:*

The hyperbolic paraboloid, $\quad \dfrac{x^2}{a^2} - \dfrac{y^2}{b^2} = nz.$

The discussion of surfaces with singular points presents no features essentially different in Cartesian coördinates from those found in the general case. If the surface has one singular point, it is a cone if the singular point is not at infinity and is a cylinder if the singular point is at infinity. If the surface has a line of singular points, it consists of two intersecting or two parallel planes according as the singular line lies in finite space or at infinity. If the surface has a plane of singular points, it consists of a plane doubly counted, which may be the plane at infinity.

95. Surfaces of second order referred to rectangular axes. In the previous section no hypotheses were made as to the angles at which the coördinate planes intersected. For that reason the coördinate planes leading to the simple forms of the equations could be chosen in an infinite number of ways. We shall now ask whether, among these planes, there exist a set in which the planes $x = 0$, $y = 0$, and $z = 0$ are mutually orthogonal.

Consider first the central surfaces without singular points for which $D \neq 0$. The plane at infinity cuts this surface in the general conic

$$ax^2 + by^2 + cz^2 + 2fyz + 2gzx + 2hxy = 0, \qquad (1)$$

where $x : y : z$ are homogeneous coördinates on the plane $t = 0$.

When the equation of the surface is referred to a self-polar tetrahedron of which the plane at infinity is one face, the curve (1) is referred to a self-polar triangle. If the axes in space are orthogonal, the triangle must also be a self-polar triangle (theorem V, § 81) to the circle at infinity

$$x^2 + y^2 + z^2 = 0. \qquad (2)$$

Our problem, therefore, is to find on the plane at infinity a triangle which is self polar at the same time with respect to (1) and (2).

By § 43 this can be done when and only when the curves (1) and (2) intersect in four distinct points or are tangent in two distinct points or are coincident.

In the first case there exists one and only one self-polar triangle common to (1) and (2), and therefore there exists only one set of mutually orthogonal planes passing through the center of the quadric and such that by use of them as coördinate planes the equation of the quadric becomes

$$ax^2 + by^2 + cz^2 + d = 0. \qquad (a \neq b \neq c \neq 0)$$

These planes are the *principal diametral planes* of the quadric, and their intersections are the *principal axes*.

In the second case there are an infinite number of planes through the origin, such that by use of them as coördinate planes the equation of the quadric becomes

$$a(x^2 + y^2) + cz^2 + d = 0. \qquad (a \neq c \neq 0)$$

Here the axis OZ is fixed, but the axes OX and OY are so far indeterminate that they may be any two lines perpendicular to OZ and to each other. The surface is a surface formed by revolving the conic $ax^2 + cz^2 + d = 0$, $y = 0$ about OZ.

In the third case any set of mutually perpendicular planes through the origin, if taken as coördinate planes, reduce the equation of the quadric to the form

$$a(x^2 + y^2 + z^2) + d = 0,$$

and the quadric is a sphere.

It is to be noticed that if the coefficients in equation (2) are real, one of the above cases necessarily occurs. For in this case the solutions of equations (1) and (2) consist of imaginary points which occur in pairs as complex imaginary points.

If we consider the noncentral quadrics without singular points and use the notation of § 94, we notice first that if the axes of coördinates are rectangular, the point B cannot be on the circle at infinity, since the line CD must be the polar of B with respect to the circle at infinity. The point B being fixed by the quadric surface, the line CD is then fixed, and consequently the line AB, since AB is the conjugate polar of CD with respect to the quadric. The point A is then fixed and is called the *vertex* of the quadric.

The points C and D must now be taken as conjugate, both with respect to the circle at infinity and with respect to the conic of intersection of the quadric and the plane at infinity. If the two straight lines into which this latter conic degenerates (cf. Ex. 1, § 86) are neither of them tangent to the circle at infinity, the points C and D are uniquely fixed. If both of these lines are tangent to the circle at infinity, the point C may be taken at pleasure on CD, and D is then fixed.

In the first case there is one tangent plane and two other planes perpendicular to it and to each other, by the use of which the equation of the quadric is reduced to the form

$$ax^2 + by^2 = nz. \qquad (a \neq b)$$

In the second case there are an infinite number of mutually orthogonal planes, one of which is a fixed tangent plane, by the use of which the equation of the quadric is reduced to the form

$$a(x^2 + y^2) = nz,$$

and the quadric is a paraboloid of revolution.

In all other cases, namely, when the point of tangency of the quadric with the plane at infinity is on the circle at infinity or when the section of the quadric with the plane at infinity consists of two straight lines, one and only one of which is tangent to the circle at infinity, the equation of the surface cannot be reduced to the above forms by the use of rectangular axes.

If the coefficients of the terms of the second order in the equation of the quadric are real, the rectangular axes always exist.

EXERCISES

Examine the following surfaces for the existence of principal axes:

1. $x^2 + y^2 + z^2 + xz + iyz + 1 = 0$.

2. $2x^2 + (1+i)y^2 + z^2 + (1+i)xy = 0$.

3. $x^2 + 2y^2 + 7z^2 + 4iyz + 1 = 0$.

4. $2x^2 + z^2 + 2ixy + 1 = 0$.

5. $3x^2 + 2y^2 + 7z^2 + 6iyz + 1 = 0$.

6. $x^2 + 2ixy - y^2 - z^2 + 2z = 0$.

7. $xz + iyz + x = 0$.

8. $x^2 - 2ixy + y^2 + 2x + 2z = 0$.

9. Examine the quadrics with singular points by the methods of this section.

96. Rulings on surfaces of second order. We have seen (§ 93) that the equation of any surface of the second order without singular points can be written as

$$x_1^2 + x_2^2 + x_3^2 + x_4^2 = 0 \tag{1}$$

if no distinction is made between reals and imaginaries or between the plane at infinity and any other plane. This equation can be written in either of the two forms

$$-\frac{x_1 + ix_2}{x_3 + ix_4} = \frac{x_3 - ix_4}{x_1 - ix_2} = \lambda, \tag{2}$$

$$\frac{x_1 + ix_2}{x_3 - ix_4} = -\frac{x_3 + ix_4}{x_1 - ix_2} = \mu; \tag{3}$$

whence follows for any point on the surface

$$x_1 : x_2 : x_3 : x_4 = \lambda\mu + 1 : i(-\lambda\mu + 1) : \lambda - \mu : i(\lambda + \mu). \tag{4}$$

From these equations the following theorems are easily proved:

I. On a surface of second order without singular points lie two families of straight lines, one defined by equations (2) and the other by equations (3).

For if λ is given any constant value in (2) the equations represent a straight line every point of which satisfies equation (1). Similarly, μ may be given a constant value in (3). The straight lines (2) and (3) are called *generators*.

II. Through each point of the surface goes one and only one line of each family.

For any point x_i of the surface determines λ and μ uniquely.

III. Each line of one family intersects each line of the other family.

For any pair of values of λ and μ leads to the solution (4).

IV. No two lines of the same family intersect.

This is a corollary to theorem II.

V. A tangent plane at any point of the surface intersects the surface in the two generators through that point.

For the two generators are tangents and hence lie in the tangent plane. But the intersection of the tangent plane with the surface is a curve of second order unless the plane lies entirely on the surface, which is impossible since the surface has no singular points. Hence the section consists of the two generators.

VI. The surface contains no other straight lines than the generators.

For if there were another line the tangent plane at any point of the line would contain it, which is impossible by theorem V.

VII. Any plane through a generator intersects the surface also in a generator of the other family and is tangent to the surface at the point of intersection of the two generators.

Consider a plane through a generator g. Its intersection with the surface is a curve of second order of which one part is known to be g. The remaining part must also be a straight line h, which is a generator by theorem VI. Since h and g are in the same plane they intersect and hence belong to different families by theorem IV. The tangent plane at the intersection of h and g contains these lines by theorem V and hence coincides with the original plane.

VIII. If two pencils of planes with their axes generators of the same family are brought into a one-to-one correspondence so that two corresponding planes intersect in a generator of the other family, the relation is projective.

Let the axes of the two pencils be taken as $x_1 = 0$, $x_2 = 0$ and $x_3 = 0$, $x_4 = 0$ respectively. Since these lines lie on the surface, the equation of the surface has the form

$$c_1 x_1 x_3 + c_2 x_1 x_4 + c_3 x_2 x_3 + c_4 x_2 x_4 = 0.$$

The equations of planes of the first pencil are

$$x_1 + \lambda x_2 = 0$$

and those of the second are

$$x_3 + \mu x_4 = 0.$$

If two such planes intersect on the surface, we have

$$\lambda = \frac{c_3\mu - c_4}{c_1\mu - c_2},$$

which proves the theorem.

IX. *The intersections of the corresponding planes of two projective pencils of planes with nonintersecting axes generate a surface of second order which contains the two axes of the pencils.*

Let the two pencils be $x_1 + \lambda x_2 = 0$ and $x_3 + \mu x_4 = 0$, where the projective relation is expressed by $\lambda = \dfrac{\alpha\mu + \beta}{\gamma\mu + \delta}$.

Then if a point is common to two corresponding planes, it satisfies the equation

$$\gamma x_1 x_3 + \alpha x_2 x_3 - \delta x_1 x_4 - \beta x_2 x_4 = 0,$$

which is also satisfied by the axes of the pencils.

X. (Dualistic to VIII.) *Lines of one family of generators cut out projective ranges on any two lines of the other family.*

As in the proof of theorem VIII, let $x_1 = 0$, $x_2 = 0$ be a generator of the surface and let $x_3 = 0$, $x_4 = 0$ be another generator of the same family. The equation of the surface is then

$$c_1 x_1 x_3 + c_2 x_1 x_4 + c_3 x_2 x_3 + c_4 x_2 x_4 = 0,$$

and the generators of the second family are

$$-\frac{x_1}{x_2} = -\frac{c_3 x_3 + c_4 x_4}{c_1 x_3 + c_2 x_4} = \lambda.$$

A generator of this family meets $x_1 = 0$, $x_2 = 0$ in the point where $x_3 : x_4 = c_4 + c_2\lambda : -c_3 - c_1\lambda$ and meets $x_3 = 0$, $x_4 = 0$ where $x_1 : x_2 = \lambda : 1$. The relation is evidently projective.

XI. (Dualistic to X.) *The lines which connect corresponding points of two projective ranges with nonintersecting bases lie on a surface of second order.*

Let one range be taken on $x_1 = 0$, $x_2 = 0$ and the other on $x_3 = 0$, $x_4 = 0$. Then the points of the two ranges are given on each base by the equations $x_3 + \lambda x_4 = 0$ and $x_1 + \mu x_2 = 0$. Let the projective relation be expressed by $\lambda = \dfrac{\alpha\mu + \beta}{\gamma\mu + \delta}$.

From these it is easy to compute that the coördinates of any point on the line connecting two corresponding points of the two ranges satisfy the equation

$$\gamma x_1 x_3 - \delta x_2 x_3 + \alpha x_1 x_4 - \beta x_2 x_4 = 0.$$

EXERCISES

1. Distinguish between the cases in which the generators are real or imaginary, assuming that the equation of the quadric is real.

2. What are the generators of a sphere?

3. Distinguish between a central quadric and a noncentral one by showing that for the latter type the generators are parallel to a plane and for the former they are not.

97. Surfaces of second class. Consider the equation

$$\sum A_{ik} u_i u_k = 0, \qquad (A_{ki} = A_{ik}) \tag{1}$$

in plane coördinates. This is a special case of the equation discussed in § 88. Equations (3), § 88, which determine the limit points, become

$$\rho x_i = A_{i1} u_1 + A_{i2} u_2 + A_{i3} u_3 + A_{i4} u_4, \qquad (i = 1, 2, 3, 4) \tag{2}$$

and equations (5), § 88, which define the singular planes, become

$$A_{i1} u_1 + A_{i2} u_2 + A_{i3} u_3 + A_{i4} u_4 = 0. \qquad (i = 1, 2, 3, 4) \tag{3}$$

If we now place

$$\Delta = \begin{vmatrix} A_{11} & A_{12} & A_{13} & A_{14} \\ A_{12} & A_{22} & A_{23} & A_{24} \\ A_{13} & A_{23} & A_{33} & A_{34} \\ A_{14} & A_{24} & A_{34} & A_{44} \end{vmatrix} \tag{4}$$

we have to distinguish four cases.

I. $\Delta \neq 0$. Equations (2) have then a single solution for $u_1 : u_2 : u_3 : u_4$, which, if substituted in (1), gives the equation of the surface enveloped by the extent of planes. This equation may be more conveniently obtained by replacing (1) by the equation

$$u_1 x_1 + u_2 x_2 + u_3 x_3 + u_4 x_4 = 0,$$

obtained from (1) by the help of (2). The elimination of u_i then gives

$$\begin{vmatrix} A_{11} & A_{12} & A_{13} & A_{14} & x_1 \\ A_{12} & A_{22} & A_{23} & A_{24} & x_2 \\ A_{13} & A_{23} & A_{33} & A_{34} & x_3 \\ A_{14} & A_{24} & A_{34} & A_{44} & x_4 \\ x_1 & x_2 & x_3 & x_4 & 0 \end{vmatrix} = 0, \tag{5}$$

which is the equation of a surface of second order.

Under the hypothesis $\Delta \neq 0$ equations (3) have no solution, so that in this case no singular plane exists. It is not difficult to show that the discriminant of equation (4) does not vanish.

We have, accordingly, the following result: *A plane extent of second class with nonvanishing discriminant consists of planes enveloping a surface of second order without singular points.*

This theorem may be otherwise expressed as follows: *A surface of second class without singular planes is also a surface of second order without singular points.*

II. $\Delta = 0$, but not all the first minors are zero. Equations (3) now have one and only one solution, so that the extent (1) has one and only one singular plane. Let it be taken as the plane $0:0:0:1$. Then $A_{14} = A_{24} = A_{34} = A_{44} = 0$, and equation (1) takes the form

$$A_{11}u_1^2 + A_{22}u_2^2 + A_{33}u_3^2 + 2A_{12}u_1u_2 + 2A_{13}u_1u_3 + 2A_{23}u_2u_3 = 0, \quad (6)$$

where the determinant

$$\begin{vmatrix} A_{11} & A_{12} & A_{13} \\ A_{12} & A_{22} & A_{23} \\ A_{13} & A_{23} & A_{33} \end{vmatrix}$$

does not vanish owing to the hypothesis that not all the first minors of the discriminant (4) vanish.

The elimination of u_i from equations (2) and equation (6) gives, then,

$$\begin{vmatrix} A_{11} & A_{12} & A_{13} & x_1 \\ A_{12} & A_{22} & A_{23} & x_2 \\ A_{13} & A_{23} & A_{33} & x_3 \\ x_1 & x_2 & x_3 & 0 \end{vmatrix} = 0, \quad x_4 = 0,$$

which are the equations of a nondegenerate conic in the plane $x_4 = 0$.

We have, accordingly, the result: *A plane extent of second class with one singular plane consists of planes which are tangent to a nondegenerate conic lying in the singular plane.*

The equation of the plane extent may be considered the equation of this conic in plane coördinates.

III. $\Delta = 0$, all the first minors are zero, but not all the second minors are zero. Equations (3) now contain only two independent equations and hence the extent contains a pencil of singular planes. If this pencil is taken as $u_1 = 0$, $u_2 = 0$, the equation of the extent becomes

$$A_{11}u_1^2 + 2 A_{12}u_1u_2 + A_{22}u_2^2 = 0, \tag{7}$$

where the determinant $A_{11}A_{22} - A_{12}^2$ does not vanish because of the hypothesis that not all the second minors of the discriminant (4) vanish.

Equation (7) factors into two distinct linear factors and hence the plane extent consists of two bundles of planes. The elimination of u_i between equations (2) and (7) gives

$$\begin{vmatrix} A_{11} & A_{12} & x_1 \\ A_{12} & A_{22} & x_2 \\ x_1 & x_2 & 0 \end{vmatrix} = 0, \quad x_3 = 0, \quad x_4 = 0,$$

which define the vertices of the two bundles.

We have, accordingly, the result: *A plane extent of second class with a pencil of singular planes consists of two bundles of planes, the singular pencil being the pencil common to the two bundles.*

IV. $\Delta = 0$, all the first and second minors are zero, but not all the third minors are zero. Equations (3) contain only one independent equation and hence the plane extent contains a bundle of singular planes. If this bundle is taken as $u_1 = 0$, the equation of the extent becomes

$$A_{11}u_1^2 = 0, \tag{8}$$

where A_{11} cannot be zero because of the hypothesis that not all third minors of (4) are zero.

Hence we have the result: *A plane extent of second class with a bundle of singular planes consists of that bundle doubly reckoned.*

It may be noticed that the elimination of u_i between equations (2) and (8) gives the meaningless result $x_1 : x_2 : x_3 : x_4 = 0 : 0 : 0 : 0$.

98. Poles and polars. The relation between poles and polars may be established by means of plane coördinates as well as by point coördinates. We shall define the pole of a plane v_i with respect to the extent (1), § 97, as the point the coördinates of which are

$$\rho x_i = A_{i1}v_1 + A_{i2}v_2 + A_{i3}v_3 + A_{i4}v_4. \qquad (i = 1, 2, 3, 4)$$

For the case in which $\Delta \neq 0$ the relation between pole and polar is the same as that defined in § 92, as the student may easily prove. In the cases in which $\Delta = 0$ the polar relation is something new.

The following theorems dualistic to those of § 92 are obvious or easily proved:

I. If a plane belongs to the extent its pole is the limit point in the plane.

II. To any plane not a singular plane of the extent corresponds a unique pole.

III. To any point corresponds a unique polar when and only when the plane extent has no singular plane.

IV. A pole lies in its polar plane when and only when the polar plane belongs to the extent.

V. The pole of any plane lies in all singular planes when such exist.

VI. If a plane p passes through the pole of a plane q, then q passes through the pole of p.

VII. All limit points lying in a plane p are the limit points of planes of the extent which pass through the polar of p.

VIII. For a surface of second class without singular planes it is possible in an infinite number of ways to construct self-polar tetrahedrons.

IX. If a line m lies in a plane p, and r and s are the planes of the extent which pass through m, and q is the plane through m and the pole of p, then p and q are harmonic conjugates to r and s.

99. Classification of surfaces of the second class. The previous sections enable us to write the simplest forms to which the equation of a surface of the second class may be reduced.

I. $\Delta \neq 0$. Since the planes envelop a surface of type I, § 93, we may take the results of that section and find the plane equation corresponding to each type there. Consequently, if no account is taken of real values the equation of the plane extent may be written as

$$u_1^2 + u_2^2 + u_3^2 + u_4^2 = 0.$$

If the coefficients in the original equation are real and the original coördinates are also real, then, by a real change of coördinates, the equation takes one or another of the forms

$$u_1^2 + u_2^2 + u_3^2 + u_4^2 = 0,$$
$$u_1^2 + u_2^2 + u_3^2 - u_4^2 = 0,$$
$$u_1^2 + u_2^2 - u_3^2 - u_4^2 = 0.$$

II. $\Delta = 0$, but not all the first minors are zero. We have already obtained equation (6), § 97, as a possible equation in this case. If no account is taken of reals this equation can be reduced to the form

$$u_1^2 + u_2^2 + u_3^2 = 0.$$

In the domain of reals there are two types:

1. Planes tangent to a real plane curve

$$u_1^2 + u_2^2 - u_3^2 = 0.$$

2. Planes tangent to an imaginary plane curve

$$u_1^2 + u_2^2 + u_3^2 = 0.$$

III. $\Delta = 0$, all the first minors are zero but not all the second minors are zero. As shown in § 97, the equation can be reduced to the single type

$$u_1^2 + u_2^2 = 0$$

if no account is taken of reals, and to the following two types in the domain of reals:

1. Two real bundles of planes

$$u_1^2 - u_2^2 = 0.$$

2. Two imaginary bundles of planes

$$u_1^2 + u_2^2 = 0.$$

IV. $\Delta = 0$, all the first and second minors are zero. As shown in § 97, there is here only one type of equation,

$$u_1^2 = 0,$$

representing a double bundle of planes.

CHAPTER XIV

TRANSFORMATIONS

100. Collineations. A collineation in space is a point transformation expressed by the equations

$$\begin{aligned}
\rho x_1' &= a_{11}x_1 + a_{12}x_2 + a_{13}x_3 + a_{14}x_4, \\
\rho x_2' &= a_{21}x_1 + a_{22}x_2 + a_{23}x_3 + a_{24}x_4, \\
\rho x_3' &= a_{31}x_1 + a_{32}x_2 + a_{33}x_3 + a_{34}x_4, \\
\rho x_4' &= a_{41}x_1 + a_{42}x_2 + a_{43}x_3 + a_{44}x_4.
\end{aligned} \tag{1}$$

We shall consider only the case in which the determinant $|a_{ik}|$ is not zero, these being the *nonsingular* collineations. Then to any point x_i corresponds a point x_i', for the right-hand members of (1) cannot simultaneously vanish. Also to any point x_i' corresponds a point x_i given by the equations obtained by solving (1),

$$\sigma x_i = A_{1i}x_1' + A_{2i}x_2' + A_{3i}x_3' + A_{4i}x_4', \tag{2}$$

where, as usual, A_{ik} is the cofactor of a_{ik} in the expansion of the determinant $|a_{ik}|$.

By means of (1) any point which lies on a plane with coördinates u_i is transformed into a point which lies on a plane with coördinates u_i', where

$$\rho u_i' = A_{i1}u_1 + A_{i2}u_2 + A_{i3}u_3 + A_{i4}u_4 \tag{3}$$

and
$$\sigma u_i = a_{1i}u_1' + a_{2i}u_2' + a_{3i}u_3' + a_{4i}u_4'. \tag{4}$$

The following theorems, similar to those of § 40, may be proved by the same methods there employed.

I. By a nonsingular collineation points, planes, and straight lines are transformed into points, planes, and straight lines respectively in a one-to-one manner.

II. The nonsingular collineations form a group.

III. If P_1, P_2, P_3, P_4, and P_5 are five arbitrarily assumed points no four of which lie in the same plane, and P_1', P_2', P_3', P_4', and P_5' are also *five arbitrarily assumed points no four of which lie in the same plane, there exists one and only one collineation by means of which P_1 is transformed into P_1', P_2 into P_2', P_3 into P_3', P_4 into P_4', and P_5 into P_5'.*

IV. *A nonsingular collineation establishes a projectivity between the points of two corresponding ranges or the planes of two corresponding pencils, and any such projectivity may be established in an infinite number of ways by a nonsingular collineation.*

V. *Any two planes which correspond by means of a nonsingular collineation are projectively transformed into each other.*

101. Types of nonsingular collineations. A collineation has a fixed point when $x_i' = x_i$ in the equations (1), § 100. Fixed points are therefore given by the equations

$$\begin{aligned}
(a_{11} - \rho)x_1 & + a_{12}x_2 & + a_{13}x_3 & + a_{14}x_4 = 0, \\
a_{21}x_1 + (a_{22} - \rho)x_2 & & + a_{23}x_3 & + a_{24}x_4 = 0, \\
a_{31}x_1 & + a_{32}x_2 + (a_{33} - \rho)x_3 & & + a_{34}x_4 = 0, \\
a_{41}x_1 & + a_{42}x_2 & + a_{43}x_3 + (a_{44} - \rho)x_4 = 0.
\end{aligned}$$

The necessary and sufficient conditions that these equations have a solution is that ρ satisfies the equation

$$\begin{vmatrix}
a_{11} - \rho & a_{12} & a_{13} & a_{14} \\
a_{21} & a_{22} - \rho & a_{23} & a_{24} \\
a_{31} & a_{32} & a_{33} - \rho & a_{34} \\
a_{41} & a_{42} & a_{43} & a_{44} - \rho
\end{vmatrix} = 0.$$

Similar conditions hold for the fixed planes. By reasoning analogous to that used in § 41 we may establish the results:

Every collineation has as many distinct fixed planes as fixed points, as many pencils of fixed planes as lines of fixed points, and as many bundles of fixed planes as planes of fixed points.

In every fixed plane lie at least one fixed point and one fixed line, through every fixed line goes at least one fixed plane, on every fixed line lies at least one fixed point, through every fixed point go at least one fixed line and one fixed plane.

With the aid of these theorems we may now classify the collineations. For brevity we shall omit much of the details of the work, which is similar to that of § 41.* In the following equations

* As in § 41, the use of Weierstrass's elementary divisors would simplify the work. See footnote, p. 86.

the letters a, b, c, d represent quantities which are distinct from each other and from zero.

A. At least four distinct fixed points not in the same plane. The four points may be taken as the vertices of the tetrahedron of reference $ABCD$ (see Fig. 52, § 82). We have, then, the following types:

TYPE I.
$$\rho x_1' = ax_1,$$
$$\rho x_2' = bx_2,$$
$$\rho x_3' = cx_3,$$
$$\rho x_4' = dx_4.$$

The collineation has the isolated fixed points A, B, C, D, and the isolated fixed planes ABC, BCD, CDA, DAB.

TYPE II.
$$\rho x_1' = ax_1,$$
$$\rho x_2' = ax_2,$$
$$\rho x_3 = cx_3,$$
$$\rho x_4' = dx_4.$$

The collineation has the isolated fixed points A, B, the line of fixed points CD, the isolated fixed planes ACD, BCD, and the pencil of fixed planes with axis AB.

TYPE III.
$$\rho x_1 = ax_1,$$
$$\rho x_2' = ax_2,$$
$$\rho x_3' = cx_3,$$
$$\rho x_4' = cx_4.$$

The collineation has the two lines of fixed points AB, CD and the two pencils of fixed planes with the axes AB, CD.

TYPE IV.
$$\rho x_1' = ax_1,$$
$$\rho x_2' = ax_2,$$
$$\rho x_3' = ax_3,$$
$$\rho x_4' = dx_4.$$

The collineation has the isolated fixed point A, the plane of fixed points BCD, the isolated fixed plane BCD, and the bundle of fixed planes with vertex A.

Type V.
$$\rho x_1' = ax_1,$$
$$\rho x_2' = ax_2,$$
$$\rho x_3' = ax_3,$$
$$\rho x_4' = ax_4.$$

All points and planes are fixed. It is the identical transformation.

B. At least three distinct fixed points not in the same straight line and no others not in the same plane. The fixed points may be taken as the points A, B, D. There are three fixed planes, one of which is ABD, and the others must intersect ABD in one of the three fixed lines AB, CD, DA. We may take one of these planes as $DBC(x_4 = 0)$. Then in that plane we have a collineation in which B and D are the only fixed points. By proper choice of the vertex C the collineations in the plane $x_4 = 0$ may be given the forms found in § 41. Hence for the space collineations we find the following types:

Type VI.
$$\rho x_1' = ax_1 + x_2,$$
$$\rho x_2' = ax_2,$$
$$\rho x_3' = cx_3,$$
$$\rho x_4 = dx_4.$$

The collineation has the isolated fixed points A, B, D and the isolated fixed planes ABD, ADC, BCD.

Type VII.
$$\rho x_1' = ax_1 + x_2,$$
$$\rho x_2' = ax_2,$$
$$\rho x_3' = cx_3,$$
$$\rho x_4' = cx_4.$$

The collineation has an isolated fixed point D, a line of fixed points AB, the isolated fixed plane ABD, and the pencil of fixed planes with the axis CD.

Type VIII.
$$\rho x_1' = ax_1 + x_2,$$
$$\rho x_2 = ax_2,$$
$$\rho x_3' = ax_3,$$
$$\rho x_4' = dx_4.$$

The collineation has the isolated fixed point A, the line of fixed points BD, the isolated fixed plane BCD, and the pencil of fixed planes with the vertex AD.

Type VIII is distinguished geometrically from Type VII by the fact that in Type VIII the line of fixed points intersects the axis of the pencil of fixed planes and in Type VII this is not the case.

TYPE IX.
$$\rho x_1' = ax_1 + x_2,$$
$$\rho x_2' = \qquad ax_2,$$
$$\rho x_3' = \qquad\qquad ax_3,$$
$$\rho x_4' = \qquad\qquad\qquad ax_4.$$

The collineation has the plane of fixed points ABD and the bundle of fixed planes with vertex D.

C. At least two distinct fixed points and no others not in the same straight line. The fixed points may be taken as B and D. There must be two distinct fixed planes of which one must pass through BD and the other may. There are two subcases each leading to two types of collineations.

1. If both fixed planes pass through BD they may be taken as $x_2 = 0$ and $x_4 = 0$. Then in each of these planes we have a collineation of Type IV or Type V of § 41. By proper choice of the points A and C we have, accordingly, the following types of space collineations:

TYPE X.
$$\rho x_1' = ax_1 + x_2,$$
$$\rho x_2' = \qquad ax_2,$$
$$\rho x_3' = \qquad\qquad bx_3 + x_4,$$
$$\rho x_4' = \qquad\qquad\qquad bx_4.$$

The collineation has the isolated fixed points B, D and the isolated fixed planes ABD, BCD.

TYPE XI.
$$\rho x_1' = ax_1 + x_2,$$
$$\rho x_2' = \qquad ax_2,$$
$$\rho x_3' = \qquad\qquad ax_3 + x_4,$$
$$\rho x_4' = \qquad\qquad\qquad ax_4.$$

The collineation has the line of fixed points BD and the pencil of fixed planes with the axis BD.

2. If only one of the fixed planes passes through BD the other must contain one of the fixed points B or D. In this case we may

take the two fixed planes as $x_4 = 0$ and $x_3 = 0$. Then in the plane BCD we have a collineation of Type IV or Type V of § 41 and in ABD one of Type VI of § 41. By proper choice of the points C and A, therefore, we have the following types:

TYPE XII.

$$\rho x_1' = ax_1 + x_2,$$
$$\rho x_2' = \qquad ax_2 + x_4,$$
$$\rho x_3' = \qquad\qquad bx_3,$$
$$\rho x_4' = \qquad\qquad\qquad ax_4.$$

The collineation has the fixed points B, D and the fixed planes BCD, ADC.

TYPE XIII.

$$\rho x_1' = ax_1 + x_2,$$
$$\rho x_2' = \qquad ax_2 + x_4,$$
$$\rho x_3' = \qquad\qquad ax_3,$$
$$\rho x_4' = \qquad\qquad\qquad ax_4.$$

The collineation has the line of fixed points BD and the pencil of fixed planes with the axis DC.

D. Only one fixed point. The fixed point may be taken as D. The fixed plane which must exist may be taken as $x_4 = 0$. Then in that plane the collineation is of Type VI, § 41, and the points C and B may be so chosen that the equations take the form of Type VI there given. To do this we first select $x_3 = 0$, $x_4 = 0$ as the fixed line in the plane $x_4 = 0$. The point A may be taken as any point outside of $x_4 = 0$. If A' is the point into which A is transformed, the line AA' may be taken as $x_1 = 0$, $x_2 = 0$. This fixes the point B. Then C is determined, as in Type VI, § 41. The result is the following type:

TYPE XIV.

$$\rho x_1' = ax_1 + x_2,$$
$$\rho x_2' = \qquad ax_2 + x_3,$$
$$\rho x_3' = \qquad\qquad ax_3 + x_4,$$
$$\rho x_4' = \qquad\qquad\qquad ax_4.$$

The above types exhaust the cases of a nonsingular collineation. In a singular collineation there exist exceptional points, lines, or planes. The discussion of these is left to the student.

EXERCISES

1. Considering the translation

$$x' = x + a, \quad y' = y + b, \quad z' = z + c$$

as a collineation, determine its fixed points and the type to which it belongs.

2. Considering the rotation

$$x' = x \cos \phi - y \sin \phi, \quad y' = x \sin \phi + y \cos \phi, \quad z' = z$$

as a collineation, determine its fixed points and the type to which it belongs.

3. Considering the screw motion

$$x' = x \cos \phi - y \sin \phi, \quad y' = x \sin \phi + y \cos \phi, \quad z' = kz$$

as a collineation, determine its fixed points and the type to which it belongs.

4. Set up the formulas for the singular collineation known as " painter's perspective," by which any point P is transformed into that point of a fixed plane p in which the line through P and a fixed point O meets p.

5. Find all possible types of nonsingular collineations.

102. Correlations. A correlation of point and plane in space is defined by the equations

$$\rho u_i' = a_{i1}x_1 + a_{i2}x_2 + a_{i3}x_3 + a_{i4}x_4, \quad (i = 1, 2, 3, 4) \tag{1}$$

where u_i are plane coördinates and x_i are point coördinates. The correlation is nonsingular when $|a_{ik}| \neq 0$, and we shall consider only such correlations. Then any point x_i is transformed into a definite plane u_i', and any plane u_i' is the transformed element of a definite point, so that the correspondence of an element and its transformed element is one-to-one. The points x_i which lie on a plane with coördinates u_i are transformed into planes u_i' which pass through a point x_i', where

$$\rho x_i' = A_{i1}u_1 + A_{i2}u_2 + A_{i3}u_3 + A_{i4}u_4, \tag{2}$$

where A_{ik} is the cofactor of a_{ik} in the determinant $|a_{ik}|$. We may say, therefore, that the plane u_i is transformed into the point x_i'. Points which lie on a line l are transformed into planes through a line l', so that we may say that the line l is transformed into the line l'.

If the point $P(x_i)$ is transformed into the plane $p'(u_i')$, then, by the same operation, the plane p' is transformed into the point $P''(x_i'')$, where, from (2),

$$\rho x_i'' = A_{i1}u_1' + A_{i2}u_2' + A_{i3}u_3' + A_{i4}u_4'.$$

The last equations solved for u_i' give

$$\rho u_i' = a_{1i}x_1'' + a_{2i}x_2'' + a_{3i}x_3'' + a_{4i}x_4''. \tag{4}$$

The points x_i and x_i'' are in general distinct. That they should coincide it is necessary and sufficient, as is seen by comparison of (1) and (4), that

$$\begin{aligned}
(a_{11}-\rho a_{11})x_1 + (a_{12}-\rho a_{21})x_2 + (a_{13}-\rho a_{31})x_3 + (a_{14}-\rho a_{41})x_4 &= 0, \\
(a_{21}-\rho a_{12})x_1 + (a_{22}-\rho a_{22})x_2 + (a_{23}-\rho a_{32})x_3 + (a_{24}-\rho a_{42})x_4 &= 0, \\
(a_{31}-\rho a_{13})x_1 + (a_{32}-\rho a_{23})x_2 + (a_{33}-\rho a_{33})x_3 + (a_{34}-\rho a_{43})x_4 &= 0, \\
(a_{41}-\rho a_{14})x_1 + (a_{42}-\rho a_{24})x_2 + (a_{43}-\rho a_{34})x_3 + (a_{44}-\rho a_{44})x_4 &= 0,
\end{aligned} \tag{5}$$

where ρ must satisfy the condition

$$\begin{vmatrix}
a_{11}-\rho a_{11} & a_{12}-\rho a_{21} & a_{13}-\rho a_{31} & a_{14}-\rho a_{41} \\
a_{21}-\rho a_{12} & a_{22}-\rho a_{22} & a_{23}-\rho a_{32} & a_{24}-\rho a_{42} \\
a_{31}-\rho a_{13} & a_{32}-\rho a_{23} & a_{33}-\rho a_{33} & a_{34}-\rho a_{43} \\
a_{41}-\rho a_{14} & a_{42}-\rho a_{24} & a_{43}-\rho a_{34} & a_{44}-\rho a_{44}
\end{vmatrix} = 0, \tag{6}$$

in order that equations (5) may have a solution.

When the coördinates of a point P satisfy equations (5), it and the plane p', into which it is transformed, form a double pair of the correlation. Since (6) is of the fourth degree we see that in general a correlation has four double pairs, but may have more.

The double pairs may be made the basis of a classification of correlations, as was done in the case of the plane, but we will not take the space to do so. Of special interest is the case in which each point of space is a point of a double pair. For this it is necessary and sufficient that equations (5) should be satisfied for all values of x. This can happen in only two cases:

1. $\rho = 1$, $a_{ki} = a_{ik}$.   2. $\rho = -1$, $a_{ii} = 0$, $a_{ki} = -a_{ik}$.

In the first case the correlation is evidently a polarity with respect to the conic $\sum a_{ik}x_ix_k = 0$, and by proper choice of coördinates it may be represented by the equations

$$\rho u_i' = x_i.$$

In the second case the correlation has the form

$$\rho u_1' = \qquad\quad a_{12}x_2 + a_{13}x_3 + a_{14}x_4,$$
$$\rho u_2' = -a_{12}x_1 \qquad\quad + a_{23}x_3 + a_{24}x_4,$$
$$\rho u_3' = -a_{13}x_1 - a_{23}x_2 \qquad\quad + a_{34}x_4,$$
$$\rho u_4' = -a_{14}x_1 - a_{24}x_2 - a_{34}x_3,$$

and represents a *null system*, which will be discussed later. It will be shown that by choice of axes the correlation may be reduced to the standard form

$$\rho u_1' = x_2,$$
$$\rho u_2' = -x_1,$$
$$\rho u_3' = x_4,$$
$$\rho u_4' = -x_3.$$

Another question of interest is to determine the condition under which a point P lies in the plane p', into which it is transformed. From equations (1) it follows at once that the coördinates of P must satisfy the equation

$$\sum a_{ik}x_ix_k = 0.$$

This equation is satisfied identically only in the case of the null system; otherwise it determines a quadric surface K_1, the locus of the points P which lie in their respective transformed planes. Similarly, the planes p which pass through their respective transformed points envelop the quadric K_2,

$$\sum A_{ik}u_iu_k = 0,$$

which is in general distinct from K_1.

EXERCISES

1. Prove that if P and p' are a double pair the plane p' is the polar plane of P with respect to the conic K_1.

2. Prove that a correlation is an involutory transformation only in the case of a polarity or a null system.

3. Explain why there is no analog of the null system in plane geometry.

4. Prove that any correlation is the product of a collineation and a polarity.

103. The projective and the metrical groups. The product of two nonsingular collineations or of two nonsingular correlations is a nonsingular collineation. Hence the totality of all collineations and correlations form a group, since this totality contains the identical substitution. Projective geometry may be defined as that geometry which is concerned with the properties of figures which are invariant under the projective group. In this geometry the plane at infinity has no unique property distinct from those of other planes nor is the imaginary circle at infinity essentially different from any other conic, and all questions of measurement disappear. Quadric surfaces are distinguished only by the presence and nature of their singular points.

Subgroups exist in great abundance in the group of projections. For example, the collineations taken without the correlations form a subgroup, but the correlations alone form no group. All collineations with the same fixed points obviously form a subgroup. Again, all collineations which leave a given quadric surface invariant form a subgroup. Of great importance among these latter is the group which leaves the imaginary circle at infinity invariant. This is the *metrical group*, which leaves angles invariant and multiplies all distances by the same constant.

The general form of a transformation of the metrical group is

$$\begin{aligned}
\rho x' &= l_1 x + m_1 y + n_1 z + p_1 t, \\
\rho y' &= l_2 x + m_2 y + n_2 z + p_2 t, \\
\rho z' &= l_3 x + m_3 y + n_3 z + p_3 t, \\
\rho t' &= t,
\end{aligned} \tag{1}$$

where the coefficients satisfy the conditions

$$l_1^2 + l_2^2 + l_3^2 = m_1^2 + m_2^2 + m_3^2 = n_1^2 + n_2^2 + n_3^2, \tag{2}$$

$$l_1 m_1 + l_2 m_2 + l_3 m_3 = m_1 n_1 + m_2 n_2 + m_3 n_3 = n_1 l_1 + n_2 l_2 + n_3 l_3 = 0. \tag{3}$$

It is easy to see that the distance between two transformed points is by this transformation k times the distance between the original points, where k^2 is the common value of the expressions in (2), and, conversely, that a collineation which multiplies all distances by the same constant is of the form (1). The preservation of angles follows from elementary theorems on similar triangles.

All transformations of the metrical group which leave a plane p fixed form a group of collineations in that plane by which the circular points at infinity are invariant. This group is therefore the metrical group in p, and the projective definitions of angle and distance given in § 50 stand.

EXERCISES

1. If D is the determinant of the coefficients l, m, n in (1), show that $D = \pm k^3$.

2. Show that the necessary and sufficient condition that (1) should represent a mechanical motion is that $D = +1$, and that it should represent a motion combined with a reflection on any plane is that $D = -1$.

3. Show that if $D = \pm 1$ in addition to conditions (2) and (3), we have

$$l_1^2 + m_1^2 + n_1^2 = l_2^2 + m_2^2 + n_2^2 = l_3^2 + m_3^2 + n_3^2 = 1,$$

$$l_1 l_2 + m_1 m_2 + n_1 n_2 = l_2 l_3 + m_2 m_3 + n_2 n_3 = l_3 l_1 + m_3 m_1 + n_3 n_1 = 0.$$

104. Projective geometry on a quadric surface. It has already been noted (§ 69) that the geometry on a surface of second order with the use of quadriplanar coördinates is dualistic to the geometry on the plane with the use of tetracyclical coördinates. For in each case we have a point defined by the ratios of four quantities x_1, x_2, x_3, x_4, bound by a quadratic relation

$$\omega(x) = 0, \tag{1}$$

which is, on the one hand, the equation of the quadric surface and, on the other hand, the fundamental relation connecting the tetracyclical coördinates.

Any point I on the quadric surface may be taken as corresponding to the point at infinity on the plane, since the point at infinity is in no way special in the analysis. Any linear equation

$$\sum a_i x_i = 0 \tag{2}$$

represents a plane section of the surface or a circle on the plane. Should the section pass through I, the circle on the plane becomes a straight line, but circles and straight lines have no analytic distinction in this geometry.

If y_i is a point on the quadric surface and we have, in (2),

$$a_i = \frac{\partial \omega}{\partial y_i}, \tag{3}$$

the plane (2) is tangent to the surface, and the circle on the plane is a point circle. The point of tangency on the surface corresponds to the center of the point circle on the plane. The intersection of the tangent plane with the quadric surface consists of two generators. In a corresponding manner the point circle on the plane consists of two one-dimensional extents. Neither alone, however, can be represented by a linear equation in x_i, and therefore they are not straight lines on the plane. If this is obscure it is to be remembered that imaginary straight lines are not defined by any geometric property, but by an analytic equation.

The intersection with the quadric surface of the tangent plane at I corresponds to the locus at infinity on the plane.

The center y_i of a point circle on the plane, or the point of tangency of a tangent plane to the surface, is found by solving (3) for y_i. The values of y_i must satisfy (1), and the substitution gives the equation

$$\eta(a) = 0, \tag{4}$$

which is the condition that a circle on the plane with tetracyclical coördinates should be a point circle, or that a plane in space should be tangent to the point circle. It is in fact simply the equation in plane coördinates of the quadric surface (1).

Two circles on the plane are perpendicular when

$$\sum b_i \frac{\partial \eta}{\partial a_i} = \eta(a, b) = 0. \tag{5}$$

In space the pole of the plane $\sum a_i x_i = 0$ with respect to the surface with the plane equation (4) is $y_i = \dfrac{\partial \eta}{\partial a_i}$, and equation (5) is the condition that this pole lie in the plane $\sum b_i x_i = 0$. Hence two orthogonal circles on the plane with tetracyclical coördinates correspond to two plane sections of the quadric surface such that each plane contains the pole of the other.

A linear substitution of the tetracyclical coördinates corresponds to a collineation in space which leaves the quadric surface invariant. The geometry of inversion on the plane is therefore dualistic to the geometry on the quadric surface which is invariant with respect to collineations which leave the surface unchanged. Two points on the plane which are inverse with respect to a circle C correspond to two points on the quadric surface such that any plane through them passes through the pole of the plane corresponding to C or, in other words, such that the line connecting them passes through the pole of the plane corresponding to C. Since the center of a circle on the plane is the inverse of the point at infinity with respect to that circle, the point on the quadric which corresponds to the center of a circle may be found by connecting the point I with the pole of the plane corresponding to the circle.

An inversion with respect to a circle corresponds in space to a collineation which transforms each point into its inverse with respect to a fixed plane. That is, if the fixed circle corresponds to the intersection of the quadric with a plane M, and K is the pole of M, an inversion with respect to M transforms any point P_1 on the quadric into the point P_2, where the line KP_1 again meets the quadric. The collineation which carries out this transformation has the plane M as a plane of fixed points and the point K as a point of fixed planes.

Consider now the parameters (λ, μ) on the surface, defined as in § 96. They may be taken as the coördinates of a point on the surface and may be interpreted dualistically to the special coördinates of § 70. The two families of generators are then dualistic to the two systems of special lines of § 70, and the locus at infinity on the plane is dualistic to the generators through the point I of the surface.

The bilinear equation

$$a_1\lambda\mu + a_2\lambda + a_3\mu + a_4 = 0 \tag{6}$$

represents a plane section of the quadric surface and is dualistic to the equilateral hyperbola on the plane with two special lines as asymptotes. A section of the quadric surface through I corresponds to an ordinary line on the plane, from which it is evident that by the use of the special coördinates the straight line has the properties of the equilateral hyperbola.

Any collineation of space which leaves the quadric surface invariant gives a linear transformation of λ and of μ. This is evident from the fact that the collineation must transform the lines of the surface into themselves in a one-to-one manner. It may also be proved analytically from the relations of § 96.

Conversely, any linear substitution of λ and μ corresponds to a collineation which leaves the quadric invariant.

Consider in fact the substitution

$$\lambda = \frac{\alpha\lambda' + \beta}{\gamma\lambda' + \delta}, \qquad \mu = \mu', \tag{7}$$

which leaves the generators of the second family fixed and transforms the generators of the first family. From (4), § 96, it is easy to compute that this is equivalent to the collineation

$$\begin{aligned}
\rho x_1 &= (\alpha + \delta)x_1' + i(\alpha - \delta)x_2' + (\gamma - \beta)x_3' - i(\beta + \gamma)x_4', \\
\rho x_2 &= i(-\alpha + \delta)x_1' + (\alpha + \delta)x_2' + i(\beta + \gamma)x_3' + (-\beta + \gamma)x_4', \\
\rho x_3 &= (\beta - \gamma)x_1' - i(\beta + \gamma)x_2' + (\alpha + \delta)x_3' + i(-\alpha + \delta)x_4', \\
\rho x_4 &= i(\beta + \gamma)x_1' + (\beta - \gamma)x_2' + i(\alpha - \delta)x_3' + (\alpha + \delta)x_4'.
\end{aligned} \tag{8}$$

Similar results can be obtained for the transformation

$$\lambda = \lambda', \qquad \mu = \frac{m\mu' + n}{p\mu' + q}, \tag{9}$$

by which the generators of the first family are fixed, and for the product of (7) and (9).

Finally, the collineation corresponding to the transformation

$$\lambda = \frac{\alpha\mu' + \beta}{\gamma\mu' + \delta}, \qquad \mu = \frac{m\lambda' + n}{p\lambda' + q}, \tag{10}$$

by which generators of the two families are interchanged, is easily computed.

EXERCISES

1. Show that if the quadric (1), § 96, is the sphere $x^2 + y^2 + z^2 = 1$, the transformation $\lambda = e^{i\phi}\lambda'$, $\mu = e^{i\phi}\mu'$ represents a rotation of the sphere about the axis OZ through an angle ϕ.

2. Show that the transformation $\lambda = -\mu'$, $\mu = -\lambda'$ replaces each point of the sphere of Ex. 1 by its diametrically opposite point.

3. Obtain a transformation of λ, μ which represents a general rotation of the sphere in Ex. 1 about any axis through its center.

105. Projective measurement. The definition of projective measurement, given in § 47 for the plane, can evidently be generalized for space, and only a concise statement of essentials is necessary here.

Let $$\omega(x) = 0 \tag{1}$$

be the equation of any quadric surface taken as the fundamental quadric for the measurement, and let

$$\Omega(u) = 0 \tag{2}$$

be the equation of the same surface in plane coördinates.

If A and B are any two points and T_1 and T_2 are the points in which the line AB meets the quadric, then the distance D between A and B is defined by the equation

$$D = K \log(AB, \ T_1 T_2);$$

or if y_i and z_i are the coördinates of A and B respectively,

$$D = K \log \frac{\omega(y, z) + \sqrt{[\omega(y, z)]^2 - [\omega(y)][\omega(z)]}}{\omega(y, z) - \sqrt{[\omega(y, z)]^2 - [\omega(y)][\omega(z)]}}. \tag{3}$$

Also, if a and b are two planes and t_1 and t_2 are the two tangent planes to the quadric through the intersection of a and b, the angle ϕ between a and b is defined by the equation

$$
\begin{aligned}
\phi &= \frac{i}{2} \log [ab, \ t_1 t_2] \\
&= \frac{i}{2} \log \frac{\Omega(u, v) + \sqrt{[\Omega(u, v)]^2 - [\Omega(u)][\Omega(v)]}}{\Omega(u, v) - \sqrt{[\Omega(u, v)]^2 - [\Omega(u)][\Omega(v)]}},
\end{aligned} \tag{4}
$$

where u_i and v_i are the coördinates of a and b respectively.

Two planes are perpendicular if each passes through the pole of the other; for, in (4), if $\Omega(u, v) = 0$, then $\phi = \frac{i}{2} \log(-1) = \frac{\pi}{2} + n\pi$.

A line is perpendicular to a plane p if every plane through the line is perpendicular to p; that is, if the line passes through the pole of p.

We may define the angle between two lines in the same plane as the angle between the two planes through the lines and perpendicular to the plane of the lines. That is the same as defining the angle between the two lines as $\frac{i}{2}$ times the logarithm of the cross ratio of the two lines and the two tangent lines drawn in their plane to the quadric surface.

Any plane cuts the quadric surface in a conic, and the definition of angle and distance is the same as in the projective measurement of § 47, in which this conic is the fundamental one. Projective plane measurement is therefore obtained by a plane section of projective space measurement.

As in Chapter VII we have three cases:

I. *The hyperbolic case.* The fundamental quadric is real, and we consider only the space inside of it. The geometry in the plane is the same as in § 48.

II. *The elliptic case.* The fundamental quadric is imaginary. The geometry in the plane is the same as in § 49.

III. *The parabolic case.* The fundamental quadric in plane coördinates may be taken as

$$u_1^2 + u_2^2 + u_3^2 = 0,$$

which is that of a plane extent consisting of planes tangent to a conic in the plane $x_4 = 0$. If this conic is the circle at infinity, the measurement becomes Euclidean.

If the conic is a real circle at infinity, for example the circle

$$x^2 + y^2 - z^2 = 0, \quad t = 0,$$

we have a measurement in which

$$D = \sqrt{(x - x')^2 + (y - y')^2 - (z - z')^2},$$

and the angle between the two planes

$$ax + by + cz + dt = 0 \quad \text{and} \quad a'x + b'y + c'z + d't = 0$$

is given by

$$\cos \phi = \frac{aa' + bb' - cc'}{\sqrt{a^2 + b^2 - c^2}\sqrt{a'^2 + b'^2 - c'^2}}.$$

Through any point in space goes a real cone, such that the distances from its vertex to points inside it are imaginary, distances from its vertex to points outside it are real, and distances from its vertex to points on it are zero. Any plane section through the vertex is divided into regions with the properties described in § 50.

106. Clifford parallels. When a system of projective measurement has been established, the concept of parallel lines may be introduced by adopting some property of parallel lines in Euclidean geometry as a definition. Perhaps the most obvious as well as the most common definition is that parallel lines are those which intersect at infinity. By this definition, in parabolic space one and only one line can be drawn through a point parallel to a given line, in hyperbolic space two such parallels can be drawn, and in elliptic space no real parallel can be drawn.

In elliptic space, however, there exist certain real lines called *Clifford parallels* which have other properties of parallel lines as they exist in Euclidean space. We will proceed to discuss these lines.

We have seen that any linear transformation of the parameters λ and μ which define a point on a quadric surface correspond to a collineation which leaves the quadric invariant. Among these transformations are those of the type

$$\lambda = \frac{\alpha\lambda' + \beta}{\gamma\lambda' + \delta}, \qquad \mu = \mu', \tag{1}$$

which transform the generators of the first family among themselves but leave each generator of the second family unchanged.

For reasons to be given later we call such a transformation a *translation of the first kind*.

Similarly, the transformation

$$\lambda = \lambda', \qquad \mu = \frac{m\mu' + n}{p\mu' + q}, \tag{2}$$

by which the generators of the second family are transformed but each of the first family is left unchanged, is called a *translation of the second kind*.

Consider a translation of the first kind. On the fundamental quadric any generator of the second family is left unchanged as a whole, but its individual points are transformed, except two fixed points, for which

$$\lambda = \frac{\alpha\lambda + \beta}{\gamma\lambda + \delta}. \tag{3}$$

This equation defines two generators of the first kind, all of whose points are fixed. Hence, *in a translation of the first kind there are, in general, two generators of the first kind which are fixed point by point.* We say "in general" because it is possible that the two roots of (3) may be equal.

Call the two fixed generators g and h. Then any line which intersects g and h is fixed, since two of its points are fixed. Also through any point P in space one and only one line can be drawn intersecting g and h. Therefore, *any point P is transformed into another point on the line which passes through P and intersects g and h.*

Since we are dealing with a case of elliptic measurement the lines g and h are imaginary. Then, if a real point P is transformed into another real point, the roots of (3) must be conjugate imaginary, since a real line intersects an imaginary quadric whose equation has real coefficients in conjugate imaginary points corresponding to conjugate imaginary values of λ and μ. Therefore, *if a translation of the first kind transforms real points into real points, there must be two distinct fixed generators corresponding to conjugate imaginary values of λ.*

This may also be established by equations (8), § 104. That these may represent a real substitution δ must be conjugate imaginary to α, and γ conjugate imaginary to $-\beta$. We therefore place $\alpha = d + ic$, $\delta = d - ic$, $\beta = -b + ia$, $\gamma = b + ia$, and have

$$
\begin{aligned}
\rho x_1 &= \quad dx_1' - cx_2' + bx_3' + ax_4', \\
\rho x_2 &= \quad cx_1' + dx_2' - ax_3' + bx_4', \\
\rho x_3 &= -bx_1' + ax_2' + dx_3' + cx_4', \\
\rho x_4 &= -ax_1' - bx_2' - cx_3' + dx_4'.
\end{aligned}
\tag{4}
$$

With these values of α, β, γ, and δ the roots of (3) are conjugate imaginary.

To find the projective distance between a point x_i and its transformed point x_i', we use equations (4) and substitute in (3), § 105, placing $K = \dfrac{i}{2}$. There results

$$
D = \frac{i}{2} \log \frac{d + i\sqrt{a^2 + b^2 + c^2}}{d - i\sqrt{a^2 + b^2 + c^2}} = \cos^{-1} \frac{d}{\sqrt{a^2 + b^2 + c^2 + d^2}},
$$

which is a constant. Hence, *by a translation of the first kind each point of space is moved through a constant projective distance on the straight line which passes through the point and meets the two fixed generators on the fundamental quadric.*

It is this property which gives to the transformation the name "translation" and to the lines which intersect the two fixed generators the name "parallels." By the transformation the points of space are moved along the Clifford parallels in a manner analogous to that in which points are moved along Euclidean parallels by a Euclidean translation.

In the projective space a dualistic property exists. Since the Clifford parallels are fixed, any plane through one of them is transformed into another plane through it. Now any plane contains one Clifford parallel, since it intersects each of the fixed generators in one point. If u_i and u_i' are the original and the transformed plane respectively, the angle between them is, by (4), § 105,

$$
\phi = \frac{i}{2} \log \frac{d + \sqrt{a^2 + b^2 + c^2}}{d - \sqrt{a^2 + b^2 + c^2}} = \cos^{-1} \frac{d}{\sqrt{a^2 + b^2 + c^2 + d^2}}.
$$

Hence, *by a translation of the first kind each plane of space is turned about the Clifford parallel in it through a constant angle which is equal to the distance through which points of the space are moved.*

Similar theorems hold for translations of the second kind. The two kinds of translations differ, however, in the sense in which the turning of the planes takes place.

By a translation of the second kind Clifford parallels of the first kind are transformed into themselves. For by the translation of the second kind all generators of the first kind are fixed, and consequently any line intersecting two such generators is transformed into a line intersecting the same two generators. Hence *two Clifford parallels are everywhere equidistant if the distance is measured on Clifford parallels of the other kind.*

Let LK and MN be two Clifford parallels of the first kind, g and h the two fixed generators which determine the parallels, and PQ any line intersecting both LK and MN. The line PQ intersects two generators g' and h' of the second kind and is therefore one of a set of Clifford parallels of the second kind. Therefore there exists a transformation of the second kind by which PQ is fixed and LK is transformed into MN, P falling on Q. Hence the angles under which PQ cuts LK and MN are equal, of course in the projective sense. That is, *if a line cuts two Clifford parallels, the corresponding angles are equal.*

In particular the line may be so drawn as to make the angle LPQ a right angle. For if Q is on MN, the point Q and the line LK determine a plane p, and in this plane a perpendicular can be drawn from Q to LK. To do this it is only necessary to connect Q with the point in which the plane p is met by the reciprocal polar of LK with respect to the quadric surface.

Hence, *from any point in one of two Clifford parallels a common perpendicular can be drawn to the two, and the portion of the perpendicular included between the two parallels is of constant length.*

107. Contact transformations. A transformation in space, expressible by means of analytic relations between the coördinates of points, may be of three kinds according as points are transformed into points, surfaces, or curves respectively. We shall find it convenient to employ Cartesian coördinates in discussing these transformations and to introduce the concept of a plane element.

Let (x, y, z) be a point in space and let $Z - z = p(X - x) + q(Y - y)$ be a plane through it. Then the five variables (x, y, z, p, q) define a *plane element*, which may be visualized as an infinitesimal portion of a plane surrounding a point. In fact, not the magnitude of the plane but simply its orientation comes into question, just as, in fixing a point, position and not magnitude is considered. If any one of the five elements is complex, then the plane element is simply a name for the set of variables (x, y, z, p, q).

Since the five variables are independent, there are ∞^5 plane elements in space. Of chief interest, however, are two-dimensional extents of plane elements. Such an extent we shall denote by M_2 and shall consider three types:

1. Let the points of the plane elements be taken in the surface $z = f(x, y)$ and let p and q be determined by the equations $p = \dfrac{\partial z}{\partial x}, \ q = \dfrac{\partial z}{\partial y}.$ More generally, let x, y, and z be defined as functions of two variables u and v, and let p and q be determined by the equation

$$dz = p\,dx + q\,dy \tag{1}$$

for all differentials du and dv. Then

$$\frac{\partial z}{\partial u} = p\frac{\partial x}{\partial u} + q\frac{\partial y}{\partial u},$$

$$\frac{\partial z}{\partial v} = p\frac{\partial x}{\partial v} + q\frac{\partial y}{\partial v};$$

whence p and q are also determined as functions of u and v.

In either definition the M_2 consists of the plane elements formed by the points of a surface and the tangent planes at those points.

2. Let the points of the plane elements be taken as functions of a single variable u and let p and q be again determined by equation (1), where one of the two (say p) is arbitrary and the other (say q) is thus determined in terms of p and u. The M_2 then consists of the points of a curve and the tangent planes to the curve at those points. The points themselves form a one-dimensional extent, and through each point goes a one-dimensional extent of planes; namely, the pencil of planes through the tangent line to the curve.

3. Let (x, y, z) be a fixed point and let p and q be arbitrary and independent. The M_2 then consists of a point with the bundle of planes through it. In this case, also, equation (1) is true, since dx, dy, and dz are all zero.

It is clear that the M_2's defined above do not exhaust all possible types of two-dimensional extents of plane elements. For example, we might take the points as points on a surface and the planes as uniquely determined at each point but not tangent to the surface; and other examples will occur to the student. The above-mentioned types exhaust all cases, however, for which equation (1) is true, as the student may verify. We shall say that a set of plane elements satisfying (1) form a *union* of elements.

Two M_2's are said to be in contact when they have a plane element in common. From this definition two surfaces, or a curve and a surface, are in contact when they are tangent in the ordinary sense, a point is in contact with a surface or a curve when it lies on the surface or the curve, two curves are in contact when they intersect, and two points are in contact when they coincide.

A contact transformation is a transformation by which two M_2's in contact are transformed into two M_2's in contact. There are three types of such transformations, which we shall proceed to discuss in the following sections.

108. Point-point transformations. This transformation is defined by three equations of the form

$$\begin{aligned}
x' &= f_1(x, y, z), \\
y' &= f_2(x, y, z), \\
z' &= f_3(x, y, z),
\end{aligned} \tag{1}$$

or, more generally,

$$\begin{aligned}
F_1(x, y, z, x', y', z') &= 0, \\
F_2(x, y, z, x', y', z') &= 0, \\
F_3(x, y, z, x', y', z') &= 0,
\end{aligned} \tag{2}$$

where we make the hypothesis that equations (1) can be solved for x, y, z and equations (2) for x, y, z and x', y', z', and that all functions are continuous and may be differentiated. Within a properly restricted region the relations between x, y, z and x', y', z' are one to one, a point goes into a point, a surface into a surface, and a curve into a curve.

A direction $dx : dy : dz$ is transformed into a direction $dx' : dy' : dz'$, where

$$dx' = \frac{\partial x'}{\partial x} dx + \frac{\partial x'}{\partial y} dy + \frac{\partial x'}{\partial z} dz,$$

$$dy' = \frac{\partial y'}{\partial x} dx + \frac{\partial y'}{\partial y} dy + \frac{\partial y'}{\partial z} dz, \qquad (3)$$

$$dz' = \frac{\partial z'}{\partial x} dx + \frac{\partial z'}{\partial y} dy + \frac{\partial z'}{\partial z} dz.$$

From this it follows that two tangent surfaces are transformed into tangent surfaces. More specifically, the relation

$$dz = p\, dx + q\, dy, \qquad (4)$$

which defines a union of line elements, is transformed into

$$\begin{vmatrix} dz' & \dfrac{\partial z'}{\partial x} + p\dfrac{\partial z'}{\partial z} & \dfrac{\partial z'}{\partial y} + q\dfrac{\partial z'}{\partial z} \\[2ex] dx' & \dfrac{\partial x'}{\partial x} + p\dfrac{\partial x'}{\partial z} & \dfrac{\partial x'}{\partial y} + q\dfrac{\partial x'}{\partial z} \\[2ex] dy' & \dfrac{\partial y'}{\partial x} + p\dfrac{\partial y'}{\partial z} & \dfrac{\partial y'}{\partial y} + q\dfrac{\partial y'}{\partial z} \end{vmatrix} = 0. \qquad (5)$$

If now we define p' and q' so that this relation is

$$dz' = p'dx' + q'dy', \qquad (6)$$

a union of plane elements (x, y, z, p, q) is transformed into a union of plane elements (x', y', z', p', q'). From equations (5) and (6),

$$p' = f_4(x, y, z, p, q),$$
$$q' = f_5(x, y, z, p, q).$$

These equations adjoined to (1) form, together with (1), the *enlarged point transformations.*

A collineation is an example of a point transformation. Another example of importance is the transformation by reciprocal radius, or inversion with respect to a sphere. If the sphere has its center at the origin and radius k, the transformation is

$$x' = \frac{k^2 x}{x^2 + y^2 + z^2},$$

$$y' = \frac{k^2 y}{x^2 + y^2 + z^2},$$

$$z' = \frac{k^2 z}{x^2 + y^2 + z^2}.$$

Discuss the properties of the inversion with respect to a sphere, especially with reference to singular points and lines.

109. Point-surface transformations. Such a transformation is defined by the equation

$$f(x, y, z, x', y', z') = 0, \tag{1}$$

with the usual hypotheses of continuity and differentiability of f. An example is a correlation since it may be expressed by the single equation

$$(a_{11}x + a_{12}y + a_{13}z + a_{14})x' + (a_{21}x + a_{22}y + a_{23}z + a_{24})y'$$
$$+ (a_{31}x + a_{32}y + a_{33}z + a_{34})z' + a_{41}x + a_{42}y + a_{43}z + a_{44} = 0.$$

By equation (1), if (x, y, z) is fixed, (x', y', z') lies on a surface m', and we say a point P is transformed into a surface m'. If $P'(x', y', z')$ is fixed, the point (x, y, z) describes a surface m, where the surfaces m' and m are not necessarily of the same character. If P' is on m' it is obvious that m contains P. In other words, if P describes a surface m, the corresponding surface, m', continues to pass through P'. We say, therefore, that the surface m is transformed into a point P'.

If P describes any surface S (differing from an m surface), the surface m' will in general envelop a surface S', the transformed surface of S. Analytically, from the general theory of envelopes, if the equation of S is

$$z = \phi(x, y), \tag{2}$$

and $p = \dfrac{\partial \phi}{\partial x}$, $q = \dfrac{\partial \phi}{\partial y}$, the equation of S' is found by eliminating x, y, and z from (1) and (2) and the two equations

$$\frac{\partial f}{\partial x} + p\frac{\partial f}{\partial z} = 0, \tag{3}$$

$$\frac{\partial f}{\partial y} + q\frac{\partial f}{\partial z} = 0. \tag{4}$$

Furthermore, the tangent plane to S' at any point is the same as the tangent plane to m' at that point, and hence, if we use p' and q' to fix that plane, we have

$$\frac{\partial f}{\partial x'} + p'\frac{\partial f}{\partial z'} = 0, \tag{5}$$

$$\frac{\partial f}{\partial y'} + q'\frac{\partial f}{\partial z'} = 0. \tag{6}$$

We now have five equations, namely (1), (3), (4), (5), and (6), establishing a relation between a plane element (x, y, z, p, q) and a plane element (x', y', z', p', q'). These equations may be solved to obtain the form

$$x' = \phi_1(x, y, z, p, q),$$
$$y' = \phi_2(x, y, z, p, q),$$
$$z' = \phi_3(x, y, z, p, q),$$
$$p' = \phi_4(x, y, z, p, q),$$
$$q' = \phi_5(x, y, z, p, q),$$

which form the enlarged point-surface contact transformation.

EXERCISES

1. Study the transformation defined by the equation
$$x^2 + y^2 + z^2 - (xx' + yy' + zz') = 0.$$

2. Study the transformation defined by the equation
$$(x - x')^2 + (y - y')^2 + (z - z')^2 = a^2.$$

110. Point-curve transformations. Consider a transformation defined by the two equations

$$f_1(x, y, z, x', y', z') = 0,$$
$$f_2(x, y, z, x', y', z') = 0. \tag{1}$$

If a point $P(x, y, z)$ is fixed, the locus of $P'(x', y', z')$ is a curve k' defined by equations (1). Similarly, if P' is fixed, the locus of P is a curve k. Hence the transformation changes points into curves.

If P describes a curve C, the curve k' takes ∞^1 positions and in general generates a surface. The ∞^1 curves k' may, however, have an envelope C', which is then the transformed curve of C. Or, finally, if C is a curve k, the corresponding curves k' pass through a point P', which we have seen to correspond to k.

If the point P describes a surface S, the corresponding curves k' form a two-parameter family of curves. The envelope of the family is a surface S' which corresponds to S.

To work analytically let us form from (1) the equation

$$f_1 + \lambda f_2 = 0. \tag{2}$$

With (x', y', z') fixed, (2) represents a pencil of surfaces through a k-curve, and the tangent plane to any one of these surfaces at a point on the k-curve has a p and a q given by the equations

$$p = -\frac{\dfrac{\partial f_1}{\partial x} + \lambda \dfrac{\partial f_2}{\partial x}}{\dfrac{\partial f_1}{\partial z} + \lambda \dfrac{\partial f_2}{\partial z}}, \qquad q = -\frac{\dfrac{\partial f_1}{\partial y} + \lambda \dfrac{\partial f_2}{\partial y}}{\dfrac{\partial f_1}{\partial z} + \lambda \dfrac{\partial f_2}{\partial z}}. \tag{3}$$

There is therefore thus defined a pencil of plane elements through a point P and tangent to a k-curve through that point.

Similarly, with (x, y, z) fixed, equation (2) defines a pencil of surfaces through a k'-curve, and a corresponding pencil of plane elements is defined by (x', y', z') and

$$p' = -\frac{\dfrac{\partial f_1}{\partial x'} + \lambda \dfrac{\partial f_2}{\partial x'}}{\dfrac{\partial f_1}{\partial z'} + \lambda \dfrac{\partial f_2}{\partial z'}}, \qquad q' = -\frac{\dfrac{\partial f_1}{\partial y'} + \lambda \dfrac{\partial f_2}{\partial y'}}{\dfrac{\partial f_1}{\partial z'} + \lambda \dfrac{\partial f_2}{\partial z'}}. \tag{4}$$

From (3) and (4) it is easy to compute that $dz - p\,dx - q\,dy$ is transformed into $dz' - p'dx' - q'dy'$ except for a factor. So that if (x, y, z, p, q) is transformed into (x', y', z', p', q') by means of (1), (3), and (4), a union of plane elements is transformed into a union of plane elements.

From the six equations (1), (3), (4) we may eliminate λ and obtain five equations which may be reduced to the form

$$x' = f_1(x, y, z, p, q),$$
$$y' = f_2(x, y, z, p, q),$$
$$z' = f_3(x, y, z, p, q),$$
$$p' = f_4(x, y, z, p, q),$$
$$q' = f_5(x, y, z, p, q),$$

which define the enlarged point-curve contact transformation derived from (1).

Consider a fixed point $P(a, b, c)$ with the M_2 of plane elements through it. Equations (1) define a k'-curve, and we may consider them solved for z' and y' in terms of x'. In (3) p and q may be taken arbitrarily. Then, if the values of z' and y' in terms of x' are substituted in (3), both λ and x' may be determined. Finally,

p' and q' are determined from (4). This shows that a definite plane element through P is transformed into a definite plane element of a k'-curve. The M_2 through P is therefore transformed into a M_2 along k'.

A pencil of plane elements through P will in general be transformed into an M_1 of plane elements forming a strip along k', but if the axis of the pencil through P is tangent to a k-curve, the pencil will be transformed into a similar pencil at a point of the k'-curve.

That being established, we see that if C is any curve, and we take an M_2 of plane elements tangent to it, we shall have correspondingly an M_2' of plane elements forming a surface. But if C is the envelope of k-curves, the M_2' consists of elements tangent to a curve C' enveloped by k'-curves.

If P describes a surface S, and we take the M_2 of tangent elements, we shall have a corresponding M_2, forming a surface S'. A plane element of the M_2 gives a definite plane element of a k-curve, as we have shown. Therefore the surface S' is made of plane elements belonging to k'-curves and is the envelope of such curves.

EXERCISE

Study in detail the transformation defined by the equations

$$(x' + iy') - z'z - x = 0,$$
$$z(x' - iy') + z' - y = 0.$$

CHAPTER XV

THE SPHERE IN CARTESIAN COÖRDINATES

111. Pencils of spheres. The equation

$$a(x^2 + y^2 + z^2) + 2fx + 2gy + 2hz + c = 0 \tag{1}$$

represents a sphere with the center $\left(\dfrac{-f}{a}, \dfrac{-g}{a}, \dfrac{-h}{a}\right)$ and the radius r, given by the equation

$$r^2 = \frac{f^2 + g^2 + h^2 - ac}{a^2}. \tag{2}$$

If $a = 0$, equation (1) represents a plane which may be regarded as a sphere with an infinite radius and with its center at infinity.

For convenience we shall denote the left-hand member of equation (1) by S. The equation

$$S_i = 0$$

shall then denote the sphere with the coefficients a_i, f_i, g_i, h_i, c_i.

Consider now two spheres

$$S_1 = 0, \qquad S_2 = 0. \tag{3}$$

They intersect at right angles when and only when the square of the distance between their centers is equal to the sum of the squares of their radii. The condition for this is easily found to be

$$2(f_1 f_2 + g_1 g_2 + h_1 h_2) - a_1 c_2 - a_2 c_1 = 0. \tag{4}$$

The spheres defined by the equation

$$S_1 + \lambda S_2 = 0, \tag{5}$$

where λ is an arbitrary parameter, form a *pencil* of spheres. If S_1 and S_2 are both planes, all spheres of the pencil are planes. Otherwise the pencil contains one and only one plane, the equation of which is found by placing $\lambda = -\dfrac{a_1}{a_2}$ in (5).

This plane, called the *radical plane* of the pencil, has accordingly the equation

$$a_2 S_1 - a_1 S_2 = 0 \tag{6}$$

or

$$2(f_1 a_2 - f_2 a_1)x + 2(g_1 a_2 - g_2 a_1)y + 2(h_1 a_2 - h_2 a_1)z + c_1 a_2 - c_2 a_1 = 0.$$

The centers of the spheres of the pencil have the coördinates

$$\left(-\frac{f_1 + \lambda f_2}{a_1 + \lambda a_2}, \ -\frac{g_1 + \lambda g_2}{a_1 + \lambda a_2}, \ -\frac{h_1 + \lambda h_2}{a_1 + \lambda a_2}\right)$$

and therefore lie in a straight line perpendicular to the radical plane. This line is the *line of centers* of the pencil.

We have three forms of a pencil of real spheres not planes :

1. When the spheres S_1 and S_2 intersect in the same real circle C. The pencil consists of all spheres through C. The radical plane is the plane of C, and the line of centers is perpendicular to that plane at the center of C.

2. When the spheres S_1 and S_2 intersect in an imaginary circle. All spheres of the pencil pass through the same imaginary circle, but in the ordinary sense the spheres do not intersect. The radical plane is a real plane containing the imaginary circle, and the line of centers is perpendicular to it.

3. When the spheres S_1 and S_2 are tangent at a point A. The spheres of the pencil are all tangent at A. The radical plane is the common tangent plane at A, and the line of centers is perpendicular to the radical plane at A.

The position of the radical plane in the second form of the pencil has been fixed only analytically. A useful geometrical property is that all the tangent lines from a fixed point of the radical plane to the spheres of the pencil are equal in length. For if P is any point of space, and M the center of a sphere of radius r, the square of the tangent from P to the sphere is $\overline{MP}^2 - r^2$. Applying this to a sphere of the pencil (5), we find the square of the length of the tangent to be

$$\frac{S_1 + \lambda S_2}{a_1 + \lambda a_2},$$

which can be written $\quad \dfrac{S_1}{a_1} - \dfrac{\lambda(a_2 S_1 - a_1 S_2)}{a_1(a_1 + \lambda a_2)}$.

If the point P is in the radical plane (6), this distance is independent of λ and hence the theorem.

It follows from this that *the radical plane is the locus of the centers of spheres orthogonal to all spheres of the pencil.*

Closely connected with this is the theorem: *A sphere orthogonal to any two spheres is orthogonal to all spheres of the pencil determined by them and has its center on the radical plane of the pencil.*

The last part of this theorem is a consequence of the previous theorem. The first part is a consequence of the linear nature of the condition (4) for orthogonality.

112. Bundles of spheres. The spheres defined by the equation

$$S_1 + \lambda S_2 + \mu S_3 = 0, \tag{1}$$

where S_1, S_2, S_3 are three spheres not belonging to the same pencil and λ, μ are arbitrary parameters, form a *bundle* of spheres.

The centers of the spheres of the bundle have the coördinates

$$\left(-\frac{f_1 + \lambda f_2 + \mu f_3}{a_1 + \lambda a_2 + \mu a_3}, \ -\frac{g_1 + \lambda g_2 + \mu g_3}{a_1 + \lambda a_2 + \mu a_3}, \ -\frac{h_1 + \lambda h_2 + \mu h_3}{a_1 + \lambda a_2 + \mu a_3} \right). \tag{2}$$

From (2) it follows that if the centers of the three spheres S_1, S_2, S_3 lie on a straight line, the centers of all spheres of the bundle lie on that line. The center may be anywhere on that line, and the radius of the sphere is then arbitrary. Hence *a special case of a bundle of spheres consists of all spheres whose centers lie on a straight line.*

More generally, if the centers of S_1, S_2, and S_3 are not on the same straight line, they will determine a plane, and the centers of all spheres of the bundle lie in this plane. This plane is the *plane of centers*, and any point in it is the center of a plane of the bundle. In this case the three spheres S_1, S_2, S_3 intersect in two points (real, imaginary, or coincident), and all spheres of the bundle pass through these points. If the two points are distinct, they are symmetrical with respect to the plane of centers; if they are coincident, they lie in the plane of centers. Hence we see that a *bundle of spheres consists in general of spheres whose centers lie in a fixed plane and which pass through a fixed point.*

The radical planes of the three spheres S_1, S_2, and S_3, taken in pairs, are

$$a_2 S_1 - a_1 S_2 = 0,$$
$$a_3 S_1 - a_1 S_3 = 0,$$
$$a_2 S_3 - a_3 S_2 = 0,$$

which evidently intersect in a straight line called the *radical axis* of the bundle. It is perpendicular to the plane of centers and passes through the points common to the spheres of the bundle. The radical plane of any two spheres of the bundle passes through the radical axis.

Any sphere orthogonal to three spheres of a bundle is orthogonal to all the spheres of the bundle because of the linear form of condition (4), § 111. The centers of such spheres lie in the radical axis of the bundle, since by § 111 they must lie in the radical plane of any two spheres of the bundle, and any point of the radical axis is the center of such a sphere. It is not difficult to show that these spheres form a pencil.

In fact, *to any bundle of spheres we may associate an orthogonal pencil of spheres and to any pencil of a sphere an orthogonal bundle. The relation of pencil and bundle is such that every sphere of the pencil is orthogonal to every sphere of the bundle, the line of centers of the pencil is the radical axis of the bundle, and the radical plane of the pencil is the plane of centers of the bundle.*

As far as the details of the above theorem have not been explicitly proved in the foregoing, the proofs are easily supplied by the student.

Closely connected with the foregoing theorem is the following: *All spheres orthogonal to two fixed spheres form a bundle and all spheres orthogonal to three fixed spheres form a pencil.*

The foregoing assumes that the three spheres S_1, S_2, S_3 are not all planes. If they are, the bundle of spheres reduces to a bundle of planes. Otherwise the bundle of spheres contains a one-dimensional extent of planes through the radical axis of the bundle.

113. Complexes of spheres. The spheres represented by the equation

$$S_1 + \lambda S_2 + \mu S_3 + \nu S_4 = 0, \tag{1}$$

where S_1, S_2, S_3, S_4 do not belong to the same bundle or pencil and λ, μ, ν are arbitrary parameters, form a *complex* of spheres.

The radical planes of the four spheres S_1, S_2, S_3, S_4 taken in pairs intersect in a point, and the radical plane of any two spheres of the complex pass through that point. This point is the *radical center* of the complex. From the properties of radical planes it follows that the square of the length of the tangents drawn from the radical center to all spheres of the complex is constant. Therefore the radical center is the center of a sphere orthogonal to all the spheres of the complex. Conversely, it is easy to see that any sphere orthogonal to this sphere belongs to the complex. That is, the *complex consists of spheres orthogonal to a fixed base sphere whose center is the radical center of the complex.*

If the four spheres intersect in a point that point is the radical center. The base sphere is then a sphere of radius zero and the complex consists of spheres passing through a point.

The above discussion assumes that the four spheres S_1, S_2, S_3, S_4 are not planes. If they are, the complex simply consists of all planes in space. In the general case the complex contains a doubly infinite set of planes which pass through the center of the base sphere.

114. Inversion. Let O be the center of a fixed sphere S, k^2 the square of its radius, and P any point. The point P may be transformed into a point P' by the condition that OPP' forms a straight line and that

$$OP \cdot OP' = k^2. \tag{1}$$

This transformation is an *inversion*, or transformation by *reciprocal radius*. The point O is the center of inversion, and the sphere S is the sphere with respect to which the inversion takes place.

If the point O has the coördinates (x_0, y_0, z_0), the equations of the transformation are

$$x' = x_0 + \frac{k^2(x - x_0)}{R^2},$$

$$y' = y_0 + \frac{k^2(y - y_0)}{R^2}, \tag{2}$$

$$z' = z_0 + \frac{k^2(z - z_0)}{R^2},$$

where $\qquad R^2 = (x - x_0)^2 + (y - y_0)^2 + (z - z_0)^2.$

In this transformation the constants may be either real or imaginary. If (x_0, y_0, z_0) is real and k^2 real and positive, the inversion is with reference to a real sphere. If (x_0, y_0, z_0) is real and k^2 real and negative, the inversion is with reference to a sphere with real center and pure imaginary radius. In this case, however, real points are transformed into real points.

From the definition and equations (2) it appears that any point P has a unique transformed point P', and, conversely, unless P is at the origin, or on a minimum line through O, or at infinity.

To handle these special cases we take O at the origin and write equations (2) with homogeneous coördinates as

$$\rho x' = k^2 xt,$$
$$\rho y' = k^2 yt,$$
$$\rho z' = k^2 zt,$$
$$\rho t' = x^2 + y^2 + z^2. \tag{3}$$

From (3) it appears that the transformed point of O is indeterminate, but that if P approaches O along the line $x:y:z = l:m:n$, the point P recedes to infinity and is transformed into the point at infinity $l:m:n:0$. Hence we may say that the center of inversion is transformed into the entire plane at infinity. Conversely, any point on the plane at infinity but not on the circle at infinity is transformed into O.

If P is on a minimum line through O but not on the imaginary circle at infinity, then $x':y':z' = x:y:z$ and $t' = 0$. That is, all points on a minimum line through O is transformed into the point in which that line meets the imaginary circle at infinity. Conversely, if P is on the imaginary circle at infinity the transformed point is indeterminate, but $x':y':z' = x:y:z$, so that any point on the circle at infinity is transformed into the minimum line through that point and the center of inversion.

Consider now a sphere S with the equation

$$a(x^2 + y^2 + z^2) + 2fx + 2gy + 2hz + c = 0. \tag{4}$$

It is transformed into

$$ak^4 + 2fk^2 x + 2gk^2 y + 2hk^2 z + c(x^2 + y^2 + z^2) = 0. \tag{5}$$

This is in general a sphere, so that in general spheres are transformed into spheres. But exceptions are to be noted:

1. If $c = 0$, $a \neq 0$, (4) is a sphere through O and (5) a plane not through O, so that spheres through the center of inversion are transformed into planes not through the center of inversion.

2. If $a = 0$, $c \neq 0$, (4) is a plane not through O and (5) a sphere through O, so that planes not through the center of inversion are transformed into spheres through the center of inversion.

3. If $a = 0$, $c = 0$, (4) and (5) represent the same plane through O, so that planes through the center of inversion are transformed into themselves.

By an inversion the angle between two curves is equal to the angle between the two transformed curves; that is, the transformation is *conformal*. To prove this we compute from (2) (with $x_0 = 0$, $y_0 = 0$, $z_0 = 0$),

$$dx' = \frac{k^2}{R^4}\{(y^2 + z^2 - x^2)\,dx - 2\,xy\,dy - 2\,xz\,dz\},$$

$$dy' = \frac{k^2}{R^4}\{-2\,xy\,dx + (x^2 - y^2 + z^2)\,dy - 2\,yz\,dz\}, \qquad (6)$$

$$dz' = \frac{k^2}{R^4}\{-2\,zx\,dx - 2\,yz\,dy + (x^2 + y^2 - z^2)\,dz\}.$$

Hence, if we place $ds'^2 = dx'^2 + dy'^2 + dz'^2$ and $ds^2 = dx^2 + dy^2 + dz^2$, we have

$$ds' = \frac{k^2}{R^2}\,ds.$$

Now, if dx, dy, dz correspond to displacements on a curve from P, and δx, δy, δz to displacements along another curve from P, the angle α between the curves is given by

$$\cos \alpha = \frac{dx\,\delta x + dy\,\delta y + dz\,\delta z}{ds\,\delta s}.$$

Similarly, the angle α' between the transformed curves is

$$\cos \alpha' = \frac{dx'\,\delta x' + dy'\,\delta y' + dz'\,\delta z'}{ds'\,ds'},$$

and it is easy to prove from (6) that $\cos \alpha = \cos \alpha'$.

Any pencil, bundle, or complex of spheres is transformed into a pencil, bundle, or complex, respectively. The line of centers of the pencil is not, however, in general transformed into the line of centers of the transformed pencil, but becomes a circle cutting the spheres of the transformed pencil orthogonally. Also the radical plane of the pencil is not transformed into the radical plane of the transformed pencil, but into one of the spheres of that pencil.

Similarly, the plane of centers of a bundle is transformed into a sphere cutting all the spheres of the bundle orthogonally, and the radical axis of the bundle is transformed into a circle orthogonal to the transformed bundle.

On the other hand, the base sphere of a complex is transformed into the base sphere of the transformed complex.

If we take a pencil of spheres intersecting in a real circle and take the center of inversion on that circle, the pencil of spheres is evidently transformed into a pencil of planes. If we take a bundle of spheres intersecting in two real points A and B, and take A as the center of inversion, the bundle of spheres becomes a bundle of planes through the inverse of B. If we take a complex of spheres and place the center of inversion on the base sphere, the complex becomes one with its base sphere a plane ; that is, it consists of all spheres whose centers are on a fixed plane.

EXERCISES

1. Prove that by an inversion with respect to a sphere S all spheres which pass through a point and its inverse are orthogonal to S.

2. Prove that a point and its inverse are harmonic conjugates with respect to the points in which the line connecting the first two points intersects the sphere of inversion.

3. Prove that the inverse of a circle is in general a circle and note the special cases.

4. Prove that if two figures are inverse with respect to a sphere S_1, their inverses with respect to a sphere S_2 whose center is not on S_1 are inverse with respect to S_1', the inverse of S_1 with respect to S_2.

5. Prove that if two figures are inverse with respect to a sphere S_1, their inverse with respect to a sphere S_2 whose center is on S_1 are symmetrical with respect to the plane P', the inverse of S_1 with respect to S_2. Conversely, if two figures are symmetrical with respect to a plane P they are inverse with respect to any sphere into which the plane P is inverted. Therefore inversion on a plane is defined as reflection on that plane.

6. Prove that if S is a sphere of radius r and S' is its inverse, the radius of S' is equal to the radius of S multiplied by the square of the radius of the sphere of inversion and divided by the absolute value of the power of the center of inversion with respect to S.

7. Prove that any two nonintersecting spheres may be inverted by an inversion on a real sphere into concentric spheres.

8. Prove that any three spheres may be inverted into three spheres of equal radius.

9. Prove that inversion on a sphere with real center and pure imaginary radius ri is equivalent to inversion on a sphere with the same center and real radius r, followed by a transformation by which each point is replaced by its symmetrical point with respect to the center of inversion.

10. A surface which is its own inverse is called *anallagmatic*. Prove that any anallagmatic surface cuts the sphere of inversion at right angles if the point of intersection is not a singular point of the surface and is the envelope of a family of spheres which cuts the sphere of inversion orthogonally.

11. Prove that the product of two inversions is equivalent to the product of an inversion and a metrical transformation or in special cases to a metrical transformation alone.

115. Dupin's cyclide. The transformation by inversion is useful in studying the class of surfaces known as *Dupin's cyclides*. These are defined as the envelope of a family of spheres which are tangent to three fixed spheres.

If the centers of the fixed spheres do not lie in a straight line we may by inversion bring them into a straight line. To do this we have simply to draw, in the plane of the centers of the three spheres, a circle orthogonal to the three spheres and take any point on that circle as the center of inversion. The circle then goes into a straight line which is orthogonal to the three transformed spheres and hence passes through their centers. This is a consequence of the conformal nature of inversion. For the same reason the surface enveloped by spheres tangent to the original three spheres is inverted into a surface enveloped by spheres tangent to three spheres whose centers lie on a straight line.

We shall study first the properties of such a surface and then by inversion deduce the properties of the general Dupin's cyclide.

Let us take the line of centers of three fixed spheres as the axis of z and the equations of the spheres as

$$\begin{aligned}
x^2 + y^2 + z^2 &= r_1^2, \\
x^2 + y^2 + (z - c_2)^2 &= r_2^2, \\
x^2 + y^2 + (z - c_3)^2 &= r_3^2.
\end{aligned} \qquad (1)$$

Then, if the sphere

$$(x - a)^2 + (y - b)^2 + (z - c)^2 = r^2 \qquad (2)$$

is tangent to each of the spheres (1), the distance between the center of (2) and that of any one of the spheres (1) must be equal to the sum or the difference of the radii of the two spheres. This gives the three equations

$$a^2 + b^2 + c^2 = (r \pm r_1)^2,$$
$$a^2 + b^2 + c^2 - 2\,c_2 c + c_2^2 = (r \pm r_2)^2, \qquad (3)$$
$$a^2 + b^2 + c^2 - 2\,c_3 c + c_3^2 = (r \pm r_3)^2,$$

which have in general four solutions of the form

$$c = \text{const.}, \quad r = \text{const.}, \quad a^2 + b^2 = \text{const.} \qquad (4)$$

Therefore the sphere (2) belongs to one of four families each of which consists of spheres with a constant radius and with their centers on a fixed circle. Each family obviously envelops a ring surface.

There are therefore in general four Dupin's cyclides determined by the condition that the enveloping spheres are tangent to three fixed spheres.

Let us take any one of the solutions (4) and change the coördinate system so that $c = 0$. The equation of the family of spheres may then be written

$$(x - a_0 \cos \theta)^2 + (y - a_0 \sin \theta)^2 + z^2 = r^2, \qquad (5)$$

where θ is an arbitrary parameter and a_0 and r are constants.

The surface enveloped by (5) is

$$(x^2 + y^2 + z^2 + a_0^2 - r^2)^2 = 4\,a_0^2 (x^2 + y^2). \qquad (6)$$

This is the equation of the *ring surface* formed by revolving about the axis of z the circle

$$(x - a_0)^2 + z^2 = r^2. \qquad (7)$$

Hence *any Dupin's cyclide is the inverse of the ring surface formed by revolving a circle about an axis not in its plane.*

The ring surface contains two families of circles forming an orthogonal network. The one family consists of the meridian circles cut out by planes through the axis of revolution, the other of circles of latitude made by sections perpendicular to that axis.

Since, by inversion, circles are transformed into circles, and angles are conserved, there exist on any Dupin's cyclide two similar families of circles also forming an orthogonal network.

The ring surface is the envelope not only of the family of spheres whose equation is (5) but also of the family with the equation

$$x^2 + y^2 + (z - a_0 \tan \theta)^2 = (a_0 \sec \theta - r)^2. \qquad (8)$$

This family consists of spheres with their centers on OZ each of which may be generated by revolving about OZ a circle with its center on OZ and tangent to the circle (7). The spheres of this family are tangent to the ring surface along the circles of latitude, while the spheres of the family (5) are tangent to the ring surface along the meridian circles. The family of spheres (8) may be determined by the condition that they are tangent in a definite manner to three spheres of (5).

Hence *any Dupin's cyclide may be generated in two ways as the envelope of a family of spheres consisting of spheres tangent to three fixed spheres. Each family of spheres is tangent to the cyclide along a family of circles, the two families of circles being orthogonal.*

The planes of each family of circles intersect in a straight line. This follows from the theorems of § 112, since the inverse spheres of the spheres (5) belong to the same bundle and the circles are intersections of spheres of that bundle, so that their planes pass through the radical axis of the bundle. Similarly for the spheres (8).

The circle (7) intersects the axis of z in two real, imaginary, or coincident points. Therefore a Dupin's cyclide has at least this number of singular points. We shall see later that it also has other singular points, but we shall confine our attention at present to these two. Call them A and B. The spheres of one of the families which envelop the cyclide intersect in A and B, as is seen in the case of the ring surface. Consequently, if one of these points, as A, is taken as the center of inversion this family of spheres becomes a family of planes, and the cyclide inverts into a surface enveloped by spheres which are tangent to three of these planes.

If A and B are distinct the planes pass through the point B', the inverse of B, and the cyclide is inverted into a cone of revolution, which is real if A and B are real, and imaginary if A and B are imaginary.

If A coincides with B the planes are parallel and the cyclide is inverted into a cylinder of revolution. We have accordingly the theorem: *A Dupin's cyclide may always be inverted into a cone of revolution which, in special cases, degenerates into a cylinder of revolution.*

Consequently we may obtain any cyclide in which the singular points A and B are distinct by inverting the cone

$$x^2 + y^2 - m^2 z^2 = 0 \tag{9}$$

from any real or imaginary center of inversion with respect to any real or imaginary sphere; or, what amounts to the same thing, we may transform the origin to any real or imaginary point and invert from the origin. The equation of the cone is then

$$(x - \alpha)^2 + (y - \beta)^2 - m^2(z - \gamma)^2 = 0, \tag{10}$$

and its inverse with respect to the origin is

$$(\alpha^2 + \beta^2 - m^2\gamma^2)(x^2 + y^2 + z^2)^2 - 2k^2(\alpha x + \beta y - m^2\gamma z)(x^2 + y^2 + z^2)$$
$$+ k^4(x^2 + y^2 - m^2 z^2) = 0. \tag{11}$$

To consider the case in which the points A and B coincide, we invert the cylinder

$$(x - \alpha)^2 + (y - \beta)^2 = r^2 \tag{12}$$

and obtain for its inverse

$$(\alpha^2 + \beta^2 - r^2)(x^2 + y^2 + z^2)^2 - 2k^2(\alpha x + \beta y)(x^2 + y^2 + z^2)$$
$$+ k^4(x^2 + y^2) = 0. \tag{13}$$

The cyclide is therefore a surface of the fourth order unless the first coefficient in either (11) or (12) vanishes. But this happens when and only when the cone (10) or the cylinder (12) passes through the center of inversion.

If now we make the equations (11) and (13) homogeneous, and place $t = 0$ to determine the section with the plane at infinity, we get the circle at infinity as a double curve when the surface is of fourth order, and the circle at infinity, together with a straight line, when the surface is of the third order.

Hence *a Dupin's cyclide is a surface of the fourth order with the circle at infinity as a double curve, or a surface of the third order with the circle at infinity as a simple curve.*

We proceed to find the singular points of equation (11). We can without loss of generality so turn the axes that $\beta = 0$, and will make the abbreviations

$$A = \alpha^2 - m^2\gamma^2,$$
$$R = x^2 + y^2 + z^2,$$
$$L = \alpha x - m^2\gamma z,$$

and write the equation as

$$AR^2 - 2k^2LR + k^4(x^2 + y^2 - m^2 z^2) = 0. \tag{14}$$

The singular points are then the solutions of this equation and the following, formed by taking the partial derivatives with respect to x, y, and z:

$$
\begin{aligned}
4\,ARx - 2\,k^2\alpha R \quad & - 4\,k^2Lx + 2\,k^4x \quad = 0, \\
4\,ARy \quad & - 4\,k^2Ly + 2\,k^4y \quad = 0, \qquad (15) \\
4\,ARz + 2\,k^2m^2\gamma R & - 4\,k^2Lz - 2\,k^4m^2z = 0.
\end{aligned}
$$

By multiplying equations (15) in order by x, y, z and adding, and subtracting the result from twice (14), we obtain

$$(AR - k^2L)R = 0. \qquad (16)$$

Also, by combining the first two of (15) we have

$$2\,k^2\alpha y R = 0. \qquad (17)$$

From (17) we have either $R = 0$ or $y = 0$. Taking first the condition $y = 0$, but $R \neq 0$, from (16) and (15),

$$x = \frac{\alpha R}{k^2}, \qquad z = \frac{\gamma R}{k^2};$$

whence

$$R = \frac{k^4}{\alpha^2 + \gamma^2}.$$

The point $\left(\dfrac{\alpha k^2}{\alpha^2 + \gamma^2},\ 0,\ \dfrac{\gamma k^2}{\alpha^2 + \gamma^2} \right)$ is therefore a singular point. It is the inverse of the vertex of the cone and is the point B of the discussion on page 276.

Consider now the solution $R = 0$ of equation (17). From (15) we have either $x = 0$, $y = 0$, $z = 0$, or $L = \dfrac{k^2}{2}$, $z = 0$. The origin is therefore a singular point, the inverse of the section of the cone with the plane at infinity, and is the point A of the discussion on page 276.

The alternative $R = 0$, $L = \dfrac{k^2}{2}$, $z = 0$ leads to the two singular points $\left(\dfrac{k^2}{2\,\alpha},\ \pm\dfrac{k^2i}{2\,\alpha},\ 0 \right)$. These points fail to exist if $\alpha = 0$, but in that case the inversion is from a point on the axis of the cone, and the surface (11) is then a ring surface.

The two singular points just found are each connected with A and B by minimum lines.

If we consider in the same way equation (13), we obtain similar results except that the singular point B coincides with A at the origin, since the assumption $y = 0$ leads to the conclusion $R = 0$. The two points $\left(\dfrac{k^2}{2\,\alpha},\ \pm\dfrac{k^2 i}{2\,\alpha},\ 0 \right)$ are again singular points unless $\alpha = 0$, when the surface (13) is a ring surface with a single singular point.

A Dupin's cyclide which is not a ring surface has in general four finite singular points two of which are connected with the other two by minimum lines. Two of these singular points may coincide, in which case the cyclide has three finite singular points two of which are connected with the third by minimum lines.

It follows, of course, that the Dupin's cyclides are not the general surfaces of fourth order with the circle at infinity as a double curve nor the general surface of third order through the circle at infinity. These more general surfaces will be noticed in the next section.

EXERCISES

1. Prove that any Dupin's cyclide is anallagmatic with respect to each sphere of two pencils of spheres.

2. Prove that the centers of each family of enveloping spheres of a Dupin's cyclide lie on a conic.

3. Prove that the two lines in which the planes of the two families of circles on the Dupin's cyclide intersect are orthogonal.

4. Prove that the circles on a Dupin's cyclide are lines of curvature. (A line of curvature on a surface is such that two normals to the surface at two consecutive points of the line of curvature intersect.)

5. Prove that the only surfaces which have two families of circles for lines of curvature are Dupin's cyclides. (Exception should be made of the sphere, plane, and minimum developable, for which all lines are lines of curvature.)

116. Cyclides. A cyclide is defined by the equation

$$u_0 (x^2 + y^2 + z^2)^2 + u_1 (x^2 + y^2 + z^2) + u_2 = 0, \tag{1}$$

where u_0 is a constant, u_1 a polynomial of the first degree, and u_2 a polynomial of the second degree in x, y, z. The Dupin's cyclides are special cases of the general cyclide.

If $u_0 \neq 0$ in equation (1) the surface is of the fourth degree and represents a biquadratic surface with the imaginary circle at infinity as a double curve.

If $u_0 = 0$, equation (1) is a general of the third degree and represents a cubic surface passing through the imaginary circle at infinity.

Degenerate cases of the cyclides may also occur if, in equation (1), $u_0 = 0$ and u_1 is identically zero. The equation then represents a quadric surface or even a plane. These cases are important only as they arise by inversion from the general cases.

In order to study the effect of inversion on the cyclide we may take the center of inversion at the origin, since the form of equation (1) is unaltered by transformation of coördinates. Such an inversion produces an equation of the same form, which is of the fourth degree if u_2 contains an absolute term and of the third degree if u_2 does not contain the absolute term but does contain linear terms. In the former case the origin is not on the surface; in the latter case the origin is on the surface, but is not a singular point. Hence

The inverse of any cyclide from a point not on it is always a cyclide of the fourth order. The inverse of any cyclide from a point on it which is not a singular point is always a cyclide of the third order.

In general the cyclide will not have a singular point. If it does we may take it as the origin. Then in equation (1) the absolute term and the terms of first order in u_2 disappear. By inversion from the origin there will then be no terms of the fourth or the third degree. Hence *the cyclide with a singular point is the inverse of a quadric surface.* Conversely, as is easily seen, *the inverse of a quadric surface is a cyclide with at least one singular point.*

Consider now a cyclide with two singular points A and B which do not lie on the same minimum line. If we invert from A the cyclide becomes a quadric surface with a singular point at B', the inverse of B. It is therefore a cone. Hence *the cyclide with two singular points not on the same minimum line is the inverse of a quadric cone.* Conversely, *the inverse of a quadric cone from a point not on it is a cyclide with at least two singular points.*

We have shown in § 115 that a Dupin's cyclide of the fourth order has in general four singular points. We shall now prove, conversely, that *a cyclide of the fourth order with four singular points is a Dupin's cyclide.*

If the four points are A, B, C, D they cannot all be connected by minimum lines, since that is an impossible configuration. We will assume that A and B are not on a minimum line, and will invert from A, thus obtaining a quadric cone F with its vertex at B', the inverse of B. Any plane section of the cyclide through AB is a curve of the fourth order with two singular points at A and B and two other singular points on the circle at infinity. It therefore breaks up into two circles and is inverted into two straight-line generators of the cone F. The cone is enveloped by a one-parameter family of planes tangent along the generators. Therefore the cyclide is enveloped by a one-parameter family of spheres tangent along the circular sections through A and B.

The plane section determined by the points A, B, and C has three singular points besides the two on the circle at infinity. Therefore it consists of a circle and two minimum lines, and since AB is not a minimum line, AC and BC are. By a similar argument AD and BD are minimum lines. Hence CD is not a minimum line.

We may accordingly invert the cyclide from C and obtain another cone with the properties of F. In particular, the straight-line generators of this cone are the inverses of circles on the cyclide, and its tangent planes are the inverses of spheres tangent to the cyclide. Therefore the cone F is enveloped by spheres, the inverse with respect to A of the last-named family. Therefore F is a cone of revolution and, by § 115, the theorem is proved.

EXERCISES

1. Prove that the envelope of spheres whose centers lie on a quadric surface and which are orthogonal to a given sphere is a cyclide.

2. Discuss the plane curves called *bicircular quartics*, defined by the equation
$$u_0 (x^2 + y^2)^2 + u_1 (x^2 + y^2) + u_2 = 0,$$
and trace the analogies to the cyclides.

3. Prove that the envelope of a circle which moves in a plane so that its center traces a fixed conic, while the circle is orthogonal to a fixed circle, is a bicircular quartic.

4. The intersection of a sphere and a quadric surface is a *spheroquadric*. Prove that a spheroquadric may be inverted into a bicircular quartic and conversely.

5. Prove that the intersection of a cyclide and a sphere is a spheroquadric.

CHAPTER XVI

PENTASPHERICAL COÖRDINATES

117. Specialized coördinates. Pentaspherical coördinates are based upon five spheres of reference, as the name implies. It is customary to define them by use of the Cartesian equations of the five spheres, but we prefer to build up the coördinate system independently of the Cartesian system, using only elementary ideas of measurement of real distance. This brings into emphasis the fact that pentaspherical coördinates are not dependent upon Cartesian coördinates, but that the two systems stand side by side, each on its own foundation. One result is that certain ideal elements pertaining to the so-called imaginary circle at infinity which are found convenient in Cartesian geometry are nonexistent in pentaspherical geometry; and, conversely, certain ideal elements of pentaspherical geometry do not appear in Cartesian geometry.

Let OX, OY, and OZ be three mutually perpendicular axes of reference intersecting at O, P any real point, OP the distance from O to P, and OL, OM, ON the three projections of OP on OX, OY, OZ respectively. Algebraic signs are to be attached to the three projections in the usual way, but OP is essentially positive. We may then take as coördinates of P the four ratios defined by the equations

$$\xi_1 : \xi_2 : \xi_3 : \xi_4 : \xi_5 = \overline{OP}^2 : OL : OM : ON : 1 \tag{1}$$

and satisfying the fundamental relation

$$\xi_2^2 + \xi_3^2 + \xi_4^2 - \xi_1\xi_5 = 0. \tag{2}$$

It is obvious that to any real point corresponds a set of real coördinates and that to any set of real coördinates corresponds one real point. The extension to imaginary and infinite points is made in the usual manner. In particular, as P recedes from O indefinitely in any direction, the coördinates approach the limiting ratios $1 : 0 : 0 : 0 : 0$, which are the coördinates of a real point at infinity. This, however, is not the only point at infinity, as will appear when we consider the formula for the distance between two points.

282

The relation (1) may be reduced to a sum of squares by replacing the coördinates ξ_i by new coördinates x_i, where

$$\rho \xi_1 = x_1 - ix_5,$$
$$\rho \xi_2 = x_2,$$
$$\rho \xi_3 = x_3, \qquad\qquad (3)$$
$$\rho \xi_4 = x_4,$$
$$\rho \xi_5 = -(x_1 + ix_5);$$

whence

$$\rho x_1 = \xi_1 - \xi_5 = \sigma(\overline{OP}^2 - 1),$$
$$\rho x_2 = 2\,\xi_2 = \sigma(2\,OL),$$
$$\rho x_3 = 2\,\xi_3 = \sigma(2\,OM), \qquad\qquad (4)$$
$$\rho x_4 = 2\,\xi_4 = \sigma(2\,ON),$$
$$\rho x_5 = i(\xi_1 + \xi_5) = \sigma i(\overline{OP}^2 + 1),$$

and the coördinates x_i satisfy the fundamental relation

$$\omega(x) = x_1^2 + x_2^2 + x_3^2 + x_4^2 + x_5^2. \qquad\qquad (5)$$

In these coördinates, which we shall use henceforth, a real point has four of its coördinates real and the fifth pure imaginary (the proportionality factor ρ being assumed real). This slight inconvenience, if it is an inconvenience, is more than balanced by the symmetry of equation (5). The coördinates of the real point at infinity are now $1 : 0 : 0 : 0 : i$.

If P_1 and P_2 are two real points with coördinates y_i and x_i respectively, the projections of the line $P_1 P_2$ on OX, OY, OZ, respectively, are easily seen to be

$$\frac{x_2}{x_1 + ix_5} - \frac{y_2}{y_1 + iy_5}, \quad \frac{x_3}{x_1 + ix_5} - \frac{y_3}{y_1 + iy_5}, \quad \frac{x_4}{x_1 + ix_5} - \frac{y_4}{y_1 + iy_5};$$

and hence, since the square of the distance of the line $P_1 P_2$ is equal to the sum of the squares of its projections, we compute readily, with the aid of (5), the *distance formula* for the distance d between two points

$$d^2 = -\frac{2(x_1 y_1 + x_2 y_2 + x_3 y_3 + x_4 y_4 + x_5 y_5)}{(x_1 + ix_5)(y_1 + iy_5)}, \qquad\qquad (6)$$

which is the same as

$$d^2 = -\frac{\omega(x, y)}{(x_1 + ix_5)(y_1 + iy_5)}, \qquad\qquad (7)$$

$\omega(x, y)$ being the polar of $\omega(x)$.

The formula (6), thus derived for real points, will be taken as the definition of distance between all kinds of points. From this it appears that d is infinite when and only when one of the points satisfies the equations $x_1 + ix_5 = 0$ and $\omega(x, y) \neq 0$. Hence *the locus of points at infinity is given by the equation* $x_1 + ix_5 = 0$.

Since the coördinates of all points satisfy (5), we have for points at infinity $x_1 + ix_5 = 0$ and $x_2^2 + x_3^2 + x_4^2 = 0$. Therefore the point $1 : 0 : 0 : 0 : i$ is the only real point at infinity. The nature of the imaginary locus at infinity will appear later.

118. The sphere. A sphere is defined as usual as the locus of points equally distant from a fixed point. This definition includes all spheres in the usual sense and all loci which are expressed by equation (6), § 117, in which y_i is fixed and $d = r$ a constant. This equation is

$$[2 y_1 + (y_1 + iy_5) r^2] x_1 + 2 y_2 x_2 + 2 y_3 x_3 + 2 y_4 x_4$$
$$+ [2 y_5 + i(y_1 + iy_5) r^2] x_5 = 0. \qquad (1)$$

This is of the type

$$a_1 x_1 + a_2 x_2 + a_3 x_3 + a_4 x_4 + a_5 x_5 = 0, \qquad (2)$$

where

$$\rho a_1 = 2 y_1 + (y_1 + iy_5) r^2,$$
$$\rho a_2 = 2 y_2,$$
$$\rho a_3 = 2 y_3, \qquad (3)$$
$$\rho a_4 = 2 y_4,$$
$$\rho a_5 = 2 y_5 + i(y_1 + iy_5) r^2.$$

From these equations and the fundamental relation $\omega(y) = 0$, we have

$$r^2 = \frac{a_1^2 + a_2^2 + a_3^2 + a_4^2 + a_5^2}{(a_1 + ia_5)^2},$$
$$\rho y_1 = a_1 - \frac{a_1 + ia_5}{2} r^2,$$
$$\rho y_2 = a_2,$$
$$\rho y_3 = a_3, \qquad (4)$$
$$\rho y_4 = a_4,$$
$$\rho y_5 = a_5 - i \cdot \frac{a_1 + ia_5}{2} r^2,$$

which give the center and the radius of any sphere (2) in terms of the coefficients a_i. We have, then, the following statement, half theorem, half definition.

Every linear equation of the type (2) *represents a sphere, the center and the radius of which are given by equations* (4).

It is convenient to represent by $\eta(a)$ the numerator of r^2 in (4); that is,

$$\eta(a) = a_1^2 + a_2^2 + a_3^2 + a_4^2 + a_5^2.$$

We have, then, the following classes of spheres:

CASE I. $\eta(a) \neq 0$. *Nonspecial spheres.*

Subcase 1. $\eta(a) \neq 0$, $a_1 + ia_5 \neq 0$. *Proper spheres.* The center and the radius of the sphere is finite, but neither is necessarily real. The sphere does not contain the real point at infinity.

Subcase 2. $\eta(a) \neq 0$, $a_1 + ia_5 = 0$. *Ordinary planes.* The radius is infinite. The center is the real point at infinity. Since a plane is the limit of a sphere with center receding to infinity and radius increasing without limit, we shall call this locus a plane. This may be justified by returning to the coördinates ξ_i. The equation then reduces to $a_2\xi_2 + a_3\xi_3 + a_4\xi_4 - a_1\xi_5 = 0$ with the condition $a_2^2 + a_2^3 + a_4^2 \neq 0$. By repetition of the familiar argument of analytical geometry this may be shown to represent a plane.

Since this case differs from the previous one essentially in that the coördinates $1 : 0 : 0 : 0 : i$ now satisfy the equation of the sphere, we may say : *A proper plane may be defined as a nonspecial sphere which passes through the real point at infinity.*

CASE II. $\eta(a) = 0$. *Special spheres.*

Subcase 1. $\eta(a) = 0$, $a_1 + ia_5 \neq 0$. *Point spheres.* The radius is zero and the center is not at infinity. It is obvious that the sphere passes through its center $y_i = a_i$, and if y_i is real the sphere contains no other real point. The sphere does not contain the real point at infinity.

Subcase 2. $\eta(a) = 0$, $a_1 + ia_5 = 0$. *Special planes.* The radius is indeterminate. The center is $a_1 : a_2 : a_3 : a_4 : ia_1$, which is a point at infinity. The equation of the sphere may be written

$$a_2\xi_2 + a_3\xi_3 + a_4\xi_4 - a_1\xi_5 = 0, \qquad (a_2^2 + a_3^2 + a_4^2 = 0)$$

which, in Cartesian geometry, would be that of a minimum plane (§ 80). In this case the sphere contains the real point at infinity.

Hence we may say : *A special plane is a point sphere which passes through the real point at infinity.*

The locus at infinity is, as we have seen, $x_1 + ix_5 = 0$. This comes under Case II, Subcase 2, and is therefore a special plane with its center at $1 : 0 : 0 : 0 : i$; that is, *the locus at infinity is a special plane whose center is the real point at infinity.*

119. Angle between spheres. The angle between two real proper spheres is equal or supplementary to the angle between their radii at any point of intersection. For precision we will take as the angle that one which is in the triangle formed by the radii to the point of intersection and the line of centers of the spheres. If θ is this angle, d the distance between the centers, and r and r' the radii, then

$$d^2 = r^2 + r'^2 - 2\,rr'\cos\theta.$$

If now the equations of the two spheres are

$$\sum a_i x_i = 0, \qquad \sum b_i x_i = 0,$$

an easy calculation by aid of formulas (4), § 118, and (6), § 117, gives

$$d^2 = -\frac{2\,(a_1 b_1 + a_2 b_2 + a_3 b_3 + a_4 b_4 + a_5 b_5)}{(a_1 + ia_5)\,(b_1 + ib_5)} + r^2 + r'^2\,;$$

whence

$$\cos\theta = \frac{a_1 b_1 + a_2 b_2 + a_3 b_3 + a_4 b_4 + a_5 b_5}{\sqrt{a_1^2 + a_2^2 + a_3^2 + a_4^2 + a_5^2}\ \sqrt{b_1^2 + b_2^2 + b_3^2 + b_4^2 + b_5^2}}. \tag{1}$$

This formula has been derived for real proper spheres intersecting in real points. We take it as the definition of the angle between any two spheres. The student may show that if one or both of the two spheres becomes a real plane, this definition of angle agrees with the usual one.

Two spheres $\sum a_i x_i = 0$, $\sum b_i x_i = 0$ *are orthogonal when*

$$a_1 b_1 + a_2 b_2 + a_3 b_3 + a_4 b_4 + a_5 b_5 = 0. \tag{2}$$

If both of the spheres are nonspecial, this agrees with the usual definition. If, however, $\sum a_i x_i = 0$ is a special sphere, the condition expresses the fact that the center of $\sum a_i x_i = 0$ lies on the sphere $\sum b_i x_i = 0$. Hence

The necessary and sufficient condition that a special sphere should be orthogonal to another sphere is that the center of the special sphere lie on the other sphere.

EXERCISE

Prove that the coefficients a_i in the equation of the sphere are proportional to the cosines of the angles made by the sphere with the coördinate spheres, and that the cosines themselves may be found by dividing a_i by $\sqrt{a_1^2 + a_2^2 + a_3^2 + a_4^2 + a_5^2}$. Compare with direction cosines in Cartesian geometry.

120. The power of a point with respect to a sphere. If C is the center of the sphere

$$\sum a_i x_i = 0,$$

with the radius r, and P is any point with coördinates y_i, the distance CP is easily calculated by (4), § 118, and (6), § 117, with the result:

$$\overline{CP}^2 = -\frac{2(a_1 y_1 + a_2 y_2 + a_3 y_3 + a_4 y_4 + a_5 y_5)}{(a_1 + ia_5)(y_1 + iy_5)} + r^2. \tag{1}$$

We shall pláce

$$S = \overline{CP}^2 - r^2 = -\frac{2(a_1 y_1 + a_2 y_2 + a_3 y_3 + a_4 y_4 + a_5 y_5)}{(a_1 + ia_5)(y_1 + iy_5)} \tag{2}$$

and shall call S the power of the point y_i with respect to the sphere. If the sphere is real and the point y_i is a real point outside the sphere, the power is the square of the length of any tangent from the point to the sphere. If the sphere is a point sphere, the power is the square of the distance from the point y_i to the center of the sphere. In all other cases equation (2) is the definition of the power.

From (2) may be obtained the important formula for a non-special sphere:

$$\frac{S}{r} = -\frac{2}{y_1 + iy_5} \cdot \frac{a_1 y_1 + a_2 y_2 + a_3 y_3 + a_4 y_4 + a_5 y_5}{\sqrt{a_1^2 + a_2^2 + a_3^2 + a_4^2 + a_5^2}}. \tag{3}$$

The above discussion fails if the sphere is a plane. We may, however, obtain the meaning of formula (3) in this case by a limit process. We have, from (2),

$$S = (PC - r)(PC + r) = PA(PC + r),$$

where PA is the shortest distance from P to the sphere. Then

$$\frac{S}{r} = PA\left(\frac{PC}{r} + 1\right).$$

Now let C recede to infinity along the line PC. The sphere becomes a plane perpendicular to PA. But the limit of $\dfrac{PC}{r}$, as r becomes infinite and $a_1 + ia_5$ approaches zero, is 1, from (1). Therefore

$$\text{Limit} \frac{S}{r} = 2\,PA,$$

where PA is the perpendicular from P to the plane. This result may be checked by replacing x_i by ξ_i and using familiar theorems of Cartesian geometry.

The equation of any nonspecial sphere may be written so that $\eta(a) = 1$. The equation is then said to be in its *normal form*, and the denominator $a_1^2 + a_2^2 + a_3^2 + a_4^2 + a_5^2$ disappears from equation (3).

121. General orthogonal coördinates. Let us make the linear substitution

$$\rho x_i' = \alpha_{i1}x_1 + \alpha_{i2}x_2 + \alpha_{i3}x_3 + \alpha_{i4}x_4 + \alpha_{i5}x_5, \quad (i = 1, 2, 3, 4, 5) \quad (1)$$

in which the determinant $|\alpha_{ik}|$ does not vanish. Then to any set of ratios x_i corresponds one set of ratios x_i', and since the quantities x_i satisfy a quadratic relation $\omega(x) = 0$, the quantities x_i' satisfy another quadratic relation $\Omega(x') = 0$.

Then values of x_i' which satisfy $\Omega(x') = 0$ correspond to one and only one set of ratios of x_i which satisfy $\omega(x) = 0$. Therefore x_i' can be taken as coördinates of a point in space and are the most general pentaspherical coördinates.

The sphere $\qquad\qquad \sum a_i x_i = 0$

becomes the sphere $\qquad \sum a_i' x_i' = 0,$

where

$$\rho a_i = \alpha_{1i}a_1' + \alpha_{2i}a_2' + \alpha_{3i}a_3' + \alpha_{4i}a_4' + \alpha_{5i}a_5', \quad (2)$$

and the condition $\eta(a) = 0$ for a special sphere goes into another quadratic condition $H(a') = 0$.

The point at infinity takes the new coördinates $\alpha_{i1} + i\alpha_{i5}$, and the condition that a sphere should be a plane is that its equation should be satisfied by these coördinates.

The coördinates ξ_i of § 117 form a special case of these general coördinates. We shall not, however, pursue the treatment of the general case, but shall restrict ourselves to the case in which the five coördinate spheres are orthogonal. In this case no sphere can be special, since, if it were, its center would lie on each of the other four spheres, and there would be four orthogonal spheres through a common point, which is obviously absurd.

We may consider that each of the equations of the coördinate spheres has been put in the normal form, so that we have, in (1),

$$\alpha_{i1}^2 + \alpha_{i2}^2 + \alpha_{i3}^2 + \alpha_{i4}^2 + \alpha_{i5}^2 = 1. \tag{3}$$

Then, by (3), § 120, the substitution is expressed by the equations

$$\rho x_i' = \frac{S_i}{r_i}, \tag{4}$$

where S_i is the power of the point x_i with respect to the sphere $x_i' = 0$, and r_i is the radius of $x_i' = 0$, since the factor $-\dfrac{2}{x_1 + ix_5}$ is the same for all five spheres. If any sphere $x_k' = 0$ is a plane, then the corresponding term $\dfrac{S_k}{r_k}$ is to be replaced by $2P_k$, where P_k is the length of the perpendicular from x_i to the plane $x_k' = 0$.

Since the five spheres in (3) are orthogonal we have

$$\alpha_{i1}\alpha_{k1} + \alpha_{i2}\alpha_{k2} + \alpha_{i3}\alpha_{k3} + \alpha_{i4}\alpha_{k4} + \alpha_{i5}\alpha_{k5} = 0 \tag{5}$$

for all pairs of values of i and k, $i \neq k$.

From a familiar theorem of algebra on orthogonal substitutions[*] it follows that

$$\alpha_{1i}^2 + \alpha_{2i}^2 + \alpha_{3i}^2 + \alpha_{4i}^2 + \alpha_{5i}^2 = 1 \tag{6}$$

and

$$\alpha_{1i}\alpha_{1k} + \alpha_{2i}\alpha_{2k} + \alpha_{3i}\alpha_{3k} + \alpha_{4i}\alpha_{4k} + \alpha_{5i}\alpha_{5k} = 0. \quad (i \neq k) \tag{7}$$

Consequently we have for x_i' the fundamental relation

$$x_1'^2 + x_2'^2 + x_3'^2 + x_4'^2 + x_5'^2 = 0, \tag{8}$$

and the condition for a special sphere is

$$a_1'^2 + a_2'^2 + a_3'^2 + a_4'^2 + a_5'^2 = 0. \tag{9}$$

Moreover, by the theory of orthogonal substitutions, equations (1) solve into

$$x_i = \rho(\alpha_{1i}x_1' + \alpha_{2i}x_2' + \alpha_{3i}x_3' + \alpha_{4i}x_4' + \alpha_{5i}x_5'). \tag{10}$$

By (4), § 118, the radius r_i' of the sphere $x_i' = 0$ is

$$r_i = \frac{1}{\alpha_{i1} + i\alpha_{i5}}. \tag{11}$$

Therefore the real point at infinity whose coördinates in the old system x_i are $1 : 0 : 0 : 0 : i$ has the new coördinates

$$\rho x_i' = \frac{1}{r_i}, \tag{12}$$

* Cf. Scott's "Theory of Determinants," p. 154.

where, if any sphere $x'_k = 0$ is a plane, the corresponding coördinate x'_k is zero, as in fact happens when $r_k = \infty$.

The equation $x_1 + ix_5 = 0$ for the locus at infinity becomes, from (10) and (11),

$$\sum \frac{x'_i}{r_i} = 0, \tag{13}$$

where, again, if any coördinate sphere is a plane the corresponding term vanishes from (13).

It is now easy to see that the formula (6), § 117, for distance becomes

$$d^2 = -\frac{2\,(x'_1 y'_1 + x'_2 y'_2 + x'_3 y'_3 + x'_4 y'_4 + x'_5 y'_5)}{\sum \dfrac{x'_i}{r_i} \sum \dfrac{y'_i}{r_i}}, \tag{14}$$

so that the equation of a sphere with center y_i and radius r is

$$2 \sum y'_i x'_i + r^2 \sum \frac{y'_i}{r_i} \sum \frac{x'_i}{r_i} = 0. \tag{15}$$

Identifying this with $\sum a'_i x'_i = 0$ \hspace{2cm} (16)

we have $\rho a'_i = y'_i + \dfrac{r^2}{2\,r_i} \sum \dfrac{y'_i}{r_i}.$ \hspace{1.5cm} (17)

From (11), with (3) and (5),

$$\sum \frac{1}{r_i^2} = 0, \tag{18}$$

so that, from (17), $\rho \sum \dfrac{a'_i}{r_i} = \sum \dfrac{y'_i}{r_i}.$ \hspace{1.5cm} (19)

By squaring (17), adding, and reducing by (8), (18), and (19), we obtain the following formulas for the radius and the center of the sphere (16):

$$r^2 = \frac{\sum a'^2_i}{\left[\sum \dfrac{a'_i}{r_i} \right]^2}, \tag{20}$$

$$\sigma y'_i = a'_i - \frac{r^2}{2\,r_i} \sum \frac{a'_i}{r_i}.$$

The formulas of § 118 are only special cases of these.

EXERCISES

1. Prove the relation $\sum \dfrac{S_i}{r_i^2} = -2.$

2. Deduce for the element of arc $ds^2 = \dfrac{\sum dx_i^2}{\left(\sum \dfrac{x_i}{r_i} \right)^2}.$

122. The linear transformation. Consider a linear transformation

$$\rho x_i' = \alpha_{i1} x_1 + \alpha_{i2} x_2 + \alpha_{i3} x_3 + \alpha_{i4} x_4 + \alpha_{i5} x_5, \tag{1}$$

in which the determinant $|\alpha_{ik}|$ does not vanish and by which the fundamental relation $\omega(x) = 0$ is invariant. Then the relation $\eta(a) = 0$ is also invariant.

The relations (1) define a one-to-one transformation of space by which a nonspecial sphere goes into a nonspecial sphere and a special sphere into a special sphere. There are two types to be distinguished.

I. *Transformations by which the real point at infinity is invariant.* By such a transformation planes are transformed into planes and, consequently, straight lines into straight lines. Since the transformation is analytic it is a collineation.

Point spheres are transformed into point spheres; therefore, expressed in Cartesian coördinates, the transformation is one by which minimum cones go into minimum cones, and consequently the circle at infinity is invariant. Hence the transformation is a metrical transformation.

Conversely, any metrical transformation may be expressed as a linear transformation of pentaspherical coördinates. This is easily seen by use of the special coördinates of § 117 and is consequently true for the general coördinates.

Hence *a linear transformation of pentaspherical coördinates by which the real point at infinity is invariant is a metrical transformation, and conversely.*

II. *Transformations by which the real point at infinity is not invariant.* Among these transformations are the *inversions.* That an inversion may be represented actually by a linear transformation of pentaspherical coördinates is evident from the example in the coördinates ξ_i, § 117,

$$\rho \xi_1' = k^4 \xi_5,$$
$$\rho \xi_2' = k^2 \xi_2,$$
$$\rho \xi_3' = k^2 \xi_3,$$
$$\rho \xi_4' = k^2 \xi_4,$$
$$\rho \xi_5' = \xi_1,$$

and in fact any inversion may be so expressed by proper choice of coördinates.

Consider now the general case of a real transformation by which the real point at infinity I is transformed into a real point A, and the same point A, or another point A', is transformed into I. Since the transformation is real A cannot be at infinity. Let this transformation be T and let S be an inversion with A as the center of inversion. Then the product ST leaves I invariant and is therefore a metrical transformation, M. Therefore $ST = M$; whence $T = S^{-1}M$. But $S^{-1} = S$. Therefore $T = SM$. Hence

Any real transformation of pentaspherical coördinates by which the real point at infinity is not invariant is either an inversion, or the product of an inversion and a metrical transformation.

This does not exhaust all cases of imaginary transformations. We may obviously have imaginary transformations of the metrical type or inversions from imaginary points, so that the above theorems hold for transformations by which the real point at infinity is transformed into itself or into any finite point. Transformations, however, by which the real point at infinity is transformed into an imaginary point at infinity are of a different type. An example of such a transformation is

$$\rho x_1' = -x_1 \qquad\qquad -2x_3 \qquad -ix_5,$$
$$\rho x_2' = \frac{3i}{2}x_1 \; +2x_2 \; -2ix_3 \qquad +\frac{5}{2}x_5,$$
$$\rho x_3' = \frac{5}{2}x_1 \; -2ix_2 \; -2x_3 \qquad -\frac{3}{2}ix_5,$$
$$\rho x_4' = \qquad\qquad\qquad 2x_4,$$
$$\rho x_5' = \quad ix_1 \; +2x_2 \qquad\qquad -x_5.$$

We shall close this section with the theorem, important in subsequent work: *If the coördinate system is orthogonal the transformation expressed by changing the sign of one of the coördinates is an inversion on the corresponding coördinate sphere.*

For let the sign of x_k be changed. Then points on the sphere $x_k = 0$ are unchanged, and any sphere orthogonal to $x_k = 0$ is transformed into itself. This characterizes an inversion on $x_k = 0$.

EXERCISES

1. Prove the last theorem analytically, using the formulas of § 121.

2. Prove that the product of five inversions with respect to five orthogonal spheres is an identity.

123. Relation between pentaspherical and Cartesian coördinates.
If we take the axes OX, OY, OZ used in § 117 to define the specialized pentaspherical coördinates as the axes also of a set of Cartesian coördinates, it is obvious that we have, for real points,

$$
\begin{aligned}
\rho x_1 &= x^2 + y^2 + z^2 - 1 &&= x^2 + y^2 + z^2 - t^2, \\
\rho x_2 &= 2x &&= 2xt, \\
\rho x_3 &= 2y &&= 2yt, \\
\rho x_4 &= 2z &&= 2zt, \\
\rho x_5 &= i(x^2 + y^2 + z^2 + 1) &&= i(x^2 + y^2 + z^2 + t^2).
\end{aligned} \tag{1}
$$

This establishes in the first place a one-to-one correspondence between real points in the two systems. It may be used also to define the correspondence between the imaginary and infinite points introduced into each system. There exists, however, no reason why such points introduced into one system should always have corresponding points in the other. As a matter of fact a failure of correspondence of such points does exist.

The Cartesian points on the imaginary circle at infinity fail to exist in pentaspherical coördinates since values of x, y, z, t which satisfy the relations $x^2 + y^2 + z^2 = 0$, $t = 0$ give $x_1 : x_2 : x_3 : x_4 : x_5 = 0 : 0 : 0 : 0 : 0$. But any Cartesian point at infinity not on the imaginary circle corresponds in pentaspherical coördinates to the real point at infinity $1 : 0 : 0 : 0 : i$.

On the other hand, we have in pentaspherical geometry imaginary points at infinity satisfying the relations $x_2^2 + x_3^2 + x_4^2 = 0$, $x_1 + ix_5 = 0$, but not having $x_2 = x_3 = x_4 = 0$. These have no corresponding points in Cartesian geometry since no values of $x : y : z : t$ in (1) give them.

This failure in the correspondence is of importance if one wishes to pass from one system to the other. They are of no significance, however, as long as one operates exclusively in one system.

The general pentaspherical coördinates are connected with Cartesian coördinates by equations of the form

$$\rho x_i' = (\alpha_{i1} + i\alpha_{i5})(x^2 + y^2 + z^2) + 2\alpha_{i2}x + 2\alpha_{i3}y + 2\alpha_{i4}z - (\alpha_{i1} - i\alpha_{i5}).$$

124. Pencils, bundles, and complexes of spheres. If $\sum a_i x_i = 0$ and $\sum b_i x_i = 0$ are two spheres, the equation

$$\sum (a_i + \lambda b_i) x_i = 0 \tag{1}$$

represents a sphere through all points common to the two spheres and intersecting neither in any other point. Such spheres together form a *pencil* of spheres.

A pencil of spheres contains one and only one plane unless it consists entirely of planes.

This follows from the fact that the condition that equation (1) should be satisfied by the coördinates of the real point at infinity consists of an equation of the first degree in λ, unless both $\sum a_i x_i = 0$ and $\sum b_i x_i = 0$ are satisfied by those coördinates. In the latter case all the spheres (1) are planes.

A pencil of spheres contains two and only two special spheres (which may be real, imaginary, or coincident) unless it consists entirely of special spheres.

The condition that (1) represents a special sphere is

$$\eta(a + \lambda b) = \eta(a) + \lambda \eta(a, b) + \lambda^2 \eta(b) = 0,$$

which determines two distinct or equal values of λ unless $\eta(a) = 0$, $\eta(b) = 0$, $\eta(a, b) = 0$. The latter case occurs when the two spheres $\sum a_i x_i = 0$, $\sum b_i x_i = 0$ are special spheres with the center of each on the other.

The theorems of § 111 and others analogous to those of § 62 are easily proved by the student.

If $\sum a_i x_i = 0$, $\sum b_i x_i = 0$, $\sum c_i x_i = 0$ are three spheres not in the same pencil, the equation

$$\sum (a_i + \lambda b_i + \mu c_i) x_i = 0$$

represents a bundle of spheres as in § 112. The bundle contains a singly infinite set of planes and a singly infinite set of special spheres. The relations between orthogonal pencils and bundles found in § 112 are easily verified here.

If $\sum a_i x_i = 0$, $\sum b_i x_i = 0$, $\sum c_i x_i = 0$, $\sum d_i x_i = 0$ are four spheres not belonging to the same bundle, the equation

$$\sum (a_i + \lambda b_i + \mu c_i + \nu d_i) x_i = 0$$

represents a complex of spheres. It consists of spheres orthogonal to a base sphere and contains a doubly infinite set of planes and a doubly infinite set of special spheres. The centers of the latter form the base sphere.

EXERCISES

1. Prove that the angle under which a sphere cuts any sphere of a pencil is determined by the angle under which it cuts two spheres of the pencil.

2. Prove that among the spheres of a pencil there is always one which cuts a given sphere orthogonally.

3. Prove that the angle under which a sphere cuts any sphere of a bundle is determined by the angles under which it cuts three spheres of the bundle.

4. Determine a sphere orthogonal to four given spheres.

5. Determine a sphere cutting five given spheres under given angles. When is the problem indeterminate?

125. Tangent circles and spheres. Let y_i, z_i, t_i be any three points given in orthogonal pentaspherical coördinates, and consider the equations

$$\rho x_i = y_i + \lambda z_i + \mu t_i. \tag{1}$$

In order that x_i should be the coördinates of a point it is necessary and sufficient that

$$\sum (y_i + \lambda z_i + \mu t_i)^2 = 0. \tag{2}$$

Since $\sum y_i^2 = 0$, $\sum z_i^2 = 0$, $\sum t_i^2 = 0$, equation (2) reduces to

$$A\lambda + B\mu + C\lambda\mu = 0, \tag{3}$$

where $A = \sum y_i z_i$, $B = \sum y_i t_i$, $C = \sum z_i t_i$.

Therefore (1) may be written

$$\rho x_i = y_i + \lambda z_i - \frac{A\lambda}{B + C\lambda} t_i, \tag{4}$$

or

$$\rho x_i = By_i + (Cy_i + Bz_i - At_i)\lambda + Cz_i \lambda^2. \tag{5}$$

This represents a one-dimensional extent of points. Any sphere which contains the three points y_i, z_i, t_i will also contain all the points x_i, and any point x_i belongs to all the spheres through y_i, z_i, t_i. Therefore (4) represents a circle, including the special case of a straight line.

Any equation $\quad f(x_1,\, x_2,\, x_3,\, x_4,\, x_5) = 0, \tag{6}$

where f is a homogeneous polynomial of the nth degree, represents a surface. To find where it is cut by any circle substitute from (5) into (6). There results an equation of degree $2n$ in λ, so that the surface is cut by any circle in $2n$ points.

If Cartesian coördinates are substituted for x_i in (6) the equation is of the $2n$th order and of the form

$$u_0(x^2 + y^2 + z^2)^n + u_1(x^2 + y^2 + z^2)^{2n-1} + \cdots + u_1 + u_0 = 0,$$

where u_k is a homogeneous polynomial of degree k not containing $(x^2 + y^2 + z^2)$ as a factor. The surface therefore contains the circle at infinity and as an n-fold curve if $u_0 \neq 0$. In the Cartesian geometry the surface is cut by any circle in $4n$ points, but the circular points at infinity count $2n$ times and do not appear in the tetracyclical geometry.

The equation in λ is

$$B^n f(y_1, y_2, y_3, y_4) + \lambda B^{n-1} \sum \frac{\partial f}{\partial y_i}(Cy_i + Bz_i - At_i) + \cdots = 0. \quad (7)$$

Now if y_i is on the surface, then $f(y) = 0$ and $\sum y_i \frac{\partial f}{\partial y_i} = 0$, the latter because f is homogeneous. Therefore one root of (7) is zero. Two roots will be zero if, in addition to y_i being on the surface, we have

$$B \sum \frac{\partial f}{\partial y_i} z_i - A \sum \frac{\partial f}{\partial y_i} t_i = 0,$$

which is the same as

$$\frac{\sum \frac{\partial f}{\partial y_i} z_i}{\sum y_i z_i} = \frac{\sum \frac{\partial f}{\partial y_i} t_i}{\sum y_i t_i}. \quad (8)$$

If this condition is satisfied by the two points z_i and t_i, the circle (1) is tangent to the surface (6) at y_i. The condition is certainly met if z_i and t_i are both on the same sphere of the pencil

$$\sum \left(\frac{\partial f}{\partial y_i} - \rho y_i \right) x_i = 0. \quad (9)$$

Any sphere of this pencil has accordingly the property that any plane section of it through y_i is a circle tangent to the surface (6). Therefore (9) *represents a pencil of tangent spheres to the surface.*

If $\frac{\partial f}{\partial y_i} = 0$, all circles through y_i meet the surface in two coincident points. The point y_i is therefore a *singular point.* It is obvious that the geometric meaning is the same as in the Cartesian geometry.

126. Cyclides in pentaspherical coördinates. Consider the surface

$$\sum a_{ik}x_ix_k = 0. \quad (a_{ki} = a_{ik}) \tag{1}$$

From § 123 and § 116 this is a cyclide. We have shown that if the cyclide has singular points, it is the inverse of a quadric surface. We shall therefore limit ourselves here to the general case in which the singular points do not exist. Since, then, the equations $\dfrac{\partial f}{\partial y_i} = 0$ have no common solution, it is necessary and sufficient that the discriminant $|a_{ik}|$ does not vanish.

It is a theorem of algebra that in this case the quadratic form may be reduced by a linear substitution to the form

$$c_1x_1^2 + c_2x_2^2 + c_3x_3^2 + c_4x_4^2 + c_5x_5^2 = 0, \tag{2}$$

(where $c_i \neq 0$), at the same time that the fundamental relation $\omega(x)$ is

$$x_1^2 + x_2^2 + x_3^2 + x_4^2 + x_5^2 = 0. \tag{3}$$

We shall therefore assume that the equation of the cyclide is in the form (2) and that the coördinates are orthogonal.

From equation (2) it is obvious that the equation of the surface is not altered by changing the sign of any one of the coördinates x_i. But this operation is equivalent to inversion on the sphere $x_i = 0$. Hence

The general cyclide is its own inverse with respect to each of five mutually orthogonal spheres.

The pencil of tangent spheres to the cyclide at any point y_i is, by § 125,

$$\sum (c_i + \lambda) y_ix_i = 0. \tag{4}$$

Hence, in order that a given sphere

$$\sum a_ix_i = 0 \tag{5}$$

should be tangent to (2), it is necessary and sufficient to determine λ and y_i so that

$$\rho a_i = (c_i + \lambda) y_i \tag{6}$$

and so that y_i should satisfy the three equations (2), (3), (5). This gives the three conditions

$$\sum \frac{c_ia_i^2}{(c_i + \lambda)^2} = 0, \quad \sum \frac{a_i^2}{(c_i + \lambda)^2} = 0, \quad \sum \frac{a_i^2}{c_i + \lambda} = 0, \tag{7}$$

of which the first is a consequence of the last two. The last two express the fact that the equation

$$\sum \frac{a_i^2}{c_i + \lambda} = 0 \tag{8}$$

has equal roots. This imposes a condition to be satisfied in order that (5) should be tangent to (2).

When λ has been determined from these equations, equations (6) determine y_i in general without ambiguity. Exceptions occur if $\lambda = -c_k$, where c_k is any one of the coefficients of (2). In that case we have in (6) $a_k = 0$, and y_k cannot be determined from (6). However, if the other four coördinates y_i are determined, y_k has two values of opposite sign but equal absolute value, determined from the fundamental relation (3). The corresponding sphere (5) is orthogonal to $x_k = 0$ and tangent to the cyclide at two points which are inverse with respect to $x_k = 0$.

The value of λ may be taken arbitrarily as $-c_k$; whence $a_k = 0$. The values of $a_i (i \neq k)$ must then be determined from (7) with $\lambda = -c_k$. Each of the first two equations contain an indeterminate term. The last equation becomes

$$\sum_i \frac{a_i^2}{c_i - c_k} = 0. \qquad (i \neq k) \tag{9}$$

The coefficients of (5) satisfy two equations, therefore, and the spheres form a family of spheres which is not linear. In this family a sphere can be found which is tangent to the cyclide at any given point. For if $\lambda = -c_k$, and y_i is any point on the cyclide, equation (6) will determine a_i, and the a_i's will satisfy (9), as has been shown. The spheres of the family therefore envelop the cyclide.

There are five such families of spheres, since λ may be any one of the five coefficients c_i. Hence

The general cyclide is enveloped by five families of spheres, each family consisting of spheres orthogonal to one of the five coördinate spheres and tangent to the surface at two points.

We shall show that *the centers of the spheres of each series lie on a quadric surface.*

Take, for example, the series for which $\lambda = -c_1$ and $a_1 = 0$. If y_i are the coördinates of the center of a sphere of the series by (20), § 121,

$$-\frac{r^2}{2}\sum \frac{a_i}{r_i} = \sigma y_1 r_1,$$

and

$$a_k = \sigma\left(y_k - \frac{y_1 r_1}{r_k}\right); \quad (k \neq 1)$$

whence

$$\rho a_k = \frac{y_k r_k - y_1 r_1}{r_k},$$

and equation (9) becomes

$$\sum_k \frac{(y_k r_k - y_1 r_1)^2}{r_k^2(c_k - c_1)} = 0, \quad (k = 2, 3, 4, 5) \tag{10}$$

which is the equation of the locus of the centers of the spheres of the family under consideration.

By (4), § 121, equation (10) may be written

$$\sum_k \frac{(S_k - S_1)^2}{r_k^2(c_k - c_1)} = 0; \tag{11}$$

and, finally, if S_k and S_1 are expressed in Cartesian coördinates, equation (11) is of the second degree, and the theorem is proved.

We may sum up in the following theorem:

The general cyclide may be generated in five ways as the envelope of a sphere subject to the two conditions that it should be orthogonal to a fixed sphere and that its center should lie on a quadric surface.

A surface which is its own inverse with respect to a sphere S is called *anallagmatic* with respect to S, which is called the *directrix sphere*. Such a surface is enveloped by a family of spheres orthogonal to S and doubly tangent to the surface. For at any point P of the surface there is a sphere tangent to the surface and orthogonal to S. By inversion this sphere is unchanged. It is therefore tangent to the surface at P', the inverse of P.

The surface on which the centers of these enveloping spheres of the anallagmatic surface lie is called the *deferent*.

The cyclide, therefore, is anallagmatic with respect to the five orthogonal spheres and has five deferents, each a quadric surface.

EXERCISES

1. If Q_k is one of the five deferents of the cyclide, and S_k the corresponding directrix sphere, prove that the tetrahedron whose vertices are the centers of the other five directrices is self-conjugate, both with respect to Q_k and with respect to S_k.

2. Prove that on the cyclide there are ten families of circles, two families corresponding to each of the five modes of generating the cyclide.

3. The focal curve of any surface being defined as the locus of the centers of point spheres which are doubly tangent to the surface, prove that the cyclide has five focal curves, each being a sphero-quadric formed by the intersection of a deferent by the corresponding directrix sphere.

REFERENCES

For more reading along the lines of Part III of this book the following references are given. As in Part II, these are not intended to form a complete bibliography or to contain journal references.

General treatises

 CLEBSCH-LINDEMAN, Vorlesungen über Geometrie. Teubner.
 DARBOUX. See reference at end of Part II.
 NIEWENGLOWSKI, Géométrie dans l'espace. Gauthier-Villars.
 SALMON-ROGERS, Geometry of Three Dimensions. Longmans, Green & Co.

Circle and spheres:

 COOLIDGE, Circle and Sphere Geometry. Oxford Clarendon Press.

Cyclides:

 BÔCHER, Potentialtheorie. Teubner.
 DARBOUX, Sur une classe remarquable de courbes et de surfaces algébriques. A. Hermann.
 DOEHLEMANN, Geometrische Transformationen, II. Teil. Göschen'sche Verlagshandlung.

These are in addition to the general treatises of Darboux and Coolidge already referred to. The first section of Bôcher's book is of interest here. Doehlemann contains figures of the Dupin cyclides.

Algebraic operations:

 BÔCHER, Introduction to Higher Algebra. The Macmillan Company.
 BROMWICH, Quadratic Forms and their Classification by Means of Invariant Factors. Cambridge University Press.

Each of these books contains geometrical illustrations. The student may refer to them for any algebraic methods we have employed and especially for an explanation of the method of elementary divisors in reducing one or a pair of quadratic forms to various types. Bromwich contains a full classification of the cyclides.

PART IV. GEOMETRY OF FOUR AND HIGHER DIMENSIONS

CHAPTER XVII

LINE COÖRDINATES IN THREE-DIMENSIONAL SPACE

127. The Plücker coördinates. The straight lines in space form a simple example of a four-dimensional extent, since a line is determined by four coördinates. In fact, the equations of a line can in general be put in the form

$$
\begin{aligned}
x &= rz + \rho, \\
y &= sz + \sigma,
\end{aligned}
\tag{1}
$$

and the quantities (r, s, ρ, σ) may be taken as the coördinates of the line. More symmetry is obtained, however, by the following device.

From equations (1) we have

$$ry - sx = r\sigma - \rho s, \tag{2}$$

and we may place $\quad r\sigma - \rho s = \eta, \tag{3}$

thus obtaining five coördinates connected by a quadratic relation.

If (x', y', z') and (x'', y'', z'') are any points on the line (1), we may easily compute

$$r:s:\rho:\sigma:\eta:1 = x'-x'':y'-y'':x''z'-x'z'':y''z'-y'z'':x'y''-x''y':z'-z'',$$

and it is the ratios on the right-hand side of this equation which were taken by Plücker as the coördinates of a line.

These coördinates, however, form only a special case, arising from the use of Cartesian coördinates, of more general coördinates obtained by the use of quadriplanar coördinates. We proceed to obtain these coördinates independently of the work just done.

The position of a straight line is fixed by two points $(x_1:x_2:x_3:x_4)$ and $(y_1:y_2:y_3:y_4)$. It should be possible, therefore, to take as coördinates of the line some functions of the coördinates of these two points. Furthermore, since any two points whose coördinates are

$\lambda x_i + \mu y_i$ may be used to define the same line as is defined by x_i and y_i, the coördinates of the line must be invariant with respect to the substitutions

$$\rho x_i' = \lambda_1 x_i + \mu_1 y_i, \qquad \rho y_i' = \lambda_2 x_i + \mu_2 y_i.$$

Simple expressions fulfilling these conditions are the ratios of determinants of the form $\begin{vmatrix} x_i & y_i \\ x_k & y_k \end{vmatrix}$. We will, accordingly, consider the expressions

$$p_{ik} = x_i y_k - x_k y_i.$$

Since $p_{ki} = - p_{ik}$, there are six of these quantities; namely,

$$p_{12} = x_1 y_2 - x_2 y_1,$$
$$p_{13} = x_1 y_3 - x_3 y_1,$$
$$p_{14} = x_1 y_4 - x_4 y_1,$$
$$p_{34} = x_3 y_4 - x_4 y_3,$$
$$p_{42} = x_4 y_2 - x_2 y_4,$$
$$p_{23} = x_2 y_3 - x_3 y_2,$$

which are connected by the relation

$$\begin{vmatrix} x_1 & x_2 & x_3 & x_4 \\ y_1 & y_2 & y_3 & y_4 \\ x_1 & x_2 & x_3 & x_4 \\ y_1 & y_2 & y_3 & y_4 \end{vmatrix} = 2(p_{12}p_{34} + p_{13}p_{42} + p_{14}p_{23}) = 0. \qquad (4)$$

It is obvious that to any straight line corresponds one and only one set of ratios of the quantities p_{ik}.

As we have seen, the ratios of p_{ik} are independent of the particular points of the line used to form p_{ik}. If in particular we take one point as the point $0 : x_2 : x_3 : x_4$, in which the line cuts the plane $x_1 = 0$, we have $p_{12} = - x_2 y_1$, $p_{13} = - x_3 y_1$, $p_{14} = - x_4 y_1$; whence $x_2 : x_3 : x_4 = p_{12} : p_{13} : p_{14}$. Using in a similar manner the points in which the line meets the other coördinate planes, we have, as the points of intersection with the four planes, the following four points:

$$\begin{array}{cccc} 0 : & p_{12} : & p_{13} : & p_{14}, \\ -p_{12} : & 0 : & p_{23} : & -p_{42}, \\ -p_{13} : & -p_{23} : & 0 : & p_{34}, \\ -p_{14} : & p_{42} : & -p_{34} : & 0. \end{array} \qquad (5)$$

The condition that these four points should lie on a straight line is exactly the relation (4).

From (5) it follows that a set of ratios p_{ik} can belong to only one line and that these ratios may have any value consistent with (4).

Hence *the ratios of p_{ik} may be taken as the coördinates of a straight line, and the relation between a straight line and its coördinates is one to one.* These coördinates are called *Plücker coördinates.*

Of course if a straight line lies completely in one of the coördinate planes, one of the sets of ratios in (5) becomes indeterminate. This cannot happen, however, for more than two of the sets at the same time, and the other two sets, together with (4), determine p_{ik}.

128. Dualistic definition. A straight line may be defined by the intersection of two planes u_i and v_i. Reasoning as in § 127 we are led to place

$$q_{12} = u_1 v_2 - u_2 v_1,$$
$$q_{13} = u_1 v_3 - u_3 v_1,$$
$$q_{14} = u_1 v_4 - u_4 v_1,$$
$$q_{34} = u_3 v_4 - u_4 v_3, \tag{1}$$
$$q_{42} = u_4 v_2 - u_2 v_4,$$
$$q_{23} = u_2 v_3 - u_3 v_2,$$

which are connected by the relation

$$2(q_{12}q_{34} + q_{13}q_{42} + q_{14}q_{23}) = 0. \tag{2}$$

To any straight line corresponds one ratio set of ratios of q_{ik}, and the four planes through the straight line and the vertices of the tetrahedron of reference have the plane coördinates

$$
\begin{array}{cccc}
0 & : & q_{12} & : & q_{13} & : & q_{14}, \\
-q_{12} & : & 0 & : & q_{23} & : & -q_{42}, \\
-q_{13} & : & -q_{23} & : & 0 & : & q_{34}, \\
-q_{14} & : & q_{42} & : & -q_{34} & : & 0.
\end{array}
\tag{3}
$$

Therefore, to any set of values of the six quantities q_{ik} which satisfy the relation (2), there corresponds one and only one line with the coördinates q_{ik}.

The relation between the quantities p_{ik} and q_{ik} is simple. From (3) the plane

$$q_{12}x_2 + q_{13}x_3 + q_{14}x_4 = 0 \tag{4}$$

passes through the line q_{ik}. If x_i and y_k are two points on the line we have, besides equation (4), the equation

$$q_{12}y_2 + q_{13}y_3 + q_{14}y_4 = 0. \tag{5}$$

From (4) and (5) we have

$$\frac{q_{12}}{p_{34}} = \frac{q_{13}}{p_{42}} = \frac{q_{14}}{p_{23}}.$$

Similarly, we may show that

$$\frac{q_{12}}{p_{34}} = \frac{q_{13}}{p_{42}} = \frac{q_{14}}{p_{23}} = \frac{q_{34}}{p_{12}} = \frac{q_{42}}{p_{13}} = \frac{q_{23}}{p_{14}}.$$

We may, accordingly, use only one set of quantities:

$$r_{12} = \rho p_{12} = \sigma q_{34},$$
$$r_{13} = \rho p_{13} = \sigma q_{42},$$
$$r_{14} = \rho p_{14} = \sigma q_{23},$$
$$r_{34} = \rho p_{34} = \sigma q_{12},$$
$$r_{42} = \rho p_{42} = \sigma q_{13},$$
$$r_{23} = \rho p_{23} = \sigma q_{14},$$

bound by the fundamental relation

$$\omega(r) = 2\,(r_{12}r_{34} + r_{13}r_{42} + r_{14}r_{23}) = 0,$$

and may interpret in point or plane coördinates at pleasure.

129. Intersecting lines. Two straight lines, one determined by the points x_i and y_i and the other by the points x_i' and y_i', intersect when the four points lie in the same plane, and only then. The necessary and sufficient condition for this is

$$\begin{vmatrix} x_1 & x_2 & x_3 & x_4 \\ y_1 & y_2 & y_3 & y_4 \\ x_1' & x_2' & x_3' & x_4' \\ y_1' & y_2' & y_3' & y_4' \end{vmatrix} = 0,$$

which is the same as

$$p_{12}p_{34}' + p_{13}p_{42}' + p_{14}p_{23}' + p_{34}p_{12}' + p_{42}p_{13}' + p_{23}p_{14}' = 0. \tag{1}$$

Also, dualistically, two lines, one determined by the planes u_i and v_i and the other by the planes u_i' and v_i', intersect when the four planes pass through the same point, and only then. The necessary and sufficient condition for this is

$$\begin{vmatrix} u_1 & u_2 & u_3 & u_4 \\ v_1 & v_2 & v_3 & v_4 \\ u_1' & u_2' & u_3' & u_4' \\ v_1' & v_2' & v_3' & v_4' \end{vmatrix} = 0,$$

which is the same as

$$q_{12}q_{34}' + q_{13}q_{42}' + q_{14}q_{23}' + q_{34}q_{12}' + q_{42}q_{13}' + q_{23}q_{14}' = 0. \tag{2}$$

Either condition (1) or (2) is in terms of r_{ik},

$$r_{12}r_{34}' + r_{13}r_{42}' + r_{14}r_{23}' + r_{34}r_{12}' + r_{42}r_{13}' + r_{23}r_{14}' = 0, \tag{3}$$

which is more compactly written as

$$\omega(r, r') = \sum r_{ik}' \frac{\partial \omega}{\partial r_{ik}} = 0,$$

where $\omega(r, r')$ is the polar of the quadratic expression $\omega(r)$.

130. General line coördinates. Consider any six quantities x_i defined as linear combinations of the six quantities r_{ik}. That is, let

$$\rho x_i = \alpha_{i1} r_{12} + \alpha_{i2} r_{13} + \alpha_{i3} r_{14} + \alpha_{i4} r_{34} + \alpha_{i5} r_{42} + \alpha_{i6} r_{23}, \tag{1}$$

with the condition that the determinant of the coefficients $|\alpha_{ik}|$ does not vanish. Then the relation between the quantities p_{ik} and x_i is one-to-one, and x_i may be used as the coördinates of a line.

By the substitution (1) the fundamental relation $\omega(r) = 0$ goes into a quadratic relation of the form

$$\xi(x) = \sum a_{ik} x_i x_k = 0. \qquad (a_{ki} = a_{ik}) \tag{2}$$

In fact, by a proper choice of the coefficients in (1), the function $\xi(x)$ may be any quadratic form of nonvanishing discriminant and, in particular, may be a sum of the six squares x_i^2. The proof of this may be given as a generalization of the similar problem in space or may be found in treatises on algebra.

By the substitution (1) the polar $\omega(r, r')$ goes into the polar

$$\xi(x, x') = \sum x_i \frac{\partial \xi}{\partial x_i'} = 0.$$

To prove this let r_{ik} and r_{ik}' represent two sets of values of the coördinates r_{ik} and let x_i and x_i' represent the corresponding values of the coördinates x_i; then $r_{ik} + \lambda r_{ik}'$ corresponds to $x_i + \lambda x_i'$ for all values of λ.

Therefore $\qquad \omega(r + \lambda r') = \xi(x + \lambda x'),$

or $\quad \omega(r) + 2\lambda\omega(r, r') + \lambda^2\omega(r') = \xi(x) + 2\lambda\xi(x, x') + \lambda^2\xi(x').$

By equating like powers of λ we have

$$\omega(r, r') = \xi(x, x').$$

Hence *the ratios of any system of six quantities x_i, bound by a homogeneous quadratic relation $\xi(x) = 0$ of nonvanishing discriminant, may be taken as the coördinates of a line in space in such a manner that the equation $\xi(x, x') = 0$ is the necessary and sufficient condition for the intersection of the two lines x_i and x_i'.*

Of particular importance are coördinates due to Klein, to which we shall refer as *Klein coördinates*. These are obtained by the substitution

$$\rho x_1 = p_{12} + p_{34},$$
$$\rho x_2 = p_{13} + p_{42},$$
$$\rho x_3 = i(p_{13} - p_{42}),$$
$$\rho x_4 = p_{14} + p_{23},$$
$$\rho x_5 = i(p_{12} - p_{34}),$$
$$\rho x_6 = i(p_{14} - p_{23}).$$

The fundamental relation is then

$$x_1^2 + x_2^2 + x_3^2 + x_4^2 + x_5^2 + x_6^2 = 0,$$

and the condition for the intersection of two lines is

$$x_1 y_1 + x_2 y_2 + x_3 y_3 + x_4 y_4 + x_5 y_5 + x_6 y_6 = 0.$$

131. Pencils and bundles of lines. I. *If a_i and b_i are two intersecting lines, then $\rho x_i = a_i + \lambda b_i$ is a line of the pencil determined by a_i and b_i, and any line of the pencil may be so expressed.*

The hypotheses are

$$\xi(a) = 0, \quad \xi(b) = 0, \quad \xi(a, b) = 0.$$

Then:

1. x_i are the coördinates of a straight line, since

$$\xi(x) = \xi(a + \lambda b) = \xi(a) + 2\lambda \xi(a, b) + \lambda^2 \xi(b) = 0.$$

2. The line x_i lies in the plane of a_i and b_i and passes through their point of intersection. To prove this let d_i be any line cutting both a_i and b_i. That is, d_i is either a line through the intersection of a_i and b_i or a line in the plane of a_i and b_i. Then $\xi(a, d) = 0$, and $\xi(b, d) = 0$. Therefore

$$\xi(x, d) = \xi(a + \lambda b, d) = \xi(a, d) + \lambda \xi(b, d) = 0.$$

Hence x_i intersects any and all of the lines d_i and therefore lies in the plane of a_i and b_i and passes through their intersection.

3. The value of λ may be so taken as to give any line of the pencil determined by a_i and b_i. To prove this let P be any point of the pencil except its vertex, and let h_i be a line through P but not in the plane of a_i and b_i. We can determine λ so that

$$\xi(x, h) = \xi(a, h) + \lambda\xi(b, h) = 0.$$

Hence x_i intersects h_i; and since h_i has only the point P in the plane of a_i and b_i, and x_i lies in that plane, x_i passes through P and is any line of the pencil. The theorem is completely proved.

II. If a_i, b_i, and c_i are three lines through the same point but not belonging to the same pencil, then $\rho x_i = a_i + \lambda b_i + \mu c_i$ is a line through the same point, and any line through that point may be so represented.

By hypothesis, $\xi(a) = 0, \xi(b) = 0, \xi(c) = 0, \xi(a, b) = 0, \xi(b, c) = 0, \xi(c, a) = 0$. Then:

1. x_i are the coördinates of some line, since $\xi(x) = 0$.

2. Any line which cuts all three lines a_i, b_i, and c_i cuts x_i. For, if $\xi(a, d) = 0$, $\xi(b, d) = 0$, and $\xi(c, d) = 0$, then $\xi(x, d) = \xi(ad) + \lambda\xi(b, d) + \mu\xi(c, d) = 0$. Therefore x_i passes through the intersection of a_i, b_i, c_i.

3. Values of λ and μ may be so determined that x_i may cut any two lines g_i and h_i which do not cut the lines a_i, b_i, and c_i. We have, in fact, to determine λ and μ from the two equations

$$\xi(a, g) + \lambda\xi(b, g) + \mu\xi(c, g) = 0,$$
$$\xi(a, h) + \lambda\xi(b, h) + \mu\xi(c, h) = 0.$$

The theorem is therefore proved.

III. If a_i, b_i, and c_i are any three lines in the same plane but not belonging to the same pencil, then $\rho x_i = a_i + \lambda b_i + \mu c_i$ is a line in the same plane, and any line in the plane may be so represented.

The proof is the same as for theorem II.

A configuration consisting of all lines through the same point is called a *bundle* of lines. A configuration consisting of all lines in a plane is a *plane* of lines. By the use of line coördinates we do not distinguish between a bundle and a plane of lines. In fact each configuration consists of a doubly infinite set of lines each of which intersects all of the others.

EXERCISES

1. Prove that the cross ratio of the four points in which a straight line meets the four planes of any tetrahedron is equal to the cross ratio of the four planes through the line and the vertices of the tetrahedron.

2. Prove that there are two and only two lines which intersect four given lines in general position.

3. Prove that if the coördinates of any five lines satisfy the six equations
$$\lambda x_i + \mu y_i + \nu z_i + \rho s_i + \sigma t_i = 0,$$
the five lines intersect each of two fixed lines.

4. Show that if the coördinates of any four lines satisfy the six equations
$$\lambda x_i + \mu y_i + \nu z_i + \rho s_i = 0,$$
any line which intersects three of them intersects the fourth, and hence the lines are four generators of a quadric surface.

5. Show that if the coördinates of three lines are connected by the six equations
$$\lambda x_i + \mu y_i + \nu z_i = 0,$$
any line which intersects two of them intersects the third. Thence deduce that the lines are three lines of a pencil.

132. Complexes, congruences, series. A *line complex* is a three-dimensional extent of lines. It may be, but is not necessarily, defined by a single equation which is satisfied by the coördinates of the lines of the complex. The *order* of a complex is the number of its lines which lie in an arbitrary plane and pass through an arbitrary point of the plane; that is, it is the number of the lines of the complex which belong to an arbitrary pencil.

A *line congruence* is a two-dimensional extent of lines. It may be defined by two simultaneous equations in line coördinates and is then composed of lines common to two complexes. The *order* of a congruence is the number of its lines which pass through an arbitrary point; its *class* is the number of its lines which lie in an arbitrary plane.

A line *series* is a one-dimensional extent of lines. It may be defined by three simultaneous equations in line coördinates. It then consists of lines common to three complexes. The *order* of a series is the number of its lines which intersect an arbitrary line.

An equation $\qquad f(x_1, x_2, x_3, x_4, x_5, x_6) = 0,$ (1)

where f is a homogeneous polynomial of the nth degree in x_i, defines a line complex of the nth order. Let a_i and b_i be any two fixed intersecting lines. Then $a_i + \lambda b_i$ is, by theorem I, § 131, a line of the pencil defined by a_i and b_i, and this line will belong to the complex (1) when λ satisfies the equation

$$f(a_1 + \lambda b_1,\ a_2 + \lambda b_2,\ a_3 + \lambda b_3,\ a_4 + \lambda b_4,\ a_5 + \lambda b_5,\ a_6 + \lambda b_6) = 0,$$

which is of the nth degree in λ.

From the above it follows that through any fixed point of space goes a configuration of lines such that n of these lines lie in each plane through the fixed point. Since the relation between the coördinates of the fixed point and those of any point on a line of the complex is an analytic one, derived from (1), it follows that *any point of space is the vertex of a cone of nth order formed by lines of the complex.*

Also if we consider a fixed plane, through every point of it go n lines of the complex. Since, as before, we have to do with an analytic equation, we infer that *in any plane the lines of a complex envelop a curve of the nth class.*

A simple example of a line complex is that which is composed of all lines which intersect a fixed line. For if a_i are the coördinates of a fixed line A, the condition that a line x_i should intersect A is, by § 130,

$$\xi(a, x) = 0,$$ (2)

which is a linear equation. Hence this complex is of the first order. In fact through an arbitrary point in an arbitrary plane goes obviously only one line intersecting A. Through a fixed point M goes a pencil of lines; namely, the lines through M in the plane determined by M and A. This is a cone of the first order. In any plane m goes a pencil of lines; namely, the lines through the point in which m intersects A. These form a line extent of the first class.

Another example of a line complex is one of second order defined by the equation

$$p_{12}^2 + p_{13}^2 + p_{14}^2 + p_{34}^2 + p_{42}^2 + p_{23}^2 = 0,$$ (3)

which, expressed in point coördinates, is

$$(x_1 y_2 - x_2 y_1)^2 + (x_1 y_3 - x_3 y_1)^2 + (x_1 y_4 - x_4 y_1)^2 + (x_3 y_4 - x_4 y_3)^2$$
$$+ (x_4 y_2 - x_2 y_4)^2 + (x_2 y_3 - x_3 y_2)^2 = 0.$$ (4)

This is not the equation of a surface, since it contains two sets of point coördinates. If, however, the coördinates y_i are fixed, (4) becomes the point equation of the cone of second order formed by lines of the complex through y_i.

If, dualistically, we express equation (3) in plane coördinates u_i and v_i and hold v_i fixed, we obtain a plane extent of second class in u_i which is intersected by the plane $v_i =$ const. in a line extent enveloping a curve of second class.

Through an arbitrary point in an arbitrary plane go two lines of the complex (3).

An example of a line congruence is that of lines intersecting two fixed lines. It is represented by two simultaneous equations similar to (2). It is of the first order, since through any point but one line can be passed intersecting the two fixed lines. It is of second class, since in a fixed plane only one line can be drawn intersecting the two fixed lines.

Another example of a line congruence consists of all lines through a point. This is of first order and zero class. Still another example consists of all lines in a plane. This is of zero order and first class.

An example of a line series is that of lines which intersect three fixed lines and is represented by three linear equations of the form (2). Such lines are one family of generators on a surface of second order (§ 96). The series is of second order, since any line in space meets two lines of the series.

133. The linear line complex. The equation

$$\alpha_1 x_1 + \alpha_2 x_2 + \alpha_3 x_3 + \alpha_4 x_4 + \alpha_5 x_5 + \alpha_6 x_6 = 0, \tag{1}$$

where x_i are general line coördinates, defines a linear line complex. An example of such a complex is, as we have seen, that which is composed of lines cutting a fixed line. Such a complex we call a *special linear line complex* or, more concisely, simply a *special complex*. The necessary and sufficient condition that (1) should represent a special complex is that the equation (1) should be equivalent to

$$\xi(x, y) = 0;$$

that is, that

$$\rho\alpha_i = \frac{\partial \xi}{\partial y_i}, \tag{2}$$

where y_i are the coördinates of a point and therefore satisfy the equation

$$\xi(y) = 0. \tag{3}$$

Equations (2) can be solved for y, since the discriminant of (3) does not vanish (§ 130). The results of the solution substituted in (3) give a relation of the form

$$\eta(\alpha) = 0, \qquad (4)$$

where $\eta(\alpha)$ is a homogeneous quadratic polynomial in α_i.

We sum up as follows:

I. A special linear complex is composed of straight lines which intersect a fixed line called the axis of the complex. A linear equation (1) *defines a special complex when and only when the coefficients* α_i *satisfy the quadratic equation* (4).

More in detail, let

$$\xi(y) = \sum a_{ik} y_i y_k, \qquad (a_{ki} = a_{ik}) \qquad (5)$$

Then equations (2) are

$$a_{i1}y_1 + a_{i2}y_2 + a_{i3}y_3 + a_{i4}y_4 + a_{i5}y_5 + a_{i6}y_6 = \rho\alpha_i, \qquad (6)$$

from which, together with (5), we have

$$\alpha_1 y_1 + \alpha_2 y_2 + \alpha_3 y_3 + \alpha_4 y_4 + \alpha_5 y_5 + \alpha_6 y_6 = 0. \qquad (7)$$

From (6) and (7) we obtain

$$\eta(\alpha) = \begin{vmatrix} a_{11} & a_{12} & a_{13} & a_{14} & a_{15} & a_{16} & \alpha_1 \\ a_{21} & a_{22} & a_{23} & a_{24} & a_{25} & a_{26} & \alpha_2 \\ a_{31} & a_{32} & a_{33} & a_{34} & a_{35} & a_{36} & \alpha_3 \\ a_{41} & a_{42} & a_{43} & a_{44} & a_{45} & a_{46} & \alpha_4 \\ a_{51} & a_{52} & a_{53} & a_{54} & a_{55} & a_{56} & \alpha_5 \\ a_{61} & a_{62} & a_{63} & a_{64} & a_{65} & a_{66} & \alpha_6 \\ \alpha_1 & \alpha_2 & \alpha_3 & \alpha_4 & \alpha_5 & \alpha_6 & 0 \end{vmatrix}$$

$$= \sum A_{ik}\alpha_i\alpha_k = 0,$$

where A_{ik} is the cofactor of a_{ik} in the expansion of $D = |a_{ik}|$.

Then $\quad \dfrac{\partial \eta}{\partial \alpha_i} = A_{i1}\alpha_1 + A_{i2}\alpha_2 + A_{i3}\alpha_3 + A_{i4}\alpha_4 + A_{i5}\alpha_5 + A_{i6}\alpha_6$

$$= \frac{D}{\rho} y_i,$$

the last result coming from the solution of equations (6) for y_i.

If we have Klein coördinates

$$\eta(\alpha) = \alpha_1^2 + \alpha_2^2 + \alpha_3^2 + \alpha_4^2 + \alpha_5^2 + \alpha_6^2,$$

$$\frac{\partial \eta}{\partial \alpha_i} = 2\alpha_i.$$

We may sum this up in the following theorem:

II. *The coördinates of the axis of the complex* (1) *when it is special are* $\dfrac{\partial \eta}{\partial \alpha_i}$. *If Klein coördinates are used, the coördinates of the axis of a special complex are the coefficients in the equation of the complex.*

Returning to the general linear complex (1) (special or non-special), consider any point P. If a_i, b_i, and c_i are any three lines through P not in the same plane, then (theorem II, § 131) any line through P has coördinates $a_i + \lambda b_i + \mu c_i$, and this line belongs to the complex when

$$\sum \alpha_i a_i + \lambda \sum \alpha_i b_i + \mu \sum \alpha_i c_i = 0. \qquad (8)$$

Equation (8) is satisfied for all values of λ and μ if the three lines a_i, b_i, and c_i belong to the complex. Otherwise, assuming that c_i does not belong to the complex, we may solve (8) for μ and write the coördinates of the point x_i in the form

$$\rho x_i = (a_i \sum \alpha_i c_i - c_i \sum \alpha_i a_i) + \lambda (b_i \sum \alpha_i c_i - c_i \sum \alpha_i b_i)$$
$$= a_i' + \lambda b_i',$$

where a_i^r and b_i' are two definitely defined lines through P, and λ is arbitrary. This proves the following theorem:

III. *Through any arbitrary point in space goes a pencil of lines of the complex unless in an exceptional manner all lines through the point belong to the complex.*

The analysis would be the same if the three lines a_i, b_i, and c_i were taken as three lines in a plane, but not through the same point (theorem III, § 131). Hence

IV. *In any arbitrary plane in space lies a pencil of lines of the complex unless in an exceptional manner all lines of the plane belong to the complex.*

To complete the information given by these two theorems we shall prove the two following:

V. *If all lines through any one point P belong to the complex, the complex is special and the point P lies on the axis of the complex.*

Let all lines through P (Fig. 56) be lines of the complex. Take h, a line not belonging to the complex, and let Q and R be two points of h. Through Q goes, by theorem III, a pencil of lines of the complex of which PQ is evidently one and h is not. Similarly, through R goes a pencil of lines of the complex of which RP is one and h is not. These two pencils lie in different planes, for if

they lay in the same plane the line h would lie in both pencils and be a line of the complex, contrary to hypothesis. The planes of the pencils intersect in a line which contains P. Call it c, and let S be any point on c.

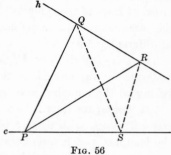

FIG. 56

The line SP belongs to the complex, since, by hypothesis, all lines through P are lines of the complex. The line SQ belongs to the complex, since it lies in the plane of the pencil with the vertex Q and passes through Q. Similarly, the line SR belongs to the complex.

Therefore we have, through the point S, three lines of the complex which are not coplanar, since c and h are not in the same plane. Hence, by theorem III, all lines through S belong to the complex. But S is any point of c, and since all lines which intersect c form a complex, the theorem is proved.

VI. *If all lines of a plane belong to the complex, the complex is special and the plane passes through the axis of the complex.*

Let all lines of a plane m (Fig. 57) belong to the complex. Take h, any line not of the complex, and let q and r be two planes through h, intersect-

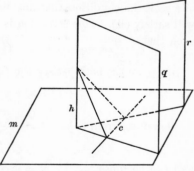

FIG. 57

ing m in the lines mq and mr. In the plane q lies, by theorem IV, a pencil of lines of the complex of which mq is one and h is not. Similarly, in the plane r lies a pencil of lines of the complex of which mr is one and h is not. These pencils have different vertices, for otherwise they would contain h. Let c be the line connecting the vertices (c, of course, lies in m). Take s, any plane through c intersecting q in the line qs and r in the line rs.

Then c is a line of the complex, since by hypothesis any line in m belongs to the complex. Also qs and rs belong to the complex, since each is a line of a pencil which has been shown to be composed of lines of the complex. The three lines do not pass through the same point because qm and rm have been shown to intersect c in different points.

Therefore, by theorem IV, all lines in s belong to the complex, and since s was any plane through c, all lines which intersect c belong to the complex, and the theorem is proved.

134. Conjugate lines. Two lines are said to be *conjugate*, or *reciprocal polars*, with respect to a line complex when every line of the complex which intersects one of the two lines intersects the other also. Let the equation of the complex in Klein coördinates be

$$a_1x_1 + a_2x_2 + a_3x_3 + a_4x_4 + a_5x_5 + a_6x_6 = 0, \tag{1}$$

and let y_i and z_i be the coördinates of any two lines. The conditions that a line x_i intersect y_i and z_i are respectively

$$y_1x_1 + y_2x_2 + y_3x_3 + y_4x_4 + y_5x_5 + y_6x_6 = 0, \tag{2}$$

$$z_1x_1 + z_2x_2 + z_3x_3 + z_4x_4 + z_5x_5 + z_6x_6 = 0. \tag{3}$$

We seek the condition that any line x_i which satisfies (1) and (2) will satisfy (3). This condition is that a quantity λ shall be found such that

$$\rho z_i = y_i + \lambda a_i. \qquad (i = 1, 2, 3, 4, 5, 6) \tag{4}$$

But y_i and z_i both satisfy the fundamental relation

$$x_1^2 + x_2^2 + x_3^2 + x_4^2 + x_5^2 + x_6^2 = 0.$$

Therefore, from (4), $\lambda = -\dfrac{2\sum a_i y_i}{\sum a_i^2}$, $\tag{5}$

and (4) becomes $\rho z_i = y_i - \dfrac{2\sum a_i y_i}{\sum a_i^2} a_i$, $\tag{6}$

which define the coördinates z_i of the conjugate line of any line y_i.

From (5) follows at once the theorem:

I. Any line has a unique conjugate with respect to any nonspecial complex.

If the line y_i belongs to the complex, then $\sum a_i y_i = 0$ and $\rho z_i = y_i$. Hence

II. *Any line of a nonspecial complex is its own conjugate.*

If the complex is special, $\sum a_i^2 = 0$. Therefore, unless also $\sum a_i y_i = 0$, $\lambda = \infty$ and $\rho z_i = a_i$. Hence

III. *The axis of a special complex is the conjugate of any line not belonging to the complex.*

If the complex is special and the line y_i belongs to it, λ is indeterminate. Hence

IV. *A line of a special complex has no determinate conjugate.*

The above theorems may also be proved easily by purely geometric methods.

If two lines have coördinates y_i and z_i which satisfy equations (6), then any values of x_i which satisfy (2) and (3) will also satisfy (1). Hence

V. *If two lines are conjugate with respect to a complex, any line which intersects both of them belongs to the complex.*

From this theorem or from the relations (6) follows at once:

VI. *Two lines conjugate with respect to a nonspecial complex do not intersect.*

We have seen (theorem IV, § 133) that in any plane m there is a unique point P which is the vertex of the pencil of complex lines in m. Similarly, through any point P goes a plane m which contains the pencil of complex lines through P. When a point and plane are so related, the point is called the *pole* of the plane, and the plane is called the *polar* of the point.

If g and h are two conjugate lines with respect to a complex, and P is any point on g, the pencil of lines from P to points on h is made up of complex lines by theorem V. Hence follow the theorems:

VII. *The polar plane of a point P on a line g is the plane determined by P and the conjugate line h. As P moves along g the polar plane turns about h.*

VIII. *The pole of any plane m through a line g is the intersection of m with the conjugate line h. As m turns about g its pole traverses h.*

135. Complexes in point coördinates. It is interesting and instructive to consider the linear complex with the use of point coördinates.

A linear equation in general line coördinates

$$\sum a_i x_i = 0 \tag{1}$$

is equivalent to a linear equation

$$\sum a_{ik} p_{ik} = 0 \qquad (a_{ii} = 0,\ a_{ki} = -a_{ik}) \tag{2}$$

in p_{ik} coördinates, and this, again, can be expressed as a bilinear equation in point coördinates:

$$\sum a_{ik}(x_i y_k - x_k y_i) = 0. \tag{3}$$

If in equation (3) we place y_i equal to constants, the equation becomes that of a plane m of which y_i is the pole.

The plane coördinates of this plane are

$$\begin{aligned}
\rho u_1 &= \phantom{-a_{12}y_1} a_{12}y_2 + a_{13}y_3 + a_{14}y_4, \\
\rho u_2 &= -a_{12}y_1 \phantom{+a_{13}y_3} + a_{23}y_3 - a_{42}y_4, \\
\rho u_3 &= -a_{13}y_1 - a_{23}y_2 \phantom{+a_{23}y_3} + a_{34}y_4, \\
\rho u_4 &= -a_{14}y_1 + a_{42}y_2 - a_{34}y_3,
\end{aligned} \tag{4}$$

and to each point y_i corresponds a unique plane unless

$$\begin{vmatrix}
0 & a_{12} & a_{13} & a_{14} \\
-a_{12} & 0 & a_{23} & -a_{42} \\
-a_{13} & -a_{23} & 0 & a_{34} \\
-a_{14} & a_{42} & -a_{34} & 0
\end{vmatrix} = 0;$$

that is, unless $\quad (a_{12}a_{34} + a_{13}a_{42} + a_{14}a_{23})^2 = 0.$

But $a_{12}a_{34} + a_{13}a_{42} + a_{14}a_{23}$ is the form which $\eta(\alpha)$ takes for the p_{ik} coördinates. Hence we have a verification of the fact that in a nonspecial complex any plane has a unique pole.

Let us take two conjugate lines as the edges AB ($x_1 = 0,\ x_2 = 0$), and CD ($x_3 = 0,\ x_4 = 0$) of the tetrahedron of reference for the point coördinates. This can always be done by a collineation which obviously amounts to a linear substitution of the line coördinates.

If $0 : 0 : y_3 : y_4$ is a point P on AB, its polar plane is, by (3),

$$a_{13}x_1 y_3 + a_{14}x_1 y_4 + a_{34}(x_3 y_4 - x_4 y_3) - a_{42}x_2 y_4 + a_{23}x_2 y_3 = 0.$$

This plane must pass through CD for all values of y_3 and y_4. Hence $a_{13} = a_{14} = a_{42} = a_{23} = 0$, and the line complex reduces to

$$a_{12}p_{12} + a_{34}p_{34} = 0, \qquad (5)$$

where neither of the coefficients can be zero if the complex is nonspecial.

It is possible to make the ratio $a_{12} : a_{34}$ equal to -1 by a collineation of space. To see this, note that if we place

$$x_1' = a_{12}x_1, \quad x_3' = -a_{34}x_3, \quad x_2' = x_2, \quad x_4' = x_4,$$

$$y_1' = a_{12}y_1, \quad y_3' = -a_{34}y_3, \quad y_2' = y_2, \quad y_4' = y_4,$$

then $p_{12}' = a_{12}p_{12}$, and $p_{34}' = -a_{34}p_{34}$, and the equation of the complex becomes

$$p_{12}' - p_{34}' = 0. \qquad (6)$$

Consider now a special complex, and let its axis be taken as the line AB ($x_1 = 0$, $x_2 = 0$), the line coördinates of which are $p_{12} = p_{13} = p_{14} = p_{42} = p_{23} = 0$. The condition that a line should intersect this line is, by (1), § 129,

$$p_{12} = 0. \qquad (7)$$

We may sum up in the following theorem:

By a projective transformation of space the equation of any special complex may be brought into the form

$$p_{12} = 0$$

and that of any nonspecial complex into the form

$$p_{12} - p_{34} = 0.$$

136. Complexes in Cartesian coördinates. We shall now consider the properties and equations of line complexes with the use of Cartesian coördinates $x : y : z : t$, by which the plane at infinity is unique and metrical properties come into evidence.

For special complexes we have two cases, according as the axis is or is not at infinity. In the former case the lines which intersect it are parallel to a fixed plane. Hence

In Cartesian geometry the special line complex consists either of all lines which intersect a fixed line or of all lines which are parallel to a fixed plane.

Consider a nonspecial complex. In the plane at infinity is a unique point I, the pole of the plane. The lines of space which pass through I form a set of parallel lines not belonging to the complex. These are called the *diameters* of the complex. Each diameter is conjugate to a line at infinity, since the conjugate to a diameter must meet all the pencil of lines of the complex whose vertex is I. Conversely, any line at infinity not through I has a diameter as its conjugate. In other words, *the polar planes of points on a diameter are parallel planes, and the poles of any pencil of parallel planes lie on a diameter.*

Consider now the pencil of parallel planes formed by planes which are perpendicular to the diameters. Their poles lie in a diameter which is unique. *Therefore there is in each nonspecial complex a unique diameter, called the axis, which has the property of being perpendicular to the polar planes of all points in it.*

Referring to (4), § 135, if we replace $x_1 : x_2 : x_3 : x_4$ by $x : y : z : t$, the pole of the plane at infinity is given by the equations

$$a_{12}y + a_{13}z + a_{14}t = 0,$$
$$- a_{12}x \qquad\quad + a_{23}z - a_{42}t = 0,$$
$$- a_{13}x - a_{23}y \qquad\quad + a_{34}t = 0,$$

which have the solution

$$x : y : z : t = a_{23} : - a_{13} : a_{12} : 0. \tag{1}$$

Any line through the point (1) is therefore a diameter, and if (x_1, y_1, z_1) is any finite point of space, the equation of the diameter through it is

$$\frac{x - x_1}{a_{23}} = \frac{y - y_1}{- a_{13}} = \frac{z - z_1}{a_{12}}.$$

The polar plane of (x_1, y_1, z_1) is, by (4), § 135,

$$(a_{12}y_1 + a_{13}z_1 + a_{14})x + (- a_{12}x_1 + a_{23}z_1 - a_{42})y$$
$$+ (- a_{13}x_1 - a_{23}y_1 + a_{34})z + (- a_{14}x_1 + a_{42}y_1 - a_{34}z_1) = 0. \tag{2}$$

The line (1) is perpendicular to the plane (2) when

$$\frac{a_{12}y_1 + a_{13}z_1 + a_{14}}{a_{23}} = \frac{- a_{12}x_1 + a_{23}z_1 - a_{42}}{- a_{13}} = \frac{- a_{13}x_1 - a_{23}y_1 + a_{34}z_1}{a_{12}}. \tag{3}$$

Consequently, if (x_1, y_1, z_1) in (3) are replaced by variable coördinates (x, y, z), equation (3) becomes the Cartesian *equation of the axis* of the complex.

Let us take this axis as the axis of z. Then, from (1), $a_{23} = 0$, $a_{13} = 0$, and, from (3), since the origin of coördinates is on the axis, $a_{14} = 0$, $a_{42} = 0$. The equation of the complex is then

$$a_{12}p_{12} + a_{34}p_{34} = 0, \tag{4}$$

which agrees with (5), § 135.

In Cartesian coördinates equation (4) is

$$xy' - x'y + k(z - z') = 0, \tag{5}$$

which associates to any point (x', y', z') its polar plane.

From (5) it is obvious that the polar plane of $P(x', y', z')$ contains the line $xy' - x'y = 0$, $z = z'$, which is the line through P perpendicular to the axis. The normal to the plane makes with the axis the angle $\cos^{-1} \dfrac{k}{\sqrt{x'^2 + y'^2 + k^2}} = \tan^{-1} \dfrac{\sqrt{x'^2 + y'^2}}{k} = \tan^{-1} \dfrac{r}{k}$, where r is the distance from P to the axis. This leads to the following result:

The polar plane of any point P contains the line through P perpendicular to the axis. If P is on the axis, its polar plane is perpendicular to the axis. As P recedes from the axis along a line perpendicular to it, the normal plane turns about this perpendicular, the direction and amount of rotation depending upon the sign and the value of k. If P moves along a line parallel to the axis, its polar plane moves parallel to itself.

Any line of a complex may be defined by a point (x, y, z) and its neighboring point $(x + dx, y + dy, z + dz)$. If in (5) we place $x' = x + dx$, $y' = y + dy$, $z' = z + dz$, we have

$$x\,dy - y\,dx - k\,dz = 0, \tag{6}$$

which may be called the *differential equation of the complex.*

Equation (6) is of the type called nonintegrable, in the sense that no solution of the form $f(x, y, z, c) = 0$ can be found for it. It is satisfied, however, in the first place, by straight lines whose equations are

$$z = c, \qquad y = mx. \tag{7}$$

In the second place, on any cylinder with the equation

$$x^2 + y^2 = a^2 \tag{8}$$

may be found curves whose direction at any point satisfies (6).

For the direction of any curve on (8) satisfies the equation

$$x\,dx + y\,dy = 0,$$

and this equation combined with (6) gives the solution

$$x^2 + y^2 = a^2, \qquad z = \frac{a^2}{k}\tan^{-1}\frac{y}{x} + c, \tag{9}$$

which are the equations of helixes with the pitch $\dfrac{2\,\pi a^2}{k}$.

It appears from the preceding that any tangent line to a helix of the form (9) is a straight line of the complex. We shall now prove, conversely, that any line of the complex, excepting only the lines (7), is tangent to such a helix.

Since z is assumed not to be constant, we may take the equation of any line not in the form (7) as

$$x = mz + b, \qquad y = nz + p, \tag{10}$$

with the condition $bn - pm = k$, which is necessary and sufficient in order that equations (10) should satisfy (6).

The distance of a point (x_1, y_1, z_1) on (10) from OZ is

$$\sqrt{x_1^2 + y_1^2} = \sqrt{(m^2 + n^2)z_1^2 + 2(mb + np)z_1 + b^2 + p^2}.$$

It is easily computed that this distance is a minimum when

$$z_1 = -\frac{mb + np}{m^2 + n^2}, \quad x_1 = \frac{nk}{m^2 + n^2}, \quad y_1 = -\frac{mk}{m^2 + n^2}.$$

The minimum distance is $\dfrac{k}{\sqrt{m^2 + n^2}}$, which we shall take as a in the equations of the helix (9). The direction of the helix at the point (x_1, y_1, z_1) is

$$dx : dy : dz = -y_1 : x_1 : \frac{a^2}{k} = m : n : 1.$$

This is the direction of the line (10), and our proposition is proved. We have, therefore, the following theorem:

A linear nonspecial complex may be considered as made up of the tangents to the helixes drawn upon cylinders whose axes coincide with the axis of the complex, the pitch of each helix being $\dfrac{2\,\pi a^2}{k}$, where a is the radius of the cylinder and k the parameter of the complex.

137. The bilinear equation in point coördinates. The equation

$$\sum a_{ik}x_iy_k = 0 \tag{1}$$

is the most general equation which is linear in each of the two sets of point coördinates $(x_1: x_2: x_3: x_4)$ and $(y_1: y_2: y_3: y_4)$.

By means of (1) a definite plane is associated to each point y_i, its equation being obtained by holding y_i constant in (1). Similarly, to each point x_i is associated a definite plane.

In this book we have met two important examples of equation (1).

I. $a_{ki} = a_{ik}$. Equation (1) then associates to each point y_i its polar plane with respect to the quadric surface

$$\sum a_{ik}x_ix_k = 0.$$

The pole does not in general lie in its polar plane. Exceptions occur only when the pole is on the quadric.

II. $a_{ki} = -a_{ik}$; whence $a_{ii} = 0$. Equation (1) associates to each point y_i its polar plane with respect to the line complex

$$\sum a_{ik}p_{ik} = 0.$$

The point y_i always lies in its polar plane. This association of point and plane forms a *null system*, mentioned in § 102, and here connected with the line complex.

EXERCISES

1. Prove that a complex is determined by any five lines, provided that they are intersected by no line.

2. Prove that a complex is determined by a pair of conjugate lines and any line not intersecting these two.

3. Prove that a complex is determined by two pairs of conjugate lines.

4. Prove that if a line describes a plane pencil its conjugate also describes a plane pencil, and if a line describes a quadric surface its conjugate does also.

5. Prove that a complex (or null system) is in general determined by any three points and their polar planes.

6. Prove that any two pairs of polar lines lie on the same quadric surface.

7. Prove that the conjugate to the axis of a nonspecial complex is the polar with respect to the imaginary circle at infinity of the pole of the plane at infinity with respect to the complex.

138. The linear line congruence. Two simultaneous linear equations in line coördinates,

$$\sum \alpha_i x_i = 0, \qquad \sum \beta_i x_i = 0, \tag{1}$$

define a congruence. Evidently equations (1) are satisfied by all lines common to two linear complexes. But all lines which belong to the two complexes defined by equations (1) belong also to all complexes of the pencil

$$\sum (\alpha_i + \lambda \beta_i) x_i = 0, \tag{2}$$

and the congruence can be defined by any two complexes obtained by giving λ two values in (2).

A complex defined by (2) is special when

$$\eta (\alpha_i + \lambda \beta_i) = 0 \ ;$$

that is, when $\quad \eta (\alpha) + 2 \lambda \eta (\alpha, \ \beta) + \lambda^2 \eta (\beta) = 0. \tag{3}$

In general equation (3) has two distinct roots. Hence we have the theorem:

In general the linear congruence consists of straight lines which intersect two fixed straight lines.

The two fixed lines are called the *directrices* of the congruence. The directrices are evident conjugate lines with respect to any nonspecial complex defined by equation (2).

If the roots of equation (3) are equal, the congruence has only one directrix and is called a *special congruence*. This congruence consists of lines which intersect the directrix and also belong to a nonspecial complex. It is clear that the directrix must be a line of this nonspecial complex, for otherwise it would have a conjugate line and the congruence would be nonspecial. Hence *a special congruence consists of lines which intersect a fixed line and such that through any point of the fixed line goes a pencil of congruence lines, the fixed line being in all cases a line of the pencil.*

As the vertex of the pencil moves along the directrix, the plane of the pencil turns about the directrix.

We have seen that a nonspecial congruence may be defined by its directrices. If the directrices intersect, the congruence separates into two sets of lines, one being all lines in the plane of the directrices (a congruence of first order and zero class), and the other being all lines through the point of intersection of the directrices (a congruence of zero order and first class).

When the directrices do not intersect, the congruence is one of first order and first class.

139. The cylindroid. We have seen that every linear complex has an axis. In a pencil of linear complexes given by equation (2), § 138, there are, therefore, ∞^1 axes which form a surface called *a cylindroid.* We may find the equation of the cylindroid in the following manner:

Let us take as the axis OZ the line which is perpendicular to the directrices of the two special complexes of the pencil, as the origin O the point halfway between the two directrices, as the plane XOY the plane parallel to the two directrices, and as OX and OY the lines in this plane which bisect the angles between the two directrices. That is, we have so chosen the axes of references that the equations of the two directrices of the special complexes of the pencil are

$$y - mx = 0, \qquad z = c, \tag{1}$$

and

$$y + mx = 0, \qquad z = -c, \tag{2}$$

respectively.

The Plücker coördinates of the line (1), which may be determined by the points $(0, 0, c)$ and $(1, m, c)$, are

$$p_{12}^{(1)} = 0, \quad p_{13}^{(1)} = -c, \quad p_{14}^{(1)} = -1, \quad p_{23}^{(1)} = -mc, \quad p_{42}^{(1)} = m, \quad p_{34}^{(1)} = 0,$$

and the special complex with this axis is therefore, by (1), § 129,

$$mp_{13} - mcp_{14} - p_{23} - cp_{42} = 0.$$

Similarly, the coördinates of (2) are

$$p_{12}^{(2)} = 0, \quad p_{13}^{(2)} = c, \quad p_{14}^{(2)} = -1, \quad p_{23}^{(2)} = -mc, \quad p_{42}^{(2)} = -m, \quad p_{34}^{(2)} = 0,$$

and the special complex with this axis is

$$-mp_{13} - mcp_{14} - p_{23} + cp_{42} = 0.$$

The pencil of complexes is therefore

$$(1 - \lambda)mp_{13} - (1 + \lambda)mcp_{14} - (1 + \lambda)p_{23} + (1 - \lambda)cp_{42} = 0.$$

By (3), § 136, the equations of the axis of any complex of the pencil are

$$\frac{(1-\lambda)\,mz-(1+\lambda)\,mc}{-(1+\lambda)} = \frac{-(1+\lambda)\,z+(1-\lambda)\,c}{-(1-\lambda)\,m}$$

$$= \frac{(1-\lambda)\,mx-(1+\lambda)\,y}{0},$$

which reduce to $\qquad\qquad y = \dfrac{1-\lambda}{1+\lambda}\,mx,$

$$[(1-\lambda)^2 m^2+(1+\lambda)^2]\,z = (1-\lambda^2)\,(1+m^2)\,c.$$

If we eliminate λ from these equations, we have

$$(x^2+y^2)\,z + \frac{(1+m^2)\,c}{m}\,xy = 0, \tag{3}$$

which is the required equation of the cylindroid.

The equations show that the surface is a cubic surface with OZ as a double line. All lines on the surface are perpendicular to OZ, and in any plane perpendicular to OZ there are two lines on the surface which are distinct, coincident, or imaginary according as the distance of the plane from O is less than, equal to, or greater than $\dfrac{(1+m^2)\,c}{2\,m}$.

We may put the equation of the cylindroid in another form. We shall denote by $2\,\alpha$ the angle between the directrices of the special complexes of the pencil, by θ the angle which any straight line on the cylindroid makes with OX, and by r the distance of that line from O. Then $m = \tan\alpha$, and $\dfrac{1-\lambda}{1+\lambda}\,m = \tan\theta$.

Equation (3) then becomes

$$r = c\,\frac{\sin 2\,\theta}{\sin 2\,\alpha}.$$

140. The linear line series. Consider three independent linear equations $\qquad \sum \alpha_i x_i = 0, \qquad \sum \beta_i x_i = 0, \qquad \sum \gamma_i x_i = 0. \tag{1}$

These equations are satisfied by the coördinates of lines which are common to the three complexes defined by the individual equations in (1) and define a line *series*. Any line of the series also belongs to each complex of the set given by the equation

$$\sum (\lambda \alpha_i + \mu \beta_i + \nu \gamma_i)\,x_i = 0, \tag{2}$$

and any three linearly independent equations formed from (2) by giving to λ, μ, and ν definite values determine the same line series that is determined by (2).

A complex of the type (2) is special when

$$\eta(\lambda\alpha + \mu\beta + \nu\gamma) = \lambda^2\eta(\alpha) + \mu^2\eta(\beta) + \nu^2\eta(\gamma) + 2\lambda\mu\eta(\alpha, \beta)$$
$$+ 2\mu\nu\eta(\beta, \gamma) + 2\nu\lambda\eta(\gamma, \alpha) = 0. \quad (3)$$

There are a singly infinite number of solutions of equation (3) in the ratios $\lambda : \mu : \nu$. Hence the lines which are defined by equations (1) intersect an infinite number of straight lines, the axes of the special complexes defined by (2) and (3). These lines are called the *directrices*.

The arrangement of the directrices depends upon the nature of equation (3). In studying that equation we may temporarily interpret $\lambda : \mu : \nu$ as homogeneous point coördinates of a point in a plane and classify equation (3) as in § 35.

Let us place

$$D = \begin{vmatrix} \eta(\alpha) & \eta(\alpha, \beta) & \eta(\alpha, \gamma) \\ \eta(\alpha, \beta) & \eta(\beta) & \eta(\beta, \gamma) \\ \eta(\alpha, \gamma) & \eta(\beta, \gamma) & \eta(\gamma) \end{vmatrix}.$$

CASE I. $D \neq 0$. This is the general case. Equation (3), interpreted as an equation in point coördinates $\lambda : \mu : \nu$, is that of a conic without singular points. To any point on this conic corresponds a special complex of the type (2) whose axis is a directrix of the series (1). To simplify our equations we shall assume that the coördinates x_i are Klein coördinates. Then (by theorem II, § 133) if $(\lambda_1 : \mu_1 : \nu_1)$ and $(\lambda_2 : \mu_2 : \nu_2)$ are two solutions of equation (2), the axes of the corresponding special complexes, or, in other words, the corresponding directrices of the series (1), are $\lambda_1\alpha_i + \mu_1\beta_i + \nu_1\gamma_i$ and $\lambda_2\alpha_i + \mu_2\beta_i + \nu_2\gamma_i$.

The condition that these two directrices intersect is

$$\eta(\lambda_1\alpha + \mu_1\beta + \nu_1\gamma, \ \lambda_2\alpha + \mu_2\beta + \nu_2\gamma) = 0,$$

which is exactly the same as the condition that each of the two points $(\lambda_1 : \mu_1 : \nu_1)$ and $(\lambda_2 : \mu_2 : \nu_2)$ should lie on the polar of the other with respect to the conic (3). This is impossible, since each of the points lies on the conic. It follows from this that *no two directrices intersect*.

From this it will also follow that *no two lines of the given series intersect*, for if they did each directrix must either lie in their plane or pass through their common point, and some of the directrices would intersect.

The lines of the series (1), on the one hand, and their directrices, on the other, form, therefore, two families of lines such that no two lines of the same family intersect, but each line of one family intersects all lines of the other. This suggests the two families of generators on a quadric surface. That the configuration is really that of a quadric surface follows from the theorem that the locus of lines which intersect three nonintersecting straight lines is a quadric surface (see Ex. 6, p. 327).

We sum up in the following words:

In the general case $(D \neq 0)$ *the lines which are common to three linear complexes form one family of generators of a quadric surface, their directrices forming the second family.*

A family of generators of a quadric surface is called a *regulus*.

CASE II. $D = 0$, but not all the first minors are zero. The curve of second order defined by (3) reduces to two intersecting straight lines and, by a linear substitution, can be reduced to the form

$$\lambda\mu = 0.$$

To do that we must define the series by three complexes such that $\eta(\alpha) = 0$, $\eta(\beta) = 0$, $\eta(c) = 0$, $\eta(b, c) = 0$, $\eta(a, c) = 0$, $\eta(\alpha, \beta) \neq 0$.

These are three special complexes such that the axes of the first two do not intersect, but the axis of the third intersects each of the axes of the first two. The axes lie, therefore, as in Fig. 58. The series consists, therefore, of two pencils of lines: one lying in the

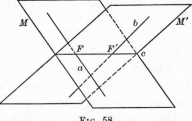

FIG. 58

plane of a and c, with its vertex at F', the point of intersection of b and c; the other lying in the plane of b and c, with its vertex at F, the intersection of a and c.

CASE III. $D = 0$, all the first minors are zero, but not all the second minors are zero. The conic defined by (3) consists of two coincident lines. Its equation may be made $\nu^2 = 0$.

We have then taken to define the series three complexes of which two are special with intersecting axes, and the third is nonspecial and contains the axis of the other two.

If a and b are the two axes of the special complexes, F their point of intersection, and m their common plane, then, since the nonspecial complex contains a and b, F is the pole of m with respect to that complex. Hence the lines common to the two complexes form a pencil of lines which must be taken double to preserve the order of the complex.

CASE IV. The case in which all the second minors of D vanish is inadmissible, for in that case the three complexes in (1) are special and their axes intersect. Then, from § 131, $\gamma_i = \alpha_i + \nu\beta_i$, and the three equations (1) are not independent.

EXERCISES

Two complexes $\sum a_i x_i = 0$ and $\sum b_i x_i = 0$ are in *involution* when $\eta(a, b) = 0$.

1. Prove that if p is a line common to two complexes in involution the correspondence of planes through p, which can be set up by taking as corresponding planes the two polar planes of each point of p with respect to the two complexes, is an involution.

2. Prove that two special complexes are in involution when their axes intersect.

3. Prove that a special complex is in involution with a nonspecial complex when the axis of the former is a line of the latter.

4. Prove that if two nonspecial complexes are in involution there exist two lines, g and h, which are conjugate with respect to the two and such that the polar planes of any point P are harmonic conjugates with respect to the two planes through P and g and through P and h respectively, and also such that the poles of any plane m with respect to the two complexes are harmonic conjugates to the points in which m meets g and h.

5. Prove that the six complexes $x_i = 0$, where x_i are Klein coördinates, are two by two in involution. Hence prove by a transformation of coördinates that there exists an infinite number of such sets of six complexes mutually in involution.

6. Prove that the locus of lines which intersect three nonintersecting lines is a quadric surface, by using Plücker coördinates and eliminating one set of point coördinates.

141. The quadratic line complex. A quadratic line complex is defined by an equation of the form

$$\sum a_{ik}x_i x_k = 0. \qquad (a_{ki} = a_{ik})$$

We .shall consider only the general case in which the above equation can be reduced to the form

$$\sum c_i x_i^2 = 0, \qquad (c_i \neq 0) \tag{1}$$

at the same time that the coördinates x_i are Klein coördinates satisfying the fundamental relation

$$\sum x_i^2 = 0. \tag{2}$$

Let us consider any fixed line y_i of the complex and any linear complex

$$\sum a_i x_i = 0, \tag{3}$$

containing y_i. In general the complex (3) will have two lines through any point P in common with (1), for P is at the same time the vertex of a pencil of lines of (3) and of a cone of lines of (1).

Analytically, we take P, a point on y_i, and z_i, any line of (3), but not of (1), through P. Then any line of the pencil determined by y_i and z_i is

$$\rho x_i = y_i + \lambda z_i,$$

and this line always belongs to (3), but belongs to (1) when and only when

$$2\lambda \sum c_i y_i z_i + \lambda^2 \sum c_i^2 z_i^2 = 0.$$

This gives in general two values of λ, of which one, $\lambda = 0$, determines the line y_i and the other determines a different line. But the two values of λ both become zero, and the line y_i is the only line through P common to (1) and (3) when

$$\sum c_i y_i z_i = 0 ;$$

that is, when z_i has been chosen as any line of the linear complex

$$\sum c_i y_i x_i = 0. \tag{4}$$

In this case the polar plane of P with respect to (4) is tangent to the complex cone of (1) at P, where P is any point whatever of y_i. The complex (4) is accordingly called the *tangent linear complex at y_i.* It is often said that the tangent linear complex contains all lines of the complex (1) which are consecutive to y_i, since any line with coördinates $y_i + dy_i$ satisfies (4). The discussion we have given makes this notion more precise.

More generally we have at y_i a pencil of tangent linear complexes. For by virtue of (2) the complex (1) may be written

$$\sum (c_i + \mu) x_i^2 = 0, \qquad (5)$$

where μ is any constant, and the tangent linear complex to (5) is

$$\sum (c_i + \mu) y_i x_i = 0. \qquad (6)$$

All these complexes have the same polar plane at any point P of y_i.

If y_i is not a line of the complex, equation (6) defines a pencil of *polar linear complexes*.

The line y_i is called a *singular line* when the tangent linear complex (4) is special. The condition for this is

$$\sum c_i^2 y_i^2 = 0, \qquad (7)$$

which says that $c_i y_i$ are the coördinates of a line, the axis of the tangent complex. At the same time all the complexes (6) are special and have the same axis.

This axis intersects y_i, since $\sum c_i y_i^2 = 0$ (because y_i is a line of the complex), and the intersection of the two lines is called a *singular point*, and their plane a *singular plane*. Any complex line y_i for which condition (7) holds is called a *singular line*.

Let P be a singular point on a singular line y_i, let z_i be any line through P, and consider the pencil of lines

$$\rho x_i = y_i + \lambda z_i. \qquad (8)$$

The condition that x_i belong to (1) is

$$\lambda^2 \sum c_i z_i^2 = 0, \qquad (9)$$

since $\sum c_i y_i^2 = 0$, because y_i is on (1), and $\sum c_i y_i z_i = 0$, because z_i intersects $c_i y_i$ at P. Then if z_i is a line of (1), all lines of the pencil (8) belong to (1). On the other hand, if z_i is any line not belonging to the complex (1), the line y_i is the only line in the plane $(y_i z_i)$ which belongs to the complex. This makes it evident that *at a singular point the complex cone splits up into two plane pencils intersecting in the singular line.*

In a similar manner we may take p as a singular plane through a singular line y_i, z_i, any line in p intersecting y_i, and again consider the pencil (8). We obtain again (9), but the interpretation is now that if z_i is any complex line in p, there is a pencil of lines in p with vertex on y_i. Consequently *in a singular plane the complex conic splits up into two pencils to which the singular line is common.*

We shall now show that *any point at which the complex cone splits into two pencils is a singular point and any plane in which the complex conic splits into two pencils is a singular plane.*

Let A be such a point, and let the two pencils be $a_i + \lambda b_i$ and $a_i + \mu e_i$. Then

$$\sum_i c_i a_i^2 = 0, \qquad \sum_i c_i a_i b_i = 0, \qquad \sum_i c_i a_i e_i = 0. \tag{10}$$

The tangent complex at a_i contains a_i, b_i, and e_i by (10). Therefore, by theorem V, § 133, it is special, and the point A lies on its axis. Hence A is a singular point. The second part of the theorem is similarly proved.

Now let a_i and b_i be two intersecting complex lines. Then

$$\sum_i a_i^2 = 0, \quad \sum_i b_i^2 = 0, \quad \sum_i a_i b_i = 0, \quad \sum_i c_i a_i^2 = 0, \quad \sum_i c_i b_i^2 = 0. \tag{11}$$

If the pencil $a_i + \lambda b_i$ belongs entirely to the complex we have also

$$\sum_i c_i a_i b_i = 0. \tag{12}$$

We shall fix a_i and take as b_i that line of the pencil which intersects a fixed line d_i which does not intersect a_i. Then

$$\sum_i b_i d_i = 0, \qquad \sum_i a_i d_i \neq 0. \tag{13}$$

To determine b_i we have five equations of which three are linear and two quadratic. There are therefore in general four sets of values of b_i, so that *on any line of the complex there are in general four singular points.*

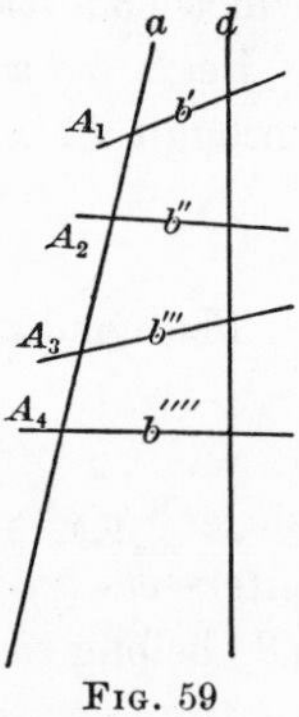

Let the four points be A_1, A_2, A_3, A_4 (Fig. 59) and the four lines be b', b'', b''', b''''. Then each of the planes (ab'), (ab''), (ab'''), (ab'''') contains a pencil of lines and hence a second one distinct or coincident. Therefore *through any line on the complex there are four singular planes.*

FIG. 59

Since the coördinates of the four lines b_i satisfy three linear equations, the lines belong in general to a regulus (§ 140) and do not intersect. Therefore the four points A are in general distinct, as are the four planes (ab). In order that two points or planes should coincide it is necessary that the regulus should degenerate, as in Case II, § 140. The condition for this is that the discriminant of the equation

$$\lambda^2 \sum a_i^2 + \mu^2 \sum d_i^2 + \nu^2 \sum c_i^2 a_i^2 + 2\lambda\mu \sum a_i d_i + 2\mu\nu \sum c_i a_i d_i + 2\nu\lambda \sum c_i a_i^2 = 0$$

should vanish. By virtue of (11), and the fact that d_i satisfies (2), the above equation reduces to

$$\nu^2 \sum c_i^2 a_i^2 + 2\lambda\mu \sum a_i d_i + 2\mu\nu \sum c_i a_i d_i = 0 \; ;$$

and the condition that its discriminant should vanish is

$$\sum c_i^2 a_i^2 = 0,$$

since $\sum a_i d_i \neq 0$, by (13).

If this condition is met, a_i is a singular line by the previous definition, two of the points A_1, A_2, A_3, A_4 coincide into one singular point on a_i, and two of the singular planes coincide. More precisely, if A_1 and A_2 coincide at A the pencils (ab') and (ab'') form the complex cone at A, the two lines b''' and b'''' intersect on d (compare § 140), and the points A_3 and A_4 are the vertices of the pencils of complex lines in the plane $(ab''' b'''')$.

142. Singular surface of the quadratic complex. The singular points and planes are determined by the complex line y_i and the intersecting line $c_i y_i$, where $\sum c_i^2 y_i^2 = 0$.

We take the pencil

$$\rho z_i = c_i y_i + \lambda y_i = (c_i + \lambda) y_i.$$

Then z_i satisfies the equations

$$\sum \frac{z_i^2}{(c_i + \lambda)^2} = \sum y_i^2 = 0, \qquad \sum \frac{c_i}{(c_i + \lambda)^2} z_i^2 = \sum c_i y_i^2 = 0 \; ;$$

or, what amounts to the same thing, the equations

$$\sum \frac{1}{c_i + \lambda} z_i^2 = 0, \qquad \sum \frac{1}{(c_i + \lambda)^2} z_i^2 = 0. \tag{1}$$

Equation (1) shows that z_i is a singular line of the complex

$$\sum \frac{1}{c_i + \lambda} x_i^2 = 0. \tag{2}$$

Since the lines z_i and $\dfrac{z_i}{c_i+\lambda}$ belong to the same pencil as y_i
and $c_i y_i$, the singular points and planes of (2) are the same as
those of $\sum c_i x_i^2 = 0$, no matter what the value of λ. The complexes (2) are called *cosingular complexes*.

We may use the cosingular complexes to prove that *on any line
in space lie four singular points of the complex $\sum c_i x_i^2 = 0$, and through
any line go four singular planes.*

Let l be any line in space. We may determine λ in (2) so
that l lies in the complex (2); in fact, this may be done in four
ways, since (2) is of the fourth order in λ by virtue of the relation
$\sum x_i^2 = 0$. Then there will be four singular points of this new complex on l by previous proof, and these points are the same as the
singular points of $\sum c_i x_i^2 = 0$.

It follows at once that *the locus of the singular points of a quadratic complex $\sum c_i x_i^2 = 0$ is a surface of the fourth order, and the
envelope of the singular planes is a surface of the fourth class.*

These two surfaces, however, are the same surface. For if two of
the singular points on l coincide, two of the singular planes through
l also coincide. Therefore, if l is tangent to one of the surfaces it
is tangent to the other. But l is any line. Therefore the two surfaces have the same tangent lines and therefore coincide.

This surface, the locus of the singular points and the envelope
of the singular planes, is called the *singular surface*.

We shall not pursue further the study of the singular surface.
Its Cartesian equation may be written down by first transforming from Klein to Plücker coördinates and replacing the latter
by their values in the coördinates of two points (x, y, z) and
(x', y', z'). Then, if (x', y', z') is constant, the equation is that
of the complex cone through (x', y', z'). The condition that this
cone should degenerate into a pair of planes is the Cartesian equation of the singular surface. It may be shown that the surface
has sixteen double points and sixteen double tangent planes
and is therefore identical with the interesting surface known as
Kummer's surface.[*]

---

[*] Cf. Salmon-Rogers, "Analytic Geometry of Three Dimensions," and Hudson,
"Kummer's Quartic Surface." The latter book contains as frontispiece a photo-
graph of the surface.

EXERCISES

1. Prove that the tangent lines of a fixed quadric surface form a quadratic complex. Find the singular surface. Note the peculiarities when the quadric is a sphere.

2. Prove that the lines which intersect the four faces of a fixed tetrahedron in points whose cross ratio is constant form a quadratic complex whose equation may be written $Ap_{12}p_{34} + Bp_{13}p_{42} + Cp_{14}p_{23} = 0$. This is the *tetrahedral complex*.

3. Prove that in a tetrahedral complex all lines through any vertex or lying in any plane of the fixed tetrahedron belong to the complex. Find the singular surface.

4. Show that lines, each of which meets a pair of corresponding lines of two projective pencils, form a tetrahedral complex.

5. Show that the lines connecting corresponding points of a collineation form a tetrahedral complex.

6. If the coördinates of two lines x_i and y_i are connected by the relations

$$\rho x_i = \frac{y_i}{\sqrt{c_i + \lambda}},$$

show that x_i belongs to the complex $\sum c_i x_i^2 = 0$ and that y_i belongs to the cosingular complex

$$\sum \frac{1}{c_i + \lambda} y_i^2 = 0.$$

7. If x_i and x_i' are two lines of a complex C, and y_i and y_i' their corresponding lines, as in Ex. 6, of a cosingular complex C_λ, prove the following propositions:

(1) If x_i intersects y_i', then x_i' intersects y_i.

(2) If x_i intersects x_i' at P, and y_i intersects y_i' at Q, the complex cone of C at P and the complex cone of C_λ at Q degenerate into plane pencils, and to a pencil of either complex corresponds a pencil of the other.

(3) If x_i intersects x_i' at P, in general y_i does not intersect y_i', and the complex cone of C at P corresponds to a regulus of C_λ. Also the complex conic in the plane of x_i and x_i' corresponds to a regulus of C_λ.

(4) Any two lines x_i and x_i' of C which do not intersect determine a cosingular complex C_λ in which the two lines y_i and y_i', corresponding to x_i and x_i', intersect. There are, therefore, two reguli of C through x_i and x_i' corresponding to the complex cone and the complex conic of C_λ determined by y_i and y_i'.

8. Prove that for an algebraic complex $f(x_1, x_2, x_3, x_4, x_5, x_6) = 0$ of the degree n the singular lines are given by the equations

$$f(x) = 0, \quad \sum \left(\frac{\partial f}{\partial x_i} \right)^2 = 0,$$

and that the singular surface is of degree $2n(n-1)^2$, where singular line and surface are defined as for the quadratic complex.

143. Plücker's complex surfaces.

In any arbitrarily assumed plane the lines which belong to a given quadratic complex envelop a conic. If the plane revolves about a fixed line, the conic describes a surface called by Plücker a *meridian surface* of the complex. If the plane moves parallel to itself, the conic describes a surface called by Plücker an *equatorial surface* of the complex. It is obvious that an equatorial surface is only a particular case of the meridian surface arising when the line about which the plane revolves is at infinity. In either case the surface has been called a *complex surface*.

It is not difficult to write down the equation of a complex surface. Let the line about which the plane revolves be determined by two fixed points, A and B, let P be any point in space, and let u_i and v_i be the coördinates of the lines PA and BP respectively.

Then the coördinates of any line of the pencil defined by PA and PB are $u_i + \lambda v_i$, and this line will belong to the quadratic complex $\sum c_i x_i^2 = 0$ when λ satisfies the equation

$$\sum c_i u_i^2 + 2\lambda \sum c_i u_i v_i + \lambda^2 \sum c_i v_i^2 = 0. \qquad (1)$$

In general there are two roots of this equation, corresponding to the geometric fact that in any plane through a fixed point there are only two complex lines, the two tangents to the complex conic in that plane. If, however, P is on that conic, the roots of (1) must be equal; that is

$$\sum c_i u_i^2 \sum c_i v_i^2 - \left\{ \sum c_i u_i v_i \right\}^2 = 0. \qquad (2)$$

Now u_i involves the point coördinates of A and P linearly, and v_i involves in a similar manner the coördinates of B and P. Hence (2) is of the fourth order in the point coördinates of P.

From the construction P is any point on the complex surface formed by the revolving plane about the line AB. Hence *Plücker's complex surfaces are of the fourth order.*

We may work in the same way with plane coördinates; that is, we may define a straight line by the intersection of two fixed planes, α and β, and take M as any plane in space. Then the three planes fix a point on l, and equation (1) determines the two lines through that point in the plane M which belong to the quadratic complex. Hence, if the coördinates of M satisfy equation (2), M is tangent to the complex cone through that point on l. A little reflection shows that such a plane is tangent to the complex surface formed by revolving a plane about the line l and that any tangent plane to the complex surface is tangent to a cone of complex lines with its vertex on l. Hence (2) is the equation in plane coördinates of the complex surface. Therefore *a complex surface is of the fourth class.*

144. The (2, 2) congruence. Consider the congruence defined by the two equations

$$\sum a_i x_i = 0, \tag{1}$$

$$\sum c_i x_i^2 = 0, \tag{2}$$

which consists of lines common to a linear and a quadratic complex. Through every point of space go two lines of the congruence; namely, those common to the pencil of lines of (1) and the complex cone of (3) through that point. Similarly, in every plane lie two congruence lines which are common to the pencil of (1) and the conic of (2) in that plane. The complex is therefore of second order and second class and is called the (2, 2) congruence.

Consider any line y_i of the congruence, and P any point on it. Through P there will go in an exceptional manner only one congruence line, when the polar plane of P with respect to (1) coincides with the polar plane of P with respect to the tangent linear complex of (2) at y_i. This will occur at two points on y_i. This may be seen without analysis from the fact that to every point on y_i may be associated two planes through y_i; namely, the polar planes with respect to (1) and to the tangent linear complex at y_i. Hence these planes are in a one-to-one correspondence, and there are two fixed points of such a correspondence.

Analytically, if the complex (1) and the tangent linear complex of (2) have at P any line z_i in common distinct from y_i, they will have the entire pencil $y_i + \lambda z_i$ in common. The conditions for this are

$$\sum y_i z_i = 0,$$

$$\sum a_i z_i = 0,$$

$$\sum c_{ij} y_i z_i = 0.$$

This determines a line series which, by § 140, degenerates into two plane pencils with vertices on y_i.

The points on y_i with the properties just described are called the *focal points* F_1 and F_2 of y_i, and the planes of the common pencil of (1) and the tangent linear complex of (3) are called the *focal planes* f_1 and f_2. The focal points are often described as the points in which y_i is intersected by a consecutive line. The meaning of this is evident from our discussion. For at F_1 and F_2 the pencil of lines of (1) is tangent to the complex cone of (2), so that through F_1 or F_2 goes only one line of the congruence doubly reckoned.

The locus of the focal points is the *focal surface*. It will be shown in the next section that the line y_i is tangent to the focal surface at each of the points F_1 and F_2, and that the planes f_1 and f_2 are tangent to the same surface at F_2 and F_1 respectively.

145. Line congruences in general. A congruence of lines consists of lines whose coördinates are functions of two independent variables. For convenience we will return to the coördinates first mentioned in § 127 and, writing the equation of a line in the form

$$x = rz + s, \qquad y = \rho z + \sigma, \tag{1}$$

will take r, s, ρ, and σ as the coördinates of the line. Then, if r, s, ρ, σ are functions of two independent variables α, β, the lines (1) form a congruence.

Let l be a line of the congruence for which $\alpha = \alpha_0$, $\beta = \beta_0$. If we place

$$\beta = \phi(\alpha), \tag{2}$$

we arrange the lines into ruled surfaces; and if we further impose on $\phi(\alpha)$ the single condition

$$\beta_0 = \phi(\alpha_0), \tag{3}$$

we shall have all ruled surfaces which are formed of lines of the congruence and which pass through l.

It is desired to know how many of these surfaces are developables. For this it is necessary and sufficient that there exist a curve C to which each of the lines of the surface are tangent. The lines of the surface being determined by (1), (2), and (3), the coördinates of C are functions of α. The direction $dx:dy:dz$ of C therefore satisfies the equations

$$dx = r\,dz + z\,dr + ds,$$
$$dy = \rho\,dz + z\,d\rho + d\sigma,$$

where $dr = \left(\dfrac{\partial r}{\partial \alpha} + \dfrac{\partial r}{\partial \beta}\,\phi'(\alpha)\right)d\alpha$, and similar expressions hold for $ds, d\rho, d\sigma$. On the other hand, the direction of the straight line (1) is given by

$$dx = r\,dz, \qquad dy = \rho\,dz,$$

so that if the straight line and curve are tangent, z must satisfy the two equations

$$z\,dr + ds = 0, \qquad z\,d\rho + d\sigma = 0,$$

and therefore we must have

$$d\rho\,ds - dr\,d\sigma = 0.$$

If we replace $dr, ds, d\rho, d\sigma$ by their values, we have as an equation for $\phi(\alpha)$ one which can be reduced to the form

$$A\phi'^2(\alpha) + B\phi(\alpha) + C = 0.$$

From this equation with the initial conditions (3) we determine two functions $\phi(\alpha)$. They have been obtained as necessary conditions for the existence of the developable surface through l, but it is not difficult to show that if $\phi(\alpha)$ is thus determined, the developable surface really exists. Hence we have the theorem:

Through any line of a congruence go two developable surfaces formed by lines of the congruences.

Of course it is not impossible that the two surfaces should coincide, but in general they will not, and we shall continue to discuss the general case.

To the two developable surfaces through l belong two curves C_1 and C_2, the cuspidal edges to which the congruence lines are tangent. The points F_1 and F_2, at which l is tangent to C_1 and C_2, are the *focal points* on l. The locus of the focal points is the *focal surface*.

It is obvious that any line of the congruence is tangent to the focal surface, for it is tangent to the cuspidal edge of the developable to which it belongs, and the cuspidal edge lies on the focal surface.

Let the line l be tangent to the focal surface at F_1 and F_2, and let C_1 be the cuspidal edge to which l is tangent at F_1. Displace l slightly along C_1 into the position l' tangent to C_1 at F_1'. The line l' is tangent to the focal surface again at F_2', and the line $F_2 F_2'$ is a chord of the focal surface. As the point F_1' approaches F_1 along C_1, the chord $F_2 F_2'$ approaches a tangent to the focal surface at F_2, and the plane of l and l' therefore approaches a tangent plane to the focal surface at F_2. But this plane is also the osculating plane of the curve C_1. Hence *the osculating plane of the curve C_1 at F_1 is tangent to the focal surface at F_2.*

An interesting and important example of a line congruence is found in the normal lines to any surface, for the normal is fully determined by the two variables which fix a point of the surface. Through any normal go two developable surfaces which cut out on the given surface two curves which are called *lines of curvature*. These curves may also be defined as curves such that normals to the given surfaces at two consecutive points intersect, for this is only one way of saying that the normals form a developable surface. Through *any point of the surface go then two lines of curvature.*

The two focal points on any normal are the centers of curvature. The distance from the focal points to the surface are the principal radii of curvature, and the focal surface is the surface of centers of curvature. The study of these properties belongs properly to the branch of geometry called differential geometry and lies outside the plan of this book. We will mention without proof the important theorem that the lines of curvature are orthogonal.

We shall, however, find room for one more theorem; namely, that *a congruence of lines normal to one surface is normal to the family of surfaces which cut off equal distances on every normal measured from points of the first surface.*

Let us write the equations of the normal in the form

$$x = \alpha + lr,$$
$$y = \beta + mr, \tag{4}$$
$$z = \gamma + nr,$$

where (α, β, γ) is a point of a surface S; l, m, n the direction cosines of the normal to S; and r the distance from S to a point P of the normal. Then

$$l^2 + m^2 + n^2 = 1;$$

whence

$$l\,dl + m\,dm + n\,dn = 0.$$

We have also

$$l\,d\alpha + m\,d\beta + n\,d\gamma = 0,$$

since the line is normal to S.

Suppose, now, we displace the normal slightly, but hold r constant. The point P goes into the point $(x + dx, \ y + dy, \ z + dz)$, where, from (4),

$$dx = d\alpha + r\,dl,$$
$$dy = d\beta + r\,dm,$$
$$dz = d\gamma + r\,dn;$$

whence

$$l\,dx + m\,dy + n\,dz = 0.$$

That is, the displacement of P takes place in a direction normal to the line (4). From this it follows that the locus of points at a normal distance r from S is another surface cutting each normal orthogonally, which is the theorem to be proved.

EXERCISES

1. Show that the focal points upon a line l of a congruence can be defined as the points at which all ruled surfaces which pass through l, and are composed of lines of the congruence, are tangent.

2. Show that the singular lines of a quadratic complex form a congruence, and that the singular surface of the complex is one nappe of the focal surface of the congruence.

3. Show that in general there does not exist a surface normal to the lines of a congruence, and that the necessary and sufficient condition that such a surface exists is that the two developable surfaces through any line of the congruence are orthogonal.

4. Show that if a ruled surface is composed of lines of a linear complex, on any line of the surface there are two points at which the tangent plane of the surface is the polar plane of the complex.

5. Consider any congruence of curves defined by

$$f_1(x, y, z, a, b) = 0,$$
$$f_2(x, y, z, a, b) = 0,$$

and define as surfaces of the congruence surfaces formed by collecting the congruence curves into surfaces according to any law. Show that on any congruence curve C there exists a certain number of focal points such that all surfaces of the congruence which contain C are tangent at these points.

6. Prove that if the curves in Ex. 5 are so assembled as to have an envelope, the envelope is composed of focal points.

CHAPTER XVIII

SPHERE COÖRDINATES

146. Elementary sphere coördinates. Another simple example of a geometric figure determined by four parameters is the sphere. We may take the quantities d, e, f, r, which fix the center and radius of the sphere

$$(x - d)^2 + (y - e)^2 + (z - f)^2 = r^2, \qquad (1)$$

as the coördinates of the sphere, and obtain a four-dimensional geometry in which the sphere is the element.

It is more convenient, however, to use the pentaspherical coördinates x_i of a point and take the ratios of the coefficients a_i in the equation

$$a_1 x_1 + a_2 x_2 + a_3 x_3 + a_4 x_4 + a_5 x_5 = 0 \qquad (2)$$

of a sphere as the sphere coördinates. This is essentially the same as taking d, e, f, and r. In fact, if x_i are the coördinates of § 117, then by (4), § 117, equation (2) can be written

$$(a_1 + ia_5)(x^2 + y^2 + z^2) + 2\, a_2 x + 2\, a_3 y + 2\, a_4 z - (a_1 - ia_5) = 0, \quad (3)$$

and the connection with (1) is obvious.

By § 119 two spheres are orthogonal when and only when

$$a_1 b_1 + a_2 b_2 + a_3 b_3 + a_4 b_4 + a_5 b_5 = 0, \qquad (4)$$

the coördinates x_i being assumed orthogonal.

Consider now any linear equation

$$c_1 u_1 + c_2 u_2 + c_3 u_3 + c_4 u_4 + c_5 u_5 = 0, \qquad (5)$$

where c_i are constants and u_i sphere coördinates. If we determine a sphere with coördinates c_i, (5) is the same as (4). Hence

A linear equation in elementary sphere coördinates represents a complex of spheres consisting of spheres orthogonal to a fixed sphere. If the fixed sphere is special the complex consists of spheres through the center of the special sphere and is called a special complex.

341

The word " complex " is used in the same sense as in § 113, for if α_i, β_i, γ_i, δ_i are four spheres which satisfy (4), any sphere which satisfies (4) has the coördinates

$$\alpha_i + \lambda\beta_i + \mu\gamma_i + \nu\delta_i.$$

Consider now the two simultaneous equations in sphere coördinates:
$$\sum c_i u_i = 0, \quad \sum d_i u_i = 0. \tag{6}$$

Spheres which satisfy both of these equations belong to two complexes. Therefore *two simultaneous linear equations in elementary sphere coördinates are satisfied by spheres which are orthogonal to two fixed spheres.* These spheres form a bundle, for if α_i, β_i, γ_i are any three spheres which satisfy (6), any sphere satisfying (6) has the coördinates $\alpha_i + \lambda\beta_i + \mu\gamma_i$.

All spheres which belong to the two complexes in (6) belong to the complex $\sum c_i u_i + \lambda\sum d_i u_i = 0$, and any two complexes of the latter form determine the bundle. Among these complexes there are in general two and only two special ones, and so we reach again the conclusion that a *bundle* of spheres consists in general of spheres through two fixed points.

Three linear equations,

$$\sum c_i u_i = 0, \quad \sum d_i u_i = 0, \quad \sum e_i u_i = 0,$$

determine spheres which are orthogonal to three base spheres. These spheres form a pencil, since if α_i and β_i are any two spheres satisfying (7), any sphere which satisfies (7) has the coördinates $\alpha_i + \lambda\beta_i$.

We shall not proceed further with the study of the elementary coördinates, as more interest attaches to the higher coördinates, defined in the next section.

EXERCISES

1. Consider the quadratic complex $\sum a_{ik} u_i u_k = 0$, $(a_{ki} = a_{ik})$ and the polar linear complex of a sphere v_i, defined by the equation $\sum a_{ik} v_i u_k = 0$. If the determinant $|a_{ik}| \neq 0$, show that to any sphere v_i corresponds one polar complex, and conversely.

2. Show that if v_i lies in the polar complex of w_i, then w_i lies in the polar complex of v_i. The two spheres v_i and w_i are said to be *conjugate*.

3. Show that the pencil of spheres defined by two conjugate spheres has in common with the quadratic complex two spheres which are harmonic conjugates of the first two spheres (the cross ratio of four spheres of a pencil is defined as in the case of pencils of planes).

4. Show that the assemblage of all special spheres forms a quadratic complex. Show that any two orthogonal spheres are conjugate with respect to this complex, and that the polar complex of any sphere v_i is the complex of spheres orthogonal to v_i.

5. Show that the planes which belong to a quadratic complex envelop a quadric surface.

6. Show that any arbitrary pencil of spheres contains two spheres which belong to a given quadratic complex, and that any arbitrary point is the center of two spheres of the complex.

7. Show that the locus of the centers of the point spheres of a complex with nonvanishing discriminant is a cyclide.

8. Define as a *simply special* complex one for which the discriminant $|a_{ik}|$ vanishes but so that all its first minors do not vanish. Show that such a complex contains one singular sphere which is conjugate to all spheres in space. Show that the complex contains all spheres of the pencil determined by the singular sphere and any other sphere of the complex, and that all spheres of such a pencil have the same polar complex.

147. Higher sphere coördinates. Let x_i be orthogonal penta-spherical coördinates whereby

$$\omega(x) = \sum x_i^2 = 0 \quad \text{and} \quad \eta(a) = \sum a_i^2, \tag{1}$$

and let

$$a_1 x_1 + a_2 x_2 + a_3 x_3 + a_4 x_4 + a_5 x_5 = 0 \tag{2}$$

be the equation of a sphere. To the five quantities a_1, a_2, a_3, a_4, a_5 we will adjoin a sixth one, a_6, defined by the relation

$$ia_6 = \sqrt{a_1^2 + a_2^2 + a_3^2 + a_4^2 + a_5^2}. \tag{3}$$

The six quantities are then bound by the quadratic relation

$$\xi(a) = a_1^2 + a_2^2 + a_3^2 + a_4^2 + a_5^2 + a_6^2 = 0, \tag{4}$$

and the ratios of these quantities are taken as the coördinates of the sphere. This is justified by the fact that if the sphere is given, the coördinates are determined; and if the coördinates are given, the sphere is determined.

More generally, if $\alpha_1, \alpha_2, \alpha_3, \alpha_4, \alpha_5, \alpha_6$ are six quantities such that

$$\rho\alpha_i = \alpha_{i1}a_1 + \alpha_{i2}a_2 + \alpha_{i3}a_3 + \alpha_{i4}a_4 + \alpha_{i5}a_5 + \alpha_{i6}a_6,$$

with the condition that the determinant $|\alpha_{ik}|$ shall not vanish, the ratios $\alpha_i : \alpha_k$ may be used as the coördinates of the sphere. Equation (4) then goes into a more general quadratic relation. We shall, however, confine ourselves to the simpler a_i.

By (20), § 121, the radius of the sphere

$$a_1x_1 + a_2x_2 + a_3x_3 + a_4x_4 + a_5x_5 = 0$$

is

$$\frac{ia_6}{\sum\limits_1^5 \dfrac{a_i}{r_i}}.$$

Consequently, to change the sign of a_6 is to change the sign of the radius of the corresponding sphere. If, then, we desire to maintain a one-to-one relation between a sphere and its coördinates, we must adopt some convention as to the meaning of a negative radius. This we shall do by considering a sphere with a positive radius as bounding that portion of space which contains its center, and a sphere with negative radius as bounding the exterior portion of space. Otherwise expressed, the positive radius goes with the inner surface of the sphere, the negative radius with the outer surface. A sphere with its radius thus determined is an *oriented sphere*.

If the sphere becomes a plane the positive value of a_6 is associated with one side of the plane, the negative value with the other. A sphere is special when and only when $a_6 = 0$.

148. Angle between spheres. By § 119 the angle between two spheres with coördinates a_i and b_i is defined by the equation

$$\cos\theta = -\frac{a_1b_1 + a_2b_2 + a_3b_3 + a_4b_4 + a_5b_5}{a_6b_6}. \tag{1}$$

Hence the angle θ is determined without ambiguity when the signs of the radii of the two spheres are known. If both radii are positive, θ is the angle interior to both spheres; if both radii are negative, θ is exterior to both spheres; and if the radii are of opposite sign, θ is interior to one sphere and exterior to the other.

For special spheres the angle defined by (1) becomes indeterminate. More precisely, if a_i is a special sphere the coördinate

$a_6 = 0$ and the other five sphere coördinates are the pentaspherical coördinates of the center of the sphere. Therefore the condition that the center of the special sphere a_i lie on another sphere b_i is

$$a_1 b_1 + a_2 b_2 + a_3 b_3 + a_4 b_4 + a_5 b_5 = 0.$$

Therefore if a_i is a special sphere, b_i any other sphere, and θ the angle between a_i and b_i, $\cos \theta$ is infinite when the center of a_i does not lie on b_i, but is $\frac{0}{0}$ when the center of a_i lies on b_i. *A special sphere therefore makes any angle with a sphere on which its center lies.*

When $\theta = (2k+1)\dfrac{\pi}{2}$, $\eta(a, b) = a_1 b_1 + a_2 b_2 + a_3 b_3 + a_4 b_4 + a_5 b_5 = 0$,

and conversely. Hence we may say:

The vanishing of the first polar of $\eta(a)$ is the condition that two spheres be orthogonal.

When $\theta = 0$, $\xi(a, b) = a_1 b_1 + a_2 b_2 + a_3 b_3 + a_4 b_4 + a_5 b_5 + a_6 b_6 = 0$, and conversely. In this case the spheres are said to be tangent, but it is to be noticed that spheres are not tangent when $\theta = \pi$. The difference between the cases in which $\theta = 0$ and those in which $\theta = \pi$ lies in the relation to each other of the space which the spheres bound. In fact, if two spheres which are tangent in the elementary sense lie outside of each other, they are tangent in the present sense only when one is the boundary of its interior space, and the other is the boundary of its exterior space; that is, the two radii have opposite signs. If two elementary spheres are tangent so that one lies inside the other, they are tangent when oriented only if the radii have the same sign. We say:

The vanishing of the first polar of $\xi(a)$ is the condition that two spheres be tangent.

Two planes are tangent when they are parallel or intersect in a minimum line (Ex. 8, § 81).

It is obvious that all these theorems are unaltered by the use of the more general sphere coördinates of § 121.

The angle θ_k made by the sphere a_i with the coördinate sphere $x_k = 0$ is given by the equation

$$\cos \theta_k = -\frac{a_k}{a_6}.$$

Consequently we have the theorem:

By the use of orthogonal coördinates x_i and the sphere coördinates a_i, the five coördinates a_1, a_2, a_3, a_4, a_5 of any sphere are proportional to the cosines of the angles which that sphere makes with the coördinate spheres.

149. The linear complex of oriented spheres.

Equation (1) of § 148 may be written

$$a_1b_1 + a_2b_2 + a_3b_3 + a_4b_4 + a_5b_5 + a_6b_6 \cos\theta = 0. \tag{1}$$

Consider now a linear equation

$$c_1u_1 + c_2u_2 + c_3u_3 + c_4u_4 + c_5u_5 + c_6u_6 = 0, \tag{2}$$

where u_i are higher sphere coördinates and c_i are constants. The spheres which satisfy this equation form a *linear complex*.

This equation may in general be identified with (1) by determining a fixed sphere, called the *base sphere*, with the coördinates

$$a_i = c_i, \; (i = 1, 2, 3, 4, 5), \quad a_6 = i\sqrt{c_1^2 + c_2^2 + c_3^2 + c_4^2 + c_5^2}, \tag{3}$$

and determining an angle θ by the equation

$$a_6 \cos\theta = c_6. \tag{4}$$

Equation (2) is then satisfied by all spheres which make the angle θ with the base sphere. This angle is equal to 0 when and only when $c_6 = a_6$; that is, when $\xi(c) = 0$. In the latter case the complex is called *special*.

We put these results in the form of the theorem:

A linear complex consists in general of spheres cutting a fixed sphere under a constant angle. If $\xi(c) = 0$ the complex is special and consists of spheres tangent to a fixed sphere.

The words "in general" have been introduced into the theorem because of the exceptional cases which arise when the base sphere is special; that is, when $a_6 = 0$. In that case the angle θ cannot be determined from (4).

If at the same time that $a_6 = 0$ the complex is special, then $c_6 = 0$, and the complex is

$$c_1u_1 + c_2u_2 + c_3u_3 + c_4u_4 + c_5u_5 = 0,$$

with $\sum c_i^2 = 0$. Then c_i are the coördinates of a point, the center of the base sphere, and hence *a special complex may consist of spheres intersecting in a point.*

If when $a_6 = 0$ the complex is not special, then $c_6 \neq 0$, and the angle θ cannot be determined. A particular case in which this may happen is when $c_1 = c_2 = c_3 = c_4 = c_5 = 0$, and the complex is

$$u_6 = 0.$$

This equation is satisfied by all special spheres. Therefore *all special spheres together form a nonspecial linear complex in which the base sphere is indeterminate.*

There remain still other cases in which $a_6 = 0$, but $c_6 \neq 0$. The base sphere is then special and the angle θ is infinite, but the complete definition of the complex is through its equation.

EXERCISES

1. Prove that the base sphere of a complex is the locus of the centers of the special spheres which belong to the complex.

2. Prove that if $c_6 = 0$ in the equation of a complex, the complex consists of spheres orthogonal to a fixed sphere, as in § 146.

3. Prove that in a special complex the coefficients in the equation of the complex are the coördinates of the base sphere.

4. Prove that all planes together make a special complex with the base sphere the locus at infinity.

5. Show that all spheres with a fixed radius form a linear complex and determine the base sphere.

6. Discuss the relation between two complexes whose equations differ only in the sign of the last term.

7. Two linear complexes $\sum c_i u_i = 0$ and $\sum d_i u_i = 0$ being said to be in *involution* when $c_1 d_1 + c_2 d_2 + c_3 d_3 + c_4 d_4 + c_5 d_5 + c_6 d_6 = 0$, show that when the base spheres of the two complexes are nonspecial, the product of the cosines of the angles which the spheres of each complex makes with its base sphere is equal to the cosine of the angle between base spheres.

8. Prove that a special complex is in involution with every complex which contains its base sphere.

9. Show that the complex consisting of spheres orthogonal to a nonspecial base sphere is in involution with the complex of all special spheres.

10. Show that the six complexes $u_i = 0$ are pair by pair in involution and determine the relations of the base spheres.

11. *Conjugate* spheres with respect to a linear complex are such that any sphere tangent to both belongs to the complex, and any sphere of the complex tangent to one is tangent to the other.

Show that if v_i is any sphere, the conjugate sphere has the coördinates

$$\rho v_i' = v_i - \frac{2 \sum c_i v_i}{\sum c_i^2} c_i.$$

12. If a complex is composed of spheres orthogonal to a base sphere, show that the conjugate of a sphere S is the inverse of S with respect to the base sphere.

13. Find without calculation and verify by the formulas the conjugate of a sphere with reference to a complex of spheres with fixed radius R.

14. Show that the conjugate of a sphere with respect to the complex of special spheres is the same sphere with the sign of the radius changed.

150. Linear congruence of oriented spheres. The spheres common to two linear complexes

$$\sum a_i u_i = 0, \qquad \sum b_i u_i = 0 \qquad (1)$$

form a *sphere congruence*. Any sphere of the congruence (1) also belongs to any complex of the form

$$\sum (a + \lambda b) u_i = 0, \qquad (2)$$

and any two complexes of form (2) can be used to define the congruence.

Now (2) represents a special complex when λ satisfies the equation

$$\xi (a + \lambda b) = 0 ;$$

that is, $$\xi (a) + 2 \lambda \xi (a, b) + \lambda^2 \xi (b) = 0. \qquad (3)$$

Hence, *in general, a sphere congruence consists of spheres tangent to two spheres, called directrix spheres.*

The exceptional cases occur when the roots of equation (3) are either illusive or equal. In the first case equation (3) is identically satisfied and all complexes of (2) are special. The congruence may then be defined in an infinite number of ways as composed of spheres tangent to two directrix spheres. The condition that (3) be identically satisfied is $\xi (a) = 0$, $\xi (b) = 0$,

$\xi(a, b) = 0$. The first two equations say that the defining complexes are special; the third equation says that the base sphere of either lies on the other.

If the two roots of (3) are equal, there is only one special complex in the pencil (2). Suppose we take this as $\sum a_i u_i = 0$. Then, since the roots of (3) are equal, $\xi(a, b) = 0$. This says that the base sphere of the special complex belongs to the complex $\sum b_i u_i = 0$.

151. Linear series of oriented spheres. Consider now the spheres common to the three complexes

$$\sum a_i u_i = 0, \quad \sum b_i u_i = 0, \quad \sum c_i u_i = 0, \tag{1}$$

which do not define the same congruence. These spheres form a *linear series*.

A sphere of the series (1) belongs also to any complex of the form

$$\sum (\lambda a_i + \mu b_i + \nu c_i) u_i = 0, \tag{2}$$

and any three linearly independent complexes (2) may be used to define the series. Among the complexes (2) there are a simply infinite set of special complexes; namely, those for which λ, μ, and ν satisfy the equation $\xi(\lambda a + \mu b + \nu c) = 0.$ (3)

The spheres of the series (1) *form, therefore, a one-dimensional extent of spheres which are tangent to a one-dimensional extent of directrix spheres.*

The nature of the series depends on the character of equation (3).

We shall assume that the discriminant of (3) does not vanish. If the quantities (λ, μ, ν) are for a moment interpreted as trilinear point coördinates in a plane, equation (3) will represent a conic without singular points; hence it is possible to find three sets of values which satisfy (3) and are linearly independent. We have corresponding to these values of (λ, μ, ν) three linearly independent special complexes, and may assume without loss of generality that they are the three complexes in equations (1).

Then any one of the directrix spheres has the coördinates (§ 149)

$$\rho v_i = \lambda a_i + \mu b_i + \nu c_i, \tag{4}$$

where $\xi(\lambda a + \mu b + \nu c) = 0, \quad \xi(a) = 0, \quad \xi(b) = 0, \quad \xi(c) = 0.$ (5)

Now if α_i, β_i, and γ_i are any three spheres of the series (1), it is obvious that the spheres v_i in (4) satisfy the three equations

$$\sum_i \alpha_i v_i = 0, \quad \sum_i \beta_i v_i = 0, \quad \sum_i \gamma_i v_i = 0. \tag{6}$$

Conversely, any sphere satisfying equations (6) satisfy (4), for three solutions of (6) are a_i, b_i, c_i, and the most general solution is therefore $\lambda a_i + \mu b_i + \nu c_i$, where (since v_i are sphere coördinates) equation (3) must be satisfied.

Hence *the directrix spheres form another linear series.*

The special complexes which may define the series (6) are

$$\sum_i (\rho \alpha_i + \sigma \beta_i + \tau \gamma_i) u_i = 0,$$

where
$$\xi (\rho \alpha_i + \sigma \beta_i + \tau \gamma_i) = 0.$$

The base spheres of these are simply the solutions of (1). Hence *the directrix spheres of the series* (6) *are the spheres of* (1).

We have, therefore, two series of spheres such that each sphere of one series is the tangent to each sphere of the other.

On the other hand, no two spheres of the same series are tangent. To prove this note that by (5) we have

$$\lambda \mu \xi (a, b) + \mu \nu \xi (b, c) + \nu \lambda \xi (c, a) = 0,$$

and no one of these coefficients can vanish under the hypothesis that the discriminant of (3) does not vanish. But a_i, b_i, c_i are any three directrix spheres, and hence the theorem.

By § 115 we are able to say immediately:

In the general case the spheres of a linear series envelop a Dupin's cyclide.

We shall not discuss the special forms of the linear series arising when the discriminant of equation (3) vanishes.

152. Pencils and bundles of tangent spheres. If a_i and b_i are any two spheres, then
$$\rho u_i = a_i + \lambda b_i \tag{1}$$

is a sphere when and only when $\sum_i a_i b_i = 0$; that is, when a_i and b_i are tangent. In this case (1) represents ∞^1 spheres, each of which is tangent to each of the others. We call this a *pencil of tangent spheres.* In the notation of § 117 the condition for a special sphere in the pencil is

$$a_6 + \lambda b_6 = 0, \tag{2}$$

so that there is only one special sphere in the pencil unless a_i and b_i, and consequently all spheres of the pencil, are special.

The condition for a plane in the pencil is

$$a_1 + ia_5 + \lambda(b_1 + ib_5) = 0, \tag{3}$$

so that there is only one plane in the pencil unless all the spheres of the pencil, including a_i and b_i, are planes.

In general the special sphere and the plane are distinct from each other. Therefore the special sphere is a point sphere whose center is in finite space. This center lies on all spheres of the pencil by § 148. Hence the pencil is composed of spheres tangent to each other at the same point. Such spheres have in common two minimum lines determined by the intersection of the point sphere and the plane of the pencil. These statements may be verified analytically by writing the equations of the spheres in the form (3), § 111.

Special forms of a tangent pencil may arise, however. For example, it may consist of spheres having two parallel minimum lines in common. The special sphere and the plane in the pencil then coincide with the minimum plane determined by these minimum lines. Again, the pencil may consist of point spheres whose centers lie on a minimum line. The plane in the pencil is then the minimum plane through that line. Or the pencil may consist of parallel planes (§ 48). The special sphere in the pencil is then the plane at infinity unless all the planes of the pencil are minimum planes and therefore special spheres. Finally, the pencil may consist of planes intersecting in the same minimum line (§ 48). The special sphere is then the minimum plane through that line.

If a_i, b_i, and c_i are three spheres not in the same pencil, then

$$\rho u_i = a_i + \lambda b_i + \mu c_i \tag{4}$$

is a sphere when and only when the three spheres are tangent each to each. In that case equation (4) defines ∞^2 spheres, each of which is tangent to each of the others. It is a *bundle of tangent spheres*. There are in the bundle ∞^1 special spheres determined by the equation

$$a_6 + \lambda b_6 + \mu c_6 = 0, \tag{5}$$

and ∞^1 planes determined by the equation

$$a_1 + ia_5 + \lambda(b_1 + ib_5) + \mu(c_1 + ic_5) = 0. \tag{6}$$

In general, equations (5) and (6) have only one common solution, so that the special spheres are point spheres. Since all spheres of the bundle are tangent, the centers of the point spheres lie on a minimum line which lies on all the spheres of the bundle. The point spheres and the planes form each a pencil in the sense already discussed, so that any point of the common minimum line is the center of a point sphere of the bundle, and any plane through the minimum line is a plane of the bundle. From that we may show that any sphere which contains that minimum line and is properly oriented belongs to the bundle. For let v_i be such a sphere and a_i' any plane of the bundle. Since v_i and a_i' have one minimum line in common, they have another minimum line in common which intersects the first one at a point P. Let b_i' be the point sphere with center P. Then v_i is tangent both to a_i' and b_i' at P, and therefore

$$\rho v_i = a_i' + \tau b_i'$$

if the proper sign is given to a_6'. But $a_i' = a_i + \lambda' b_i + \mu' c_i$ and $b_i' = a_i + \lambda'' b_i + \mu'' c_i$, so that

$$\rho v_i = a_i + \lambda_1 b_i + \mu_1 c_i ;$$

whence v_i belongs to the bundle.

Summing up, we say: *In general a bundle of tangent spheres consists of all the ∞^2 spheres which have a minimum line in common and of no other spheres.*

To avoid misunderstanding the student should remember that we are dealing with oriented spheres and that, for example, three elementary tangent spheres which lie so that two of them are tangent internally to the third, but externally to each other, cannot be so oriented as to be tangent in the sense in which we now use the word.

Special forms of bundles deserve some mention. In the first place, we notice that not all the spheres can be point spheres ; since, if they were, the centers of three spheres would be finite points not in the same line but in the same plane, so that each is connected with the other by a minimum line, which is impossible.

The spheres of the bundle may, however, all be planes. Then the special spheres must be minimum planes, which, since they are tangent, must form a pencil of minimum planes tangent to the circle at infinity at the same point (§ 48). All planes of the bundle must pass through this point, and it is evident that any two planes through this point either intersect in a minimum line or are parallel, and in each case are tangent. Hence, *as a special case a bundle of tangent spheres may consist of ∞^2 planes through the same point on the imaginary circle at infinity.*

153. Quadratic complex of oriented spheres. Consider the quadratic complex defined by the equation

$$\sum_i c_i u_i^2 = 0. \tag{1}$$

This is the form to which in general an equation of the second degree in x_i can be reduced, and we shall consider only this case. Since the sphere coördinates satisfy the equation

$$\sum_i u_i^2 = 0, \tag{2}$$

the same complex (1) is represented by any equation of the form

$$\sum_i (c_i + \mu) u_i^2 = 0. \tag{3}$$

Now let y_i be a sphere of (3), and z_i any sphere tangent to y_i, and consider the pencil of tangent spheres

$$\rho u_i = y_i + \lambda z_i. \tag{4}$$

This pencil has in common with (3) the two spheres corresponding to the values of λ obtained by substituting from (4) in (3). This gives, with reference to the fact that y_i satisfies (3),

$$2\lambda \sum_i (c_i + \mu) y_i z_i + \lambda^2 \sum_i (c_i + \mu) z_i^2 = 0.$$

The one common sphere is, then, always y_i, as it should be, but the other is in general distinct from y_i and coincides with it when and only when z_i satisfies the relation

$$\sum_i (c_i + \mu) y_i z_i = 0 \; ;$$

that is, when z_i lies on the linear complex

$$\sum_i (c_i + \mu) y_i u_i = 0. \tag{5}$$

This complex is called a *tangent linear complex.*

From the derivation a tangent linear complex through a sphere y_i is a linear complex which contains y_i and has the property that any pencil of tangent spheres belonging to the linear complex which contains y_i has, in common with the quadratic complex, only the sphere y_i doubly reckoned, unless the pencil lies entirely in the quadratic complex.

This definition is analogous to that given in point space for a tangent plane to a surface by means of coincident points of intersection of a line in the tangent plane. The exceptional cases of pencils entirely on the complex are analogous to tangent lines which lie entirely on the surface.

It may also be noted that if $y_i + dy_i$ is any sphere of (1) adjacent to y_i, so that $\sum c_i y_i dy_i = 0$ and, from (2), $\sum y_i dy_i = 0$, the sphere lies also in (5). The tangent linear complex contains all spheres of the quadratic complex adjacent to y_i.

Since μ is arbitrary in (5) the quadratic complex (1) has a pencil of tangent linear complexes through any sphere y_i. Among these there is in general one and only one which is a special complex, for the condition that (5) be special is

$$\sum (c_i + \mu)^2 y_i^2 = 0,$$

which, if we replace μ by $\dfrac{\mu_1}{\mu_2}$ and use (1) and (2), becomes

$$\mu_2^2 \sum c_i^2 y_i^2 = 0.$$

The special linear tangent complex is then in general $(\mu_2 = 0)$

$$\sum y_i u_i = 0.$$

In an exceptional manner, however, all tangent linear complexes are special when

$$\sum c_i^2 y_i^2 = 0. \tag{6}$$

When this condition is satisfied the sphere y_i is called a *singular sphere*.

The conditions to be satisfied by the coördinates of a singular sphere are, accordingly,

$$\sum y_i^2 = 0, \quad \sum c_i y_i^2 = 0, \quad \sum c_i^2 y_i^2 = 0, \tag{7}$$

which express respectively that y_i satisfies the fundamental equation for sphere coördinates, that the sphere y_i is in the complex (1), and that it is a singular sphere.

The last equation also expresses the fact that $c_i y_i$ are the coördinates of some sphere, and the second equation tells us that the sphere $c_i y_i$ is tangent to the sphere y_i. The two spheres therefore define a pencil. On the sphere y_i there is, therefore, a definite point P, the center of the point sphere of the pencil. The locus of P is an ∞^2 extent of points forming the *surface of singularities*.

In order to determine the degree of the surface of singularities we shall take z_i, any sphere of the pencil of tangent spheres defined by y_i and $c_i y_i$, so that

$$\rho z_i = (c_i + \lambda)\, y_i. \tag{8}$$

Substitution in (7) gives the equations

$$\sum \frac{z_i^2}{(a_i + \lambda)^2} = 0, \quad \sum \frac{c_i z_i^2}{(c_i + \lambda)^2} = 0, \quad \sum \frac{c_i^2 z_i^2}{(c_i + \lambda)^2} = 0,$$

but simple linear combinations of these show that they are equivalent to the three equations

$$\sum z_i^2 = 0, \quad \sum \frac{z_i^2}{c_i + \lambda} = 0, \quad \sum \frac{z_i^2}{(c_i + \lambda)^2} = 0. \tag{9}$$

Conversely, if z_i is any solution of (9) and we place $u_i = \dfrac{z_i}{c_i + \lambda}$, it is clear that u_i is a singular sphere of the quadratic complex (1). Therefore equations (9) are satisfied by all spheres belonging to any pencil of tangent spheres defined by a singular sphere y_i and the sphere $c_i y_i$, and, conversely, any sphere which satisfies (9) belongs to such a pencil.

Let us now adjoin the condition that z_i should be a point sphere; namely,

$$z_6 = 0. \tag{10}$$

Equations (9) and (10), then, define the points P.

Consider now any straight line l defined as the intersections of two planes M and N. Take

$$\sum m_i z_i = 0 \tag{11}$$

as the equation of any linear complex which has M as a base sphere, and

$$\sum n_i z_i = 0 \tag{12}$$

as the equation of any linear complex which has N as a base sphere.

The point spheres of the complex (11) have centers on M, and the point spheres of the complex (12) have centers on N, so that the point spheres belonging to M and N have centers on the line l.

Hence the simultaneous solutions of equations (9), (10), (11), and (12) give the point spheres whose centers lie both on the surface of singularities and on the line l. The number of these solutions is the number of points in which l meets the surface of singularities; that is, the degree of the surface.

To solve these equations we may begin by eliminating λ from the last two of equations (9). Since the third equation of (9) is the derivative of the second with respect to λ, the elimination of λ gives the condition that the second equation should have equal roots in λ. Since the second equation in (9) is of the fourth order in λ, by virtue of the first equation in (9), the result of the elimination of λ is an equation of the sixth degree in z_i^2 or the twelfth degree in z_i. This equation, combined with the first of equations (9) and the linear equations (10), (11), (12), gives twenty-four solutions. Therefore *the equation of singularities is of the twenty-fourth order.*

Equations (9)–(12) may be otherwise interpreted by considering (11) and (12) as the equations of two complexes with base spheres which are not planar and therefore intersect in a circle, which may be any circle. The special spheres of the complexes have their centers on this circle, and the special spheres which also satisfy (7)–(9) are point spheres, since the condition that they be planar adds a new equation which in general cannot be satisfied. Hence, by the argument above, any circle, as well as any straight line, meets the surface of singularities in twenty-four finite points.

If the equations are expressed in Cartesian coördinates, the circle will meet a surface of the twenty-fourth order in forty-eight points. We have accounted for twenty-four finite points; the other twenty-four must lie on the imaginary circle at infinity. Since the plane of the finite circle meets the circle at infinity in two points, we have the theorem: *The surface of singularities contains the imaginary circle at infinity as a twelvefold line.*

Return, now, to the pencil (8). There is one plane p in the pencil which is tangent to y_i at P and is uniquely determined by y_i. Such planes form an ∞^2 extent which envelop a surface. To show that this surface is the surface of singularities let $y_i + dy_i$ be a singular sphere neighboring to y_i, so that

$$\sum y_i dy_i = 0, \quad \sum c_i y_i dy_i = 0, \quad \sum c_i^2 y_i dy_i = 0. \tag{13}$$

The pencil of tangent spheres defined by $y_i + dy_i$ and $c_i(y_i + dy_i)$ is

$$\rho v_i = (c_i + \mu)(y_i + dy_i), \tag{14}$$

and the condition that v_i should be tangent to z_i is satisfied by virtue of (7) and (13). Hence, in particular, the point P, the center of the point sphere of (8), lies in the plane p' of the pencil (14); that is, P is the limit point of intersection of two neighboring planes p and is therefore a point of the surface enveloped by p. This establishes the identity of the surface which is the locus of P and that enveloped by p.

The class of the surface of singularities is the number of the planes p which pass through an arbitrary line. To determine this number we may again set up equations (9), (11), and (12), but replace (10) by

$$u_1 + iu_5 = 0, \tag{15}$$

which is the condition that u_i should be a plane.

Any plane of either of the complexes (11) or (12) intersects the base plane M or N respectively in a straight line, and therefore the planes common to M and N pass through the line l. The solutions of equations (9), (11), (12), and (15) give, therefore, the planes tangent to the surface of singularities which pass through l. Hence *the surface of singularities is of the twenty-fourth class.*

154. Duality of line and sphere geometry. Since line coördinates and higher sphere coördinates each consist of the ratios of six quantities connected by a quadratic relation, there is duality between them. To bring out the dualistic properties we shall interpret the ratios of six quantities x_i connected by the relation

$$x_1^2 + x_2^2 + x_3^2 + x_4^2 + x_5^2 + x_6^2 = 0,$$

on the one hand, as the sphere coördinates a_i' of § 147 and, on the other hand, as the Klein line coördinates of § 130.

It is to be noticed that for a real line, as shown in § 130, we have x_1, x_2, x_4 real and x_3, x_5, x_6 pure imaginary. On the other hand it follows from §§ 146, 147 that for a real sphere we have x_1, x_2, x_3, x_4 real and x_5, x_6 pure imaginary. Hence configurations which are real in either the line or the sphere space will be imaginary in the other.

It is also to be noticed that a sphere for which $x_6 = 0$ is peculiar, being a special sphere, but the line for which $x_6 = 0$ has no special geometric properties. The complex of lines $x_6 = 0$ has, however, a peculiar rôle in the dualistic relations. We shall call this complex C. Its equation in Plücker coördinates is $p_{14} - p_{23} = 0$.

Two spheres whose coördinates differ only in the sign of x_6 are the same in the elementary sense, but two lines whose coördinates differ in the same way are distinct and conjugate with respect to the complex C. The relation between sphere and line is therefore in one sense one-to-two, but becomes one-to-one by the convention of distinguishing between two spheres which differ in the sign of the radius.

Any sphere for which $x_1 + ix_5 = 0$ is a plane, but the corresponding line has no special geometric property. The complex of lines $x_1 + ix_5 = 0$, however, will have a peculiar rôle in the duality. We shall call this complex S. It is special and consists of lines intersecting the line with coördinates $1 : 0 : 0 : 0 : i$. Its equation in Plücker coördinates is $p_{34} = 0$.

We have now as immediate consequences of our previous results the following dualistic relations:

Line space	*Sphere space*
A straight line.	A sphere.
A line of the complex C.	A special sphere.
A line of the complex S.	A plane.
A line of C but not of S.	A point sphere.
A line of S but not of C.	An ordinary plane.
A line of C and of S.	A minimum plane.
Two lines conjugate with respect to C.	Two spheres differing only in the sign of the radius.
Two intersecting lines.	Two tangent spheres.
A nonspecial complex.	A nonspecial complex.
A special complex consisting of lines intersecting a fixed line.	A special complex consisting of spheres tangent to a fixed sphere.
A linear congruence consisting of lines intersecting two lines.	A linear congruence consisting of spheres tangent to two spheres.
A linear series forming one set of generators of a quadric surface.	A linear series forming one of the families of spheres which envelop a Dupin's cyclide.
A quadratic line complex with its singular surface.	A quadratic sphere complex with its singular surface.

A pencil of lines corresponds to a pencil of tangent spheres, and a bundle of lines to a bundle of tangent spheres. Consider a point P and the ∞^2 lines through it. They correspond in general to a bundle of tangent spheres which have in common a minimum line p (§ 152). It is therefore possible in this way to set up a correspondence of the line space and the sphere space by which any point of the line space corresponds to a minimum line of the sphere space.

An exception occurs when the point P of the line space lies on the axis of the complex S. Then all lines through P belong to S, and the corresponding bundle of spheres consists of planes which have in common only a point on the imaginary circle at infinity.

Consider two points P and Q connected by a line l corresponding to a sphere s. P corresponds in the first place to a bundle of spheres containing s and therefore, in the second place, to a minimum line p on s. Similarly, Q corresponds to a minimum line q, also on s. If p and q intersect in a finite point M, the point sphere with center M belongs to both the bundle of spheres containing p and that containing q. Therefore the line corresponding to this point sphere must pass through P and Q. Hence l, since it corresponds to a point sphere, is in this case a line of the complex C.

Conversely, if l is any line of the complex C the minimum lines corresponding to P and Q lie on a special sphere and intersect.

Otherwise, if l is not a line of the complex C the minimum lines do not intersect in a finite point and hence are two generators of the same family on s.

Consider now the line l' conjugate to l with respect to the complex C. The points of this line correspond to generators of the same sphere s. But points of l and l' are connected by a line of C, and therefore the generators given by l' intersect those given by l. Therefore the generators given by points of l and l' belong to different families.

Consider now the lines of a plane. They form a bundle which corresponds to a bundle of tangent spheres. It is therefore possible to set up a correspondence of line space and sphere space by which a plane corresponds to a minimum line. We have nothing new, however, since the lines which lie in a plane are conjugate with respect to C of the lines which pass through a point. In fact, if we keep to the correspondence of point and minimum line it is not difficult to show that the ∞^2 points of a plane correspond to ∞^2 minimum lines, which can be arranged in ∞^1 spheres which have a minimum line in common, so that in this way a plane corresponds to a minimum line.

We may exhibit these results in the following table:

Line space	Sphere space
A point.	A minimum line.
The points of a general line l.	One set of generators of a sphere s.
The points of l' conjugate to l with respect to C.	The other set of generators of s.
The points on a line of C but not of S.	The minimum lines on a point sphere (the lines of a minimum cone).
The points of a line of S but not of C and the points of the conjugate line with respect to C.	The two families of minimum lines of a plane.
The points of a line common to C and S.	The single family of minimum lines on a minimum plane.

Consider now any surface F in the line space. We may find a corresponding surface in the sphere space as follows. Let P be any point on F and consider the pencil of tangent lines to F at P. These lines if infinitesimal in length determine a surface element.

Corresponding to the pencil of tangent lines there is in the sphere space a pencil of tangent spheres which determine a point P' and a tangent plane; that is, another surface element. It may be noticed that the point P' is the center of the point sphere which corresponds to the line of the complex C in the pencil of lines which lie in the surface element of F.

We have in this way associated to a surface element in the line space a surface element of the sphere space. When the surface elements in the line space are associated into a surface F, the surface elements in the sphere space form another surface, F', which corresponds to F.

To any tangent line of F at P corresponds a tangent sphere of F' at P'. It is known from surface theory that consecutive to P there are two points Q and R on F such that a tangent line at either coincides with a tangent line at P. The tangents PQ and PR are the principal tangents at P. If the directions of one of these tangents is followed on the surface, we have a principal tangent line (or an asymptotic line) on F.

Corresponding to this, there are in the sphere space two consecutive points Q' and R' on F' such that a tangent sphere at either coincides with a tangent sphere at P'. If one of the directions $P'Q'$ or $P'R'$ is followed on F', we have a line of curvature of F'.

Therefore, *in the correspondence before us principal tangent lines on a surface in the line space correspond to lines of curvature on the corresponding surface in the sphere space.*

EXERCISES

1. Show that the relation between line space and sphere space may be expressed by the equations

$$-Zz = Tx - (X - iY)t,$$
$$(X + iY)z = Ty - Zt,$$

where $x : y : z : t$ are Cartesian point coördinates in the line space and $X : Y : Z : T$ are similar coördinates in the sphere space. Verify all the results of the text.

2. Trace the analogies between the four-dimensional sphere geometry and the three-dimensional point geometry with pentaspherical coördinates.

CHAPTER XIX

FOUR-DIMENSIONAL POINT COÖRDINATES

155. Definitions. We shall now develop the elements of a four-dimensional geometry in which the ideas and methods of the elementary three-dimensional point geometry are used and which stands in essentially the same relation to that geometry as that does to the geometry of the plane.

We shall define as a *point* in a four-dimensional space any set of values of the four ratios $x_1 : x_2 : x_3 : x_4 : x_5$ of five variables. In a nonhomogeneous form the point is a set of values of the four variables (x, y, z, w).

A *straight line* is defined as a one-dimensional extent determined by the equations

$$\rho x_i = y_i + \lambda z_i, \qquad (i = 1, 2, 3, 4, 5) \tag{1}$$

where y_i and z_i are two fixed points and λ is an independent variable.

A *plane* is defined as a two-dimensional extent determined by the equations

$$\rho x_i = y_i + \lambda z_i + \mu w_i, \qquad (i = 1, 2, 3, 4, 5) \tag{2}$$

where x_i, y_i, z_i are three fixed points not on the same straight line and λ, μ are independent variables.

A *hyperplane* is defined as a three-dimensional extent determined by the equations

$$\rho x_i = y_i + \lambda z_i + \mu w_i + \nu u_i, \qquad (i = 1, 2, 3, 4, 5) \tag{3}$$

where y_i, z_i, w_i, u_i are four fixed points not in the same plane and λ, μ, ν are independent variables.

From these definitions follows at once the theorem :

I. A straight line is completely and uniquely determined by any two of its points, a plane by any three of its points which are not collinear, and a hyperplane by any four of its points which are not coplanar.

The forms of equations (1), (2), (3) show that if the fixed points are given, the corresponding locus is completely determined. The theorem asserts that any points on the locus which are the same in number and satisfy the same condition as the given points may be used to define the locus. We shall show this for the plane (2). Let Y_i be a point defined by equations (2) when $\lambda = \lambda_1$, $\mu = \mu_1$; that is, let

$$Y_i = y_i + \lambda_1 z_i + \mu_1 w_i. \tag{4}$$

Equations (2) may then be written

$$\rho x_i = Y_i + (\lambda - \lambda_1) z_i + (\mu - \mu_1) w_i,$$

which are of the type $\quad \rho x_i = Y_i + \lambda' z_i + \mu' w_i. \tag{5}$

Then any point which can be obtained from (2) can also be obtained from (5), and conversely.

The discussion, however, assumes that Y_i is not on the same straight line through z_i and w_i; for if it were, the coördinates of Y_i would not be of the form (4). In fact, to obtain from (2) points on the line $y_i z_i$ in the plane (2) it is necessary to replace λ and μ by the fractional forms $\dfrac{\lambda}{\nu}$, $\dfrac{\mu}{\nu}$, write the equation of the plane as

$$\rho x_i = \nu y_i + \lambda z_i + \mu w_i,$$

and then place $\nu = 0$.

We have shown that in equations (2) the point y_i may be replaced by any point not on the same straight line with z_i and w_i. In the same manner each of the other points may be replaced, and the theorem is proved for the plane.

The student will have no difficulty in proving the theorem for straight line and hyperplane.

Another immediate consequence of the definitions is the theorem:

II. *If two points lie in a plane, the line determined by them lies in the plane; if three points lie in a hyperplane, the plane determined by them lies in the hyperplane.*

The proof is left to the student.

If we eliminate ρ, λ, μ, ν from equations (3) we have the result

$$\begin{vmatrix} x_1 & y_1 & z_1 & w_1 & u_1 \\ x_2 & y_2 & z_2 & w_2 & u_2 \\ x_3 & y_3 & z_3 & w_3 & u_3 \\ x_4 & y_4 & z_4 & w_4 & u_4 \\ x_5 & y_5 & z_5 & w_5 & u_5 \end{vmatrix} = 0. \tag{6}$$

Hence:

III. *Any hyperplane may be represented by a linear equation in the coördinates* x_i.

Conversely:

IV. *Any linear equation in* x_i *represents a hyperplane.*

Let
$$\sum a_i x_i = 0 \tag{7}$$

be such an equation, and let y_i, z_i, w_i, u_i be four points satisfying the equation but not on the same straight line. Then we have

$$\sum a_i y_i = 0, \quad \sum a_i z_i = 0, \quad \sum a_i w_i = 0, \quad \sum a_i u_i = 0,$$

and by eliminating a_i from these equations and (7) we have an equation of the form (6) and thence equations of form (3).

If we eliminate ρ, λ, μ from equations (2) we have the two equations

$$\begin{vmatrix} x_1 & y_1 & z_1 & w_1 \\ x_2 & y_2 & z_2 & w_2 \\ x_3 & y_3 & z_3 & w_3 \\ x_4 & y_4 & z_4 & w_4 \end{vmatrix} = 0, \quad \begin{vmatrix} x_1 & y_1 & z_1 & w_1 \\ x_2 & y_2 & z_2 & w_2 \\ x_3 & y_3 & z_3 & w_3 \\ x_5 & y_5 & z_5 & w_5 \end{vmatrix} = 0. \tag{8}$$

That is:

V. *Any plane may be represented by two linear equations in the coördinates* x_i.

Conversely:

VI. *Any two independent linear equations represent a plane.*

Let
$$\sum a_i x_i = 0, \quad \sum b_i x_i = 0 \tag{9}$$

be such equations. Since they are independent, at least one of the determinants $\begin{vmatrix} a_i & a_k \\ b_i & b_k \end{vmatrix}$ is not zero. Let us assume that $\begin{vmatrix} a_4 & a_5 \\ b_4 & b_5 \end{vmatrix} \neq 0$. The two equations can then be solved for x_4 and x_5, and thus reduced to two of the type (9) with $a_5 = 0$ and $b_4 = 0$. If y_i, z_i, w_i are three points satisfying the equations but not on the same straight line, we may then eliminate a_i and b_i and obtain equations of the form (8) and finally of the form (2).

In the same manner we may easily prove:

VII. *Any straight line may be represented by three linear equations, and any three independent linear equations represent a straight line.*

As a special case of theorem IV, any one of the five equations $x_i = 0$ represents a hyperplane. Consider in particular $x_5 = 0$. The points in this hyperplane have the coördinates $x_1 : x_2 : x_3 : x_4$, as in projective three-dimensional space, and the definitions of straight line and plane are the usual definitions. The two equations which represent a plane consist of the equation $x_5 = 0$ and any other linear equation. If, then, the equation $x_5 = 0$ is assumed once for all, a plane is represented by a single equation. Similarly, a straight line in $x_5 = 0$ is represented by two equations besides the equation $x_5 = 0$. Obviously the difference between the representations of a plane in three-dimensional and four-dimensional geometry is similar to that between the representations of a straight line in two-dimensional and three-dimensional geometry.

Just as plane geometry is a section of space geometry, so space geometry is a section of four-dimensional geometry, the three-dimensional space being a hyperplane of the four-dimensional space.

156. Intersections. We shall proceed to give theorems concerning the intersections of lines, planes, and hyperplanes. In reading these it may be helpful for the student to bear in mind that within the same hyperplane these theorems are the same as those of the ordinary three-dimensional geometry, but differences emerge as we consider figures in different hyperplanes.

I. Two hyperplanes intersect in a plane. All hyperplanes through the same plane form a pencil, and any two of these hyperplanes may be used to define the plane.

The first part of this theorem follows immediately from theorem VI, § 155. For the latter part we notice that any hyperplanes of the pencil $\sum_i a_i x_i + \lambda \sum_i b_i x_i = 0$ intersect in the plane determined by $\sum_i a_i x_i = 0$ and $\sum_i b_i x_i = 0$.

II. Three hyperplanes not in the same pencil intersect in a straight line. All hyperplanes through the same line form a bundle, and any three of them not in the same pencil determine the line.

This follows at once from theorem VII, § 155. The bundle of hyperplanes is given by the equation $\sum_i a_i x_i + \lambda \sum_i b_i x_i + \mu \sum_i c_i x_i = 0$.

III. Four hyperplanes not in the same bundle intersect in a point. All hyperplanes through the same point form a three-dimensional extent, and any four of them not in the same bundle determine the point.

This follows from the fact that the four equations

$$\sum a_i x_i = 0, \quad \sum b_i x_i = 0, \quad \sum c_i x_i = 0, \quad \sum d_i x_i = 0$$

determine in general a single point. The exceptions are when the four equations represent hyperplanes of the same bundle.

IV. *A plane and a hyperplane intersect in a straight line unless the plane lies entirely in the hyperplane.*

For the equations which determine the points common to a plane and a hyperplane are three linear equations which in general determine a line. If, however, the plane lies in the hyperplane, the latter may be taken as one of the equations of the plane (theorem I), and we have only two equations. Furthermore, if the plane intersect the hyperplane in three points not in the same straight line, it lies entirely in the hyperplane by theorem II, § 155.

V. *Two planes intersect in a single point unless they lie in the same hyperplane. In that case they intersect in a line, or coincide.*

For the points common to two planes must in general satisfy four linear equations and hence reduce to a single point. If, however, the planes are in the same hyperplane, the equation of that hyperplane may be taken as one of the equations of each of the planes, and the points common to them have only to satisfy three equations. Furthermore, if the two planes intersect in a line, the hyperplane determined by four points, two on the line of intersection and one on each of the planes, will contain both planes (theorem II, § 155).

VI. *Three planes not in the same hyperplane do not in general intersect, but may intersect in a single point or in a straight line. Three planes in the same hyperplane intersect in a point or a straight line.*

The points of intersection of three planes must satisfy six equations, which is in general impossible. If the planes are in the same hyperplane, however, the number of equations is reduced to at least four by taking the equation of that hyperplane as one of the equations of each of the three planes.

But consider four hyperplanes intersecting in a point. It is possible in a number of ways to pair these hyperplanes so as to determine three planes which have the point in common but are not in the same hyperplane.

Or, again, consider any two planes intersecting in a point A. It is easily possible to select two points B and C which shall not lie in the same hyperplane with either of the given planes. The plane ABC has the point A in common with the first two planes, but they do not lie in the same hyperplane.

Similarly, let two planes intersect in a line AB. A plane may be passed through AB and a point C not in the same hyperplane with the first two planes. Of course any two of these planes lie in the same hyperplane (theorem V).

VII. *A straight line and a hyperplane intersect in a single point unless the line lies entirely in the hyperplane.*

The reason is obvious.

VIII. *A straight line and a plane do not intersect unless they lie in the same hyperplane. In the latter case they either intersect in a point or the line lies entirely in the plane.*

The points common to a straight line and a plane must satisfy five equations, which is in general impossible. If, however, the line and plane are in the same hyperplane, the number of equations may be reduced to four.

Again, let the line and plane intersect in the point A. Three other points may be taken: B on the line, and C, D on the plane. The hyperplane determined by A, B, C, D then contains both the line and the plane.

IX. *Two straight lines do not intersect unless they lie in the same plane. In the latter case they intersect in a point or coincide throughout.*

The points common to two lines must satisfy six equations, which is in general impossible. If, however, they lie in the same plane, the number of equations may be reduced to four.

Again, let the two lines intersect in a point A. The plane determined by A and two other points, one on each line, contains both lines.

We close this section with two theorems on the determination of planes and hyperplanes which have already been foreshadowed.

X. *A plane may be determined by (1) three points not in the same line; (2) a line and a point not on it; (3) two intersecting lines.*

XI. *A hyperplane may be determined by* (1) *four points not in the same plane;* (2) *a plane and a point not on it;* (3) *a plane and a line intersecting it;* (4) *two planes intersecting in a line;* (5) *three lines not in the same plane intersecting in a point.*

157. Euclidean space of four dimensions.

We shall consider now a four-dimensional space in which metrical properties analogous to those of three-dimensional Euclidean space are assumed. For that purpose let us replace the ratios $x_1 : x_2 : x_3 : x_4 : x_5$ by $x : y : z : w : t$, and place

$$X = \frac{x}{t}, \quad Y = \frac{y}{t}, \quad Z = \frac{z}{t}, \quad W = \frac{w}{t}.$$

Then if $t \neq 0$ the coördinates X, Y, Z, W are finite, and the values (X, Y, Z, W) are said to represent a point in finite space. If $t = 0$ one or more of the coördinates X, Y, Z, W is infinite, and the ratios $x : y : z : w : 0$ are said to represent a point at infinity.

The equation $t = 0$ represents, then, the hyperplane at infinity.

The *distance* between two points is defined by the equation in the nonhomogeneous coördinates

$$d^2 = (X_2 - X_1)^2 + (Y_2 - Y_1)^2 + (Z_2 - Z_1)^2 + (W_2 - W_1)^2, \quad (1)$$

or in the homogeneous coördinates

$$d^2 = \frac{(x_2 t_1 - x_1 t_2)^2 + (y_2 t_1 - y_1 t_2)^2 + (z_2 t_1 - z_1 t_2)^2 + (w_2 t_1 - w_1 t_2)^2}{t_1^2 t_2^2}, \quad (2)$$

from which it appears that the distance between two finite points is finite and that the distance between a finite point and an infinite point is in general infinite.

The equations of a straight line are in nonhomogeneous coördinates

$$X = \frac{X_1 + \lambda X_1}{1 + \lambda}, \quad Y = \frac{Y_1 + \lambda Y_1}{1 + \lambda}, \quad Z = \frac{Z_1 + \lambda Z_1}{1 + \lambda}, \quad W = \frac{W_1 + \lambda W_1}{1 + \lambda}; \quad (3)$$

whence follows $\dfrac{X - X_1}{X_2 - X_1} = \dfrac{Y - Y_1}{Y_2 - Y_1} = \dfrac{Z - Z_1}{Z_2 - Z_1} = \dfrac{W - W_1}{W_2 - W_1},$ (4)

which may be written

$$\frac{X - X_1}{A} = \frac{Y - Y_1}{B} = \frac{Z - Z_1}{C} = \frac{W - W_1}{D}. \quad (5)$$

The ratios $A : B : C : D$ are independent of the two points used to determine the line and will be defined as the *direction* of the line. It is readily seen that a line may be drawn through the point (X_1, Y_1, Z_1, W_1) with any given direction and that two lines through that point with the same direction coincide throughout. There is, therefore, a one-to-one relation between the lines drawn through a fixed point and the ratios we have used to define direction. This justifies the use of the word.

Two lines with the directions $A_1:B_1:C_1:D_1$ and $A_2:B_2:C_2:D_2$ respectively are said to make with each other the angle θ, defined by the equation

$$\cos \theta = \frac{A_1A_2 + B_1B_2 + C_1C_2 + D_1D_2}{\sqrt{A_1^2 + B_1^2 + C_1^2 + D_1^2}\sqrt{A_2^2 + B_2^2 + C_2^2 + D_2^2}}. \tag{6}$$

Consider the hyperplane $W = 0$. Any point in that hyperplane is fixed by the coördinates (X, Y, Z), and the distance between two points reduces to the Euclidean distance. The equation of any straight line in that hyperplane is

$$\frac{X - X_1}{A} = \frac{Y - Y_1}{B} = \frac{Z - Z_1}{C},$$

so that $D = 0$. Hence the definitions of distance and angle become those of Euclidean distance and angle. Therefore the geometry in the hyperplane $W = 0$ is Euclidean.

Similarly, the geometry in each of the hyperplanes $X = 0$, $Y = 0$, $Z = 0$ is Euclidean. The same will be shown later to be true for any hyperplane except the hyperplane at infinity and certain exceptional imaginary hyperplanes. We accordingly call this four-dimensional geometry Euclidean.

In the hyperplane at infinity, $t = 0$, a point is fixed by the homogeneous coördinates $x:y:z:w$, and we may apply to this plane the methods and formulas of three-dimensional geometry with quadriplanar coördinates.

It is important to notice the connection between figures in the four-dimensional space and their intercepts with the hyperplane at infinity. These intercepts we shall sometimes call *traces*.

The equation (5) of a straight line with direction $A:B:C:D$ may be written in homogeneous coördinates as

$$\frac{xt_1 - x_1t}{A} = \frac{yt_1 - y_1t}{B} = \frac{zt_1 - z_1t}{C} = \frac{wt_1 - w_1t}{D}; \tag{7}$$

whence it appears at once that its intercept with $t = 0$ is the point $A : B : C : D$.

The equation of a hyperplane is

$$Ax + By + Cz + Dw + Et = 0,$$

and its trace on the hyperplane at infinity is the plane

$$Ax + By + Cz + Dw = 0.$$

Similarly, the equations of a plane are

$$A_1x + B_1y + C_1z + D_1w + E_1t = 0,$$
$$A_2x + B_2y + C_2z + D_2w + E_2t = 0,$$

and its trace on the hyperplane at infinity is the straight line

$$A_1x + B_1y + C_1z + D_1w = 0,$$
$$A_2x + B_2y + C_2z + D_2w = 0.$$

A *hypersphere* is defined as the locus of points whose distances from a fixed point are equal. It is easy to show from (2) that the equation of a hypersphere is

$$a_0(x^2 + y^2 + z^2 + w^2) + 2\,a_1xt + 2\,a_2yt + 2\,a_3zt + 2\,a_4wt + a_5t^2 = 0, \quad (8)$$

and that its intercept with the hyperplane at infinity is the quadric surface

$$x^2 + y^2 + z^2 + w^2 = 0. \tag{9}$$

This surface, which we call the *absolute*, plays a rôle in four-dimensional geometry analogous to that played by the imaginary circle at infinity in three-dimensional geometry. All hyperspheres contain the absolute. The hyperplane $w = 0$ intersects the absolute in the imaginary circle at infinity in the space of the coördinates x, y, z. The same thing is true of all hyperplanes, with the exception of the minimum hyperplanes, to be considered later.

158. Parallelism. Any two of the configurations, straight line, plane, or hyperplane, are said to be parallel if their complete intersection is at infinity.

This definition gives us nothing new concerning parallel lines. For example, we have, at once, the following theorem:

I. Through any point in space goes a single line parallel to a fixed line. Any two parallel lines lie in the same plane and determine the plane.

Neither do we find anything new concerning a line parallel to a plane. We have already seen that a line will not meet a plane unless it lies in the same hyperplane. In the latter case the line may intersect the plane in a finite point or be parallel to it. We have the following theorem:

II. *If a line is parallel to a plane the two lie in the same hyperplane and determine that hyperplane. Through any point in space goes a pencil of lines parallel to a fixed plane.*

When we consider parallel planes we have to distinguish two cases. Two planes are said to be *completely parallel* if they intersect in a line at infinity, and are said to be *simply parallel* if they intersect in a single point at infinity and in no other point.

From theorem XI, (4), § 156, we have, at once, the theorem:

III. *If two planes are completely parallel they lie in the same hyperplane.*

In fact, completely parallel planes are the parallel planes of the ordinary three-dimensional geometry. On the other hand, two simply parallel planes do not lie in the same hyperplane and consequently cannot appear in three-dimensional geometry. A distinction between completely and simply parallel planes is brought out in the following theorem:

IV. *If two planes are completely parallel, any line of one is parallel to some line of the other and, in fact, to a pencil of lines. If two planes are simply parallel, there is a unique direction in each plane such that lines with that direction in either plane are parallel to lines with the same direction in the other, but lines with any other direction in one plane are parallel to no lines of the other.*

To understand this theorem note that if two completely parallel planes intersect in the line l at infinity, any line in one plane will meet l in some point P, and any line through P in the second plane will be parallel to the first plane. If, however, two simply parallel planes intersect in a single point P at infinity, the only lines in the two planes which are parallel are those which intersect in P. It may be noticed that this property of a unique direction is found also in two intersecting planes, the unique direction being that of the line of intersection.

A plane is parallel to a hyperplane if they intersect in a straight line at infinity. Let this line be l. Then any line in the plane meets l in a point P, and a bundle of lines may be drawn in the hyperplane through P. Then each line of the bundle is parallel to the given line. The hyperplane meets the plane at infinity in a plane m, in which the line l lies. Any plane in the hyperplane intersects m in a line l', which has at least one point in common with l but which may coincide with l. From these considerations we state the theorem:

V. *If a plane and a hyperplane are parallel, any line in the plane is parallel to each line of a bundle in the hyperplane, and any plane in the hyperplane is at least simply parallel to the given plane.*

Two hyperplanes are parallel if they intersect in the same plane at infinity. Let that plane be m. Any plane in one hyperplane meets m in a straight line l, and through l may be passed a pencil of planes in the other hyperplane. Again, consider any two planes, one in each of the hyperplanes. They meet m in two lines, l and l', which intersect in a point unless they coincide. The two planes can have no other point in common unless they are in the same hyperplane. Hence we have the theorem:

VI. *If two hyperplanes are parallel, any plane of one is completely parallel to some plane and hence to a pencil of planes of the other, and any plane of one is simply parallel to any plane whatever of the other to which it is not completely parallel.*

The analytic conditions for parallelism are easily given. The necessary and sufficient condition that two lines with the directions

$$A_1 : B_1 : C_1 : D_1 \quad \text{and} \quad A_2 : B_2 : C_2 : D_2$$

should be parallel is that $A_1 : B_1 : C_1 : D_1 = A_2 : B_2 : C_2 : D_2$.

Also the necessary and sufficient condition that two hyperplanes

$$A_1 x + B_1 y + C_1 z + D_1 w + E_1 t = 0$$

and

$$A_2 x + B_2 y + C_2 z + D_2 w + E_2 t = 0$$

should be parallel is that $A_1 : B_1 : C_1 : D_1 = A_2 : B_2 : C_2 : D_2$.

Since two planes are simply parallel when they intersect in a single point at infinity, the necessary and sufficient condition that the two planes

$$\left\{\begin{array}{l} A_1 x + B_1 y + C_1 z + D_1 w + E_1 t = 0, \\ A_2 x + B_2 y + C_2 z + D_2 w + E_2 t = 0 \end{array}\right\} \tag{1}$$

and

$$\left\{\begin{array}{l} A_3 x + B_3 y + C_3 z + D_3 w + E_3 t = 0, \\ A_4 x + B_4 y + C_4 z + D_4 w + E_4 t = 0 \end{array}\right\} \tag{2}$$

should be simply parallel is that

$$\begin{vmatrix} A_1 & B_1 & C_1 & D_1 \\ A_2 & B_2 & C_2 & D_2 \\ A_3 & B_3 & C_3 & D_3 \\ A_4 & B_4 & C_4 & D_4 \end{vmatrix} = 0, \tag{3}$$

but that not all the other fourth-order determinants of the matrix

$$\begin{Vmatrix} A_1 & B_1 & C_1 & D_1 & E_1 \\ A_2 & B_2 & C_2 & D_2 & E_2 \\ A_3 & B_3 & C_3 & D_3 & E_3 \\ A_4 & B_4 & C_4 & D_4 & E_4 \end{Vmatrix}$$

should vanish.

That the two planes (1) and (2) should be completely parallel their traces on the hyperplane at infinity must coincide. Now the determinants of the matrix

$$\begin{Vmatrix} A_1 & B_1 & C_1 & D_1 \\ A_2 & B_2 & C_2 & D_2 \end{Vmatrix}$$

are Plücker coördinates for the trace of the plane. Therefore the necessary and sufficient condition that the two planes (1) and (2) should be parallel is that the determinants of the matrix

$$\begin{Vmatrix} A_1 & B_1 & C_1 & D_1 \\ A_2 & B_2 & C_2 & D_2 \end{Vmatrix}$$

should have a constant ratio to the corresponding determinants of the matrix

$$\begin{Vmatrix} A_3 & B_3 & C_3 & D_3 \\ A_4 & B_4 & C_4 & D_4 \end{Vmatrix}.$$

159. Perpendicularity. In accordance with (6), § 157, two lines with the directions $A_1 : B_1 : C_1 : D_1$ and $A_2 : B_2 : C_2 : D_2$ are said to be perpendicular when

$$A_1 A_2 + B_1 B_2 + C_1 C_2 + D_1 D_2 = 0. \tag{1}$$

This condition may be given a useful interpretation in the hyperplane at infinity. The polar plane of a point $x_1 : y_1 : z_1 : w_1$ in the hyperplane $t = 0$, with respect to the absolute $x^2 + y^2 + z^2 + w^2 = 0$, is $x_1 x + y_1 y + z_1 z + w_1 w = 0$. Equation (1) therefore shows that two perpendicular lines meet the hyperplane at infinity in two points, each of which is on the polar plane of the other with respect to the absolute. Or, otherwise expressed, *the necessary and sufficient condition that two lines are perpendicular is that their traces on the hyperplane at infinity are harmonic conjugates with respect to the two points in which the line connecting the traces meets the absolute.*

A line is said to be perpendicular to a hyperplane when it is perpendicular to every line in the hyperplane. For this to happen it is necessary and sufficient that the hyperplane meet the hyperplane at infinity in the polar plane of the trace of the line. From this follows at once the theorem:

I. Through any point either in or without a hyperplane one and only one straight line can be drawn perpendicular to the hyperplane; and from any point in or without a straight line one and only one hyperplane can be drawn perpendicular to it.

Since in the plane at infinity the polar plane with respect to the absolute of the point $A : B : C : D$ is the plane $Ax + By + Cz + Dw = 0$, we have the theorem:

II. Any line perpendicular to the hyperplane $Ax + By + Cz + Dw + E = 0$ has the direction $A : B : C : D$, and conversely.

Any three lines of a hyperplane which are not coplanar, and no two of which are parallel, determine three noncollinear points of the trace of the hyperplane at infinity. The line perpendicular to these three lines passes through the pole of the plane determined by the three points. Consequently we have the theorem:

III. A line perpendicular to three lines of a hyperplane which are not coplanar, and no two of which are parallel, is perpendicular to the hyperplane.

In particular the three lines may intersect in the same point. Consequently we have the theorem:

IV. A line may be drawn perpendicular to three lines intersecting in a point but not in the same plane, and it is then perpendicular to the hyperplane determined by the three lines.

A line is perpendicular to a plane if it is perpendicular to every line in that plane. From this we have the theorem:

V. If a line is perpendicular to a hyperplane, it is perpendicular to every plane in the hyperplane.

The definition of perpendicularity of line and plane is the same as in three-dimensional geometry. The theorem, however, that from a point in a plane only one line can be drawn perpendicular to it is no longer true.

In fact, consider a plane l and any point P in it, and let the trace of l on $t = 0$ be the line L. Further, let L' be the conjugate polar line of L with respect to the absolute (§ 92). Then any point on L' is the harmonic conjugate of any point on L. Hence any two lines, one of which intersects L and the other L', are perpendicular. From P a pencil of lines may be drawn to meet L'. Therefore we have the theorem:

VI. All lines perpendicular to a plane at a fixed point lie in a plane. The two planes are such that every line of one is perpendicular to every line of the other.

These planes are said to be *completely perpendicular*. Obviously they do not exist in ordinary three-dimensional space.

The point P considered above need not lie in the plane l. Hence we have the more general theorem:

VII. Through any point of space one plane, and only one, can be passed completely perpendicular to a given plane.

With the same notation as before let l be a given plane, P a point which may or may not lie in l, and PA a line perpendicular to l, where A lies on L'. Through PA pass a plane m intersecting $t = 0$ in a line M through A. If M' is the conjugate polar of M, M' intersects L in a point B, by the theory of conjugate polar lines. Then if Q is any point of l, the line QB lies in l and is perpendicular to m. Therefore we have the following theorem:

VIII. If a plane m contains a line perpendicular to a plane l, the plane l contains a line perpendicular to m.

Two planes such that each contains a line perpendicular to the other we shall call *semiperpendicular* planes.

From the foregoing we easily deduce the following theorem:

IX. The necessary and sufficient condition that two planes should be semiperpendicular is that the trace at infinity of either should intersect in one point the conjugate polar with respect to the absolute of the trace of the other. The necessary and sufficient condition that two planes should be completely perpendicular is that the trace of either should be the conjugate polar of the trace of the other.

If two semiperpendicular planes lie in the same hyperplane, they intersect in a line and are the ordinary perpendicular planes of three-dimensional geometry. If two semiperpendicular planes are not in the same hyperplane, they intersect in a single point. If this point is at infinity, the two planes are also simply parallel. In these cases the traces L and M intersect in a point C, which is harmonic conjugate to both A and B. From this follows the theorem:

X. Two semiperpendicular planes may be simply parallel. The direction of the parallel lines of the two planes is then orthogonal to the directions of the perpendicular lines.

It is to be noticed that in this case the direction of the parallel lines is similar to that of the line of intersection of semiperpendicular planes in the same hyperplane.

A plane l is perpendicular to a hyperplane h when it contains a normal line to the hyperplane. The trace L of the plane then passes through the pole of the trace H of the hyperplane, and the conjugate polar L' of L lies in H. Therefore:

XI. If a plane is perpendicular to a hyperplane, it is completely perpendicular to each plane of a pencil of parallel planes of the hyperplane and semiperpendicular to every other plane of the hyperplane.

The angle between two hyperplanes may be defined as the angle between their normal lines. Hence two hyperplanes,

$$A_1 x + B_1 y + C_1 z + D_1 w + E_1 t = 0$$

and
$$A_2 x + B_2 y + C_2 z + D_2 w + E_2 t = 0,$$

are perpendicular when and only when

$$A_1 A_2 + B_1 B_2 + C_1 C_2 + D_1 D_2 = 0.$$

This is the condition that the traces at infinity of the two hyperplanes are such that each contains the pole of the other, as might be inferred from the definition. From this we have the theorems:

XII. *If two hyperplanes are perpendicular, the normal to either from any point of their intersection lies in the other.*

XIII. *Any hyperplane passed through a normal to another hyperplane is perpendicular to that hyperplane.*

Since in $t = 0$ the intersection of two planes is the conjugate polar of the line connecting the poles of the planes, we have the theorem:

XIV. *The plane of intersection of two perpendicular hyperplanes is completely perpendicular to any plane determined by two intersecting normals to the hyperplanes.*

In the hyperplane at infinity we may, in an infinite number of ways, select a tetrahedron $ABCD$ which shall be self-conjugate with respect to the absolute. From any finite point O draw the lines OA, OB, OC, OD. We have a configuration, the properties of which are given in the following theorem:

XV. *From any point in space may be drawn, in an infinite number of ways, four mutually perpendicular lines. Every three of these lines determines a hyperplane perpendicular to the hyperplane determined by any other three. Every pair of the lines determines a plane which is completely perpendicular to that determined by the other pair of the lines.*

A special case of the configuration described above is that formed by the coördinate hyperplanes $X = 0$, $Y = 0$, $Z = 0$, $W = 0$.

By (6), § 157, the cosines of the angles made with the coördinate hyperplanes by the hyperplane

$$Ax + By + Cz + Dw + E = 0$$

are

$$\frac{A}{\sqrt{A^2 + B^2 + C^2 + D^2}}, \qquad \frac{B}{\sqrt{A^2 + B^2 + C^2 + D^2}},$$

$$\frac{C}{\sqrt{A^2 + B^2 + C^2 + D^2}}, \qquad \frac{D}{\sqrt{A^2 + B^2 + C^2 + D^2}},$$

when

$$A^2 + B^2 + C^2 + D^2 \neq 0.$$

We may denote these by l, m, n, r respectively, and write the equation of the hyperplane in the form

$$lx + my + nz + rw + p = 0,$$

with $l^2 + m^2 + n^2 + r^2 = 1$. The equation is then in the *normal form*, and it is easy to show that p is the length of the perpendicular from the origin to the plane. Also by the same methods as in three-dimensional geometry we may show that the length of the perpendicular from any point (x_1, y_1, z_1, w_1) is $lx_1 + my_1 + nz_1 + rw_1 + p$.

Let us now take any configuration described in theorem XV, and, writing the equation of each of the four hyperplanes in the normal form, make the transformation of coördinates given by the equations in nonhomogeneous coördinates:

$$x' = l_1 x + m_1 y + n_1 z + r_1 w + p_1,$$
$$y' = l_2 x + m_2 y + n_2 z + r_2 w + p_2,$$
$$z' = l_3 x + m_3 y + n_3 z + r_3 w + p_3,$$
$$w' = l_4 x + m_4 y + n_4 z + r_4 w + p_4,$$

with the conditions $\qquad l_i^2 + m_i^2 + n_i^2 + r_i^2 = 1,$

$$l_i l_k + m_i m_k + n_i n_k + r_i r_k = 0. \qquad (i \neq k)$$

The new coördinates are the distances from four orthogonal hyperplanes, and, in fact, our discussion shows that the same is true of the original coördinates.

In the new system the equation for distance is unaltered, namely,

$$d = \sqrt{(x_2' - x_1')^2 + (y_2' - y_1')^2 + (z_2' - z_1')^2 + (w_2' - w_1')^2},$$

and if we place $w' = 0$ we have the ordinary Euclidean geometry in three dimensions. This justifies the statement already made in anticipation, which we now give as a theorem:

XVI. *In four-dimensional Euclidean space the geometry in any hyperplane, for which $A^2 + B^2 + C^2 + D^2 \neq 0$, is that of the usual three-dimensional Euclidean geometry.*

160. Minimum lines, planes, and hyperplanes. In the discussion of the previous section we have had to make exception of the cases in which the direction quantities A, B, C, D satisfy the condition

$$A^2 + B^2 + C^2 + D^2 = 0. \qquad (1)$$

We shall now examine the exceptional cases.

Obviously the necessary and sufficient condition that the direction quantities of a straight line satisfy equation (1) is that the line intersects the absolute, or, in other words, that the trace at infinity of the line lies on the absolute. The necessary and sufficient condition that the quantities A, B, C, D in an equation of a hyperplane satisfy (1) is that the trace at infinity of the hyperplane is tangent to the absolute. In this case the hyperplane is said to be tangent to the absolute.

The straight lines which intersect the absolute are the minimum lines of three-dimensional geometry.

In fact, the hyperplane $w = 0$, which by theorem XVI, § 159, represents any ordinary hyperplane, meets the absolute in the imaginary circle at infinity, and the lines in the hyperplane which meet the absolute are therefore the minimum lines of the hyperplane. Also, if any line meets the absolute in a point P, a hyperplane can evidently be determined in an infinite number of ways so as to contain the line and not be tangent to the absolute. We have, therefore, nothing new to add to the three-dimensional properties of minimum lines.

In four-dimensional space there go through every point ∞^2 minimum lines, one to each of the points of the absolute. These lines form a hypercone. A hyperplane through the vertex intersects the hypercone in general in an ordinary cone of minimum lines, and a plane through the vertex intersects the hypercone in general in two minimum lines.

Consider now any plane. Its trace in the hyperplane at infinity is a straight line which may have any one of three relations to the absolute: (1) it may intersect the absolute in two distinct points; (2) it may be tangent to the absolute; (3) it may lie entirely on the absolute.

The first case is the ordinary plane, the second the minimum plane of three-dimensional geometry. In fact, if any plane of character (1) or (2) is given, it is clearly possible to find a hyperplane which will contain it and not be tangent to the absolute. The ordinary plane is characterized by the property that through any point of it go two minimum lines, and the minimum plane of three-dimensional type by the property that through every point of it goes one minimum line.

The third type of plane is, however, not found in the ordinary three-dimensional geometry. For if a plane meets the absolute in a straight line, any hyperplane containing it contains this line and therefore intersects the absolute in two straight lines. The geometry in this hyperplane is therefore a geometry in which the imaginary circle at infinity is replaced by two intersecting straight lines. Its properties will therefore differ from those of Euclidean space.

A plane at infinity intersecting the absolute in two straight lines is tangent to it. Therefore a plane of the third type lies only in hyperplanes tangent to the absolute. A unique property of these planes is that any straight line in them meets the absolute and is therefore a minimum line. In other words, the distance between any two points on planes of this type is zero. We shall refer to a plane of this type as a *minimum plane of the second kind*.

Consider now a hyperplane which is tangent to the absolute. The equation of such a hyperplane is

$$Ax + By + Cz + Dw + E = 0$$

with $A^2 + B^2 + C^2 + D^2 = 0$. From analogy to three-dimensional geometry we shall call such a hyperplane a *minimum hyperplane*. It has already been remarked that in a minimum hyperplane we have at infinity two intersecting straight lines instead of an imaginary circle. There will be a unique direction in the hyperplane; namely, that toward the point of intersection of the two imaginary lines at infinity. For convenience we shall call a line with this direction an *axis* of the hyperplane.

Through every point of the hyperplane goes an axis, and through every axis go two minimum planes of the second kind, each containing one of the two intersecting lines at infinity. Any other plane through the axis is an ordinary minimum plane. The cone of minimum lines through a point splits up, then, into two intersecting planes.

Any plane not containing the axis intersects the absolute in two distinct points and is therefore an ordinary plane.

Since a minimum hyperplane intersects $t = 0$ in a plane tangent to the absolute, the normal to the hyperplane passes through the point of tangency, which is the point of intersection of the two straight lines at infinity. Hence the axes of a minimum hyperplane are the normals to the hyperplane. The axes are therefore normal also to every plane in the minimum hyperplane.

Let the plane of the figure (Fig. 60) be the plane of intersection of a minimum hyperplane with the hyperplane at infinity, and let the two lines OA and OB be the intersection of the plane with the absolute. Then, if L is the trace of any ordinary plane, the normal to the plane passes through O and is an axis of the hyperplane.

Two ordinary planes in the minimum hyperplane, therefore, cannot be perpendicular to each other.

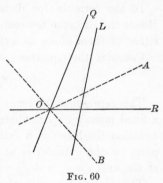

Fig. 60

But consider a minimum plane of the first kind whose trace on the hyperplane at infinity is the line OQ. The conjugate polar of the line OQ is a line OR. Consequently any two minimum planes of the first kind whose traces are OQ and OR respectively are completely perpendicular. This state of two completely perpendicular planes lying in the same hyperplane cannot be met in an ordinary hyperplane and is therefore not found in Euclidean geometry. This is due to the fact that in an ordinary hyperplane only one minimum plane can be passed through a minimum line, while in a minimum hyperplane a pencil of minimum planes can be passed through an axis of the hyperplane, and these planes are paired into completely perpendicular planes.

Finally, it may be remarked that a minimum plane of the second kind is, in a sense, completely perpendicular to itself, for the lines OA and OB are each self-conjugate.

For the sake of an analytic treatment let us suppose that a minimum hyperplane has the equation $z - iw = 0$, and let us make the nonorthogonal change of coördinates expressed by the equations

$$z' = z + iw,$$

$$w' = z - iw.$$

Then the formula for distance becomes

$$d^2 = (x_2 - x_1)^2 + (y_2 - y_1)^2 + (z_2' - z_1')(w_2' - w_1').$$

In the hyperplane $w' = 0$ a point is fixed by the coördinates x, y, z', and the distance between two points becomes

$$d = (x_2 - x_1)^2 + (y_2 - y_1)^2.$$

The equation of the two straight lines at infinity is

$$x^2 + y^2 = 0,$$

and the equations of any axis of the hyperplane is $x = x_0$, $y = y_0$. In the formula for distance the coördinate z' does not occur. Hence the distance between two points is unaltered by displacing either of them along an axis.

Consider the equation

$$(x - x_0)^2 + (y - y_0) = a^2.$$

This represents the locus of points at a constant distance a from a fixed point x_0, y_0, z, where z is arbitrary. From the form of the equation the locus is a cylinder whose elements are axes. Every point on the cylinder is at a constant distance a from each point of the axis $x = x_0$, $y = y_0$.

The above are some of the peculiar properties of a minimum hyperplane.

161. Hypersurfaces of second order. Consider the equation

$$\sum a_{ik} x_i x_k = 0 \qquad (a_{ki} = a_{ik}) \tag{1}$$

in the homogeneous coördinates of a four-dimensional space in which no hyperplane is singled out to be given special significance as the hyperplane at infinity. The space is, therefore, a projective space. The student will have no difficulty in showing, by the methods of § 82, that the coördinates may, if desired, be interpreted as equal to the distances from five hyperplanes, each distance multiplied by an arbitrary constant. However, we shall make no use of this property, and mention it only for the analogy between the present coördinates and quadriplanar coördinates in three-dimensional space.

Equation (1) represents a hypersurface of the second order. If y_i and z_i are any fixed points, the line

$$\rho x_i = y_i + \lambda z_i \tag{2}$$

intersects the hypersurface in general in two distinct or coincident points or lies entirely on it. Therefore any hyperplane intersects the hypersurface in a two-dimensional extent which is met by any

line in two points and is therefore a quadric surface, or else the
hyperplane lies entirely on the hypersurface. Similarly, any plane
intersects the hypersurface (1) in a conic or lies entirely on it.

Let us consider these intersections more carefully. If in equation (2) the point y_i is taken on the hypersurface, the line will meet
the hypersurface (1) in two distinct points unless the equation

$$\sum a_{ik} y_i z_k = 0 \tag{3}$$

is satisfied by the point z_i. In the latter case the line (2) meets
(1) in two points coinciding with y_i, unless also z_i is on the hypersurface, in which case the line lies entirely on the hypersurface.

This means that if y_i is on the hypersurface (1), any point on
the hyperplane

$$\sum a_{ik} y_i x_k = 0 \tag{4}$$

but not on the hypersurface, if connected with y_i, determines a
straight line tangent to the hypersurface, and this property is
enjoyed by no other point. Hence the hyperplane is the locus of
tangent lines at y_i and is called the *tangent hyperplane*.

The hyperplane (4) intersects the hypersurface in an extent of
two dimensions which has the property that any point on it determines with y_i a line entirely on it. It is therefore a cone of second
order. Therefore, *through any point of the hypersurface goes a cone
of straight lines lying entirely on the hypersurface*.

An exception to the above occurs when y_i is a point satisfying
the equations $a_{i1}y_1 + a_{i2}y_2 + a_{i3}y_3 + a_{i4}y_4 + a_{i5}y_5 = 0.$ (5)

Such a point, if it exists, is a *singular point*. At a singular point
the equation of the tangent hyperplane becomes illusive. Any line
through a singular point meets the hypersurface in two coincident
points, and if any point on the hypersurface is connected with the
singular point by a straight line, the line lies entirely on the hypersurface. Equations (5) do not always have a solution; but if they
have, the solution is a point of the surface, since equation (1) is
homogeneous.

If y_i is any point, whether on the hypersurface or not, equation (4)
defines a hyperplane called the *polar hyperplane* of y_i. If the equation
of the polar hyperplane is written in the form

$$u_1 x_1 + u_2 x_2 + u_3 x_3 + u_4 x_4 + u_5 x_5 = 0,$$

we have $\qquad \rho u_i = a_{i1} y_1 + a_{i2} y_2 + a_{i3} y_3 + a_{i4} y_4 + a_{i5} y_5.$ (6)

From this it follows that any point has a definite polar hyperplane. The converse is true, however, only if the determinant

$$\begin{vmatrix} a_{11} & a_{12} & a_{13} & a_{14} & a_{15} \\ a_{12} & a_{22} & a_{23} & a_{24} & a_{25} \\ a_{13} & a_{23} & a_{33} & a_{34} & a_{35} \\ a_{14} & a_{24} & a_{34} & a_{44} & a_{45} \\ a_{15} & a_{25} & a_{35} & a_{45} & a_{55} \end{vmatrix}$$

does not vanish. The vanishing of this determinant is the necessary and sufficient condition that equations (5) should have a solution. Therefore we say:

If a hyperplane of the second order has no singular points, to every point in space corresponds a unique polar hyperplane, and to every hyperplane corresponds a unique pole. The necessary and sufficient condition for this to occur is that the discriminant $|a_{ik}|$ should not vanish.

If the hypersurface has a singular point, it is easy to see that every polar hyperplane passes through that point. Therefore only hyperplanes through the singular points can have poles.

The properties of polar hyperplanes are similar to those of polar planes of three-dimensional geometry, and the theorems of § 92 may, with slight modifications, be repeated for the four dimensions.

We may also employ some of the methods of § 93 in classifying hypersurfaces of the second order. Let us take the general case in which no singular points occur. There is then no difficulty in applying these methods to show that the equation may be reduced to

$$x_1^2 + x_2^2 + x_3^2 + x_4^2 + x_5^2 = 0.$$

The cases of hypersurfaces with singular points are more tedious if the elementary methods are used. It is preferable in these cases to use the methods of elementary divisors.

162. Duality between line geometry in three dimensions and point geometry in four dimensions. Since the straight line in a three-dimensional space is determined by four coördinates, it will be dualistic with the point in four dimensions. In order to have coördinates of the four-dimensional space which are dualistic with the Klein coördinates of the straight line, we will introduce hexaspherical coördinates in four-dimensional space analogous to the pentaspherical coördinates of three-dimensional space.

Following the analogy of §§ 117, 123, let us place

$$\rho x_1 = X^2 + Y^2 + Z^2 + W^2 - 1,$$
$$\rho x_2 = 2X,$$
$$\rho x_3 = 2Y,$$
$$\rho x_4 = 2Z, \tag{1}$$
$$\rho x_5 = 2W,$$
$$\rho x_6 = i(X^2 + Y^2 + Z^2 + W^2 + 1), \tag{2}$$

where $\qquad x_1^2 + x_2^2 + x_3^2 + x_4^2 + x_5^2 + x_6^2 = 0.$

The coördinates x_i are hexaspherical coördinates. The locus at infinity has the equation $x_1 + ix_6 = 0$, and the real point at infinity has the coördinates $1 : 0 : 0 : 0 : 0 : i$.

The equation

$$a_1 x_1 + a_2 x_2 + a_3 x_3 + a_4 x_4 + a_5 x_5 + a_6 x_6 = 0$$

is that of the hypersphere

$$(a_1 + ia_6)(X^2 + Y^2 + Z^2 + W^2) + 2a_1 X + 2a_2 Y + 2a_3 Z + 2a_4 W - (a_1 - ia_6) = 0.$$

There are four varieties of hyperspheres:

1. Proper hyperspheres, $\quad \sum a_i^2 \neq 0, \quad a_1 + ia_6 \neq 0.$

2. Proper hyperplanes, $\quad \sum a_i^2 \neq 0, \quad a_1 + ia_6 = 0.$

3. Point hyperspheres, $\quad \sum a_i^2 = 0, \quad a_1 + ia_6 \neq 0.$

4. Minimum hyperplanes, $\sum a_i^2 = 0, \quad a_1 + ia_6 = 0.$

On the other hand, we may interpret the coördinates x_i as Klein coördinates of a straight line in a space of three dimensions.

For convenience we will denote by S_3 the three-dimensional point space in which x_i are line coördinates, and by Σ_4 the four-dimensional point space in which x_i are hexaspherical coördinates of a point. Then the coördinates $1 : 0 : 0 : 0 : 0 : i$, which in Σ_4 represent the real point at infinity, represent in S_3 a straight line l, which has no peculiar relation to the line space. In fact, l acquires its unique significance only because of its dualistic relation to Σ_4. Also the equation $x_1 + ix_6 = 0$, which, in Σ_4, represents the hyperplane at infinity, represents in S_3 a special line complex c, of which the line l is the axis. With these preliminary remarks we may exhibit in parallel columns the relation between S_3 and Σ_4.

Σ_4	S_3
Point.	Line.
Real point at infinity.	Line l.
Proper hypersphere.	Nonspecial line complex not containing l.
Proper hyperplane.	Nonspecial complex containing l.
Point hypersphere.	Special complex not containing l.
Center of point hypersphere.	Axis of special complex.
Minimum hyperplane.	Special complex containing l.
Hyperplane at infinity.	Special complex c with axis l.
Two points on same minimum line.	Two intersecting lines.
Any imaginary point at infinity.	Line intersecting l.
Points common to two hyperspheres.	Line congruence.
Vertices of two point hyperspheres which pass through the intersections of two hyperspheres.	Axes of line congruence.
Circle defined by the intersection of three hyperspheres.	Regulus.
Two circles such that each point of one is the center of a point hypersphere passing through the other.	Two reguli generating the same quadric surface.

The use of hexaspherical coördinates gives a four-dimensional space in which the ideal elements differ from those introduced by the use of Cartesian coördinates, as has been explained in § 123. Such a space is in a one-to-one relation with the manifold of straight lines in S_3.

If we wish to retain in Σ_4 the ideal elements of the Cartesian geometry, the relation between S_3 and Σ_4 ceases to be one-to-one for certain exceptional elements. To show this we will modify equations (1) by introducing homogeneous coördinates in Σ_4 and have

$$\rho x_1 = x^2 + y^2 + z^2 + w^2 - t^2,$$
$$\rho x_2 = 2\,xt,$$
$$\rho x_3 = 2\,yt,$$
$$\rho x_4 = 2\,zt, \tag{3}$$
$$\rho x_5 = 2\,wt,$$
$$\rho x_6 = i\,(x^2 + y^2 + z^2 + w^2 + t^2).$$

If we use these equations to establish the relation between the lines of S_3 and the points of Σ_4, we shall have the same results as before, with the following exceptions, all of which relate to the ideal elements of Σ_4. Any point in Σ_4 on the hyperplane at infinity, but not on the absolute, corresponds to the line l; and the line l corresponds to all points on $t = 0$, but not on the absolute.

Any point on the absolute corresponds to a line in S_3 which at first sight seems entirely indeterminate, but if we write equations (3) in the form

$$x_1 + ix_6 : x_2 : x_3 : x_4 : x_5 : x_1 - ix_6 = - t : x : y : z : w : \frac{x^2 + y^2 + z^2 + w^2}{t},$$

it appears that a point on the absolute corresponds to a line for which

$$x_1 : x_6 = 1 : i, \qquad x_2 : x_3 : x_4 : x_5 = x : y : z : w.$$

This is a one-dimensional extent of lines. One line of the extent is always l, and another is $1 : x : y : z : w : i$. The general line may be written as $(1 + \lambda) : x : y : z : w : i(1 + \lambda)$. By § 131 the extent is, therefore, a pencil containing l. Then, to any point on the absolute corresponds any line of a certain pencil containing l.

It is easy to show that any line which intersects l corresponds to a definite point on the absolute.

It is, of course, possible to interpret equation $t = 0$ in equations (3) as the equation of any hyperplane in a projective space with the coördinates $x : y : z : w : t$. The absolute is then replaced by a quadric surface Φ in the hyperplane $t = 0$. The correspondence between S_3 and Σ_4 is then less special than the one we have considered.

EXERCISES

1. Show that orthogonal hyperspheres correspond to complexes in involution.

2. Define inversion with respect to a hypersphere F in Σ_4 and show that two inverse points with respect to F correspond to two lines in S_3 which are conjugate polars with respect to the line complex which corresponds to F.

CHAPTER XX

GEOMETRY OF N DIMENSIONS

163. Projective space. We shall say that a point in n dimensions is defined by the n ratios of $n+1$ coördinates; namely,

$$x_1 : x_2 : x_3 : \cdots : x_n : x_{n+1}. \tag{1}$$

The values of the coördinates may be real or imaginary, but the indeterminate ratios $0:0:\cdots:0:0$ shall not be allowed. The totality of points thus obtained is a space of n dimensions denoted by S_n.

A straight line in S_n is defined by the equations

$$\rho x_i = y_i + \lambda z_i, \qquad (i = 1, 2, \cdots, n+1) \tag{2}$$

where y_i and z_i are constants and λ is an independent variable. Obviously y_i and z_i are coördinates of two points on the line, which is thus uniquely determined by any two points in S_n. Also, any two points of a straight line may be used to define it.

A plane in S_n is defined by the equations

$$\rho x_i = y_i + \lambda z_i + \mu w_i, \qquad (i = 1, 2, \cdots, n+1) \tag{3}$$

where y_i, z_i, w_i are the coördinates of three points not on the same straight line, and λ, μ are independent variables. Therefore a plane is uniquely determined by any three noncollinear points of S_n, and any three such points on a plane may be used to define it.

In general, a manifold of r dimensions lying in S_n may be defined by the equations

$$\rho x_i = y_i^{(1)} + \lambda_1 y_i^{(2)} + \cdots + \lambda_r y_i^{(r+1)}, \qquad (i = 1, 2, \cdots, n+1) \tag{4}$$

where y_i are constants not connected by linear relations of the same form as (4), and λ_k are r independent variables. Such a manifold is called a *linear space of r dimensions* and will be denoted by S_r'. It is also called an *r-flat*. A straight line is therefore a linear space of one dimension (S_1'), a plane is a linear space of two dimensions

(S'_2), and S_n itself is a linear space of n dimensions. From the definition follow at once the theorems:

I. *A linear space of r dimensions is uniquely determined by any $r+1$ points of S_n not lying in a linear space of lower dimensions, and any $r+1$ points of an S'_r may be used to define it.*

II. *A linear space of r dimensions is determined by a linear space of $r-1$ dimensions and any point not in that latter space.*

It is easy to see that a linear space of $n-1$ dimensions is also defined by a linear equation

$$a_1x_1 + a_2x_2 + \cdots + a_nx_n + a_{n+1}x_{n+1} = 0, \tag{5}$$

which is analogous to the equation of a plane in three dimensions. An S'_{n-1} is therefore called a *hyperplane*.

It is also easy to see that the coördinates x_i which satisfy equations (4) satisfy $n-r$ equations of the form (5), and conversely. Therefore

III. *A linear space of r dimensions may be defined by $n-r$ independent linear equations, and is therefore the intersection of $n-r$ hyperplanes.*

In S_n we shall be interested in projective geometry; that is, in properties of the space which are unaltered by the transformation

$$\rho X_i = \sum_{k=1}^{k=n+1} a_{ik}x_k, \tag{6}$$

where the determinant $|a_{ik}|$ does not vanish. Accordingly, if we are concerned with geometry in an S'_r we may equate to X_{r+2}, X_{r+3}, $\cdots$, X_{n+1}, respectively, the left-hand members of the $n-r$ equations which define it, while leaving $x_1, x_2, \cdots, x_{r+1}$ unchanged. Now placing X_{r+2}, X_{r+3}, $\cdots$, X_{n+1} equal to zero, we have left the $r+1$ homogeneous coördinates $x_1, x_2, \cdots, x_{r+1}$ to define a point in S'_r. It follows that an S'_r is an S_n with a smaller number of dimensions, and that any projective properties of S_n which are independent of the value of n apply to any S'_r.

Besides the linear spaces there may exist in S_n other spaces. Such spaces may be defined by equations of the form

$$\rho x_i = \phi_i(\lambda_1, \lambda_2, \cdots, \lambda_r), \tag{7}$$

where ϕ_i are functions of r independent variables λ_k. If ϕ_i are algebraic functions, equations (7) define an *algebraic space*. If we substitute the values of x_i from (7) in the r equations,

$$a_1^{(1)}x_1 + a_2^{(1)}x_2 + \cdots + a_{n+1}^{(1)}x_{n+1} = 0,$$
$$\vdots \qquad\qquad\qquad\qquad \vdots$$
$$a_1^{(r)}x_1 + a_2^{(r)}x_2 + \cdots + a_{n+1}^{(r)}x_{n+1} = 0,$$

which define an S'_{n-r}, we shall have r equations to determine the r variables λ_k. The solutions of these equations used in (7) give the number of points of the space (7) which lie in an S'_{n-r}. Let this number be g. Then g is called the *degree* of the space (7), and that space is denoted by S_r^g, where r gives the dimensions of the space and g the number of points in which it is cut by a general S'_{n-r}. Thus S_1^g represents a curve which is cut by any hyperplane in g points, and S_{n-1}^g a hypersurface which is cut by any straight line in g points.

A space S_r^g may also be defined by $n - r$ simultaneous equations. Usually the same space may be represented by either this method or by that of equations (7), but sometimes this is not possible. If S_{n-1}^g is represented by a single algebraic equation, g represents the degree of the equation. If S_r^g is represented by $n - r$ equations, g is in general the product of the degrees of the equations.

In this chapter we shall confine our attention to $S_{n-1}^{(2)}$ defined by the equation

$$\sum_{i=1}^{i=n+1} \sum_{k=1}^{k=n+1} a_{ik}x_i x_k = 0, \qquad (a_{ki} = a_{ik})$$

and sections of the same.

164. Intersection of linear spaces. Consider two linear spaces S'_{r_1} and S'_{r_2}. A point x_i, which is common to the two, must satisfy the $2n - r_1 - r_2$ equations in $n + 1$ homogeneous variables:

$$a_1^{(1)}x_1 \quad + a_2^{(1)}x_2 \quad + \cdots + a_{n+1}^{(1)}x_{n+1} = 0,$$
$$\vdots \qquad\qquad\qquad\qquad\qquad \vdots$$
$$a_1^{(n-r_1)}x_1 + a_2^{(n-r_1)}x_2 + \cdots + a_{n+1}^{(n-r_1)}x_{n+1} = 0,$$
$$b_1^{(1)}x_1 \quad + b_2^{(1)}x_2 \quad + \cdots + b_{n+1}^{(1)}x_{n+1} = 0,$$
$$\vdots \qquad\qquad\qquad\qquad\qquad \vdots$$
$$b_1^{(n-r_2)}x_1 + b_2^{(n-r_2)}x_2 + \cdots + b_{n+1}^{(n-r_2)}x_{n+1} = 0.$$

$$(1)$$

We have three cases to distinguish:

1. If $2n - r_1 - r_2 > n$, equations (1) have in general no solution. There results the theorem:

I. *Two linear spaces S'_{r_1} and S'_{r_2} have in general no point in common when $r_1 + r_2 < n$.*

For an example consider two straight lines in S_3 or a straight line and a plane in S_4.

2. If $2n - r_1 - r_2 = n$, equations (1) have in general one solution. There results the theorem:

II. *Two linear spaces S'_{r_1} and S'_{r_2} intersect in general in one point when $r_1 + r_2 = n$.*

Examples are two straight lines in S_2, a line and a plane in S_3, and two planes in S_4.

3. If $2n - r_1 - r_2 < n$, equations (1) have in general an infinite number of solutions. Let us suppose that $r_1 + r_2 = n + a$. The number of equations (1) is then $n - a$, and they therefore define an S'_a. There results the theorem:

III. *Two linear spaces S'_{r_1} and S'_{r_1}, where $r_1 + r_r = n + a$, intersect in general in an S'_a.*

Examples of this theorem are that in S_3 two planes intersect in a straight line, and that in S_4 two hyperplanes intersect in a plane.

Of course any two linear spaces may so lie as to intersect in more points than the above general theorems call for. Let us suppose then that S'_{r_1} and S'_{r_2} intersect in an S'_a. Now S'_{r_1} is defined by $r_1 + 1$ points, of which $a + 1$ may be taken in S'_a. Similarly, S'_{r_2} is defined by $r_2 + 1$ points, of which $a + 1$ may be taken in S'_a. If, therefore, we take $a + 1$ points in S'_a, $r_1 - a$ other points in S'_{r_1} but not in S'_a, and $r_2 - a$ points in S'_{r_2} but not in S'_a, we have $r_1 + r_2 - a + 1$ points, which may be used to define an $S'_{r_1 + r_2 - a}$. This $S'_{r_1 + r_2 - a}$ contains all of S'_{r_1} and all of S'_{r_2} since it contains $r_1 + 1$ points of the former and $r_2 + 1$ points of the latter.

Therefore we have the theorem:

IV. *If S'_{r_1} and S'_{r_2} intersect in an S'_a, they lie in an $S'_{r_1 + r_2 - a}$.*

An example of this theorem is that in S_3 if two straight lines (S'_1) intersect in a point (S'_0), they lie in a plane (S'_2). Another example is that in S_4 if two planes (S_2') intersect in a straight line (S_1'), they lie in an S_3'.

Conversely, we have the theorem:

V. *If S_{r_1} and S_{r_1}' lie in an $S_m'(m < n)$, they intersect in an $S_{r_1+r_2-m}'$ if $r_1 + r_2 \geqq m$.*

This is only a restatement of theorem III, since by the previous section we have only to consider the S_m' in which the two linear spaces lie.

Similar theorems may be proved for the intersections of the curved spaces $S_{r_1}^{g_1}$ and $S_{r_2}^{g_2}$. These we leave for the student.

EXERCISES

1. Show that the hyperplanes in S_n may be considered as points in a space of n dimensions Σ_n.

2. Show that if S_m' contains $p + 1$ points of S_p' it contains all points of S_p'.

3. Show that through any S_k' may be passed ∞^{n-k-1} hyperplanes, any $n - k$ of which determine S_k'; that is, in the notation of Ex. 1 any S_k' is common to a Σ_{n-k-1}'.

4. Show that two algebraic spaces S_m^g and $S_{m'}^{g'}$ do not in general intersect if $m + m' < n$, and intersect in an $S_a^{gg'}$ if $m + m' = n + a$.

5. Show that every S_m^2 is contained in an S_{m+1}'.

6. Show that every curve of order g is contained in a linear space of a number of dimensions not superior to g.

165. The quadratic hypersurface. The equation

$$\phi(x_i) = \sum_{i=1}^{i=n+1} \sum_{k=1}^{k=n+1} a_{ik} x_i x_k = 0, \qquad (a_{ki} = a_{ik}) \tag{1}$$

defines an S_{n-1}^2, which we shall call a *quadratic hypersurface* or, more concisely, a *quadric*. For convenience we shall denote the surface by ϕ.

Any line $$\rho x_i = y_i + \lambda z_i \tag{2}$$

meets ϕ in two points corresponding to values of λ given by the equation

$$\sum a_{ik} y_i y_k + 2 \lambda \sum a_{ik} y_i z_k + \lambda^2 \sum a_{ik} z_i z_k = 0. \tag{3}$$

If $\sum a_{ik}y_iz_k = 0$, the points y_i and z_i are harmonic conjugates with respect to the points in which the line (2) intersects ϕ, and are called *conjugate points*. Therefore, if y_i is fixed, any point on the locus

$$\sum a_{ik}y_ix_k = 0 \tag{4}$$

is a harmonic conjugate of y_i. This locus is a hyperplane called the *polar hyperplane* of y_i with respect to the quadric.

If y_i is also on the quadric, both roots of (3) are zero, and the line (2) touches the hypersurface in two coincident points at y_i, or lies entirely on ϕ. The polar (4) then becomes the tangent hyperplane, the locus of all lines tangent to ϕ at y_i. In no other case does the polar contain the point y_i.

It follows directly, either from the harmonic property or from equation (4), that if a point P is on the polar of a point Q, then Q is on the polar of P.

More generally, let y_i describe an S_r' defined by

$$\rho y_i = y_i^{(1)} + \lambda_1 y_i^{(2)} + \cdots + \lambda_r y_i^{(r+1)}. \tag{5}$$

The polar hyperplanes are

$$\sum a_{ik}(y_i^{(1)} + \lambda_1 y_i^{(2)} + \cdots + \lambda_r y_i^{(r+1)})x_k = 0.$$

Values of x_i common to these hyperplanes satisfy the $r+1$ equations

$$\sum a_{ik}y_i^{(l)}x_k = 0, \qquad (l = 1, 2, \cdots, r+1) \tag{6}$$

and therefore form an S_{n-r-1}'. The two spaces S_r' and S_{n-r-1}' are *conjugate polar spaces*. Each point of one is conjugate to each point of the other. Conjugate polar lines in S_3 form a simple example.

If the equation of the polar hyperplane is written in the form

$$\sum u_k x_k = 0,$$

we have

$$\rho u_k = \sum_{i=1}^{i=n+1} a_{ik}y_i. \tag{7}$$

Let us consider first the case in which the determinant $|a_{ik}|$, which is the *discriminant* of (1), does not vanish. Then if the quantities u_k in (7) are replaced by zero, the equations have no solution. Therefore all possible values of y_i give definite values of u_k which cannot all become zero. Again, equations (7), as they stand, can be solved for y_i, so that any assumed values of u_k determine unique values of y_i which cannot all be zero. Summing up, we have the theorem:

If the discriminant of ϕ does not vanish, every point of S_n has a definite polar hyperplane, and every hyperplane in S_n is the polar of a definite point. In particular, at every point of ϕ there is a definite tangent plane.

Consider now the case in which the discriminant $|a_{ik}|$ vanishes. There will then be solutions of the equations

$$\sum_{i=1}^{i=n+1} a_{ik}y_i = 0. \qquad (k = 1, 2, \cdots, n+1) \qquad (8)$$

Any point whose coördinates satisfy (8) lies on ϕ, since its coördinates satisfy the equation

$$\sum_{ik} a_{ik}y_iy_k = 0,$$

and is called a singular point of ϕ.

Obviously, at a singular point the tangent hyperplane is indeterminate, and in a sense any hyperplane through a singular point may be called a tangent hyperplane.

Equation (3) shows that any line through a singular point cuts the quadric in two points coincident with the singular point, which is thus a double point of the quadric. It also appears from (3) that any point of ϕ may be joined to any singular point by a straight line lying entirely on ϕ.

Any point y_i not a singular point has a definite polar hyperplane

$$\sum_{k=1}^{k=n+1} \left\{ \sum_{i=1}^{i=n+1} a_{ik}y_i \right\} x_k = 0;$$

and since this may be written

$$\sum_{i=1}^{i=n+1} \left\{ \sum_{k=1}^{k=n+1} a_{ik}x_x \right\} y_i = 0,$$

it passes through all the singular points.

The number of the singular points of ϕ will depend upon the vanishing, or not, of the minors of $|a_{ik}|$. In the simplest case, in which $|a_{ik}|$ vanishes but not all of its first minors vanish, equations (8) have one and only one solution, and ϕ has one singular point. Therefore the quadric consists of ∞^{n-2} lines passing through the singular point.

Suppose, more generally, the minors of $|a_{ik}|$ which contain $n + 2 - r$ or more rows vanish, but that at least one minor with $n + 1 - r$ rows does not vanish. The equations (8) then contain $n - r + 1$ independent equations, and the singular points therefore form an S'_{r-1}. The quadric is then said to be *r-fold specialized*. The number r is so chosen that a onefold specialized quadric has a single singular point, a twofold specialized quadric has a line of singular points, and so on.

Any S'_r which is determined by the S'_{r-1} of singular points and another point P on ϕ lies entirely on ϕ. This follows from the fact that all points of the S'_r lie on some line through P and a singular point, and, as we have seen, these lines lie entirely on ϕ. In particular, if $r = 2$, the quadric consists of planes through a singular line; if $r = 3$, the quadric consists of spaces of three dimensions through a singular plane; and so forth.

A group of $n + 1$ points which are two by two conjugate with respect to ϕ form a self-conjugate $(n + 1)$-gon. There always exist such $(n + 1)$-gons if the quadric is nonspecialized. This may be seen by extending the procedure used in § 92. By a change of coördinates the $n + 1$ hyperplanes which are determined by each set of n-points in the $(n + 1)$-gon may be used in place of the original hyperplanes $x_i = 0$. In the new coördinates any point whose coördinates are of the form $x_k = 1$, $x_i = 0$ $(i \neq k)$ has the hyperplane $x_k = 0$ for its polar. The equation of ϕ then becomes

$$c_1 x_1^2 + c_2 x_2^2 + \cdots + c_{n+1} x_{n+1}^2 = 0. \tag{9}$$

Now the vanishing of the discriminant and its minors denotes geometric properties which are independent of the coördinates used. Hence we infer that for the general quadric all the coefficients c_i differ from zero. If the quadric is r-fold specialized, it may be shown that equation (9) may still be obtained, but that r of the coefficients vanish.

If the quadric is general, by another change of coördinates equation (9) may be put in the form

$$x_1^2 + x_2^2 + \cdots + x_{n+1}^2 = 0. \tag{10}$$

EXERCISES

1. Prove that all points of any S'_r through the S'_{r-1} of singular points have the same polar hyperplane, which passes through S'_{r-1}, and that, conversely, any hyperplane through the singular S'_{r-1} has for its pole any point of a certain S'_r.

2. Show that for any quadric which is r-fold specialized, any tangent hyperplane at an ordinary point is tangent to the quadric at all points of an S'_r lying on ϕ and determined by the point of contact and the singular S'_{r-1}.

3. Show that if ϕ is more than once specialized, any hyperplane is a tangent hyperplane at one or more of the points of the singular S'_{r-1}.

4. Prove that every S'_m through a point y_i intersects ϕ in an $S^{(2)}_{m-1}$ and intersects the polar hyperplane of y_i in an S'_{m-1}, which is the polar hyperplane of y_i with respect to the $S^{(2)}_{m-1}$ in the space S'_m.

5. Prove that if S'_r and S'_{n-r-1} are conjugate polar spaces, the tangent hyperplanes to ϕ at points of the intersections of ϕ with one of these are exactly the tangent hyperplanes of ϕ which pass through the other.

6. Prove that any plane through the vertex of a hypercone intersects it in general in two straight lines, but that if $n > 3$, it may lie entirely on the hypercone.

166. Intersection of a quadric by hyperplanes. Let ϕ be a quadric hypersurface in n-space with the equation

$$\sum a_{ik}x_i x_k = 0. \qquad (a_{ki} = a_{ik}) \qquad (1)$$

It is intersected by any hyperplane H in a quadric hypersurface ϕ' lying in H. To prove this we have simply to note that the equation of H may be taken as $x_{n+1} = 0$ without changing the form of (1).

We proceed to determine the conditions under which ϕ' is specialized. If ϕ' has a singular point P, any line in H through P intersects ϕ', and therefore ϕ, in two coincident points in P. Therefore, either H is tangent to ϕ at P, or P is a singular point of ϕ. Conversely, if H is tangent to ϕ at a point P, or if H passes through a singular point P of ϕ, then ϕ' has a singular point at P.

If ϕ is a nonspecialized quadric, the hyperplane H has at most one point of tangency. Hence:

I. A nonspecialized quadric is intersected by any nontangent hyperplane in a nonspecialized quadric of one lower dimension, and is intersected by a tangent hyperplane in a once-specialized quadric with its singular point at the point of tangency.

If the quadric ϕ is once specialized, having a singular point A, any hyperplane which is tangent to ϕ at a point B distinct from A is also tangent to ϕ at all points of the line AB (Ex. 2, § 165). Hence:

II. *If the quadric ϕ has one singular point A, any hyperplane which does not pass through A intersects ϕ in a nonspecialized quadric of one lower dimension; any hyperplane through A but not tangent at any other point intersects ϕ in a once-specialized quadric, with a singular point at A; and any hyperplane tangent along the line AB intersects ϕ in a twice-specialized quadric with the line AB as a singular line.*

More generally, let ϕ be an r-fold specialized quadric containing a singular S'_{r-1}, which we shall call S. Any hyperplane meets S in an S'_{r-2} or else completely contains S. Moreover, if H is tangent to ϕ at some point P not in S, it is tangent at all points of the S'_r determined by P and S, and therefore contains S. From these facts we have the following theorem:

III. *If the quadric ϕ is r-fold specialized, having a singular $(r-1)$-flat S, any hyperplane H not containing S intersects ϕ in an $(r-1)$-fold specialized quadric whose singular $(r-2)$-flat is the intersection of H and S; any hyperplane containing S but not tangent to ϕ intersects ϕ in an r-fold specialized quadric whose singular $(r-1)$-flat is S; and any hyperplane tangent to ϕ at P intersects ϕ in an $(r+1)$-fold specialized quadric whose singular r-flat is determined by P and S.*

Consider, now, the intersection of ϕ and the two hyperplanes

$$\sum a_i x_i = 0, \qquad \sum b_i x_i = 0, \tag{2}$$

which we shall call H_1 and H_2 respectively. H_1 intersects ϕ in a quadric ϕ' lying in S_{n-1}, and H_2 intersects ϕ' in a quadric ϕ'', which lies in the S_{n-2} formed by the intersection of H_1 and H_2. Hence the common intersection of the quadric (1) and the hyperplanes (2) is a quadric of $n-3$ dimensions lying in a space of $n-2$ dimensions. This quadric is also the intersection of the quadric determined by ϕ and H_1 and that determined by ϕ and H_2.

This quadric may also be obtained as the intersection of ϕ and any two hyperplanes of the pencil

$$\sum (a_i + \lambda b_i) x_i = 0, \tag{3}$$

in which there are in general two hyperplanes tangent to ϕ and fixing two points of tangency on ϕ. Hence we have the theorem:

IV. The intersection of a quadric surface ϕ by an S'_{n-2} formed by two hyperplanes consists in general of an $S_{n-3}^{(2)}$ formed by the intersection of two hypercones lying on ϕ. The $S_{n-3}^{(2)}$ has the property that any point on it may be joined to each of two fixed points on ϕ by straight lines lying entirely on ϕ.

Of course the fixed points and the straight lines mentioned do not in general belong to the $S_{n-3}^{(2)}$.

We shall examine this configuration more in detail for the case in which ϕ is not specialized, and shall assume the equation of ϕ in the form

$$\sum x_i^2 = 0. \tag{4}$$

Then the condition that a hyperplane of the pencil (3) is tangent is

$$\sum a_i^2 + 2\lambda \sum a_i b_i + \lambda^2 \sum b_i^2 = 0. \tag{5}$$

If the roots of equation (5) are distinct, there are two tangent hyperplanes in the pencil (3), and we have the general case described in theorem IV. If the roots of (5) are equal, there is only one tangent hyperplane, and the corresponding hypercone on ϕ is not sufficient to determine the $S_{n-3}^{(2)}$, but must be taken with another hyperplane section.

Finally, equation (5) may be identically satisfied. This happens when

$$\sum a_i^2 = 0, \quad \sum a_i b_i = 0, \quad \sum b_i^2 = 0, \tag{6}$$

which express the facts that each of the hyperplanes H_1 and H_2 given by equations (2) are tangent to ϕ, and that the point of tangency of each lies on the other. Then any one of the hyperplanes of the pencil (3) is tangent to ϕ, and the point of tangency is $a_i + \lambda b_i$, so that the points of tangency lie on a straight line. The pencil of hyperplanes (3) consists, therefore, of the hyperplanes tangent to ϕ at the points of a straight line on ϕ. Let us call this line h. Then all points on the $S_{n-3}^{(2)}$ determined by ϕ, H_1, and H_2 may be joined to any point of h by means of a straight line lying on ϕ. Let y_i be a point on $S_{n-3}^{(2)}$. Then any point on the line joining y_i to a point of h is $a_i + \lambda b_i + \mu y_i$. The coördinates of this point satisfy equations (2) and (4) by virtue of (6) and the hypothesis that y_i satisfies these equations. Consequently in this case $S_{n-3}^{(2)}$ is a specialized quadric with h as a singular line.

Consider, now, the intersection of ϕ by an S'_{n-3} defined by the hyperplanes

$$\sum a_i x_i = 0, \quad \sum b_i x_i = 0, \quad \sum c_i x_i = 0. \tag{7}$$

These determine with ϕ an $S_{n-4}^{(2)}$, which may also be determined as the intersection of ϕ, and any three linearly independent hyperplanes of the bundle defined by

$$\sum (a_i + \lambda b_i + \mu c_i) x_i = 0. \tag{8}$$

Among these there are ∞^1 tangent hyperplanes. If the equation of ϕ is in the form (4), the tangent hyperplanes are given by values of λ and μ, which satisfy the equation

$$\sum (a_i + \lambda b_i + \mu c_i)^2 = 0, \tag{9}$$

and the points of tangency of these hyperplanes are then $a_i + \lambda b_i + \mu c_i$. These points of tangency therefore form an $S_1^{(2)}$, or curve of second order lying on ϕ, and every point of the $S_{n-4}^{(2)}$ which we are considering may be joined to each point of this curve by a straight line on ϕ.

Equation (8) is identically satisfied when each of the hyperplanes (7) is tangent to ϕ and the points of tangency of each lies on the other two. Each hyperplane (8) is then a tangent hyperplane, and the points of tangency are $a_i + \lambda b_i + \mu c_i$, where λ, μ are unrestricted. The bundle therefore consists of all hyperplanes whose points of tangency are the points of a plane lying on ϕ. Therefore each point of the $S_{n-4}^{(2)}$ is joined to each point of this special plane by lines lying on ϕ and on the $S_{n-4}^{(2)}$. Therefore the $S_{n-4}^{(2)}$ is in this case a specialized quadric with that plane as a singular plane.

Consider, now, the general case of the intersection of ϕ by the S'_{n-k} defined by the k hyperplanes

$$\sum a_i^{(l)} x_i = 0. \qquad (l = 1, 2, \cdots, k) \tag{10}$$

This is an $S_{n-k-1}^{(2)}$, which may also be obtained as the intersection of ϕ and any k hyperplanes of the system

$$\sum (a_i^{(1)} + \lambda_1 a_i^{(2)} + \cdots + \lambda_{k-1} a_i^{(k)}) x_i = 0, \tag{11}$$

in which there are generally ∞^{k-2} tangent hyperplanes.

In fact, if we limit ourselves to a nonspecialized ϕ and take its equation as (4), the condition that a hyperplane (11) should be tangent is

$$\sum (a_i^{(1)} + \lambda_1 a_i^{(2)} + \cdots + \lambda_{k-1} a_i^{(k)})^2 = 0, \tag{12}$$

and the points of tangency are then $a_i^{(1)} + \lambda_1 a_i^{(2)} + \cdots + \lambda_{k-1} a_i^{(k)}$, where, of course, λ_i satisfy (12). These points form, therefore, a $S_{k-2}^{(2)}$ on ϕ, and any hypercone with its vertex on this $S_{k-2}^{(2)}$ passes through the $S_{n-k-1}^{(2)}$ which we are discussing. We have, therefore, the theorem:

V. The intersection of a nonspecialized quadric ϕ by an S'_{n-k} defined by k hyperplanes is an $S_{n-k-1}^{(2)}$ which, in general, has the property that each of its points may be joined to each point of a certain $S_{k-2}^{(2)}$ on ϕ by straight lines lying on ϕ.

According to this theorem we have on ϕ two spaces, $S_{n-k-1}^{(2)}$ and $S_{k-2}^{(2)}$, such that each point of either is connected to each point of the other by straight lines on ϕ. It is obvious that the condition must hold $2 \equiv k \equiv n-1$.

If $n = 3$, the two spaces are $S_0^{(2)}$ and $S_0^{(2)}$, each of which consists of a pair of points. If $n = 4$, the two spaces are $S_1^{(2)}$ and $S_0^{(2)}$, one of which is a curve of second order and the other a pair of points. If $n = 5$, we have either an $S_2^{(2)}$ connected by straight lines with an $S_0^{(2)}$, or an $S_1^{(2)}$ connected in a similar manner with another $S_1^{(2)}$.

In the first and last of the examples just given we have two spaces of the same number of dimensions occupying with respect to each other the special relation described in the theorem. In order that this should happen, it is necessary that $n - k - 1 = k - 2$; whence $k = \dfrac{n+1}{2}$. Hence it is only in spaces of odd dimensions that two quadric spaces of an equal number of dimensions should so lie on the quadric ϕ that each point of one is connected with each point of the other by straight lines on ϕ. The number of dimensions of these spaces is one less than half the number of dimensions of the quadric.

Returning to equation (12) we see that it is identically satisfied when the hyperplanes (10) are each tangent to ϕ and the point of tangency of each lies on each of the others. Then the system (11) consists of hyperplanes tangent to ϕ at the points of an S'_{k-1} lying on ϕ. The $S^{(2)}_{n-k-1}$ determined by ϕ and (10) is then a k-fold specialized quadric with the aforementioned S'_{k-1} as a singular locus.

167. Linear spaces on a quadric. It is a familiar fact that straight lines lie on a quadric in three dimensions. We shall generalize this property by determining the linear spaces which lie on a quadric in n dimensions. Let the quadric ϕ be given as in § 166, and let S'_r be a linear space defined by the $n+1$ equations

$$\rho x_i = y_i^{(1)} + \lambda_1 y_i^{(2)} + \cdots + \lambda_r y_i^{(r+1)}. \tag{1}$$

The necessary and sufficient condition that x_i of (1) should lie on ϕ for all values of λ_k is that y_i should satisfy the $r+1$ equations

$$\sum_i \sum_k a_{ik} y_i^{(l)} y_k^{(l)} = 0 \qquad (l = 1, 3, \cdots, r+1) \tag{2}$$

and the $\dfrac{r(r+1)}{2}$ equations

$$\sum_i \sum_k a_{ik} y_i^{(l)} y_k^{(m)} = 0, \quad (l \neq m), \quad (l, m = 1, 2, \cdots, r+1) \tag{3}$$

of which the first set express the fact that each point $y_i^{(l)}$ is on ϕ, and the second set say that each point is in the tangent hyperplane to ϕ at each of the other points.

Take any point P_1 on ϕ and let T_1 be the tangent hyperplane at P_1. Then T_1 intersects ϕ in a specialized quadric $S^{(2)}_{n-2}$. Take P_2, any point on $S^{(2)}_{n-2}$. The line $P_1 P_2$ then lies on ϕ by the conditions (2) and (3) and on $S^{(2)}_{n-2}$, because $S^{(2)}_{n-2}$ is specialized. The hyperplane T_2 tangent to ϕ at P_2 is also tangent to $S^{(2)}_{n-2}$ and intersects the latter in an $S^{(2)}_{n-3}$ which contains $P_1 P_2$. T_2 will also contain other points of $S^{(2)}_{n-3}$ if $n - 3 > 1$; that is, $n > 4$. If this condition is met, take P_3 in $S^{(2)}_{n-3}$ but not in $P_1 P_2$. The three points P_1, P_2, P_3 determine an S'_2 which lies on ϕ by virtue of equations (2) and (3).

The hyperplane T_3, which is tangent to ϕ at P_3, is also tangent to $S^{(2)}_{n-3}$ and intersects it in an $S^{(2)}_{n-4}$ which contains S'_2. It will contain other points of $S^{(2)}_{n-4}$ if $n - 4 > 2$; that is, $n > 6$. If this condition is met we may take another point, P_4, on this $S^{(2)}_{n-4}$ but not on S'_2. The four points P_1, P_2, P_3, P_4 now determine an S'_3 which is on ϕ by the conditions (2) and (3).

This process may be continued as long as the condition for the value of n found at each step is met. Suppose we have determined in this way an S'_{r-1} lying on ϕ by means of r points, the tangent hyperplanes at which have in common with ϕ an $S^{(2)}_{n-r-1}$ containing S'_{r-1}. If $n-r-1 > r-1$, that is, if $r < \dfrac{n}{2}$, this $S^{(2)}_{n-r-1}$ has points which are not on S'_{r-1}. Take P_{r+1}, one such point. It determines with S'_{r-1} an S'_r lying on ϕ. The process may be continued as long as $r < \dfrac{n}{2}$, but not longer. Since the dimensions of the quadric ϕ are $n-1$, we shall write the condition for r as $r \lesseqgtr \dfrac{n-1}{2}$ and state the theorem:

I. A nonspecialized quadric contains linear spaces of any number of dimensions equal to or less than half the number of dimensions of the quadric, but contains no linear space of greater dimensions.

To find how many such linear spaces lie on the quadric, we notice that the point P_1 may be determined in ∞^{n-1} ways, the point P_2 in ∞^{n-2} ways, and so on until finally the point P_{r+1} is determined in ∞^{n-r-1} ways. The $r+1$ points may therefore be chosen in $\infty^{\frac{r+1}{2}(2n-r-2)}$ ways; but since in any S'_r, $r+1$ points may be chosen in $\infty^{r(r+1)}$ ways, the total number of S'_r on the quadric is $\infty^{\frac{r+1}{2}(2n-3r-2)}$.

The number of S'_r which pass through a fixed point may be determined by noticing that with P_1 fixed, the r points $P_2, \cdots, P_{r+1}$ may be determined in $\infty^{\frac{r}{2}(2n-r-3)}$ ways, and that in any S'_r the r points may be chosen in ∞^{r^2} ways, so that the number of different S'_r through a point is $\infty^{\frac{r}{2}(2n-3r-3)}$. We sum up in the theorem:

II. Upon a nonspecialized quadric there exist $\infty^{\frac{r+1}{2}(2n-3r-2)}$ S'_r, of which $\infty^{\frac{r}{2}(2n-3r-3)}$ pass through any fixed point on the quadric.

If n is odd, the greatest value of r is $\dfrac{n-1}{2}$, and there are $\infty^{\frac{1}{4}(n^2-1)}$ linear spaces of these dimensions on the quadric; if n is even, the greatest value of r is $\dfrac{n-2}{2}$, and there are $\infty^{\frac{1}{4}n(n+2)}$ linear spaces of these dimensions on the quadric.

Let us consider more in detail the case in which n is odd, and let us place $n = 2p+1$. We shall limit ourselves to a nonspecialized quadric ϕ and shall write its equation in the form

$$u_1^2 + u_2^2 + \cdots + u_{p+1}^2 - x_1^2 - x_2^2 - \cdots - x_{p+1}^2 = 0, \qquad (4)$$

as may be done without loss of generality. The linear space of the largest number of dimensions on ϕ is then S_p', and its equations may be written

$$
\begin{aligned}
u_1 &= a_{11}x_1 + a_{12}x_2 + \cdots + a_{1,p+1}x_{p+1}, \\
u_2 &= a_{21}x_1 + a_{22}x_2 + \cdots + a_{2,p+1}x_{p+1}, \\
&\quad\cdots\cdots\cdots\cdots\cdots\cdots\cdots \\
u_{p+1} &= a_{p+1,1}x_1 + a_{p+2,2}x_2 + \cdots + a_{p+1,p+1}x_{p+1},
\end{aligned}
\tag{5}
$$

where the coefficients satisfy the relations

$$
\begin{aligned}
\sum_{i=1}^{i=p+1} a_{ik}^2 &= 1, &&(k=1, 2, \cdots, p+1) \\
\sum_{i=1}^{i=p+1} a_{ik}a_{il} &= 0. &&(k \neq l = 1, 2, \cdots, p+1)
\end{aligned}
\tag{6}
$$

In fact, any S_p' is defined by $p+1$ linear equations connecting the variables u_i and x_i, and these equations may be put in the form (5), provided no one of the variables u_i is missing from the equations. But if one of these variables is missing, it is clear that the S_p' cannot lie on (5). The conditions (6) are found by direct substitution from (5) in (4).

As a consequence of equations (6), the determinant $|a_{ik}| = \pm 1$,[*] and we may divide the S_p' into two families, according to the value of this determinant. Hence we have the theorem:

III. *On a nonspecialized quadric of dimensions $2p$ in a space of odd dimensions $2p+1$ there are two families of linear spaces of dimensions p.*

Now the equations of any one S_p' on (4) may be written by a proper choice of coördinates without changing the form of (4), as

$$
u_i = x_i. \qquad (i=1, 2, \cdots, p+1) \tag{7}
$$

In fact, we have simply to make a change of coördinates by which the right-hand members of equations (5) are taken equal to x_i' and then to drop the primes.

Consider, then, the intersection of (7) with any S_p' whose equations are in the form (5) with $|a_{ik}| = e$, where $e = \pm 1$. Then (5) is of the

* Scott's "Theory of Determinants," p. 157.

same family as (7) when $e = 1$, and is of the opposite family when $e = -1$. The condition for the intersection of the two S_p' is

$$\begin{vmatrix} a_{11} - 1 & a_{12} & \cdots & a_{1, p+1} \\ a_{21} & a_{22} - 1 & \cdots & a_{2, p+1} \\ \cdot & \cdot & \cdots & \cdot \\ a_{p+1, 1} & a_{p+1, 2} & \cdots & a_{p+1, p+1} - 1 \end{vmatrix} = 0. \tag{8}$$

If p is odd, equation (8) is satisfied* always when $e = -1$, but is not satisfied when $e = 1$ unless other relations than (6) exist between the coefficients. If p is even, equation (8) is always satisfied when $e = 1$, but is not satisfied in general when $e = -1$. Hence we have the theorem:

IV. *If p is an odd number, two linear spaces S_p' of opposite families on a quadric in a space of $2p + 1$ dimensions always intersect, and two S_p' of the same family do not in general intersect. If p is an even number, two S_p' of the same family always intersect, and two S_p' of opposite families do not in general intersect.*

It is easily shown that any point P_1 on ϕ may be given the coördinates $u_i = 0$, $x_i = 0$, $(i = 1, 2, \cdots, p)$, $u_{p+1} : x_{p+1} = 1 : 1$ without changing the form of the equation (4). The tangent hyperplane T_1 at P_1 is then $u_{p+1} - x_{p+1} = 0$, and its intersection with ϕ is the $S_{2p-1}^{(2)}$

$$u_1^2 + u_2^2 + \cdots u_p^2 - x_1^2 - x_2^2 - \cdots - x_p^2 = 0.$$

Any point P_2 on this locus may be given the coördinates $u_i = 0$, $x_i = 0$, $(i = 1, 2, \cdots, p-1)$, $u_p : u_{p+1} : x_p : x_{p+1} = 1 : 1 : 1 : 1$. The line $P_1 P_2$ is then on ϕ. The tangent hyperplane to ϕ at P_2 is then $u_p + u_{p+1} - x_p - x_{p+1} = 0$ and intersects $S_{2p-1}^{(2)}$ in the $S_{2p-2}^{(2)}$

$$u_1^2 + u_2^2 + \cdots + u_{p-1}^2 - x_1^2 - x_2^2 - \cdots - x_{p-1}^2 = 0.$$

Any point P_3 on this locus can now be given the coördinates $u_i = 0$, $x_i = 0$, $(i = 1, 2, \cdots, p-2)$, $u_{p-1} : u_p : u_{p+1} : x_{p-1} : x_p : x_{p+1} = 1 : 1 : 1 : 1 : 1 : 1$, and the S_2' determined by the three points P_1, P_2, P_3 lies on ϕ and has the equations $u_1 = \cdots = u_{p-2} = x_1 = \cdots = x_{p-2} = 0$, $u_{p-1} = x_{p-1}$, $u_p = x_p$, $u_{p+1} = x_{p+1}$.

---

* Scott, "Theory of Determinants," p. 234.

Proceeding in this way we may show that any $S_k'(k < p)$ lying on ϕ can be given the equations

$$
\begin{aligned}
u_1 &= x_1 = 0, \\
&\;\cdots\cdots\cdots \\
u_{p-k} &= x_{p-k} = 0, \\
u_{p-k+1} &= x_{p-k+1}, \\
&\;\cdots\cdots\cdots \\
u_{p+1} &= x_{p+1},
\end{aligned}
\tag{9}
$$

without changing the form of equation (4).

Any S_p' on ϕ has, as we have seen, the equations (5), and if it also contains all points of (9), its equations reduce to the form

$$
\begin{aligned}
u_1 &= a_{11}\; x_1 + \cdots + a_{1,p-k} x_{p-k}, \\
&\;\cdots\cdots\cdots\cdots\cdots\cdots\cdots \\
u_{p-k} &= a_{p-k,1} x_1 + \cdots + a_{p-k,p-k} x_{p-k}, \\
u_{p-k+1} &= \qquad\qquad\qquad\quad x_{p-k+1}, \\
&\;\cdots\cdots\cdots\cdots\cdots\cdots\cdots \\
u_{p+1} &= \qquad\qquad\qquad\quad x_{p+1},
\end{aligned}
\tag{10}
$$

where the coefficients satisfy conditions similar to (6) and

$$
|a_{ik}| = \begin{vmatrix} a_{11} & \cdots & a_{1,p-k} \\ \cdot & \cdots\cdots & \cdot \\ a_{p-k,1} & \cdots & a_{p-k,p-k} \end{vmatrix} = e.
$$

Without change of the form of equation (4) or (9) any one of these S_p' can be given the equations

$$
u_i = x_i.
\tag{12}
$$

In fact, we have simply to make a change of variables by which the right-hand members of equations (10) become x_i' and then to drop the primes.

The S_p' given by (12) will intersect any S_p' given by (10) always in the points of S_k' given by (9). In order that (12) and (10) should intersect in some other point not in S_k', it is necessary and sufficient that

$$
\begin{vmatrix} a_{11}-1 & \cdots & a_{1,p-k} \\ \cdot & \cdots\cdots & \cdot \\ a_{p-k,1} & \cdots & a_{p-k,p-k}-1 \end{vmatrix} = 0.
\tag{13}
$$

Now if $p - k$ is an odd number, equation (13) is always satisfied when $e = 1$; and if $p - k$ is an even number, it is always satisfied when $e = -1$. Further, we notice that if (12) and (10) have in common a point P which is outside of S_k', they have in common the S_{k+1}' determined by S_k' and P; and since (12) and (10) are on ϕ, this S_{k+1}' is on ϕ. Moreover, $p - k$ is odd if p is odd and k even or if p is even and k odd, and $p - k$ is even if both p and k are odd or if both p and k are even.

From this we have the following results:

1. If p is odd and two S_p' of the same family intersect in an S_k' where k is even, they intersect in at least an S_{k+1}'.

2. If p is odd and two S_p' of opposite families intersect in an S_k' where k is odd, they intersect in at least an S_{k+1}'.

3. If p is even and two S_p' of the same family intersect in an S_k' where k is odd, they intersect in at least an S_{k+1}'.

4. If p is even and two S_p' of opposite families intersect in an S_k' where k is even, they intersect in at least an S_{k+1}'.

This may be put into the following theorem, with reference also to theorem IV:

V. If p is odd, two S_p' of the same family do not in general intersect, but may intersect in an S_k' where k is odd; and two S_p' of opposite families intersect in general in a point, but may intersect in an S_k' where k is even. If p is even, two S_p' of the same family intersect in general in a single point, but may intersect in an S_k' where k is even; and two S_p' of opposite families do not in general intersect, but may intersect in an S_k' where k is odd.

If in equations (10) we take $k = p - 1$, they reduce to

$$u_1 = a_{11}x_1, \qquad u_i = x_i, \qquad (i = 2, 3, \cdots, p+1)$$

with $a_{11} = e = \pm 1$. Hence we have the theorem:

VI. Through any S_{p-1}' on ϕ go two S_p', one of each family.

More generally the number of independent coefficients in (10) is known from the theory of determinants to be $\dfrac{(p-k)(p-k-1)}{2}$. Hence we have the theorem:

VII. Through any S_k' on ϕ go $\infty^{\frac{1}{2}(p-k)(p-k-1)}$ S_p' of each family.

EXERCISES

1. Show that if S'_r lies on ϕ it must lie in its reciprocal polar space. From that deduce the condition $r \lesseqgtr \dfrac{n-1}{2}$.

2. Prove that there are $\infty^{\frac{r+1}{2}(2n-3r-2)}$ S'_r on ϕ by determining the number of solutions of equations (2) and (3), remembering that each of the $r+1$ points may be taken arbitrarily on S'_r.

3. Show that through every S'_k lying on ϕ there pass $\infty^{\frac{r-k}{2}(2n-3r-k-3)}S'_r$ which lie on the quadric $\left(k < r \lesseqgtr \dfrac{n-1}{2} \right)$.

168. Stereographic projection of a quadric in S_n upon S'_{n-1}. Let ϕ be a quadric hypersurface of dimensions $n-1$ in S_n, Σ any hyperplane in S_n, so that Σ is an S'_{n-1}, and O any point on ϕ. Straight lines through O intersect ϕ and Σ in general in one point each, and set up, therefore, a point correspondence of ϕ and Σ which in general is one-to-one. There are, however, on both ϕ and Σ exceptional points. On ϕ the point O is exceptional, since lines through O and no other point of ϕ lie in the tangent hyperplane at O, the intersection of which, with Σ, is an S'_{n-2} which we shall call π. Hence O corresponds to any point of π. On Σ the points in which the straight lines on ϕ through O intersect Σ are exceptional, since each of these points corresponds to an entire straight line on ϕ. These straight lines are the intersections of ϕ $(S^{(2)}_{n-1})$ and the tangent hyperplane (S'_{n-1}) at O, and therefore intersect Σ (S'_{n-1}) in an $S^{(2)}_{n-3}$ which we shall call Ω. Evidently Ω lies in π.

These statements, which are geometrically evident, may be verified by the use of coördinates. Let $x_1 : x_2 : \cdots : x_{n+1}$ be coördinates of a point in S_n, and let

$$x_1^2 + x_2^2 + \cdots + x_{n+1}^2 = 0 \tag{1}$$

be the equation of ϕ. Without loss of generality we may take O as $0 : 0 : \cdots : i : 1$ and the equation of Σ as $x_n = 0$.

The equations of a straight line through O and any point P of ϕ are, then,

$$\rho X_1 = 0 + \lambda x_1,$$
$$\vdots \qquad \vdots \qquad \vdots$$
$$\rho X_{n=1} = 0 + \lambda x_{n-1},$$
$$\rho X_n = i + \lambda x_n, \tag{2}$$
$$\rho X_{n+1} = 1 + \lambda x_{n+1};$$

and OP meets Σ in the point Q, obtained by placing $X_n = 0$ in (2). This determines λ, and the coördinates of Q are found to be

$$\xi_1 : \xi_2 : \cdots : \xi_{n-1} : 0 : \xi_n = x_1 : x_2 : \cdots : x_{n-1} : 0 : ix_n + x_{n+1},$$

where ξ_i are coördinates of points in Σ, and x_i are coördinates of points on ϕ. Since x_i satisfy equation (1) we may write the relation between P and its projection Q in the form

$$
\begin{aligned}
\rho x_1 &= \xi_1 \xi_n, \\
&\vdots \\
\rho x_{n-1} &= \xi_{n-1} \xi_n, \\
\rho(ix_n + x_{n+1}) &= \xi_n^2, \\
\rho(ix_n - x_{n+1}) &= \xi_1^2 + \xi_2^2 + \cdots + \xi_{n-1}^2.
\end{aligned}
\tag{3}
$$

Equations (3) show that to a definite point P corresponds a definite point Q, except that the point O gives an indeterminate Q on the locus $\xi_n = 0$, which is, therefore, the equation of π in Σ. Also any point Q corresponds to a definite point P, except that any point in the locus $\xi_n = 0$, $\xi_1^2 + \xi_2^2 + \cdots + \xi_{n-1}^2 = 0$ gives an indeterminate point P, but such that P and Q lie on a straight line through O. Therefore

$$\xi_n = 0, \quad \xi_1^2 + \xi_2^2 + \cdots + \xi_{n-1}^2 = 0 \tag{4}$$

are the equations which define the quadric Ω. We may note that any point Q which is on π but not on Ω gives the definite point O.

Any S_k' which lies on ϕ projects into an S_k' on Σ. For the equations
$$\rho x_i = x_i^{(1)} + \lambda_1 x_i^{(2)} + \cdots + \lambda_k x_i^{(k+1)}$$
become by the transformation (3)
$$\rho \xi_i = \xi_i^{(1)} + \mu_1 \xi_i^{(2)} + \cdots + \mu_k \xi_i^{(k+1)}.$$

An S_k' on ϕ intersects the tangent hyperplane at O in an S_{k-1}' which projects into an S_{k-1}' in Σ. But all points of the tangent hyperplane project into points on Ω, and therefore this S_{k-1}' lies entirely on Ω. Therefore we say:

I. *By stereographic projection any linear space S_k' lying on a quadric hypersurface ϕ in a space of n dimensions is brought into correspondence with a linear space S_{k-1}' lying on a quadric surface Ω in a space of $n - 2$ dimensions.*

This being proved, let us consider the case in which n is an odd number $2p + 1$. Then ϕ is of dimensions $2p$, and Ω is of dimensions

$2p - 2$. On ϕ there exist linear spaces S_p' which project into linear spaces of the same number of dimensions, which we call Σ_p' since they are in Σ. Any two Σ_p' intersect in at least a point, since they lie in a space of $2p$ dimensions (§ 164). If that point of intersection is not on Ω, it corresponds to an intersection of the two S_p' on ϕ, since outside of Ω any point of Σ corresponds to a definite point of ϕ. If, however, the intersection of two Σ_p' lies on Ω, the two corresponding S_p' on ϕ do not in general intersect. In fact, the intersection of two Σ_p' on Ω simply means that a straight line from O in the tangent hyperplane at O meets each of the two corresponding S_p'. Since we are talking of two S_p' in general, their intersection in the tangent hyperplane at O may be considered as exceptional, so that we have the theorem:

II. If two S_p' on the quadric ϕ intersect, the corresponding S_{p-1}' on the quadric Ω do not in general intersect; and if two S_p' on ϕ do not intersect, their corresponding S_{p-1}' on Ω in general intersect in a point.

In a similar manner the question of the intersections of linear spaces S_{p-1}' on an $S_{2p-2}^{(2)}$ may be reduced to the question of the intersection of two S_{p-2}' on an $S_{2p-4}^{(2)}$, and eventually to the intersection of two S_1' on an $S_2^{(2)}$; that is, of two straight lines on a quadric surface in ordinary three space.

We may, accordingly, divide the S_p' on ϕ into two families, according as they correspond by this successive projection to the two families of generators on an ordinary quadric surface. From theorem II, however, it is evident that we have the same classification as that made algebraically in § 167; for it follows that two S_p' of the same family do or do not intersect according as p is even or odd, and two S_p' of opposite families do or do not intersect according as p is odd or even. Exceptions may, of course, occur, as has been shown in § 167.

Let us consider now the intersection of ϕ by any hyperplane

$$a_1 x_1 + a_2 x_2 + \cdots + a_n x_n + a_{n+1} x_{n+1} = 0,$$

which passes or does not pass through the center of projection O, according as $i a_n + a_{n+1}$ is or is not 0. The intersection with ϕ is an $S_{n-2}^{(2)}$ which projects upon Σ into a $\Sigma_{n-2}^{(2)}$, with the equation

$$(i a_n + a_{n+1})(\xi_1^2 + \cdots + \xi_{n-1}^2) - 2\, a_1 \xi_1 \xi_n - \cdots - 2\, a_{n-1} \xi_{n-1} \xi_n$$
$$- (i a_n - a_{n+1}) \xi_n^2 = 0.$$

This is in general a $\Sigma_{n-1}^{(2)}$ which contains Ω, but if $ia_n + a_{n+1} = 0$, it splits up into the hyperplane π and a general hyperplane γ. Hence the theorem:

If an $S_{n-2}^{(2)}$ upon ϕ does not pass through O, it projects into a quadric in Σ which contains Ω; if an $S_{n-2}^{(2)}$ on ϕ does pass through O, it projects into a hyperplane in Σ together with the hyperplane π.

EXERCISES

1. Show that any S_m^g on ϕ not passing through O projects into a Σ_m^g in Σ which intersects π in a Σ_{m-1}^g contained in Ω.

2. Show that any S_{n-1}^i not passing through O intersects ϕ in an S_{n-2}^{2i} which projects into a Σ_{n-2}^{2i} which passes i times through Ω.

169. Application to line geometry. Since line coördinates consist of six homogeneous variables connected by a quadratic relation, a straight line in ordinary space may be considered as a point on a quadric surface in an S_5. We shall proceed to interpret in line geometry some of the general results we have obtained. In so doing we shall, to avoid confusion, designate a point, line, and plane in S_5 by the symbols S_0', S_1', S_2', respectively, reserving the words "point," "line," and "plane" for the proper configurations in S_3. Let ϕ be the quadric whose equation is the fundamental relation connecting the coördinates of a straight line. Then an S_0' on ϕ is a straight line, an S_1' on ϕ is a pencil of straight lines, and an S_2' on ϕ is either a bundle of lines or a plane of lines. These statements are established by comparing the analytical conditions for pencils and bundles of lines given in § 131 with those for S_1' and S_2' on ϕ.

The two families of S_2' on ϕ are easily distinguished, the one consisting of lines through a point, the other of lines in a plane. It is evident that two S_2' of the same family intersect in an S_0', for two bundles of lines or two planes of lines have always one line in common. On the other hand, a bundle of lines and a plane of lines do not in general have a line in common; that is, two S_2' of different families do not in general intersect. If, however, a point of lines and a plane of lines have one line in common, they will have a pencil in common; that is, *if two S_2' of different families on ϕ intersect in an S_0', they intersect in an S_1'.* This is in accord with theorem V, § 167.

A linear line complex is an $S_3^{(2)}$ formed by the intersection of ϕ and an S_4'. If the S_4' is tangent to ϕ, the complex is special and consists of $\infty^2 S_1'$ joining the points of the complex to a fixed S_0'. The special linear complex in line geometry consists, therefore, of ∞^2 pencils of lines containing a fixed line.

A linear line congruence consists of an $S_2^{(2)}$ formed by the intersection of ϕ and two S_4'. Therefore it consists in general of lines each of which belongs to two pencils containing, respectively, one of two fixed lines. When the two fixed lines intersect, the congruence splits up into a bundle of lines and a plane of lines, with a pencil in common. That suggests the theorem that on ϕ, *if the two fixed S_0' connected with a congruence $S_2^{(2)}$ lie on an S_1' of ϕ, the $S_2^{(2)}$ splits up into two S_2' of different families intersecting in this S_1'.*

A linear series is an $S_1^{(2)}$ determined by the intersection of ϕ and three S_4'. From the general theory we see that the series consists of ∞^1 lines, each of which lies in a pencil containing each of ∞^1 fixed lines. It therefore consists in general of ∞^1 lines intersecting another ∞^1 lines. We leave to the student the task of considering the special cases of a line series.

A linear complex

$$a_1 x_1 + a_2 x_2 + \cdots + a_{n+1} x_{n+1} = 0 \tag{1}$$

is fully determined by the ratios $a_1 : a_2 : \cdots : a_{n+1}$, which may be taken as the coördinates of the complex, and we may have a geometry in which the line complex is the element.

The quantities $a_1 : a_2 : \cdots : a_{n+1}$ are also the coördinates of a point in S_5, which is the pole of the hyperplane (1). Therefore the point a_i is not on the quadric ϕ unless the complex is special. An S_0' in S_5 is therefore a line complex. The lines of the complex a_i correspond to the points in which the polar (1) of the point a_i intersects ϕ. If S_0' is on ϕ, the complex is special and may be replaced by its axis so as not to contradict the previous statement that an S_0' on ϕ is a straight line. In fact, if the equation of ϕ is taken as $\sum x_i^2 = 0$, the coördinates of a special complex and of its axis are the same.

Consider now two complexes a_i and b_i as two points S_0' in S_5. They are said to be in *involution* if each S_0' lies on the polar plane of the other. From this it follows at once that if one of the complexes is special, its axis is a line of the other; so that if both are special, their axes intersect, and conversely. In case neither complex is special, the S_0' defined by a_i and b_i are not lines in S_3, and we must look for other geometric properties of complexes in involution.

In S_5 the coördinates a_i and b_i have a dualistic significance. On the one hand, they are coördinates of two S_0'; on the other hand, they are coördinates of two hyperplanes, the polars of these points. The two S_0' determine a pencil of S_0' which lie in an S_1', and the two hyperplanes a pencil of hyperplanes which have an S_3' in common. The pencil of S_0' contains two S_0' on ϕ, and the pencil of hyperplanes contains two hyperplanes tangent to ϕ. It is then evident that *two complexes are in involution when the two S_0' in S_5 which represent them are harmonic conjugates with respect to the quadric ϕ,* or, what is the same thing, when the two hyperplanes defining the complexes are harmonic conjugates to the two tangent hyperplanes to ϕ which are contained in the pencil defined by the two complexes.

It is clear that in any pencil of complexes the relation between a complex and its involutory complex is one-to-one.

If we consider a fixed complex a_i, all complexes in involution to it are represented by points in an S_4', which is the polar hyperplane of a_i with respect to ϕ.

This relation can be generalized. Let S_k' be a linear space of points in S_5, and let S_{4-k}' be the conjugate polar space with respect to ϕ, so that any point in S_k' is the harmonic conjugate with respect to ϕ of any point in S_{4-k}'. We have, then, two series of complexes, each of which is in involution with each one of the other series. The points in which S_k' intersect ϕ are special complexes. Their axes, therefore, must lie in each of the complexes in S_{4-k}', as has been shown above. In other words, the *axes of the special complexes of one series are the straight lines common to the complexes of the involutory series, and conversely.* The proof of the converse is left to the student.

For example, consider the pencil of complexes $a_i + \lambda b_i$ in involution with the series of complexes $c_i + \lambda' d_i + \mu' e_i + \nu' f_i$. The pencil of complexes have in general a congruence of straight lines in common, and these are the axes of the special complexes of the series. On the other hand, the series of complexes have in general two lines in common which are the axes of the special complexes of the pencil. Again, consider the bundles of complexes $a_i + \lambda b_i + \mu c_i$ and $e_i + \lambda' f_i + \mu' g_i$ in involution. The complexes of either bundle have in common the ∞^1 straight lines of a regulus which are the axes of the special complexes of the other bundle.

Any collineation of S_5 is a transformation of S_3 by which a linear line complex goes into a linear line complex, and any linear series of complexes goes into another such series. If, in addition, the quadric ϕ is transformed into itself, straight lines in S_3 are transformed into straight lines, and any S_2' on ϕ is transformed into another S_2' on ϕ. But as there are two systems of S_2' on ϕ, the transformation may transform an S_2' either into one of the same system or into one of the other system. In the first case, points in S_3' are transformed into points; in the second case, points in S_3 are transformed into planes. We have, accordingly, the theorem:

A collineation in S_5 which leaves the quadric ϕ unaltered is either a collineation or a correlation in S_3.

EXERCISES

1. Discuss oriented circles in a plane as points on a quadric in S_4.

2. Discuss oriented spheres in ordinary space as points on a quadric in S_5.

170. Metrical space of n dimensions. We have been considering spaces in which a point is defined by the ratios of homogeneous variables. We may, however, consider equally well a space in which the point is defined directly by n coördinates $u_1, u_2, \cdots, u_n$, and where the equations are not homogeneous. All equations may be made homogeneous, however, by placing

$$u_1 = \frac{x_1}{t}, \quad u_2 = \frac{x_2}{t}, \quad \cdots, \quad u_n = \frac{x_n}{t}. \tag{1}$$

The discussion is then reduced to the homogeneous case, but the use of t as the $n+1st$ coördinate emphasizes the unique character of that coördinate. In fact, when $t = 0$, some or all of the original coördinates become infinite. This enables us to handle infinite values of the original coördinates. Such sets of values may be distinguished from each other by the ratios of x_i, so that

$$a_1 : a_2 : \cdots : a_n : 0$$

is said to define a definite point at infinity. We have, therefore, a special case of projective space with a unique hyperplane $t = 0$. We may define a distance in a manner analogous to that used in three dimensions, by the equation

$$d^2 = (u_1' - u_1)^2 + (u_2' - u_2)^2 + \cdots + (u_n' - u_n)^2, \qquad (2)$$

or, in homogeneous form,

$$d^2 = \frac{(u_1't - u_1t')^2 + (u_2't - u_2t')^2 + \cdots + (u_n't - u_nt')^2}{t^2t'^2}. \qquad (3)$$

From this it appears that the distance between two points can be infinite only if t or t' is zero. Conversely, with the exception noted below, a point for which $t = 0$ is at an infinite distance from any point for which $t' \neq 0$. Therefore $t = 0$ is called *the hyperplane at infinity*.

On the hyperplane at infinity the coördinates are projective coördinates in S_{n-1} defined by the ratios $x_1 : x_2 : \cdots : x_n$.

An exception to the statement that points on the hyperplane at infinity are at an infinite distance from points not on that hyperplane occurs for points on the locus

$$t = 0, \quad x_1^2 + x_2^2 + \cdots + x_n^2 = 0, \qquad (4)$$

since the distance of any point on this locus from any other point is indeterminate. This locus, which is an S_{n-2}^2, or a quadric hypersurface in the hyperplane at infinity, is called *the absolute*.

The following properties of metrical space are such obvious generalizations of those of three-dimensional space that a mere statement of them is sufficient.

A *hypersphere* is the locus of points equidistant from a fixed point. Its equation is

$$(x_1 - a_1)^2 + (x_2 - a_2)^2 + \cdots + (x_n - a_n)^2 = r^2, \qquad (5)$$

and it is obvious that all hyperspheres contain the absolute, but no other point at infinity.

A straight line may be defined by the equations

$$\frac{x_1 - a_1}{l_1} = \frac{x_2 - a_2}{l_2} = \cdots = \frac{x_n - a_n}{l_n}. \qquad (6)$$

This line meets the hyperplane at infinity in the point $l_1 : l_2 : \cdots : l_n$. Hence, through any point in space go ∞^{n-1} lines distinguished by the ratios of the quantities l_i. We say that these quantities determine the direction of the line, direction being that property which distinguishes between straight lines through the same point.

Two lines with the same direction meet the hyperplane at infinity in the same point and are called parallel. Two lines with directions l_i and l_i' meet the hyperplane at infinity in two points with coördinates l_i and l_i', and the straight line connecting these two points meets the absolute in two points such that the cross ratio of the four points is

$$\frac{l_1 l_1' + l_2 l_2' + \cdots + l_n l_n'}{\sqrt{(l_1^2 + l_2^2 + \cdots + l_n^2)}\sqrt{l_1'^2 + l_2'^2 + \cdots + l_n'^2}}.$$

We shall define this as the cosine of the angle between the two lines; namely,

$$\cos\theta = \frac{\sum l_i l_i'}{\sqrt{\sum l_i^2}\sqrt{\sum l_i'^2}}.$$

In particular two lines are perpendicular when

$$l_1 l_1' + l_2 l_2' + \cdots + l_n l_n' = 0.$$

A line meets the absolute when, and only when,

$$l_1^2 + l_2^2 + \cdots + l_n^2 = 0.$$

In that case the distance between any two points on the line is zero, and the line is a minimum line. Through any point of space go, then, ∞^{n-2} minimum lines forming a hypercone of ∞^{n-1} points.

A tangent hyperplane to a hypersphere intersects it in ∞^{n-3} lines, and since the sphere contains the absolute these are minimum lines.

Any hyperplane

$$a_1 x_1 + a_2 x_2 + \cdots + a_n x_n + a_{n+1} t = 0$$

meets $t = 0$ in the locus

$$a_1 x_1 + a_2 x_2 + \cdots + a_n x_n = 0,$$

which is a hyperplane in the S_{n-1} defined by $t = 0$. It is tangent to the absolute when $\sum a_i^2 = 0$.

Hyperplanes satisfying this condition are minimum hyperplanes; all others are ordinary hyperplanes.

The intersection of an ordinary hyperplane with $t = 0$ has a pole with respect to the absolute whose coördinates are $a_1 : a_2 : \cdots : a_n$, and any straight line with the direction $a_1 : a_2 : \cdots : a_n$ is said to be perpendicular to the hyperplane. In fact, from the definition of perpendicular lines already given, this line is perpendicular to any line in the hyperplane, and conversely.

Two hyperplanes are perpendicular when the pole of the trace at infinity of either contains the pole of the trace of the other. Therefore the condition for two perpendicular hyperplanes is

$$a_1 b_1 + a_2 b_2 + \cdots + a_n b_n = 0.$$

It follows that the n hyperplanes

$$x_1 = 0, \quad x_2 = 0, \cdots, \quad x_n = 0$$

are mutually perpendicular hyperplanes intersecting at O. Through O or any point of space pass an infinite number of such mutually orthogonal hyperplanes; for, as seen in § 165, we may find in $t = 0$ an infinite number of coördinate systems such that the absolute retains the form $\sum_i x_i^2 = 0$, and the lines drawn from O to the points $x_i = 0$, $x_k \neq 0$ $(k \neq i)$ determine the hyperplanes required.

In this way any ordinary hyperplane may be made the plane $x_n = 0$. The coördinates in this hyperplane are $x_1 : x_2 : \cdots : x_{n-1} : t$, and its absolute is $t = 0$, $x_1^2 + x_2^2 + \cdots + x_{n-1}^2 = 0$.

Therefore *the geometry in any ordinary hyperplane differs from that in the original space only in the number of the dimensions.*

Two linear spaces, S'_{r_1} and S'_{r_2}, are said to be completely *parallel* if they intersect only at infinity and if the section of S'_{r_1} at infinity is completely contained in the section of S'_{r_2} at infinity $(r_1 \leqq r_2)$. Since the section of S'_{r_1} at infinity is an S'_{r_1-1}, it is necessary that S'_{r_1} and S'_{r_2} should lie in an $S'_{r_1+r_2-(r_1-1)} = S'_{r_2+1}$ (theorem IV, § 164). Moreover, if we take r_1 points in the S'_{r_1-1} at infinity, one other point not at infinity in S'_{r}, and $r_2 - r_1 + 1$ points not at infinity in S'_{r_2}, we have $r_2 + 2$ points to determine an S'_{r_2+1}. Therefore,

If two linear spaces S'_{r_1} and S'_{r_2} $(r_1 \leqq r_2)$ are completely parallel, they lie in an S'_{r_2+1} and completely determine it.

Consider now two spaces, S'_{r_1} and S'_{r_2} $(r_1 \leqq r_2)$, which do not intersect $(r_1 + r_2 < n)$. They determine in the hyperplane at infinity two nonintersecting spaces, S'_{r_1-1} and S'_{r_2-1}. If we take r_1 points in S'_{r_1-1}, and r_2 points in S'_{r_2-1}, we determine, by means of these points, an $S'_{r_1+r_2-1}$ in the hyperplane at infinity which contains both S'_{r_1-1}

and S'_{r_2-1}. By means of this $S'_{r_1+r_2-1}$ and one other point in S'_{r_1} not at infinity, we determine an $S'_{r_1+r_2}$ which contains S'_{r_1} because it contains r_1+1 of its points, and is parallel to S'_{r_2} since the intersection with infinity of S'_{r_2} is completely contained in that of $S'_{r_1+r_2}$. Hence,

If S'_{r_1} and S'_{r_2} are two nonintersecting linear spaces with $r_1 \gtreqqless r_2$, it is possible to pass a linear space $S'_{r_1+r_2}$ through S'_{r_1} parallel to S'_{r_2}.

It is obviously possible to define as partially parallel two linear spaces which intersect at infinity and nowhere else. This would lead to a series of theorems of which those in § 158 are examples, but we shall not pursue this line of investigation.

Two linear spaces will be defined as completely perpendicular when each straight line in one is perpendicular to each straight line of the other. If S'_{r_1} and S'_{r_2} are two linear spaces intersecting the hyperplane at infinity in S'_{r_1-1} and S'_{r_2-1}, respectively, it follows that the necessary and sufficient condition that S'_{r_1} should be completely perpendicular to S'_{r_2} is that S'_{r_1-1} should lie in the conjugate polar space of S'_{r_2-1} with respect to the absolute, when, of course, S'_{r_2-1} will also lie in the conjugate polar space of S'_{r_1-1} with respect to the absolute.

Now the conjugate polar space of S'_{r_1} in S'_{n-1} (the hyperplane at infinity) is, by § 165, S'_{n-r_1-1}. If S'_{r_1} is given, its intercept on the plane at infinity S'_{r_1-1} is determined, and the reciprocal polar space S'_{n-r_1-1} is also uniquely determined. One other point in finite space then determines with this S'_{n-r_1-1} an S'_{n-r_1} which is completely perpendicular to the given S'_{r_1}. Hence the theorem.

Through any point in space one and only one S'_{n-r} can be passed which is completely perpendicular to a given S'_r. Any linear space contained in S'_{n-r} is then completely perpendicular to any linear space in S'_r.

It is possible to define as partially perpendicular, spaces each of which contains a straight line perpendicular to the other, as in § 166, but we shall not do this.

Let us consider the stereographic projection of a hypersphere upon a hyperplane. Here we have merely to use the results of § 168, interpreting the quadric ϕ as a hypersphere, and the plane $x_{n+1}=0$

as the hyperplane at infinity in S_n. Then π is the hyperplane at infinity in S_{n-1}, and Ω is the absolute. We have at once the theorem :

By the stereographic projection of a hypersphere in S_n upon a hyperplane S_{n-1}, hyperplanar sections of ϕ go into hyperplanes or hyperspheres of S_{n-1} according as the hyperplanar sections of ϕ do or do not contain the center of projection.

A collineation in S_n by which ϕ is invariant gives a point transformation on ϕ by which hyperplanar sections go into hyperplanes. There is a corresponding transformation in S_{n-1} by which a hyperplane or a hypersphere goes into either a hyperplane or a hypersphere. If the collineation in S_n leaves O as well as ϕ invariant, hyperplanes of S_{n-1} are transformed into hyperplanes, and the transformation is a collineation. But the transformation in S_n leaves the tangent hyperplane at O unchanged, and therefore the corresponding transformation in S_{n-1} leaves the absolute unchanged. Hence,

Collineations in S_n which leave ϕ and the point O on ϕ unchanged determine collineations in S_{n-1} which leave the absolute unchanged and which are therefore metrical transformations.

Collineations in S_n which leave ϕ but not O unchanged determine point transformations in S_{n-1} by which hyperspheres go into hyperspheres, a hyperplane being considered a special case of a hypersphere.

We have used in § 168 one set of coördinates (x_i) for the points of ϕ, and another set (ξ_i) for the points of S_{n-1}, but clearly the coördinates x_i may also be used to determine points in S_{n-1}.

We shall have, then, for the points of S_{n-1} $n+1$ homogeneous coördinates connected by a quadratic relation, and such that a linear equation between them represents a hypersphere with the hyperplane as a special case. Each of the coördinates x_i equated to zero represents a hypersphere. We may, accordingly, call them $(n+1)$-polyspherical coördinates of the points of S_{n-1}. They are a generalization of the pentaspherical coördinates of S_3. We say :

Projective coördinates of points on a hypersphere in S_n are polyspherical coördinates of points on an S_{n-1} into which the hypersphere is stereographically projected. Collineations of S_n which leave the hypersphere invariant are linear transformations of the polyspherical coördinates of S_{n-1}.

171. Minimum projection of S_n upon S_{n-1}. Consider in S_n, with nonhomogeneous metrical coördinates, the minimum hypercone

$$(x_1 - a_1)^2 + (x_2 - a_2)^2 + \cdots + (x_n - a_n)^2 = 0. \qquad (1)$$

The section of this by the hyperplane $x_n = 0$ is

$$(x_1 - a_1)^2 + (x_2 - a_2)^2 + \cdots + (x_{n-1} - a_{n-1})^2 + a_n^2 = 0, \qquad (2)$$

which is a hypersphere in the S_{n-1} defined by $x_n = 0$. We say that the vertex a_i of the minimum hypercone (1) in S_n is projected minimally into the hypersphere (2) in S_{n-1}. Obviously, in order that the hypersphere (2) should be real the vertex of (1) must be imaginary. More exactly the coefficients $a_1, a_2, \cdots, a_{n-1}$ must be real and a_n pure imaginary.

The coördinates of the vertex of a hypercone in S_n are then essentially elementary coördinates (§ 146) of a hypersphere in S_{n-1}, but the radius of the sphere is ia_n instead of a_n. Let us, however, introduce into S_n polyspherical coördinates based upon $n + 2$ hyperspheres. The coördinates of the vertex of a hypercone in S_n and, consequently, of a hypersphere in S_{n-1} are then $n + 2$ homogeneous coördinates connected by a quadratic relation. They are therefore higher sphere coördinates of oriented hyperspheres in S_{n-1}. But we have seen that the polyspherical coördinates in S_n are projective coördinates of points on a hypersphere in S_{n+1}. We have, therefore:

The projective coördinates of a point on a hypersphere in S_{n+1} become, by stereographic projection, the $n + 2$ polyspherical coördinates of a point in S_n, and, by further minimum projection, the higher sphere coördinates of a hypersphere in S_{n-1}.

We have in this way obtained a geometric construction by which, for example, oriented spheres in S_3 may be brought into a one-to-one relation with points on a hypersphere in S_5.

EXERCISES

1. Show analytically that a point $x_1 : x_2 : \cdots : x_{n+1}$ on the hypersphere $x_1^2 + x_2^2 + \cdots + x_{n+1}^2 = 0$ in S_n projects by the double projection of the text into the hypersphere $(ix_n + x_{n+1})(\xi_1^2 + \cdots + \xi_{n-2}^2) - 2x_1\xi_1 - \cdots - 2x_{n-1}\xi_{n-2} + (ix_n - x_{n+1}) = 0$ in Σ_{n-2}.

2. Establish the following relations between S_5, S_4, and S_3, ϕ being a hypersphere in S:

S_5	S_4	S_3
A point on ϕ.	A point.	A sphere.
A hyperplane section of ϕ.	A sphere.	A sphere complex.
A section of ϕ by a tangent hyperplane.	A point sphere.	A special sphere complex.
A minimum line on ϕ.	A minimum line.	A pencil of tangent spheres.
A minimum plane on ϕ.	A minimum plane of second kind.	A bundle of tangent spheres.
A section of ϕ by any S_4^q.	A hypersurface of order g.	A sphere complex of order g.
A minimum curve on ϕ.	A minimum curve.	A series of ∞^1 spheres, each of which is tangent to the consecutive one.

REFERENCES

Sphere geometry :

COOLIDGE, Line and Sphere Geometry (see reference at end of Part III).

Line geometry :

HUDSON, Kummer's Quadric Surface. Cambridge University Press.

JESSOP, Treatise on the Line Complex. Cambridge University Press.

KŒNIGS, La géométrie réglée et ses applications. Gauthier-Villars.

PLÜCKER, Neue Geometrie des Raumes. Teubner.

Plücker's work is the original authority. It is quoted here for its historical value. The student will probably find it more convenient to consult the other texts, the scope of which is sufficiently indicated by their titles.

Geometry of n dimensions :

JOUFFRET, Géométrie à quatre dimensions. Gauthier-Villars.

MANNING, Geometry of Four Dimensions. The Macmillan Company.

Manning's book is synthetic, Jouffret's analytic. Especial mention should be made of the historical account in Manning's introduction, with copious references to the literature.

For general *n*-dimensional geometry reference will be made to the following journal articles, which the author has found especially useful in preparing his text :

KLEIN, "Ueber Liniengeometrie und metrische Geometrie." *Mathematische Annalen*, Vol. V, 1872.

SEGRE, "Studio sulle quadriche in uno spazio lineare ad un numero qualunque di dimensioni." *Memorie della reale accademia delle scienze di Torino*. Second Series, Vol. XXXVI, 1885.

VERONESE, "Behandlung der projectivischen Verhältnisse der Raüme von verschiedenen Dimensionen durch das Princip des Projicirens und Schneidens." *Mathematische Annalen*, Vol. XIX, 1882.

INDEX

COORDINATE GEOMETRY
by Luther Pfahler Eisenhart

"Coordinate Geometry" offers a thorough, complete, and unified introduction to the subject. An unusual presentation affords an exceptional insight into coordinate Geometry: where other studies cover all aspects of the 2nd dimension before going on to the 3rd, Professor Eisenhart advances in dimension within each topic. The sphere and circle are treated together; 3-dimensional coordinate systems are introduced along with polar coordinates; quadric surfaces directly follow conic sections.

Extensive use is made of determinants, but no previous knowledge of them is assumed. They are introduced from the beginning as a natural tool for coordinate geometry. Invaraints of conic sections and quadric surfaces are fully treated. Algebriac equations of the last degree in 2 and 3 unknowns are carefully reviewed and carried farther than is usual in algebra courses. Throughout the book, results are formulated precisely, with theorems clearly and sharply stated. Professor Eisenhart offers the only discussion, in any introductory text to analytic geometry, of the axiomatic basis of the subject. He gives axioms for coordinated geometry and shows that they are the algebraic equivalent of Hilbert's axioms for synthetic geometry.

The more than 500 exercises throughout the text will prove particularly helpful. They incorporate, often in rather novel settings, each idea after it has been carefully and fully explained.

Introduction. Appendix. Index. Over 500 exercises. Bibliography. 43 illustrations. xi + 298pp. 5⅜ x 8. S600 Paperbound **$1.65**

THE WORKS OF ARCHIMEDES WITH THE METHOD OF ARCHIMEDES
edited by T.L. Heath

The modern mathematician, physicist, science historian, logician, and every person interested in the most powerful mathematical mind of antiquity will be fascinated by this compilation of **all** the known works of Archimedes. In addition Sir Thomas Heath has contributed a scholarly introduction which clarifies many intricate points of the life and thought of the great geometer and of the scientific thought of the entire ancient world.

In the works proper, the famous problems of the ratio of the areas of a cylinder and an inscribed sphere, the measurement of a circle, the properties of conoids, spheroids and spirals, the quardrature of the parabola, and others are given in their entirety. THE METHOD OF ARCHIMEDES is the only extant work in which an ancient mathematician reveals his method of analysis. As such, it gives an invaluable insight into the steps which led to the immaculate demonstrations of Greek mathematics which otherwise seem to have been conceived in a perfect state with no prior development.

In the 186 page introduction to Greek mathematics, Sir Thomas discusses the relation of Archimedes to his predecessors and gives a very complete and lucid account of both arithmetic problems such as approximations to $\sqrt{3}$ and other irrational numbers, algebraic-geometric problems such as the trisection of the angle, proportionals, the cubic equation, and the anticipation of the integral calculus through the construction of inscribed and circumscribed polygons to a closed curve.

Preface. Bibliography. 563pp. 5⅜ x 8.

S9 Paperbound $2.00

ADVANCED EUCLIDEAN GEOMETRY
("Modern Geometry")
by Roger A. Johnson

This work is an elementary treatise on advanced Euclidean geometry, and requires no further preparation than high school geometry and trigonometry.

For many years this has been the standard textbook in this area of classical mathematics; no other book has covered the subject quite as well.

The author deals with the geometry of the triangle and the circle, concentrating on extensions of Euclidean theory, and exploring in unusual detail the many theorems that have been developed by relatively recent geometers. Several hundred of these theorems and corollaries are formulated and proved completely in the text. Since many of these theorems and proofs are available only in widely scattered journals, this book also has value as a time-saver and reference work to geometers and teachers of geometry. In addition the author has included a number of theorems left unproved, to be used by the student as exercises.

Johnson makes liberal use of circular inversion, the theory of pole and polar, and many other modern and powerful geometric tools throughout the book. A particularly valuable feature is his use throughout of the concept of "directed angles," a method that furnishes the shortest and most elegant form of statement for several common theorems and is besides a powerful method of proof.

CONTENTS: Introduction, Similar Figures, Coaxial Circles, Inversion, Triangles and Polygons, Geometry of Circles, Tangent Circles, The Theorem of Miquel, Theorems of Ceva and Menelaus, Three Notable Points, Inscribed and Escribed Circles, The Nine Point Circle, Symmedian Point and Other Notable Points, Triangles in Perspective, Pedal Triangles and Circles, Shorter Topics, The Brocard Configuration, Equibrocardal Triangles, Three Similar Figures.

Formerly titled "Modern Geometry." Unabridged republication of 1929 edition. Index. 107 diagrams. xiii + 319pp. 5⅜ x 8.   S669 Paperbound **$1.65**

NON-EUCLIDEAN GEOMETRY
by Roberto Bonola

This is an excellent historical and mathematical view by a renowned Italian geometer of the geometries that have arisen from a study of Euclid's 5th postulate on parallel lines. Students, teachers and mathematicians will find here a ready reference source and guide to a field that has now become overwhelmingly important.

NON-EUCLIDEAN GEOMETRY first examines the various attempts to prove Euclid's parallel postulate — by the Greeks, by the Arabs, by mathematicians of the Renaissance. Then, ranging through the 17th, 18th and 19th centuries, it considers the forerunners and founders of non-Euclidean geometry, such as Saccheri, Lambert, Legendre, W. Bolyai, Gauss, Schweikart, Taurinus, J. Bolyai and Lobatschewsky. In a discussion of later developments, the author treats the work of Riemann, Helmholtz and Lie; the impossibility of proving Euclid's postulate, and similar topics. The complete text of two of the founding monographs is appended to Bonola's study: "The Science of Absolute Space" by John Bolyai and "Geometrical Researches on the Theory of Parallels" by Nicholas Lobatschewsky.

"Firmly recommended to any scientific reader with some mathematical inclination" JOURNAL OF THE ROYAL NAVAL SCIENTIFIC SERVICE. "Classics on the subject," SCIENTIFIC AMERICAN.

Translation with additional appendices by H. S. Carslaw. 256 bibliographic footnote references. Introduction by Federigo Enriques. Index. 181 diagrams. 431pp. 5⅜ x 8.

S27 Paperbound **$1.95**

THE GEOMETRY OF RENÉ DESCARTES

This is an unabridged re-publication of the definitive English translation of one of the very greatest classics of science. Originally published in 1637, it has been characterized as "the greatest single step ever made in the progress of the exact sciences" (John Stuart Mill); as a book which "remade geometry and made modern geometry possible," (Eric Temple Bell). It "revolutionized the entire conception of the object of mathematical science," (J. Hadamard).

With this volume Descartes founded modern analytical geometry. Reducing geometry to algebra and analysis, and conversely showing that analysis may be translated into geometry, it opened the way for modern mathematics. Descartes was the first to classify curves systematically, and to demonstrate algebraic solution of geometric curves. His geometric interpretation of negative quantities led to later concepts of continuity and the theory of function. The third book contains important contributions to the theory of equations.

This edition contains the entire definitive Smith-Latham translation of Descartes' three books: **Problems the Construction of which Requires Only Straight Lines and Circles; On the Nature of Curved Lines; On the Construction of Solid or Supersolid Problems.** Interleaved page by page with the translation is a complete facsimile of the 1637 French text, together with all Descartes' original illustrations, 248 footnotes explain the text and add further bibliography.

Translated by David E. Smith and Marcia L. Latham. Preface. Index. 50 figures. xiii+244pp. 5⅜ x 8.   S68   Paperbound **$1.50**

ELEMENTS OF PROJECTIVE GEOMETRY
by Luigi Cremona

The outstanding work of one of the foremost 19th century European geometers, this treatise has remained one of the best and most complete treatments of projective geometry for more than 75 years. Written originally in Italian, it has been translated into French, German, and English. It was perhaps the main force in spreading a knowledge of projective geometry throughout the Continent and the British Isles, and has come to be accepted as a classic in its field.

The book provides a comprehensive coverage of the entire field of projective geometry as constructed on the basis of Euclidean geometry, including detailed proofs of all its fundamental principles. Over 150 examples and problems are not only answered, but worked out and solved completely. In addition, stress throughout the book is placed on the constructive aspects of projective geometry, with more than 250 diagrams included to help the student understand basic principles by the practical construction of figures. Anyone with a knowledge of ordinary geometry can begin this book with no further preparation

Cremona covers homology, the law of duality, geometric forms, harmonic sections, anharmonic ratios, the theorems of Pascal and Briachon, conjugate diameters, Desargues' theorem, foci, the construction of projective forms, the theory of involution, Carnot's theorem, the theory of pole and polar, problems of the second degree, the center and diameter of a conic, polar reciprocal figures, and self-corresponding elements. Besides these general problems, the author also treats scores of specific cases, giving theorems, construction problems, and proofs for each.

Unabridged republication of 1913 printing. Index. Over 150 examples and problems. 252 diagrams. xx + 302 pp. 5⅜ x 8.   S668 Paperbound **$1.75**

A TREATISE ON THE DIFFERENTIAL GEOMETRY OF CURVES AND SURFACES

by Luther P. Eisenhart

Professor of Mathematics, Emeritus, Princeton

This is an introductory treatise on differential geometry written especially for the graduate student. An outgrowth of the author's own courses at Princton, it has been highly successful as a textbook for many years. It is more detailed and more concrete in its approach than most more recent books, and is thereby still of great use to a student or a teacher. L. P. Eisenhart is recognized as a leading writer on mathematics, whose treatises on advanced topics are already considered modern classics.

In this book, he gives a thorough explanation of the geometry of curves and surfaces, concentrating on the problems a student will find most helpful. New ideas are not only explained fully and clearly in the text, but are also illustrated and extended by hundreds of examples and problems.

Chapter I, devoted to the theory of space curves, covers parametric equations, tangents to a curve, osculating planes, and normals, and develops the concept of moving axes used throughout the remainder of the book. The author goes on to deal with the geometry of a surface in the neighborhood of a point, Gauss' method, envelopes, the moving trihedral, differential parameters, systems of curves, geodesics, conformal representation, and applications of the theory to quadrics, ruled surfaces and others.

The last part of the book, drawn from a more advanced course in differential geometry, deals with the deformation of surfaces, rectilinear congruences, cyclic systems, and triply orthogonal systems of surfaces.

Unabridged and unaltered republication of 1909 edition. Index. 683 problems. 30 diagrams. xii + 474pp. S667 Paperbound **$2.75**

FAMOUS PROBLEMS OF ELEMENTARY GEOMETRY

by Felix Klein

This expanded version of the famous 1894 Easter lectures at Göttingen University has been accepted as a modern mathematical classic, and has been translated into four different languages. Using techniques of modern mathematics, it examines three famous problems which were intensely investigated in premodern mathematics: doubling the volume of a cube, trisecting an angle, squaring a circle.

Written with all Felix Klein's mathematical breadth, clarity, and profundity, this volume provides answers to modern problems connected with these three problems of the past. It is especially interesting to the modern student in answering such questions as: Under what circumstances is a geometric construction possible? By what means can a geometric construction be effected? What are transcendental numbers, and how can you prove that e and pi are transcendental? Treatment is simple, and no knowledge of higher mathematics is required.

CONTENTS. I. THE POSSIBILITY OF THE CONSTRUCTION OF ALGEBRAIC EXPRESSIONS. 1. Algebraic equations solvable by square roots. The delian problem and the trisection of the angle. The division of the circle into equal parts. The construction of the regular polygon of 17 sides. General considerations of algebraic constructions. II. TRANSCENDENTAL NUMBERS AND THE QUADRATURE OF THE CIRCLE. Cantor's demonstration of the existence of transcendental numbers. Historical survey of the attempts at the computation and construction of pi. Transcendence of the number e. Transcendence of pi. Integraph and the geometric construction of pi. Notes by R. C. Archibald discuss in detail Gaussian polygons, Fermat's theorem, the irrationality of pi, and similar topics.

Translated by W. W. Beman, D. E. Smith from the second revised edition. 16 figures. xi + 92pp. 5⅜ x 8.

T298 Paperbound $1.00

GEOMETRY OF FOUR DIMENSIONS
by H. P. Manning

Manning's GEOMETRY OF FOUR DIMENSIONS is unique in English as a clear and concise introduction to a branch of modern mathematics now in application as an indispensable part of mathematical physics (algebra, analysis, relativity).

Proceeding by the synthetic method the author will make clear to you the geometry of the fourth dimension, aiding you to reason about four-dimensional figures. Treatment is based mostly on Euclidean geometry, although in some cases, as hyperplanes at infinity, non-Euclidean geometry is used. After a discussion of the history of dimensions, with references to Moebius, Riemann, Lobatchevsky, and others, the author discusses the foundations of fourth dimensional geometry; perpendicular and simple angles; angles of two planes and of higher order; symmetry, order, motion, hyperpyramids; hypercones; hyperspheres; Euclidean geometry, figures with parallel elements; measurement of volume and hypervolume in hyperspace; regular polyhedroids.

"Clearly written . . . an excellent book," SCIENTIFIC AMERICAN. "Of particular interest . . . The author shows that the knowledge of the new geometries has clarified and sometimes corrected men's understanding even of Euclidean geometry," MODERN SCHOOLMAN. "A standard treatise for students of mathematics," SKY AND TELESCOPE.

Complete unabridged reproduction of the first edition. Preface. Historical introduction. 179 footnotes, mostly bibliographical. Glossary of terms. Index. 76 figures, including 3 full-page plates. ix+348 pp. 5⅜ x 8.

S182 Paperbound **$1.95**

Catalogue of Dover
SCIENCE BOOKS

BOOKS THAT EXPLAIN SCIENCE

THE NATURE OF LIGHT AND COLOUR IN THE OPEN AIR, M. Minnaert. Why is falling snow sometimes black? What causes mirages, the fata morgana, multiple suns and moons in the sky; how are shadows formed? Prof. Minnaert of U. of Utrecht answers these and similar questions in optics, light, colour, for non-specialists. Particularly valuable to nature, science students, painters, photographers. "Can best be described in one word—fascinating!" Physics Today. Translated by H. M. Kremer-Priest, K. Jay. 202 illustrations, including 42 photos. xvi + 362pp. 5⅜ x 8. T196 Paperbound **$1.95**

THE RESTLESS UNIVERSE, Max Born. New enlarged version of this remarkably readable account by a Nobel laureate. Moving from sub-atomic particles to universe, the author explains in very simple terms the latest theories of wave mechanics. Partial contents: air and its relatives, electrons and ions, waves and particles, electronic structure of the atom, nuclear physics. Nearly 1000 illustrations, including 7 animated sequences. 325pp. 6 x 9. T412 Paperbound **$2.00**

MATTER AND LIGHT, THE NEW PHYSICS, L. de Broglie. Non-technical papers by a Nobel laureate explain electromagnetic theory, relativity, matter, light, radiation, wave mechanics, quantum physics, philosophy of science. Einstein, Planck, Bohr, others explained so easily that no mathematical training is needed for all but 2 of the 21 chapters. "Easy simplicity and lucidity . . . should make this source-book of modern physcis available to a wide public," Saturday Review. Unabridged. 300pp. 5⅜ x 8. T35 Paperbound **$1.60**

THE COMMON SENSE OF THE EXACT SCIENCES, W. K. Clifford. Introduction by James Newman, edited by Karl Pearson. For 70 years this has been a guide to classical scientific, mathematical thought. Explains with unusual clarity basic concepts such as extension of meaning of symbols, characteristics of surface boundaries, properties of plane figures, vectors, Cartesian method of determining position, etc. Long preface by Bertrand Russell. Bibliography of Clifford. Corrected. 130 diagrams redrawn. 249pp. 5⅜ x 8. T61 Paperbound **$1.60**

THE EVOLUTION OF SCIENTIFIC THOUGHT FROM NEWTON TO EINSTEIN, A. d'Abro. Einstein's special, general theories of relativity, with historical implications, analyzed in non-technical terms. Excellent accounts of contributions of Newton, Riemann, Weyl, Planck, Eddington, Maxwell, Lorentz, etc., are treated in terms of space, time, equations of electromagnetics, finiteness of universe, methodology of science. "Has become a standard work," Nature. 21 diagrams. 482pp. 5⅜ x 8. T2 Paperbound **$2.00**

BRIDGES AND THEIR BUILDERS, D. Steinman, S. R. Watson. Engineers, historians, everyone ever fascinated by great spans will find this an endless source of information and interest. Dr. Steinman, recent recipient of Louis Levy Medal, is one of the great bridge architects, engineers of all time. His analysis of great bridges of history is both authoritative and easily followed. Greek, Roman, medieval, oriental bridges; modern works such as Brooklyn Bridge, Golden Gate Bridge, etc. described in terms of history, constructional principles, artistry, function. Most comprehensive, accurate semi-popular history of bridges in print in English. New, greatly revised, enlarged edition. 23 photographs, 26 line drawings. xvii + 401pp. 5⅜ x 8. T431 Paperbound **$1.95**

CONCERNING THE NATURE OF THINGS, Sir William Bragg. Christmas lectures at Royal Society by Nobel laureate, dealing with atoms, gases, liquids, and various types of crystals. No scientific background is needed to understand this remarkably clear introduction to basic processes and aspects of modern science. "More interesting than any bestseller," London Morning Post. 32pp. of photos. 57 figures. xii + 232pp. 5⅜ x 8. **T31 Paperbound $1.35**

THE RISE OF THE NEW PHYSICS, A. d'Abro. Half million word exposition, formerly titled "The Decline of Mechanism," for readers not versed in higher mathematics. Only thorough explanation in everyday language of core of modern mathematical physical theory, treating both classical, modern views. Scientifically impeccable coverage of thought from Newtonian system through theories of Dirac, Heisenberg, Fermi's statistics. Combines history, exposition; broad but unified, detailed view, with constant comparison of classical, modern views. "A must for anyone doing serious study in the physical sciences," J. of the Franklin Inst. "Extraordinary faculty . . . to explain ideas and theories . . . in language of everyday life," Isis. Part I of set: philosophy of science, from practice of Newton, Maxwell, Poincaré, Einstein, etc. Modes of thought, experiment, causality, etc. Part II: 100 pp. on grammar, vocabulary of mathematics, discussions of functions, groups, series, Fourier series, etc. Remainder treats concrete, detailed coverage of both classical, quantum physics: analytic mechanics, Hamilton's principle, electromagnetic waves, thermodynamics, Brownian movement, special relativity, Bohr's atom, de Broglie's wave mechanics, Heisenberg's uncertainty, scores of other important topics. Covers discoveries, theories of d'Alembert, Born, Cantor, Debye, Euler, Foucault, Galois, Gauss, Hadamard, Kelvin, Kepler Laplace, Maxwell, Pauli, Rayleigh Volterra, Weyl, more than 180 others. 97 illustrations. ix + 982pp. 5⅜ x 8.
T3 Vol. 1 Paperbound $2.00
T4 Vol. II Paperbound $2.00

SPINNING TOPS AND GYROSCOPIC MOTION, John Perry. Well-known classic of science still unsurpassed for lucid, accurate, delightful exposition. How quasi-rigidity is induced in flexible, fluid bodies by rapid motions; why gyrostat falls, top rises; nature, effect of internal fluidity on rotating bodies; etc. Appendixes describe practical use of gyroscopes in ships, compasses, monorail transportation. 62 figures. 128pp. 5⅜ x 8. **T416 Paperbound $1.00**

FOUNDATIONS OF PHYSICS, R. B. Lindsay, H. Margenau. Excellent bridge between semipopular and technical writings. Discussion of methods of physical description, construction of theory; valuable to physicist with elementary calculus. Gives meaning to data, tools of modern physics. Contents: symbolism, mathematical equations; space and time; foundations of mechanics; probability; physics, continua; electron theory; relativity; quantum mechanics; causality; etc. "Thorough and yet not overdetailed. Unreservedly recommended," Nature. Unabridged corrected edition. 35 illustrations. xi + 537pp. 5⅜ x 8. **S377 Paperbound $2.45**

FADS AND FALLACIES IN THE NAME OF SCIENCE, Martin Gardner. Formerly entitled "In the Name of Science," the standard account of various cults, quack systems, delusions which have masqueraded as science: hollow earth fanatics, orgone sex energy, dianetics, Atlantis, Forteanism, flying saucers, medical fallacies like zone therapy, etc. New chapter on Bridey Murphy, psionics, other recent manifestations. A fair reasoned appraisal of eccentric theory which provides excellent innoculation. "Should be read by everyone, scientist or nonscientist alike," R. T. Birge, Prof. Emeritus of Physics, Univ. of Calif; Former Pres., Amer. Physical Soc. x + 365pp. 5⅜ x 8. **T394 Paperbound $1.50**

ON MATHEMATICS AND MATHEMATICIANS, R. E. Moritz. A 10 year labor of love by discerning, discriminating Prof. Moritz, this collection conveys the full sense of mathematics and personalities of great mathematicians. Anecdotes, aphorisms, reminiscences, philosophies, definitions, speculations, biographical insights, etc. by great mathematicians, writers: Descartes, Mill, Locke, Kant, Coleridge, Whitehead, etc. Glimpses into lives of great mathematicians, from Archimedes to Euler, Gauss, Weierstrass. To mathematicians, a superb browsing-book. To laymen, exciting revelation of fullness of mathematics. Extensive cross index. 410pp. 5⅜ x 8. **T489 Paperbound $1.95**

GUIDE TO THE LITERATURE OF MATHEMATICS AND PHYSICS, N. G. Parke III. Over 5000 entries under approximately 120 major subject headings, of selected most important books, monographs, periodicals, articles in English, plus important works in German, French, Italian, Spanish, Russian (many recently available works). Covers every branch of physics, math, related engineering. Includes author, title, edition, publisher, place, date, number of volumes, number of pages. 40 page introduction on basic problems of research, study provides useful information on organization, use of libraries, psychology of learning, etc. Will save you hours of time. 2nd revised edition. Indices of authors, subjects. 464pp. 5⅜ x 8. **S447 Paperbound $2.49**

THE STRANGE STORY OF THE QUANTUM, An Account for the General Reader of the Growth of Ideas Underlying Our Present Atomic Knowledge, B. Hoffmann. Presents lucidly, expertly, with barest amount of mathematics, problems and theories which led to modern quantum physics. Begins with late 1800's when discrepancies were noticed; with illuminating analogies, examples, goes through concepts of Planck, Einstein, Pauli, Schroedinger, Dirac, Sommerfield, Feynman, etc. New postscript through 1958. "Of the books attempting an account of the history and contents of modern atomic physics which have come to my attention, this is the best," H. Margenau, Yale U., in Amer. J. of Physics. 2nd edition. 32 tables, illustrations. 275pp. 5⅜ x 8. **T518 Paperbound $1.45**

DOVER SCIENCE BOOKS

HISTORY OF SCIENCE
AND PHILOSOPHY OF SCIENCE

THE VALUE OF SCIENCE, Henri Poincaré. Many of most mature ideas of "last scientific universalist" for both beginning, advanced workers. Nature of scientific truth, whether order is innate in universe or imposed by man, logical thought vs. intuition (relating to Weierstrass, Lie, Riemann, etc), time and space (relativity, psychological time, simultaneity), Herz's concept of force, values within disciplines of Maxwell, Carnot, Mayer, Newton, Lorentz, etc. iii + 147pp. 5⅜ x 8.   S469 Paperbound **$1.35**

PHILOSOPHY AND THE PHYSICISTS, L. S. Stebbing. Philosophical aspects of modern science examined in terms of lively critical attack on ideas of Jeans, Eddington. Tasks of science, causality, determinism, probability, relation of world physics to that of everyday experience, philosophical significance of Planck-Bohr concept of discontinuous energy levels, inferences to be drawn from Uncertainty Principle, implications of "becoming" involved in 2nd law of thermodynamics, other problems posed by discarding of Laplacean determinism. 285pp. 5⅜ x 8.   T480 Paperbound **$1.65**

THE PRINCIPLES OF SCIENCE, A TREATISE ON LOGIC AND THE SCIENTIFIC METHOD, W. S. Jevons. Milestone in development of symbolic logic remains stimulating contribution to investigation of inferential validity in sciences. Treats inductive, deductive logic, theory of number, probability, limits of scientific method; significantly advances Boole's logic, contains detailed introduction to nature and methods of probability in physics, astronomy, everyday affairs, etc. In introduction, Ernest Nagel of Columbia U. says,"[Jevons] continues to be of interest as an attempt to articulate the logic of scientific inquiry." liii + 786pp. 5⅜ x 8.   S446 Paperbound **$2.98**

A HISTORY OF ASTRONOMY FROM THALES TO KEPLER, J. L. E. Dreyer. Only work in English to give complete history of cosmological views from prehistoric times to Kepler. Partial contents: Near Eastern astronomical systems, Early Greeks, Homocentric spheres of Euxodus, Epicycles, Ptolemaic system, Medieval cosmology, Copernicus, Kepler, much more. "Especially useful to teachers and students of the history of science . . . unsurpassed in its field," Isis. Formerly "A History of Planetary Systems from Thales to Kepler." Revised foreword by W. H. Stahl. xvii + 430pp. 5⅜ x 8.   S79 Paperbound **$1.98**

A CONCISE HISTORY OF MATHEMATICS, D. Struik. Lucid study of development of ideas, techniques, from Ancient Near East, Greece, Islamic science, Middle Ages, Renaissance, modern times. Important mathematicians described in detail. Treatment not anecdotal, but analytical development of ideas. Non-technical—no math training needed. "Rich in content, thoughtful in interpretations," U.S. Quarterly Booklist. 60 illustrations including Greek, Egyptian manuscripts, portraits of 31 mathematicians. 2nd edition. xix + 299pp. 5⅜ x 8.   S255 Paperbound **$1.75**

THE PHILOSOPHICAL WRITINGS OF PEIRCE, edited by Justus Buchler. A carefully balanced expositon of Peirce's complete system, written by Peirce himself. It covers such matters as scientific method, pure chance vs. law, symbolic logic, theory of signs, pragmatism, experiment, and other topics. "Excellent selection . . . gives more than adequate evidence of the range and greatness," Personalist. Formerly entitled "The Philosophy of Peirce." xvi + 368pp.   T217 Paperbound **$1.95**

SCIENCE AND METHOD, Henri Poincaré. Procedure of scientific discovery, methodology, experiment, idea-germination—processes by which discoveries come into being. Most significant and interesting aspects of development, application of ideas. Chapters cover selection of facts, chance, mathematical reasoning, mathematics and logic; Whitehead, Russell, Cantor, the new mechanics, etc. 288pp. 5⅜ x 8.   S222 Paperbound **$1.35**

SCIENCE AND HYPOTHESIS, Henri Poincaré. Creative psychology in science. How such concepts as number, magnitude, space, force, classical mechanics developed, how modern scientist uses them in his thought. Hypothesis in physics, theories of modern physics. Introduction by Sir James Larmor. "Few mathematicians have had the breadth of vision of Poincaré, and none is his superior in the gift of clear exposition," E. T. Bell. 272pp. 5⅜ x 8.   S221 Paperbound **$1.35**

ESSAYS IN·EXPERIMENTAL LOGIC, John Dewey. Stimulating series of essays by one of most influential minds in American philosophy presents some of his most mature thoughts on wide range of subjects. Partial contents: Relationship between inquiry and experience; dependence of knowledge upon thought; character logic; judgments of practice, data, and meanings; stimuli of thought, etc. viii + 444pp. 5⅜ x 8.   T73 Paperbound **$1.95**

WHAT IS SCIENCE, Norman Campbell. Excellent introduction explains scientific method, role of mathematics, types of scientific laws. Contents: 2 aspects of science, science and nature, laws of chance, discovery of laws, explanation of laws, measurement and numerical laws, applications of science. 192pp. 5⅜ x 8.   S43 Paperbound **$1.25**

FROM EUCLID TO EDDINGTON: A STUDY OF THE CONCEPTIONS OF THE EXTERNAL WORLD, Sir **Edmund Whittaker.** Foremost British scientist traces development of theories of natural philosophy from western rediscovery of Euclid to Eddington, Einstein, Dirac, etc. 5 major divisions: Space, Time and Movement; Concepts of Classical Physics; Concepts of Quantum Mechanics; Eddington Universe. Contrasts inadequacy of classical physics to understand physical world with present day attempts of relativity, non-Euclidean geometry, space curvature, etc. 212pp. 5⅜ x 8. T491 Paperbound **$1.35**

THE ANALYSIS OF MATTER, Bertrand Russell. How do our senses accord with the new physics? This volume covers such topics as logical analysis of physics, prerelativity physics, causality, scientific inference, physics and perception, special and general relativity, Weyl's theory, tensors, invariants and their physical interpretation, periodicity and qualitative series. "The most thorough treatment of the subject that has yet been published," The Nation. Introduction by L. E. Denonn. 422pp. 5⅜ x 8. T231 Paperbound **$1.95**

LANGUAGE, TRUTH, AND LOGIC, A. Ayer. A clear introduction to the Vienna and Cambridge schools of Logical Positivism. Specific tests to evaluate validity of ideas, etc. Contents: function of philosophy, elimination of metaphysics, nature of analysis, a priori, truth and probability, etc. 10th printing. "I should like to have written it myself," Bertrand Russell. 160pp. 5⅜ x 8. T10 Paperbound **$1.25**

THE PSYCHOLOGY OF INVENTION IN THE MATHEMATICAL FIELD, J. Hadamard. Where do ideas come from? What role does the unconscious play? Are ideas best developed by mathematical reasoning, word reasoning, visualization? What are the methods used by Einstein, Poincaré, Galton, Riemann? How can these techniques be applied by others? One of the world's leading mathematicians discusses these and other questions. xiii + 145pp. 5⅜ x 8. T107 Paperbound **$1.25**

GUIDE TO PHILOSOPHY, C. E. M. Joad. By one of the ablest expositors of all time, this is not simply a history or a typological survey, but an examination of central problems in terms of answers afforded by the greatest thinkers: Plato, Aristotle, Scholastics, Leibniz, Kant, Whitehead, Russell, and many others. Especially valuable to persons in the physical sciences; over 100 pages devoted to Jeans, Eddington, and others, the philosophy of modern physics, scientific materialism, pragmatism, etc. Classified bibliography. 592pp. 5⅜ x 8. T50 Paperbound **$2.00**

SUBSTANCE AND FUNCTION, and **EINSTEIN'S THEORY OF RELATIVITY, Ernst Cassirer.** Two books bound as one. Cassirer establishes a philosophy of the exact sciences that takes into consideration new developments in mathematics, shows historical connections. Partial contents: Aristotelian logic, Mill's analysis, Helmholtz and Kronecker, Russell and cardinal numbers, Euclidean vs. non-Euclidean geometry, Einstein's relativity. Bibliography. Index. xxi + 464pp. 5⅜ x 8. T50 Paperbound **$2.00**

FOUNDATIONS OF GEOMETRY, Bertrand Russell. Nobel laureate analyzes basic problems in the overlap area between mathematics and philosophy: the nature of geometrical knowledge, the nature of geometry, and the applications of geometry to space. Covers history of non-Euclidean geometry, philosophic interpretations of geometry, especially Kant, projective and metrical geometry. Most interesting as the solution offered in 1897 by a great mind to a problem still current. New introduction by Prof. Morris Kline, N.Y. University. "Admirably clear, precise, and elegantly reasoned analysis," International Math. News. xii + 201pp. 5⅜ x 8. S233 Paperbound **$1.60**

THE NATURE OF PHYSICAL THEORY, P. W. Bridgman. How modern physics looks to a highly unorthodox physicist—a Nobel laureate. Pointing out many absurdities of science, demonstrating inadequacies of various physical theories, weighs and analyzes contributions of Einstein, Bohr, Heisenberg, many others. A non-technical consideration of correlation of science and reality. xi + 138pp. 5⅜ x 8. S33 Paperbound **$1.25**

EXPERIMENT AND THEORY IN PHYSICS, Max Born. A Nobel laureate examines the nature and value of the counterclaims of experiment and theory in physics. Synthetic versus analytical scientific advances are analyzed in works of Einstein, Bohr, Heisenberg, Planck, Eddington, Milne, others, by a fellow scientist. 44pp. 5⅜ x 8. S308 Paperbound **60¢**

A SHORT HISTORY OF ANATOMY AND PHYSIOLOGY FROM THE GREEKS TO HARVEY, Charles Singer. Corrected edition of "The Evolution of Anatomy." Classic traces anatomy, physiology from prescientific times through Greek, Roman periods, dark ages, Renaissance, to beginning of modern concepts. Centers on individuals, movements, that definitely advanced anatomical knowledge. Plato, Diocles, Erasistratus, Galen, da Vinci, etc. Special section on Vesalius. 20 plates. 270 extremely interesting illustrations of ancient, Medieval, Renaissance, Oriental origin. xii + 209pp. 5⅜ x 8. T389 Paperbound **$1.75**

SPACE-TIME-MATTER, Hermann Weyl. "The standard treatise on the general theory of relativity," (Nature), by world renowned scientist. Deep, clear discussion of logical coherence of general theory, introducing all needed tools: Maxwell, analytical geometry, non-Euclidean geometry, tensor calculus, etc. Basis is classical space-time, before absorption of relativity. Contents: Euclidean space, mathematical form, metrical continuum, general theory, etc. 15 diagrams. xviii + 330pp. 5⅜ x 8. S267 Paperbound **$1.75**

MATTER AND MOTION, James Clerk Maxwell. Excellent exposition begins with simple particles, proceeds gradually to physical systems beyond complete analysis; motion, force, properties of centre of mass of material system; work, energy, gravitation, etc. Written with all Maxwell's original insights and clarity. Notes by E. Larmor. 17 diagrams. 178pp. 5⅜ x 8.
S188 Paperbound **$1.25**

PRINCIPLES OF MECHANICS, Heinrich Hertz. Last work by the great 19th century physicist is not only a classic, but of great interest in the logic of science. Creating a new system of mechanics based upon space, time, and mass, it returns to axiomatic analysis, understanding of the formal or structural aspects of science, taking into account logic, observation, a priori elements. Of great historical importance to Poincaré, Carnap, Einstein, Milne. A 20 page introduction by R. S. Cohen, Wesleyan University, analyzes the implications of Hertz's thought and the logic of science. 13 page introduction by Helmholtz. xlii + 274pp. 5⅜ x 8.
S316 Clothbound **$3.50**
S317 Paperbound **$1.75**

FROM MAGIC TO SCIENCE, Charles Singer. A great historian examines aspects of science from Roman Empire through Renaissance. Includes perhaps best discussion of early herbals, penetrating physiological interpretation of "The Visions of Hildegarde of Bingen." Also examines Arabian, Galenic influences; Pythagoras' sphere, Paracelsus; reawakening of science under Leonardo da Vinci, Vesalius; Lorica of Gildas the Briton; etc. Frequent quotations with translations from contemporary manuscripts. Unabridged, corrected edition. 158 unusual illustrations from Classical, Medieval sources. xxvii + 365pp. 5⅜ x 8.
T390 Paperbound **$2.00**

A HISTORY OF THE CALCULUS, AND ITS CONCEPTUAL DEVELOPMENT, Carl B. Boyer. Provides laymen, mathematicians a detailed history of the development of the calculus, from beginnings in antiquity to final elaboration as mathematical abstraction. Gives a sense of mathematics not as technique, but as habit of mind, in progression of ideas of Zeno, Plato, Pythagoras, Eudoxus, Arabic and Scholastic mathematicians, Newton, Leibniz, Taylor, Descartes, Euler, Lagrange, Cantor, Weierstrass, and others. This first comprehensive, critical history of the calculus was originally entitled "The Concepts of the Calculus." Foreword by R. Courant. 22 figures. 25 page bibliography. v + 364pp. 5⅜ x 8.
S509 Paperbound **$2.00**

A DIDEROT PICTORIAL ENCYCLOPEDIA OF TRADES AND INDUSTRY, Manufacturing and the Technical Arts in Plates Selected from "L'Encyclopédie ou Dictionnaire Raisonné des Sciences, des Arts, et des Métiers" of Denis Diderot. Edited with text by C. Gillispie. First modern selection of plates from high-point of 18th century French engraving. Storehouse of technological information to historian of arts and science. Over 2,000 illustrations on 485 full page plates, most of them original size, show trades, industries of fascinating era in such great detail that modern reconstructions might be made of them. Plates teem with men, women, children performing thousands of operations; show sequence, general operations, closeups, details of machinery. Illustrates such important, interesting trades, industries as sowing, harvesting, beekeeping, tobacco processing, fishing, arts of war, mining, smelting, casting iron, extracting mercury, making gunpowder, cannons, bells, shoeing horses, tanning, papermaking, printing, dying, over 45 more categories. Professor Gillispie of Princeton supplies full commentary on all plates, identifies operations, tools, processes, etc. Material is presented in lively, lucid fashion. Of great interest to all studying history of science, technology. Heavy library cloth. 920pp. 9 x 12.
T421 2 volume set **$18.50**

DE MAGNETE, William Gilbert. Classic work on magnetism, founded new science. Gilbert was first to use word "electricity," to recognize mass as distinct from weight, to discover effect of heat on magnetic bodies; invented an electroscope, differentiated between static electricity and magnetism, conceived of earth as magnet. This lively work, by first great experimental scientist, is not only a valuable historical landmark, but a delightfully easy to follow record of a searching, ingenious mind. Translated by P. F. Mottelay. 25 page biographical memoir. 90 figures. lix + 368pp. 5⅜ x 8.
S470 Paperbound **$2.00**

HISTORY OF MATHEMATICS, D. E. Smith. Most comprehensive, non-technical history of math in English. Discusses lives and works of over a thousand major, minor figures, with footnotes giving technical information outside book's scheme, and indicating disputed matters. Vol. I: A chronological examination, from primitive concepts through Egypt, Babylonia, Greece, the Orient, Rome, the Middle Ages, The Renaissance, and to 1900. Vol. II: The development of ideas in specific fields and problems, up through elementary calculus. "Marks an epoch . . . will modify the entire teaching of the history of science," George Sarton. 2 volumes, total of 510 illustrations, 1355pp. 5⅜ x 8. Set boxed in attractive container.
T429, 430 Paperbound, the set **$5.00**

THE PHILOSOPHY OF SPACE AND TIME, H. Reichenbach. An important landmark in development of empiricist conception of geometry, covering foundations of geometry, time theory, consequences of Einstein's relativity, including: relations between theory and observations; coordinate definitions; relations between topological and metrical properties of space; psychological problem of visual intuition of non-Euclidean structures; many more topics important to modern science and philosophy. Majority of ideas require only knowledge of intermediate math. "Still the best book in the field," Rudolf Carnap. Introduction by R. Carnap. 49 figures. xviii + 296pp. 5⅜ x 8.
S443 Paperbound **$2.00**

FOUNDATIONS OF SCIENCE: THE PHILOSOPHY OF THEORY AND EXPERIMENT, N. Campbell.
A critique of the most fundamental concepts of science, particularly physics. Examines why certain propositions are accepted without question, demarcates science from philosophy, etc. Part I analyzes presuppositions of scientific thought: existence of material world, nature of laws, probability, etc; part 2 covers nature of experiment and applications of mathematics: conditions for measurement, relations between numerical laws and theories, error, etc. An appendix covers problems arising from relativity, force, motion, space, time. A classic in its field. "A real grasp of what science is," Higher Educational Journal.
xiii + 565pp. 5⅝ x 8⅜.   S372 Paperbound **$2.95**

THE STUDY OF THE HISTORY OF MATHEMATICS and **THE STUDY OF THE HISTORY OF SCIENCE, G. Sarton.** Excellent introductions, orientation, for beginning or mature worker. Describes duty of mathematical historian, incessant efforts and genius of previous generations. Explains how today's discipline differs from previous methods. 200 item bibliography with critical evaluations, best available biographies of modern mathematicians, best treatises on historical methods is especially valuable. 10 illustrations. 2 volumes bound as one.
113pp. + 75pp. 5⅜ x 8.   T240 Paperbound **$1.25**

MATHEMATICAL PUZZLES

MATHEMATICAL PUZZLES OF SAM LOYD, selected and edited by **Martin Gardner.** 117 choice puzzles by greatest American puzzle creator and innovator, from his famous "Cyclopedia of Puzzles." All unique style, historical flavor of originals. Based on arithmetic, algebra, probability, game theory, route tracing, topology, sliding block, operations research, geometrical dissection. Includes famous "14-15" puzzle which was national craze, "Horse of a Different Color" which sold millions of copies. 120 line drawings, diagrams. Solutions.
xx + 167pp. 5⅜ x 8.   T498 Paperbound **$1.00**

SYMBOLIC LOGIC and THE GAME OF LOGIC, Lewis Carroll. "Symbolic Logic" is not concerned with modern symbolic logic, but is instead a collection of over 380 problems posed with charm and imagination, using the syllogism, and a fascinating diagrammatic method of drawing conclusions. In "The Game of Logic" Carroll's whimsical imagination devises a logical game played with 2 diagrams and counters (included) to manipulate hundreds of tricky syllogisms. The final section, "Hit or Miss" is a lagniappe of 101 additional puzzles in the delightful Carroll manner. Until this reprint edition, both of these books were rarities costing up to $15 each. Symbolic Logic: Index. xxxi + 199pp. The Game of Logic: 96pp.
2 vols. bound as one. 5⅜ x 8.   T492 Paperbound **$1.50**

PILLOW PROBLEMS and A TANGLED TALE, Lewis Carroll. One of the rarest of all Carroll's works, "Pillow Problems" contains 72 original math puzzles, all typically ingenious. Particularly fascinating are Carroll's answers which remain exactly as he thought them out, reflecting his actual mental process. The problems in "A Tangled Tale" are in story form, originally appearing as a monthly magazine serial. Carroll not only gives the solutions, but uses answers sent in by readers to discuss wrong approaches and misleading paths, and grades them for insight. Both of these books were rarities until this edition, "Pillow Problems" costing up to $25, and "A Tangled Tale" $15. Pillow Problems: Preface and Introduction by Lewis Carroll. xx + 109pp. A Tangled Tale: 6 illustrations. 152pp. Two vols.
bound as one. 5⅜ x 8.   T493 Paperbound **$1.50**

NEW WORD PUZZLES, G. L. Kaufman. 100 brand new challenging puzzles on words, combinations, never before published. Most are new types invented by author, for beginners and experts both. Squares of letters follow chess moves to build words; symmetrical designs made of synonyms; rhymed crostics; double word squares; syllable puzzles where you fill in missing syllables instead of missing letter; many other types, all new. Solutions. "Excellent," Recreation. 100 puzzles. 196 figures. vi + 122pp. 5⅜ x 8.
                                                     T344 Paperbound **$1.00**

MATHEMATICAL EXCURSIONS, H. A. Merrill. Fun, recreation, insights into elementary problem solving. Math expert guides you on by-paths not generally travelled in elementary math courses—divide by inspection, Russian peasant multiplication; memory systems for pi; odd, even magic squares; dyadic systems; square roots by geometry; Tchebichev's machine; dozens more. Solutions to more difficult ones. "Brain stirring stuff . . . a classic," Genie.
50 illustrations. 145pp. 5⅜ x 8.   T350 Paperbound **$1.00**

THE BOOK OF MODERN PUZZLES, G. L. Kaufman. Over 150 puzzles, absolutely all new material based on same appeal as crosswords, deduction puzzles, but with different principles, techniques. 2-minute teasers, word labyrinths, design, pattern, logic, observation puzzles, puzzles testing ability to apply general knowledge to peculiar situations, many others. Solutions. 116 illustrations. 192pp. 5⅜ x 8.   T143 Paperbound **$1.00**

MATHEMAGIC, MAGIC PUZZLES, AND GAMES WITH NUMBERS, R. V. Heath. Over 60 puzzles, stunts, on properties of numbers. Easy techniques for multiplying large numbers mentally, identifying unknown numbers, finding date of any day in any year. Includes The Lost Digit, 3 Acrobats, Psychic Bridge, magic squares, triangles, cubes, others not easily found elsewhere. Edited by J. S. Meyer. 76 illustrations. 128pp. 5⅜ x 8.   T110 Paperbound **$1.00**

DOVER SCIENCE BOOKS

PUZZLE QUIZ AND STUNT FUN, J. Meyer. 238 high-priority puzzles, stunts, tricks—math puzzles like The Clever Carpenter, Atom Bomb, Please Help Alice; mysteries, deductions like The Bridge of Sighs, Secret Code; observation puzzlers like The American Flag, Playing Cards, Telephone Dial; over 200 others with magic squares, tongue twisters, puns, anagrams. Solutions. Revised, enlarged edition of "Fun-To-Do." Over 100 illustrations. 238 puzzles, stunts, tricks. 256pp. 5⅜ x 8.   T337 Paperbound **$1.00**

101 PUZZLES IN THOUGHT AND LOGIC, C. R. Wylie, Jr. For readers who enjoy challenge, stimulation of logical puzzles without specialized math or scientific knowledge. Problems entirely new, range from relatively easy to brainteasers for hours of subtle entertainment. Detective puzzles, find the lying fisherman, how a blind man identifies color by logic, many more. Easy-to-understand introduction to logic of puzzle solving and general scientific method. 128pp. 5⅜ x 8.   T367 Paperbound **$1.00**

CRYPTANALYSIS, H. F. Gaines. Standard elementary, intermediate text for serious students. Not just old material, but much not generally known, except to experts. Concealment, Transposition, Substitution ciphers; Vigenere, Kasiski, Playfair, multafid, dozens of other techniques. Formerly "Elementary Cryptanalysis." Appendix with sequence charts, letter frequencies in English, 5 other languages, English word frequencies. Bibliography. 167 codes. New to this edition: solutions to codes. vi + 230pp. 5⅜ x 8⅜.
                                                             T97 Paperbound **$1.95**

CRYPTOGRAPY, L. D. Smith. Excellent elementary introduction to enciphering, deciphering secret writing. Explains transposition, substitution ciphers; codes; solutions; geometrical patterns, route transcription, columnar transposition, other methods. Mixed cipher systems; single, polyalphabetical substitutions; mechanical devices; Vigenere; etc. Enciphering Japanese; explanation of Baconian biliteral cipher; frequency tables. Over 150 problems. Bibliography. Index. 164pp. 5⅜ x 8.   T247 Paperbound **$1.00**

MATHEMATICS, MAGIC AND MYSTERY, M. Gardner. Card tricks, metal mathematics, stage mind-reading, other "magic" explained as applications of probability, sets, number theory, etc. Creative examination of laws, applications. Scores of new tricks, insights. 115 sections on cards, dice, coins; vanishing tricks, many others. No sleight of hand—math guarantees success. "Could hardly get more entertainment . . . easy to follow," Mathematics Teacher. 115 illustrations. xii + 174pp. 5⅜ x 8.   T335 Paperbound **$1.00**

AMUSEMENTS IN MATHEMATICS, H. E. Dudeney. Foremost British originator of math puzzles, always witty, intriguing, paradoxical in this classic. One of largest collections. More than 430 puzzles, problems, paradoxes. Mazes, games, problems on number manipulations, unicursal, other route problems, puzzles on measuring, weighing, packing, age, kinship, chessboards, joiners', crossing river, plane figure dissection, many others. Solutions. More than 450 illustrations. viii + 258pp. 5⅜ x 8.   T473 Paperbound **$1.25**

THE CANTERBURY PUZZLES H. E. Dudeney. Chaucer's pilgrims set one another problems in story form. Also Adventures of the Puzzle Club, the Strange Escape of the King's Jester, the Monks of Riddlewell, the Squire's Christmas Puzzle Party, others. All puzzles are original, based on dissecting plane figures, arithmetic, algebra, elementary calculus, other branches of mathematics, and purely logical ingenuity. "The limit of ingenuity and intricacy," The Observer. Over 110 puzzles, full solutions. 150 illustrations. viii + 225 pp. 5⅜ x 8.   T474 Paperbound **$1.25**

MATHEMATICAL PUZZLES FOR BEGINNERS AND ENTHUSIASTS, G. Mott-Smith. 188 puzzles to test mental agility. Inference, interpretation, algebra, dissection of plane figures, geometry, properties of numbers, decimation, permutations, probability, all are in these delightful problems. Includes the Odic Force, How to Draw an Ellipse, Spider's Cousin, more than 180 others. Detailed solutions. Appendix with square roots, triangular numbers, primes, etc. 135 illustrations. 2nd revised edition. 248pp. 5⅜ x 8.   T198 Paperbound **$1.00**

MATHEMATICAL RECREATIONS, M. Kraitchik. Some 250 puzzles, problems, demonstrations of recreation mathematics on relatively advanced level. Unusual historical problems from Greek, Medieval, Arabic, Hindu sources; modern problems on "mathematics without numbers," geometry, topology, arithmetic, etc. Pastimes derived from figurative, Mersenne, Fermat numbers: fairy chess; latruncles: reversi; etc. Full solutions. Excellent insights into special fields of math. "Strongly recommended to all who are interested in the lighter side of mathematics," Mathematical Gaz. 181 illustrations. 330pp. 5⅜ x 8.
                                                             T163 Paperbound **$1.75**

FICTION

FLATLAND, E. A. Abbott. A perennially popular science-fiction classic about life in a 2-dimensional world, and the impingement of higher dimensions. Political, satiric, humorous, moral overtones. This land where women are straight lines and the lowest and most dangerous classes are isosceles triangles with 3° vertices conveys brilliantly a feeling for many concepts of modern science. 7th edition. New introduction by Banesh Hoffmann. 128pp. 5⅜ x 8.   T1 Paperbound **$1.00**

7

SEVEN SCIENCE FICTION NOVELS OF H. G. WELLS. Complete texts, unabridged, of seven of Wells' greatest novels: The War of the Worlds, The Invisible Man, The Island of Dr. Moreau, The Food of the Gods, First Men in the Moon, In the Days of the Comet, The Time Machine. Still considered by many experts to be the best science-fiction ever written, they will offer amusements and instruction to the scientific minded reader. "The great master," Sky and Telescope. 1051pp. 5⅜ x 8. T264 Clothbound **$3.95**

28 SCIENCE FICTION STORIES OF H. G. WELLS. Unabridged! This enormous omnibus contains 2 full length novels—Men Like Gods, Star Begotten—plus 26 short stories of space, time, invention, biology, etc. The Crystal Egg, The Country of the Blind, Empire of the Ants, The Man Who Could Work Miracles, Aepyornis Island, A Story of the Days to Come, and 20 others "A master . . . not surpassed by . . . writers of today," The English Journal. 915pp. 5⅜ x 8. T265 Clothbound **$3.95**

FIVE ADVENTURE NOVELS OF H. RIDER HAGGARD. All the mystery and adventure of darkest Africa captured accurately by a man who lived among Zulus for years, who knew African ethnology, folkways as did few of his contemporaries. They have been regarded as examples of the very best high adventure by such critics as Orwell, Andrew Lang, Kipling. Contents: She, King Solomon's Mines, Allan Quatermain, Allan's Wife, Maiwa's Revenge. "Could spin a yarn so full of suspense and color that you couldn't put the story down," Sat. Review. 821pp. 5⅜ x 8. T108 Clothbound **$3.95**

CHESS AND CHECKERS

LEARN CHESS FROM THE MASTERS, Fred Reinfeld. Easiest, most instructive way to improve your game—play 10 games against such masters as Marshall, Znosko-Borovsky, Bronstein, Najdorf, etc., with each move graded by easy system. Includes ratings for alternate moves possible. Games selected for interest, clarity, easily isolated principles. Covers Ruy Lopez, Dutch Defense, Vienna Game openings; subtle, intricate middle game variations; all-important end game. Full annotations. Formerly "Chess by Yourself." 91 diagrams. viii + 144pp. 5⅜ x 8. T362 Paperbound **$1.00**

REINFELD ON THE END GAME IN CHESS, Fred Reinfeld. Analyzes 62 end games by Alekhine, Flohr, Tarrasch, Morphy, Capablanca, Rubinstein, Lasker, Reshevsky, other masters. Only 1st rate book with extensive coverage of error—tell exactly what is wrong with each move you might have made. Centers around transitions from middle play to end play. King and pawn, minor pieces, queen endings; blockage, weak, passed pawns, etc. "Excellent . . . a boon," Chess Life. Formerly "Practical End Play." 62 figures. vi + 177pp. 5⅜ x 8. T417 Paperbound **$1.25**

HYPERMODERN CHESS as developed in the games of its greatest exponent, ARON NIMZO-VICH, edited by Fred Reinfeld. An intensely original player, analyst, Nimzovich's approaches startled, often angered the chess world. This volume, designed for the average player, shows how his iconoclastic methods won him victories over Alekhine, Lasker, Marshall, Rubinstein, Spielmann, others, and infused new life into the game. Use his methods to startle opponents, invigorate play. "Annotations and introductions to each game . . . are excellent," Times (London). 180 diagrams. viii + 220pp. 5⅜ x 8. T448 Paperbound **$1.35**

THE ADVENTURE OF CHESS, Edward Lasker. Lively reader, by one of America's finest chess masters, including: history of chess, from ancient Indian 4-handed game of Chaturanga to great players of today; such delights and oddities as Maelzel's chess-playing automaton that beat Napoleon 3 times; etc. One of most valuable features is author's personal recollections of men he has played against—Nimzovich, Emanuel Lasker, Capablanca, Alekhine, etc. Discussion of chess-playing machines (newly revised). 5 page chess primer. 11 illustrations. 53 diagrams. 296pp. 5⅜ x 8. S510 Paperbound **$1.45**

THE ART OF CHESS, James Mason. Unabridged reprinting of latest revised edition of most famous general study ever written. Mason, early 20th century master, teaches beginning, intermediate player over 90 openings; middle game, end game, to see more moves ahead, to plan purposefully, attack, sacrifice, defend, exchange, govern general strategy. "Classic . . . one of the clearest and best developed studies," Publishers Weekly. Also included, a complete supplement by F. Reinfeld, "How Do You Play Chess?", invaluable to beginners for its lively question-and-answer method. 448 diagrams. 1947 Reinfeld-Bernstein text. Bibliography. xvi + 340pp. 5⅜ x 8. T463 Paperbound **$1.85**

MORPHY'S GAMES OF CHESS, edited by P. W. Sergeant. Put boldness into your game by flowing brilliant, forceful moves of the greatest chess player of all time. 300 of Morphy's best games, carefully annotated to reveal principles. 54 classics against masters like Anderssen, Harrwitz, Bird, Paulsen, and others. 52 games at odds; 54 blindfold games; plus over 100 others. Follow his interpretation of Dutch Defense, Evans Gambit, Giuoco Piano, Ruy Lopez, many more. Unabridged reissue of latest revised edition. New introduction by F. Reinfeld. Annotations, introduction by Sergeant. 235 diagrams. x + 352pp. 5⅜ x 8. T386 Paperbound **$1.75**

WIN AT CHECKERS, M. Hopper. (Formerly "Checkers.") Former World's Unrestricted Checker Champion discusses principles of game, expert's shots, traps, problems for beginner, standard openings, locating best move, end game, opening "blitzkrieg" moves to draw when behind, etc. Over 100 detailed questions, answers anticipate problems. Appendix. 75 problems with solutions, diagrams. 79 figures. xi + 107pp. 5⅜ x 8.   T363 Paperbound **$1.00**

HOW TO FORCE CHECKMATE, Fred Reinfeld. If you have trouble finishing off your opponent, here is a collection of lightning strokes and combinations from actual tournament play. Starts with 1-move checkmates, works up to 3-move mates. Develops ability to look ahead, gain new insights into combinations, complex or deceptive positions; ways to estimate weaknesses, strengths of you and your opponent. "A good deal of amusement and instruction," Times, (London). 300 diagrams. Solutions to all positions. Formerly "Challenge to Chess Players." 111pp. 5⅜ x 8.   T417 Paperbound **$1.25**

A TREASURY OF CHESS LORE, edited by Fred Reinfeld. Delightful collection of anecdotes, short stories, aphorisms by, about masters; poems, accounts of games, tournaments, photographs; hundreds of humorous, pithy, satirical, wise, historical episodes, comments, word portraits. Fascinating "must" for chess players; revealing and perhaps seductive to those who wonder what their friends see in game. 49 photographs (14 full page plates). 12 diagrams. xi + 306pp. 5⅜ x 8.   T458 Paperbound **$1.75**

WIN AT CHESS, Fred Reinfeld. 300 practical chess situations, to sharpen your eye, test skill against masters. Start with simple examples, progress at own pace to complexities. This selected series of crucial moments in chess will stimulate imagination, develop stronger, more versatile game. Simple grading system enables you to judge progress. "Extensive use of diagrams is a great attraction," Chess. 300 diagrams. Notes, solutions to every situation. Formerly "Chess Quiz." vi + 120pp. 5⅜ x 8.   T433 Paperbound **$1.00**

MATHEMATICS:
ELEMENTARY TO INTERMEDIATE

HOW TO CALCULATE QUICKLY, H. Sticker. Tried and true method to help mathematics of everyday life. Awakens "number sense"—ability to see relationships between numbers as whole quantities. A serious course of over 9000 problems and their solutions through techniques not taught in schools: left-to-right multiplications, new fast division, etc. 10 minutes a day will double or triple calculation speed. Excellent for scientist at home in higher math, but dissatisfied with speed and accuracy in lower math. 256pp. 5 x 7¼.   Paperbound **$1.00**

FAMOUS PROBLEMS OF ELEMENTARY GEOMETRY, Felix Klein. Expanded version of 1894 Easter lectures at Göttingen. 3 problems of classical geometry: squaring the circle, trisecting angle, doubling cube, considered with full modern implications: transcendental numbers, pi, etc. "A modern classic . . . no knowledge of higher mathematics is required," Scientia. Notes by R. Archibald. 16 figures. xi + 92pp. 5⅜ x 8.   T298 Paperbound **$1.00**

HIGHER MATHEMATICS FOR STUDENTS OF CHEMISTRY AND PHYSICS, J. W. Mellor. Practical, not abstract, building problems out of familiar laboratory material. Covers differential calculus, coordinate, analytical geometry, functions, integral calculus, infinite series, numerical equations, differential equations, Fourier's theorem probability, theory of errors, calculus of variations, determinants. "If the reader is not familiar with this book, it will repay him to examine it," Chem. and Engineering News. 800 problems. 189 figures. xxi + 641pp. 5⅜ x 8.   S193 Paperbound **$2.25**

TRIGONOMETRY REFRESHER FOR TECHNICAL MEN, A. A. Klaf. 913 detailed questions, answers cover most important aspects of plane, spherical trigonometry—particularly useful in clearing up difficulties in special areas. Part I: plane trig, angles, quadrants, functions, graphical representation, interpolation, equations, logs, solution of triangle, use of slide rule, etc. Next 188 pages discuss applications to navigation, surveying, elasticity, architecture, other special fields. Part 3: spherical trig, applications to terrestrial, astronomical problems. Methods of time-saving, simplification of principal angles, make book most useful. 913 questions answered. 1738 problems, answers to odd numbers. 494 figures. 24 pages of formulas, functions. x + 629pp. 5⅜ x 8.   T371 Paperbound **$2.00**

CALCULUS REFRESHER FOR TECHNICAL MEN, A. A. Klaf. 756 questions examine most important aspects of integral, differential calculus. Part I: simple differential calculus, constants, variables, functions, increments, logs, curves, etc. Part 2: fundamental ideas of integrations, inspection, substitution, areas, volumes, mean value, double, triple integration, etc. Practical aspects stressed. 50 pages illustrate applications to specific problems of civil, nautical engineering, electricity, stress, strain, elasticity, similar fields. 756 questions answered. 566 problems, mostly answered. 36pp. of useful constants, formulas. v + 431pp. 5⅜ x 8.   T370 Paperbound **$2.00**

MONOGRAPHS ON TOPICS OF MODERN MATHEMATICS, edited by J. W. A. Young. Advanced mathematics for persons who have forgotten, or not gone beyond, high school algebra. 9 monographs on foundation of geometry, modern pure geometry, non-Euclidean geometry, fundamental propositions of algebra, algebraic equations, functions, calculus, theory of numbers, etc. Each monograph gives proofs of important results, and descriptions of leading methods, to provide wide coverage. "Of high merit," Scientific American. New introduction by Prof. M. Kline, N.Y. Univ. 100 diagrams. xvi + 416pp. 6⅛ x 9¼.
S289 Paperbound **$2.00**

MATHEMATICS IN ACTION, O. G. Sutton. Excellent middle level application of mathematics to study of universe, demonstrates how math is applied to ballistics, theory of computing machines, waves, wave-like phenomena, theory of fluid flow, meteorological problems, statistics, flight, similar phenomena. No knowledge of advanced math required. Differential equations, Fourier series, group concepts, Eigenfunctions, Planck's constant, airfoil theory, and similar topics explained so clearly in everyday language that almost anyone can derive benefit from reading this even if much of high-school math is forgotten. 2nd edition. 88 figures. viii + 236pp. 5⅜ x 8.
T450 Clothbound **$3.50**

ELEMENTARY MATHEMATICS FROM AN ADVANCED STANDPOINT, Felix Klein. Classic text, an outgrowth of Klein's famous integration and survey course at Göttingen. Using one field to interpret, adjust another, it covers basic topics in each area, with extensive analysis. Especially valuable in areas of modern mathematics. "A great mathematician, inspiring teacher, . . . deep insight," Bul., Amer. Math Soc.

Vol. I. ARITHMETIC, ALGEBRA, ANALYSIS. Introduces concept of function immediately, enlivens discussion with graphical, geometric methods. Partial contents: natural numbers, special properties, complex numbers. Real equations with real unknowns, complex quantities. Logarithmic, exponential functions, infinitesimal calculus. Transcendence of e and pi, theory of assemblages. Index. 125 figures. ix + 274pp. 5⅜ x 8.
S151 Paperbound **$1.75**

Vol. II. GEOMETRY. Comprehensive view, accompanies space perception inherent in geometry with analytic formulas which facilitate precise formulation. Partial contents: Simplest geometric manifold; line segments, Grassman determinant principles, classification of configurations of space. Geometric transformations: affine, projective, higher point transformations, theory of the imaginary. Systematic discussion of geometry and its foundations. 141 illustrations. ix + 214pp. 5⅜ x 8.
S151 Paperbound **$1.75**

A TREATISE ON PLANE AND ADVANCED TRIGONOMETRY, E. W. Hobson. Extraordinarily wide coverage, going beyond usual college level, one of few works covering advanced trig in full detail. By a great expositor with unerring anticipation of potentially difficult points. Includes circular functions; expansion of functions of multiple angle; trig tables; relations between sides, angles of triangles; complex numbers; etc. Many problems fully solved. "The best work on the subject," Nature. Formerly entitled "A Treatise on Plane Trigonometry." 689 examples. 66 figures. xvi + 383pp. 5⅜ x 8.
S353 Paperbound **$1.95**

NON-EUCLIDEAN GEOMETRY, Roberto Bonola. The standard coverage of non-Euclidean geometry. Examines from both a historical and mathematical point of view geometries which have arisen from a study of Euclid's 5th postulate on parallel lines. Also included are complete texts, translated, of Bolyai's "Theory of Absolute Space," Lobachevsky's "Theory of Parallels." 180 diagrams. 431pp. 5⅜ x 8.
S27 Paperbound **$1.95**

GEOMETRY OF FOUR DIMENSIONS, H. P. Manning. Unique in English as a clear, concise introduction. Treatment is synthetic, mostly Euclidean, though in hyperplanes and hyperspheres at infinity, non-Euclidean geometry is used. Historical introduction. Foundations of 4-dimensional geometry. Perpendicularity, simple angles. Angles of planes, higher order. Symmetry, order, motion; hyperpyramids, hypercones, hyperspheres; figures with parallel elements; volume, hypervolume in space; regular polyhedroids. Glossary. 78 figures. ix + 348pp. 5⅜ x 8.
S182 Paperbound **$1.95**

MATHEMATICS: INTERMEDIATE TO ADVANCED

GEOMETRY (EUCLIDEAN AND NON-EUCLIDEAN)

THE GEOMETRY OF RENÉ DESCARTES. With this book, Descartes founded analytical geometry. Original French text, with Descartes's own diagrams, and excellent Smith-Latham translation. Contains: Problems the Construction of Which Requires only Straight Lines and Circles; On the Nature of Curved Lines; On the Construction of Solid or Supersolid Problems. Diagrams. 258pp. 5⅜ x 8.
S68 Paperbound **$1.50**

DOVER SCIENCE BOOKS

THE WORKS OF ARCHIMEDES, edited by T. L. Heath. All the known works of the great Greek mathematician, including the recently discovered Method of Archimedes. Contains: On Sphere and Cylinder, Measurement of a Circle, Spirals, Conoids, Spheroids, etc. Definitive edition of greatest mathematical intellect of ancient world. 186 page study by Heath discusses Archimedes and history of Greek mathematics. 563pp. 5⅜ x 8. S9 Paperbound **$2.00**

COLLECTED WORKS OF BERNARD RIEMANN. Important sourcebook, first to contain complete text of 1892 "Werke" and the 1902 supplement, unabridged. 31 monographs, 3 complete lecture courses, 15 miscellaneous papers which have been of enormous importance in relativity, topology, theory of complex variables, other areas of mathematics. Edited by R. Dedekind, H. Weber, M. Noether, W. Wirtinger. German text; English introduction by Hans Lewy. 690pp. 5⅜ x 8. S226 Paperbound **$2.85**

THE THIRTEEN BOOKS OF EUCLID'S ELEMENTS, edited by Sir Thomas Heath. Definitive edition of one of very greatest classics of Western world. Complete translation of Heiberg text, plus spurious Book XIV. 150 page introduction on Greek, Medieval mathematics, Euclid, texts, commentators, etc. Elaborate critical apparatus parallels text, analyzing each definition, postulate, proposition, covering textual matters, refutations, supports, extrapolations, etc. This is the full Euclid. Unabridged reproduction of Cambridge U. 2nd edition. 3 volumes. 995 figures. 1426pp. 5⅜ x 8. S88, 89, 90, 3 volume set, paperbound **$6.00**

AN INTRODUCTION TO GEOMETRY OF N DIMENSIONS, D. M. Y. Sommerville. Presupposes no previous knowledge of field. Only book in English devoted exclusively to higher dimensional geometry. Discusses fundamental ideas of incidence, parallelism, perpendicularity, angles between linear space, enumerative geometry, analytical geometry from projective and metric views, polytopes, elementary ideas in analysis situs, content of hyperspacial figures. 60 diagrams. 196pp. 5⅜ x 8. S494 Paperbound **$1.50**

ELEMENTS OF NON-EUCLIDEAN GEOMETRY, D. M. Y. Sommerville. Unique in proceeding step-by-step. Requires only good knowledge of high-school geometry and algebra, to grasp elementary hyperbolic, elliptic, analytic non-Euclidean Geometries; space curvature and its implications; radical axes; homopethic centres and systems of circles; parataxy and parallelism; Gauss' proof of defect area theorem; much more, with exceptional clarity. 126 problems at chapter ends. 133 figures. xvi + 274pp. 5⅜ x 8. S460 Paperbound **$1.50**

THE FOUNDATIONS OF EUCLIDEAN GEOMETRY, H. G. Forder. First connected, rigorous account in light of modern analysis, establishing propositions without recourse to empiricism, without multiplying hypotheses. Based on tools of 19th and 20th century mathematicians, who made it possible to remedy gaps and complexities, recognize problems not earlier discerned. Begins with important relationship of number systems in geometrical figures. Considers classes, relations, linear order, natural numbers, axioms for magnitudes, groups, quasi-fields, fields, non-Archimedean systems, the axiom system (at length), particular axioms (two chapters on the Parallel Axioms), constructions, congruence, similarity, etc. Lists: axioms employed, constructions, symbols in frequent use. 295pp. 5⅜ x 8. S481 Paperbound **$2.00**

CALCULUS, FUNCTION THEORY (REAL AND COMPLEX), FOURIER THEORY

FIVE VOLUME "THEORY OF FUNCTIONS" SET BY KONRAD KNOPP. Provides complete, readily followed account of theory of functions. Proofs given concisely, yet without sacrifice of completeness or rigor. These volumes used as texts by such universities as M.I.T., Chicago, N.Y. City College, many others. "Excellent introduction . . . remarkably readable, concise, clear, rigorous," J. of the American Statistical Association.

ELEMENTS OF THE THEORY OF FUNCTIONS, Konrad Knopp. Provides background for further volumes in this set, or texts on similar level. Partial contents: Foundations, system of complex numbers and Gaussian plane of numbers, Riemann sphere of numbers, mapping by linear functions, normal forms, the logarithm, cyclometric functions, binomial series. "Not only for the young student, but also for the student who knows all about what is in it," Mathematical Journal. 140pp. 5⅜ x 8. S154 Paperbound **$1.35**

THEORY OF FUNCTIONS, PART I, Konrad Knopp. With volume II, provides coverage of basic concepts and theorems. Partial contents: numbers and points, functions of a complex variable, integral of a continuous function, Cauchy's intergral theorem, Cauchy's integral formulae, series with variable terms, expansion and analytic function in a power series, analytic continuation and complete definition of analytic functions, Laurent expansion, types of singularities. vii + 146pp. 5⅜ x 8. S156 Paperbound **$1.35**

THEORY OF FUNCTIONS, PART II, Konrad Knopp. Application and further development of general theory, special topics. Single valued functions, entire, Weierstrass. Meromorphic functions: Mittag-Leffler. Periodic functions. Multiple valued functions. Riemann surfaces. Algebraic functions. Analytical configurations, Riemann surface. x + 150pp. 5⅜ x 8. S157 Paperbound **$1.35**

PROBLEM BOOK IN THE THEORY OF FUNCTIONS, VOLUME I, Konrad Knopp. Problems in elementary theory, for use with Knopp's "Theory of Functions," or any other text. Arranged according to increasing difficulty. Fundamental concepts, sequences of numbers and infinite series, complex variable, integral theorems, development in series, conformal mapping. Answers. viii + 126pp. 5⅜ x 8. S 158 **Paperbound $1.35**

PROBLEM BOOK IN THE THEORY OF FUNCTIONS, VOLUME II, Konrad Knopp. Advanced theory of functions, to be used with Knopp's "Theory of Functions," or comparable text. Singularities, entire and meromorphic functions, periodic, analytic, continuation, multiple-valued functions, Riemann surfaces, conformal mapping. Includes section of elementary problems. "The difficult task of selecting . . . problems just within the reach of the beginner is here masterfully accomplished," AM. MATH. SOC. Answers. 138pp. 5⅜ x 8.
S159 Paperbound **$1.35**

ADVANCED CALCULUS, E. B. Wilson. Still recognized as one of most comprehensive, useful texts. Immense amount of well-represented, fundamental material, including chapters on vector functions, ordinary differential equations, special functions, calculus of variations, etc., which are excellent introductions to these areas. Requires only one year of calculus. Over 1300 exercises cover both pure math and applications to engineering and physical problems. Ideal reference, refresher. 54 page introductory review. ix + 566pp. 5⅜ x 8.
S504 Paperbound **$2.45**

LECTURES ON THE THEORY OF ELLIPTIC FUNCTIONS, H. Hancock. Reissue of only book in English with so extensive a coverage, especially of Abel, Jacobi, Legendre, Weierstrass, Hermite, Liouville, and Riemann. Unusual fuliness of treatment, plus applications as well as theory in discussing universe of elliptic integrals, originating in works of Abel and Jacobi. Use is made of Riemann to provide most general theory. 40-page table of formulas. 76 figures. xxiii + 498pp. 5⅜ x 8. S483 Paperbound **$2.55**

THEORY OF FUNCTIONALS AND OF INTEGRAL AND INTEGRO-DIFFERENTIAL EQUATIONS, Vito Volterra. Unabridged republication of only English translation. General theory of functions depending on continuous set of values of another function. Based on author's concept of transition from finite number of variables to a continually infinite number. Includes much material on calculus of variations. Begins with fundamentals, examines generalization of analytic functions, functional derivative equations, applications, other directions of theory, etc. New introduction by G. C. Evans. Biography, criticism of Volterra's work by E. Whittaker. xxxx + 226pp. 5⅜ x 8. S502 Paperbound **$1.75**

AN INTRODUCTION TO FOURIER METHODS AND THE LAPLACE TRANSFORMATION, Philip Franklin. Concentrates on essentials, gives broad view, suitable for most applications. Requires only knowledge of calculus. Covers complex qualities with methods of computing elementary functions for complex values of argument and finding approximations by charts; Fourier series; harmonic anaylsis; much more. Methods are related to physical problems of heat flow, vibrations, electrical transmission, electromagnetic radiation, etc. 828 problems, answers. Formerly entitled "Fourier Methods." x + 289pp. 5⅜ x 8.
S452 Paperbound **$1.75**

THE ANALYTICAL THEORY OF HEAT, Joseph Fourier. This book, which revolutionized mathematical physics, has been used by generations of mathematicians and physicists interested in heat or application of Fourier integral. Covers cause and reflection of rays of heat, radiant heating, heating of closed spaces, use of trigonometric series in theory of heat, Fourier integral, etc. Translated by Alexander Freeman. 20 figures. xxii + 466pp. 5⅜ x 8.
S93 Paperbound **$2.00**

ELLIPTIC INTEGRALS, H. Hancock. Invaluable in work involving differential equations with cubics, quatrics under root sign, where elementary calculus methods are inadequate. Practical solutions to problems in mathematics, engineering, physics; differential equations requiring integration of Lamé's, Briot's, or Bouquet's equations; determination of arc of ellipse, hyperbola, lemiscate; solutions of problems in elastics; motion of a projectile under resistance varying as the cube of the velocity; pendulums; more. Exposition in accordance with Legendre-Jacobi theory. Rigorous discussion of Legendre transformations. 20 figures. 5 place table. 104pp. 5⅜ x 8. S484 Paperbound **$1.25**

THE TAYLOR SERIES, AN INTRODUCTION TO THE THEORY OF FUNCTIONS OF A COMPLEX VARIABLE, P. Dienes. Uses Taylor series to approach theory of functions, using ordinary calculus only, except in last 2 chapters. Starts with introduction to real variable and complex algebra, derives properties of infinite series, complex differentiation, integration, etc. Covers biuniform mapping, overconvergence and gap theorems, Taylor series on its circle of convergence, etc. Unabridged corrected reissue of first edition. 186 examples, many fully worked out. 67 figures. xii + 555pp. 5⅜ x 8. S391 Paperbound **$2.75**

LINEAR INTEGRAL EQUATIONS, W. V. Lovitt. Systematic survey of general theory, with some application to differential equations, calculus of variations, problems of math, physics. Includes: integral equation of 2nd kind by successive substitutions; Fredholm's equation as ratio of 2 integral series in lambda, applications of the Fredholm theory, Hilbert-Schmidt theory of symmetric kernels, application, etc. Neumann, Dirichlet, vibratory problems. ix + 253pp. 5⅜ x 8. S175 Clothbound **$3.50**
S176 Paperbound **$1.60**

12

DICTIONARY OF CONFORMAL REPRESENTATIONS, H. Kober. Developed by British Admiralty to solve Laplace's equation in 2 dimensions. Scores of geometrical forms and transformations for electrical engineers, Joukowski aerofoil for aerodynamics, Schwartz-Christoffel transformations for hydro-dynamics, transcendental functions. Contents classified according to analytical functions describing transformations with corresponding regions. Glossary. Topological index. 447 diagrams. 6⅛ x 9¼. .S160 Paperbound **$2.00**

ELEMENTS OF THE THEORY OF REAL FUNCTIONS, J. E. Littlewood. Based on lectures at Trinity College, Cambridge, this book has proved extremely successful in introducing graduate students to modern theory of functions. Offers full and concise coverage of classes and cardinal numbers, well ordered series, other types of series, and elements of the theory of sets of points. 3rd revised edition. vii + 71pp. 5⅜ x 8.   S171 Clothbound **$2.85**
S172 Paperbound **$1.25**

INFINITE SEQUENCES AND SERIES, Konrad Knopp. 1st publication in any language. Excellent introduction to 2 topics of modern mathematics, designed to give student background to penetrate further alone. Sequences and sets, real and complex numbers, etc. Functions of a real and complex variable. Sequences and series. Infinite series. Convergent power series. Expansion of elementary functions. Numerical evaluation of series. v + 186pp. 5⅜ x 8.
S152 Clothbound **$3.50**
S153 Paperbound **$1.75**

THE THEORY AND FUNCTIONS OF A REAL VARIABLE AND THE THEORY OF FOURIER'S SERIES, E. W .Hobson. One of the best introductions to set theory and various aspects of functions and Fourier's series. Requires only a good background in calculus. Exhaustive coverage of: metric and descriptive properties of sets of points; transfinite numbers and order types; functions of a real variable; the Riemann and Lebesgue integrals; sequences and series of numbers; power-series; functions representable by series sequences of continuous functions; trigonometrical series; representation of functions by Fourier's series; and much more. "The best possible guide," Nature. Vol. I: 88 detailed examples, 10 figures. Index. xv + 736pp. Vol. II: 117 detailed examples, 13 figures. x + 780pp. 6⅛ x 9¼.
Vol. I: S387 Paperbound **$3.00**
Vol. II: S388 Paperbound **$3.00**

ALMOST PERIODIC FUNCTIONS, A. S. Besicovitch. Unique and important summary by a well known mathematician covers in detail the two stages of development in Bohr's theory of almost periodic functions: (1) as a generalization of pure periodicity, with results and proofs; (2) the work done by Stepanof, Wiener, Weyl, and Bohr in generalizing the theory. xi + 180pp. 5⅜ x 8.   S18 Paperbound **$1.75**

INTRODUCTION TO THE THEORY OF FOURIER'S SERIES AND INTEGRALS, H. S. Carslaw. 3rd revised edition, an outgrowth of author's courses at Cambridge. Historical introduction, rational, irrational numbers, infinite sequences and series, functions of a single variable, definite integral, Fourier series, and similar topics. Appendices discuss practical harmonic analysis, periodogram analysis, Lebesgue's theory. 84 examples. xiii + 368pp. 5⅜ x 8.
S48 Paperbound **$2.00**

SYMBOLIC LOGIC

THE ELEMENTS OF MATHEMATICAL LOGIC, Paul Rosenbloom. First publication in any language. For mathematically mature readers with no training in symbolic. logic. Development of lectures given at Lund Univ., Sweden, 1948. Partial contents: Logic of classes, fundamental theorems, Boolean algebra, logic of propositions, of propositional functions, expressive languages, combinatory logics, development of math within an object language, paradoxes, theorems of Post, Goedel, Church, and similar topics. iv + 214pp. 5⅜ x 8.
S227 Paperbound **$1.45**

INTRODUCTION TO SYMBOLIC LOGIC AND ITS APPLICATION, R. Carnap. Clear, comprehensive, rigorous, by perhaps greatest living master. Symbolic languages analyzed, one constructed. Applications to math (axiom systems for set theory, real, natural numbers), topology (Dedekind, Cantor continuity explanations), physics (general analysis of determination, causality, space-time topology), biology (axiom system for basic concepts). "A masterpiece," Zentralblatt für Mathematik und Ihre Grenzgebiete. Over 300 exercises. 5 figures. xvi + 241pp. 5⅜ x 8.   S453 Paperbound **$1.85**

AN INTRODUCTION TO SYMBOLIC LOGIC, Susanne K. Langer. Probably clearest book for the philosopher, scientist, layman—no special knowledge of math required. Starts with simplest symbols, goes on to give remarkable grasp of Boole-Schroeder, Russell-Whitehead systems, clearly, quickly. Partial Contents: Forms, Generalization, Classes, Deductive System of Classes, Algebra of Logic, Assumptions of Principia Mathematica, Logistics, Proofs of Theorems, etc. "Clearest . . . simplest introduction . . . the intelligent non-mathematician should have no difficulty," MATHEMATICS GAZETTE. Revised, expanded 2nd edition. Truth-value tables. 368pp. 5⅜ 8.   S164 Paperbound **$1.75**

TRIGONOMETRICAL SERIES, Antoni Zygmund. On modern advanced level. Contains carefully organized analyses of trigonometric, orthogonal, Fourier systems of functions, with clear adequate descriptions of summability of Fourier series, proximation theory, conjugate series, convergence, divergence of Fourier series. Especially valuable for Russian, Eastern European coverage. 329pp. 5⅜ x 8. S290 Paperbound **$1.50**

THE LAWS OF THOUGHT, George Boole. This book founded symbolic logic some 100 years ago. It is the 1st significant attempt to apply logic to all aspects of human endeavour. Partial contents: derivation of laws, signs and laws, interpretations, eliminations, conditions of a perfect method, analysis, Aristotelian logic, probability, and similar topics. xvii + 424pp. 5⅜ x 8. S28 Paperbound **$2.00**

SYMBOLIC LOGIC, C. I. Lewis, C. H. Langford. 2nd revised edition of probably most cited book in symbolic logic. Wide coverage of entire field; one of fullest treatments of paradoxes; plus much material not available elsewhere. Basic to volume is distinction between logic of extensions and intensions. Considerable emphasis on converse substitution, while matrix system presents supposition of variety of non-Aristotelian logics. Especially valuable sections on strict limitations, existence theorems. Partial contents: Boole-Schroeder algebra; truth value systems, the matrix method; implication and deductibility; general theory of propositions; etc. "Most valuable," Times, London. 506pp. 5⅜ x 8. S170 Paperbound **$2.00**

GROUP THEORY AND LINEAR ALGEBRA, SETS, ETC.

LECTURES ON THE ICOSAHEDRON AND THE SOLUTION OF EQUATIONS OF THE FIFTH DEGREE, Felix Klein. Solution of quintics in terms of rotations of regular icosahedron around its axes of symmetry. A classic, indispensable source for those interested in higher algebra, geometry, crystallography. Considerable explanatory material included. 230 footnotes, mostly bibliography. "Classical monograph . . . detailed, readable book," Math. Gazette. 2nd edition. xvi + 289pp. 5⅜ x 8. S314 Paperbound **$1.85**

INTRODUCTION TO THE THEORY OF GROUPS OF FINITE ORDER, R. Carmichael. Examines fundamental theorems and their applications. Beginning with sets, systems, permutations, etc., progresses in easy stages through important types of groups: Abelian, prime power, permutation, etc. Except 1 chapter where matrices are desirable, no higher math is needed. 783 exercises, problems. xvi + 447pp. 5⅜ x 8. S299 Clothbound **$3.95**
S300 Paperbound **$2.00**

THEORY OF GROUPS OF FINITE ORDER, W. Burnside. First published some 40 years ago, still one of clearest introductions. Partial contents: permutations, groups independent of representation, composition series of a group, isomorphism of a group with itself, Abelian groups, prime power groups, permutation groups, invariants of groups of linear substitution, graphical representation, etc. "Clear and detailed discussion . . . numerous problems which are instructive," Design News. xxiv + 512pp. 5⅜ x 8. S38 Paperbound **$2.45**

COMPUTATIONAL METHODS OF LINEAR ALGEBRA, V. N. Faddeeva, translated by C. D. Benster. 1st English translation of unique, valuable work, only one in English presenting systematic exposition of most important methods of linear algebra—classical, contemporary. Details of deriving numerical solutions of problems in mathematical physics. Theory and practice. Includes survey of necessary background, most important methods of solution, for exact, iterative groups. One of most valuable features is 23 tables, triple checked for accuracy, unavailable elsewhere. Translator's note. x + 252pp. 5⅜ x 8. S424 Paperbound **$1.95**

THE CONTINUUM AND OTHER TYPES OF SERIAL ORDER, E. V. Huntington. This famous book gives a systematic elementary account of the modern theory of the continuum as a type of serial order. Based on the Cantor-Dedekind ordinal theory, which requires no technical knowledge of higher mathematics, it offers an easily followed analysis of ordered classes, discrete and dense series, continuous series, Cantor's transfinite numbers. "Admirable introduction to the rigorous theory of the continuum . . . reading easy," Science Progress. 2nd edition. viii + 82pp. 5⅜ x 8. S129 Clothbound **$2.75**
S130 Paperbound **$1.00**

THEORY OF SETS, E. Kamke. Clearest, amplest introduction in English, well suited for independent study. Subdivisions of main theory, such as theory of sets of points, are discussed, but emphasis is on general theory. Partial contents: rudiments of set theory, arbitrary sets, their cardinal numbers, ordered sets, their order types, well-ordered sets, their cardinal numbers. vii + 144pp. 5⅜ x 8. S141 Paperbound **$1.35**

CONTRIBUTIONS TO THE FOUNDING OF THE THEORY OF TRANSFINITE NUMBERS, Georg Cantor. These papers founded a new branch of mathematics. The famous articles of 1895-7 are translated, with an 82-page introduction by P. E. B. Jourdain dealing with Cantor, the background of his discoveries, their results, future possibilities. ix + 211pp. 5⅜ x 8. S45 Paperbound **$1.25**

NUMERICAL AND GRAPHICAL METHODS, TABLES

JACOBIAN ELLIPTIC FUNCTION TABLES, L. M. Milne-Thomson. Easy-to-follow, practical, not only useful numerical tables, but complete elementary sketch of application of elliptic functions. Covers description of principle properties; complete elliptic integrals; Fourier series, expansions; periods, zeros, poles, residues, formulas for special values of argument; cubic, quartic polynomials; pendulum problem; etc. Tables, graphs form body of book: Graph, 5 figure table of elliptic function sn (u m); cn (u m); dn (u m). 8 figure table of complete elliptic integrals K, K′, E, E′, nome q. 7 figure table of Jacobian zeta-function Z(u). 3 figures. xi + 123pp. 5⅜ x 8.   S194 Paperbound **$1.35**

TABLES OF FUNCTIONS WITH FORMULAE AND CURVES, E. Jahnke, F. Emde. Most comprehensive 1-volume English text collection of tables, formulae, curves of transcendent functions. 4th corrected edition, new 76-page section giving tables, formulae for elementary functions not in other English editions. Partial contents: sine, cosine, logarithmic integral; error integral; elliptic integrals; theta functions; Legendre, Bessel, Riemann, Mathieu, hypergeometric functions; etc. "Out-of-the-way functions for which we know no other source." Scientific Computing Service, Ltd. 212 figures. 400pp. 5⅝ x 8⅜.   S133 Paperbound **$2.00**

MATHEMATICAL TABLES, H. B. Dwight. Covers in one volume almost every function of importance in applied mathematics, engineering, physical sciences. Three extremely fine tables of the three trig functions, inverses, to 1000th of radian; natural, common logs; squares, cubes; hyperbolic functions, inverses; $(a^2 + b^2)$ exp. ½a; complete elliptical integrals of 1st, 2nd kind; sine, cosine integrals; exponential integrals; Ei(x) and Ei(−x); binomial coefficients; factorials to 250; surface zonal harmonics, first derivatives; Bernoulli, Euler numbers, their logs to base of 10; Gamma function; normal probability integral; over 60pp. Bessel functions; Riemann zeta function. Each table with formulae generally used, sources of more extensive tables, interpolation data, etc. Over half have columns of differences, to facilitate interpolation. viii + 231pp. 5⅜ x 8.   S445 Paperbound **$1.75**

PRACTICAL ANALYSIS, GRAPHICAL AND NUMERICAL METHODS, F. A. Willers. Immensely practical hand-book for engineers. How to interpolate, use various methods of numerical differentiation and integration, determine roots of a single algebraic equation, system of linear equations, use empirical formulas, integrate differential equations, etc. Hundreds of short-cuts for arriving at numerical solutions. Special section on American calculating machines, by T. W. Simpson. Translation by R. T. Beyer. 132 illustrations. 422pp. 5⅜ x 8.
S273 Paperbound **$2.00**

NUMERICAL SOLUTIONS OF DIFFERENTIAL EQUATIONS, H. Levy, E. A. Baggott. Comprehensive collection of methods for solving ordinary differential equations of first and higher order. 2 requirements: practical, easy to grasp; more rapid than school methods. Partial contents: graphical integration of differential equations, graphical methods for detailed solution. Numerical solution. Simultaneous equations and equations of 2nd and higher orders. "Should be in the hands of all in research and applied mathematics, teaching," Nature. 21 figures. viii + 238pp. 5⅜ x 8.   S168 Paperbound **$1.75**

NUMERICAL INTEGRATION OF DIFFERENTIAL EQUATIONS, Bennet, Milne, Bateman. Unabridged republication of original prepared for National Research Council. New methods of integration by 3 leading mathematicians: "The Interpolational Polynomial," "Successive Approximation," A. A. Bennett, "Step-by-step Methods of Integration," W. W. Milne. "Methods for Partial Differential Equations," H. Bateman. Methods for partial differential equations, solution of differential equations to non-integral values of a parameter will interest mathematicians, physicists. 288 footnotes, mostly bibliographical. 235 item classified bibliography. 108pp. 5⅜ x 8.   S305 Paperbound **$1.35**

Write for free catalogs!

Indicate your field of interest. Dover publishes books on physics, earth sciences, mathematics, engineering, chemistry, astronomy, anthropology, biology, psychology, philosophy, religion, history, literature, mathematical recreations, languages, crafts, art, graphic arts, etc.

Write to Dept. catr
Dover Publications, Inc.
Science A
180 Varick St., N. Y. 14, N. Y.